THE
DIGITAL IC HANDBOOK

To William J. Walsh

THE
DIGITAL IC
HANDBOOK

MICHAEL S. MORLEY

TAB Professional and Reference Books

Division of TAB BOOKS Inc.

Blue Ridge Summit, PA

FIRST EDITION
FIRST PRINTING

Copyright © 1988 by TAB BOOKS Inc.
Printed in the United States of America

Library of Congress Cataloging in Publication Data

Morley, M.S.
The digital IC handbook / by Michael S. Morley.
p. cm.
Includes indexes.
ISBN 0-8306-9302-5
1. Digital integrated circuits—Handbooks, manuals, etc.
I. Title.

TK7868.D5M63 1988   88-11918
621.381'73—dc19   CIP

Questions regarding the content of this book
should be addressed to:

Reader Inquiry Branch
TAB BOOKS Inc.
Blue Ridge Summit, PA 17294-0214

Contents

Introduction

The purpose of this book is to aid electronics circuit designers in the selection of standard digital integrated circuits (ICs). This book is intended to be a companion volume to *The Linear IC Handbook*, also published by TAB Professional and Reference Books, Division of TAB BOOKS Inc., and was written for engineers, technicians, and hobbyists—in short, anyone who designs electronic digital systems.

This book uses tables extensively. It includes two types of tables that I have compiled for my own use as an electronics designer. The first type of table is the *index table*. The index tables are included in Appendices A through I. Each table includes the part number type, the temperature grade, a description, the pin count, the maximum power, 100-piece price, and supplier codes for specific series or families of digital ICs. I have used these tables to baseline existing designs and evaluate potential design approaches in terms of IC count, total power, IC board area, and cost.

My criterion for each entry in the index tables is this: if it was listed in the manufacturer's price list *and* I had a data sheet that included the minimum information used in the index table, then I listed the part in the index table. The manufacturer's price list is the only guarantee that a part really exists as far as I am concerned. This criterion purges obsolete parts and eliminates the assumption of the availability of "dream" parts for which there might be a glowing data sheet but no silicon.

Unfortunately, this rule prevented me from listing ICs for which I could not obtain either price lists or data sheets. Because of a lack of price lists, the

Japanese suppliers are not represented in this book. Because I work for a government contractor that forbids the use of non-military or off-shore devices (from the Japanese, primarily), this has not affected me personally. However, if you work for a commercial company, you will have to obtain pricing information formally by having your purchasing department contact these suppliers or their representatives directly.

Because of a lack of data sheets, some new but very real parts are not listed in this book. This will always be a problem with this type of book. For new parts you will have to rely on the suppliers and their sales and applications engineering staffs.

The second type of table in this book is the *selection guide table*. The selection guide tables initially were created from the index tables. All of the entries in the index tables were sorted by function. The logic IC index tables were sorted into tables for gates, flip-flops, counters, and so forth. The memory index table was sorted into static RAMs, dynamic RAMs, PROMs, and erasable PROMs. The microprocessor indexes (6500 Family Index, the 6800/68000 Family Index, etc.) were sorted by data bus width into 8, 16, and 32-bit processor tables. Some of these functions were further sorted if the tables were too large to allow the reader to be able to do a quick visual search. With the exception of the Analog Devices and Integrated Device Technology multipliers (and multiplier/accumulators), every IC in the selection guide tables also appears in the index tables.

Note that not every IC in the index tables is in the selection guide tables. Some function groups contained too few ICs to be included or they were too specialized to be included.

After performing the functional sort, each selection guide table was amended to include data that was specific to that functional group—specification data that would be a key selection criterion for that functional group: delay times for gates, set-up and hold times for flip-flops, maximum count frequencies for counters, address acquisition times for memories, address and data bus sizes and clock rates for microprocessors, to name a few.

The price data is found in both types of tables even though I knew the data would be old by the time you read this. Price is an important factor in system design. Never buy a more expensive part than you absolutely need. You should perform trade studies on different hardware design approaches to determine the optimum design with respect to price, power consumption, and board area. And although the price data in this book are out of date, it gives you the *relative* cost of a function. Keep in mind that price data on the older parts (most of the logic ICs) will probably not change and that the price of advanced ICs will fall dramatically as volume production ramps up.

Experienced designers, who are already familiar with all the IC families and probably a great many of the parts in each family, should be able to go directly to the index tables and the selection guide tables. New designers, or persons who want to learn the basics of digital ICs, memories, and microprocessors, are invited to read the text material.

The purpose of the text material is to introduce concepts that the manufacturer's data books assume that you already know. The text material is not intended to be a complete tutorial, however. The only assumption I make is that the reader has had a basic electronics course.

A second purpose of the text is to provide functional descriptions of specific digital ICs, to provide additional technical data that is not in the selection guide tables, and to point out differences between similar part types.

The structure of the book is as follows:

Chapter 1 compares the two basic logic families: the 54/74 families and the 4000 Series CMOS families. Basic characteristics are defined. The thirteen subfamilies of the 54/74 group and three subfamilies of the 4000 Series are discussed.

Chapters 2 through 6 present functional descriptions and selection guides for the various categories of the 54/74 and 4000 Series parts: gates (Chapter 2); flip-flops, latches, and multivibrators (Chapter 3); buffers and transceivers (Chapter 4); decoders, encoders, and data selectors (Chapter 5); and counters and shift registers (Chapter 6).

Chapter 7 presents functional descriptions and selection guides for arithmetic circuits from the 54/74 families, the 4000 Series CMOS, and from the 2900 Family (TTL compatible, from AMD), the ADSP-1000 series (CMOS from Analog Devices), and the IDT7200 series (CMOS from Integrated Device Technology).

Chapter 8 presents functional descriptions and selection guides for memories. This group includes very few ICs from the 54/74 families and none from the 4000 series.

Chapter 9 presents microprocessors: from the 6502 8-bit microprocessor to the 80386 32-bit microprocessor to the "roll-your-own," bit-slice microprocessor.

Appendices A-I are the IC index tables. Appendix J gives the explanation for the supplier codes used in the index tables.

Chapter 1
Comparison of Logic Families

The two most popular logic families are the 54/74 Family and the 4000 Series CMOS Family. The 54/74 Family began in the 1960s with the Standard TTL Family (first manufactured by Texas Instruments) and has grown to 13 subfamilies in the military temperature range (the 54 Family) and 13 subfamilies in commercial and/or industrial temperature range (the 74 Family). Eight of the 13 subfamilies in the 54 Family and the 74 Family are fabricated using bipolar IC technology. The remaining five subfamilies are fabricated using CMOS technology. Some of these 13 subfamilies of either the 54 Family or the 74 Family are obsolete. New members, such as 54/74F (F stands for FAST, an acronym for Fairchild Advanced Schottky TTL) and 54/74HC (HC stands for High Speed CMOS), are fabricated from either advanced bipolar technologies or advanced silicon-gate CMOS technologies. An index to the 54/74 families is contained in Appendix A.

The 4000 Series CMOS Family consists of three subfamilies in the military temperature range and three subfamilies in the industrial temperature range. The 4000 Series is fabricated using metal-gate CMOS technology. Although the 4000 Series is considered an obsolete logic family, major suppliers such as RCA (the originator of the Series), Motorola, and National continue to sell a full catalog of part types. An index to the 4000 Series is contained in Appendix B.

The purpose of this chapter is to explain the basic characteristics of the 54/74 Family and the 4000 Series CMOS Family. The approach used will be to provide definitions of the basic characteristics, provide tables that compare each of the logic families in terms of these characteristics, and provide a schematic

1

and short discussion of a basic logic circuit from each family or family type.

1.1 DEFINITIONS OF BASIC CHARACTERISTICS

A *logic family* may be defined as a set of digital ICs that are electrically compatible with each other. For example, if a NAND gate in one IC package is connected to a NOR gate in another IC package, then the output characteristics of the NAND gate must be compatible with the input characteristics of the NOR gate in order for the combination of the two gates to perform the intended logic function. Choosing a NAND gate and the NOR gate from the same logic family guarantees the required compatibility.

The input and output characteristics of the 54/74 families and the 4000 Series families are shown in Tables 1-1 and 1-2. 54 families and 4000 Series families that operate over the military temperature range are compared in Table 1-1. 74 families and 4000 Series families that operate over the commercial and/or industrial temperature ranges are compared in Table 1-2. The input and output characteristics data in these tables is over the operating temperature range unless otherwise noted.

1.1.1 Input Characteristics

The input characteristics are V_{IH}, V_{IL}, I_{IH}, I_{IL}.

☐ V_{IH} (Input Voltage, HIGH) is defined as the minimum HIGH voltage on an input pin that guarantees that the output is in the proper logic state, HIGH or LOW, depending on the logic function. For example, for an inverter, a HIGH on the input causes a LOW on the output. Therefore, for an inverter, V_{IH} is the minimum HIGH voltage on the input pin that will guarantee that the output will be LOW. For 5-volt logic families (the nominal power supply voltage V_{CC} = 5 V), the input voltage is ideally 5 volts for HIGH. In actuality, the input will always be something less than 5 volts. For Standard TTL (see logic family "54" in Table 1-1 or logic family "74" in Table 1-2), the input pin of a logic function can be as low as 2 volts and the output is guaranteed to be in the proper logic state.

☐ V_{IL} (Input Voltage, LOW) is defined as the maximum LOW voltage on an input pin that will guarantee that the output will be in the proper logic state. For Standard TTL, the input pin of a logic function can be as high as 0.8 volts and the output is guaranteed to be in the proper logic state.

☐ I_{IH} (Input Current, HIGH) is defined as the maximum current into (plus sign) or out of (minus sign) the input pin of a logic function when the voltage on the input pin is HIGH. Tables 1-1 and 1-2 show absolute values for I_{IH}. Logic families that show I_{IH} = 1 μA are CMOS and the I_{IH} is actually + or − 1 μA. The other logic families are bipolar and the circuit

Table 1-1. Comparison of Logic Families, Military Temperature Range.

Logic Family	Min TEMP (C)	Max TEMP (C)	Min Vcc (V)	Max Vcc (V)	Min VIH (V)	Max VIL (V)	Max IIH (μA)	Max IIL (mA)	Min VOH (V)	Max VOL (V)	Max IOH (mA)	Max IOL (mA)	Max ICC (mA)	Max DELAY (nS)	Notes
54	-55	125	4.5	5.5	2	0.8	40	1.6	2.4	0.4	0.4	16	22	22	1,2
54AC	-55	125	2	6	3.15	1.35	1	1 μA	3.7	0.4	24	24	0.1	8.5	1,3
54ACT	-55	125	2	6	2	0.8	1	1 μA	3.7	0.4	24	24	0.1	12.5	1,3
54ALS	-55	125	4.5	5.5	2	0.7	20	0.1	2.5	0.4	0.4	4	3	16	1
54AS	-55	125	4.5	5.5	2	0.8	20	0.5	2.5	0.5	2	20	17.4	5	1
54C	-55	125	3	15	3.5	1.5	1	1 μA	4.5	0.5	0.01	0.01	15 μA	90	1,2,4
54F	-55	125	4.5	5.5	2	0.8	20	0.6	2.5	0.5	1	20	10.2	7	1
54H	-55	125	4.5	5.5	2	0.8	50	2	2.4	0.4	0.5	20	40	10	1,2
54HC	-55	125	2	6	3.15	0.9	1	1 μA	3.7	0.4	4	4	40 μA	27	1,5
54HCT	-55	125	2	5.5	2	0.8	1	1 μA	3.7	0.4	4	4	40 μA	30	1
54L	-55	125	4.5	5.5	2	0.7	10	0.18	2.4	0.3	0.1	2	2.04	60	1,2
54LS	-55	125	4.5	5.5	2	0.7	20	0.4	2.5	0.4	0.4	4	4.4	15	1,2
54S	-55	125	4.5	5.5	2	0.8	50	2	2.5	0.5	1	20	36	5	1,2
4000A	-55	125	3	12	3.5	1.5	1	1 μA	4.95	0.05	0.35	0.28	3 μA	95	2,6,7,8,9
4000B	-55	125	3	18	3.5	1.5	1	1 μA	4.95	0.05	0.36	0.36	7.5 μA	250	2,6,8,10,11
4000UB	-55	125	3	18	4	1	1	1 μA	4.95	0.05	0.36	0.36	7.5 μA	120	2,6,8,10,11

Table 1-2. Comparison of Logic Families, Commercial and Industrial Temperature Ranges.

Logic Family	Min TEMP (C)	Max TEMP (C)	Min Vcc (V)	Max Vcc (V)	Min VIH (V)	Max VIL (V)	Max IIH (μA)	Max IIL (mA)	Min VOH (V)	Max VOL (V)	Max IOH (mA)	Max IOL (mA)	Max Icc (mA)	Max DELAY (nS)	Notes
74	0	70	4.75	5.25	2	0.8	40	1.6	2.4	0.4	0.4	16	22	22	1,2
74AC	−40	85	2	6	3.15	1.35	1	1 μA	3.76	0.37	24	24	0.05	8.5	1,3
74ACT	−40	85	2	6	2	0.8	20	1 μA	3.76	0.37	24	24	0.05	12.5	1,3
74ALS	0	70	4.5	5.5	2	0.8	20	0.1	2.5	0.5	0.4	8	3	11	1
74AS	0	70	4.5	5.5	2	0.8	20	0.5	2.5	0.5	2	20	17.4	4.5	1
74C	−40	85	3	15	3.5	1.5	1	1 μA	4.5	0.5	0.01	0.01	15 μA	90	1,2,4
74F	0	70	4.75	5.25	2	0.8	20	0.6	2.7	0.5	1	20	10.2	6	1
74H	0	70	4.75	5.25	2	0.8	50	2	2.4	0.4	0.5	20	40	10	1,2
74HC	−40	85	2	6	3.15	0.9	1	1 μA	3.84	0.33	4	4	20 μA	23	1,5
74HCT	−40	85	2	5.5	2	0.8	10	1 μA	3.84	0.33	4	4	20 μA	25	1
74L	0	70	4.75	5.25	2	0.7	10	0.18	2.4	0.4	0.2	3.6	2.04	60	1,2
74LS	0	70	4.75	5.25	2	0.8	20	0.4	2.7	0.5	0.4	8	4.4	15	1,2
74S	0	70	4.75	5.25	2	0.8	50	2	2.7	0.5	1	20	36	5	1,2
4000A	−40	85	3	12	3.5	1.5	1	1 μA	4.95	0.05	0.24	0.24	15 μA	120	2,6,7,8,9
4000B	−40	85	3	18	3.5	1.5	1	1 μA	4.95	0.05	0.42	0.42	7.5 μA	250	2,6,8,10,11
4000UB	−40	85	3	18	4	1	1	1 μA	4.95	0.05	0.42	0.42	7.5 μA	120	2,6,8,10,11

Notes For Tables 1-1 and 1-2:

1. I_{CC} and DELAY data are for type '00 Quad 2-Input NAND Gate.
2. DELAY is at V_{CC} = 5 V and TEMP = 25 C.
3. V_{CC} = 4.5 V to 5.5 V.
4. V_{CC} = 5 V except for I_{IH}, I_{IL}, and I_{CC} are specified at V_{CC} = 15 V.
5. V_{CC} = 4.5 V to 6 V.
6. I_{CC} and DELAY data are for type 4000 Dual 3-Input NOR Gate Plus Inverter.
7. V_{CC} = 5 V except I_{IH} and I_{IL} are specified at V_{CC} = 15 V.
8. V_{OH} and V_{OL} at I_{OH} and I_{OL} less than 1 μA.
9. I_{OH} at V_{OH} = 2.5 V and I_{OL} at V_{OL} = 0.4
10. V_{CC} = 5 V except I_{IH} and I_{IL} are specified at V_{CC} = 18 V.
11. I_{OH} at V_{OH} = 4.6 V and I_{OL} at V_{OL} = 0.4.

design is such that I_{IH} is into the input pin or positive. I_{IH} for the bipolar logic families is usually specified at maximum V_{CC} with the input voltage equal to the value of minimum V_{OH} (2.4 V or 2.5 V). I_{IH} for the CMOS logic families is specified for the input voltage equal to either zero volts or V_{DD} (the power supply voltage symbol for CMOS).

□ I_{IL} (Input Current, LOW) is defined as the maximum current into (plus sign) or out of (minus sign) the input pin of a logic function when the voltage on the input pin is LOW. Tables 1-1 and 1-2 show absolute values for I_{IL}. Logic families that show $I_{IL} = 1\ \mu A$ are CMOS and the I_{IL} is actually + or − 1 μA. The other logic families are bipolar and the circuit design is such that I_{IH} is out of the input pin or negative. I_{IL} for the bipolar logic families is usually specified at maximum V_{CC} with the input voltage equal to the value of maximum V_{OL} (0.3 V to 0.5 V). I_{IL} for the CMOS logic families is specified for the input voltage equal to either zero volts or V_{DD}.

1.1.2 Output Characteristics

The output characteristics are V_{OH}, V_{OL}, I_{OH}, I_{OL}.

□ V_{OH} (Output Voltage, HIGH) is defined as the minimum HIGH voltage on an output pin when the proper input conditions are applied to the logic function such that the output is intended to be in the logic HIGH state. For example, for an inverter, a LOW on the input causes a HIGH on the output. Therefore, for an inverter, V_{OH} is the minimum HIGH voltage on the output pin when the input pin is LOW. For 5-volt logic families the output voltage is ideally 5 volts for a logic HIGH. In actuality, the output will always be something less than 5 volts. For Standard TTL, the output pin of a logic function can be as low as 2.4 volts for a logic HIGH output. Note that the minimum V_{OH} is always greater than the minimum V_{IH} for a given logic family in order to guarantee output/input compatibility between two logic functions in different packages. Also, V_{OH} is specified for a given I_{OH} and minimum V_{CC}.

□ V_{OL} (Output Voltage, LOW) is defined as the maximum LOW voltage on an output pin when the proper input conditions are applied to the logic function such that the output is intended to be in the LOW state. For 5-volt logic families the output voltage is ideally zero volts for a logic LOW. In actuality, the output will always be something greater than zero volts. For Standard TTL, the output pin of a logic function can be as high as 0.4 volts for a logic LOW output. Note that the maximum V_{OL} is always less than the maximum V_{IL} for a given logic family in order to guarantee output/input compatibility between two logic functions in different packages.

☐ I_{OH} (Output Current, HIGH) is defined as the maximum current out of the output pin of a logic function when the output is in the logic HIGH state. I_{OH} is normally shown as a negative number; however the minus signs have been omitted in Tables 1-1 and 1-2. The value of I_{OH} determines how many inputs the logic function may drive when the output is in the HIGH state. For Standard TTL, the minimum guaranteed I_{OH} is -0.4 mA, which is sufficient to drive 10 Standard TTL inputs at 40 μA each in the HIGH state. I_{OH} is considered an operating condition that is not to be exceeded. If it is exceeded, then the minimum V_{OH} is not guaranteed.

☐ I_{OL} (Output Current, LOW) is defined as the maximum current into the output pin of a logic function when the output is in the logic LOW state. The value of I_{OL} determine how many inputs the logic function may drive when the output is in the LOW state. For Standard TTL the minimum guaranteed I_{OL} is 16 mA, which is sufficient to drive 10 Standard TTL inputs at 1.6 mA each in the LOW state. I_{OL} is considered an operating condition that is not to be exceeded. If it is exceeded, then the maximum V_{OL} is not guaranteed.

In addition to the input and output characteristics, Tables 1-1 and 1-2 show the following characteristics for each logic family: operating temperature range (TEMP), operating voltage range (V_{CC}), maximum power supply current (I_{CC}), and maximum propagation delay (DELAY). I_{CC} is specified at maximum V_{CC}, unless otherwise noted. Voltage waveforms for propagation delay times are shown in Fig. 1-1. See supplier data books for input rise and fall times and the values of the measurement reference points on the input and output waveforms. The delay data in Tables 1-1 and 1-2 may be either t_{PLH} or t_{PHL}, whichever is worse. For 54/74 families, I_{CC} and delay data are for a type '00 Quad 2-Input NAND Gate. For 4000 Series families, the power supply current and propagation delay data are for a type 4000 Dual 3-Input NOR Gate Plus Inverter.

The sources for the data in Tables 1-1 and 1-2 are Texas Instruments' data books, except as follows:

Fairchild data books:	54/74AC, 54/74ACT, 54/74F
National data book:	54/74C
RCA data book:	4000A, 4000B, 4000UB

In the remainder of this chapter, I present schematics and brief discussions of the particular characteristics of each of the logic families. The bipolar logic families are covered first and are presented in historical order (as opposed to the alphabetic order shown in Tables 1-1 and 1-2).

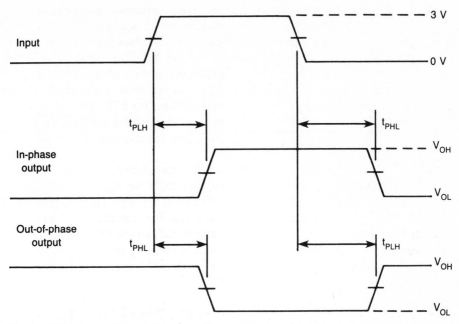

Fig. 1-1. Voltage waveforms for propagation delay times.

1.2 54/74 STANDARD TTL

Figure 1-2 shows the schematic of a Standard TTL NAND gate. The figure shown is a schematic of one of four circuits of either the 5400 or the 7400 Quad 2-Input NAND gate. TTL stands for Transistor-Transistor Logic, a logic family of ICs implemented in a bipolar process technology that combines NPN transistors, PN diodes, and diffused resistors in a single monolithic structure. This logic family quickly became the dominant logic family of the late 1960s and 70s, obsoleting the earlier logic families of RTL (Resistor-Transistor Logic) and DTL (Diode-Transistor Logic).

Q1 is a two-emitter transistor and is equivalent to two NPN transistors in parallel with the base terminals tied together and the collector terminals tied together. When both the A or B inputs are HIGH (V_{IH} = 2 V minimum), current flows through R1 and the base-collector diode of Q1 and into the base of Q2, turning Q2 ON. Q2 saturates (about 0.1 volts collector to emitter), Q3 is turned OFF and Q4 is turned ON. The Y terminal output voltage V_{OL} is 0.4 V maximum (0.2 V typical) when sinking 16 mA from external loads (inputs of logic functions in other packages). Maximum input current I_{IH} is 40 μA leakage current into the pin.

When either the A or B input is LOW (V_{IL} = 0.8 V minimum), current flows through R1 and the base-emitter diode of Q1. Q2 is OFF, Q4 is OFF, and

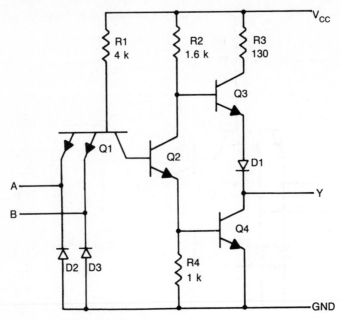

Fig. 1-2. Schematic of 54/7400 NAND gate.

Q3 is ON. The output voltage is V_{CC} minus the voltage drop across R1 (R1 times Q3 base current), the Q3 base-emitter voltage, and the forward voltage across D1. V_{OH} is 2.4 V minimum (3.4 V typical) with minimum V_{CC} and sourcing 0.4 mA. The input current I_{IL} is 1.6 mA maximum (at maximum V_{CC}) out of the input pin and is equal to V_{CC} minus the Q1 base-emitter voltage divided by R1, or $(V_{CC} - V_{BE1})/R1$.

The 54/7400 Quad NAND Gate I_{CC} is 22 mA maximum (for all four gates; 12 mA typical) when the output is LOW and 8 mA maximum (4 mA typical) when the output is HIGH. The propagation delay (the time difference between when the input changes and the output changes) for each gate is 22 nS maximum (11 nS typical) when the output is changing from LOW to HIGH and 15 nS maximum (7 nS typical) when changing from HIGH to LOW with a load resistance of 400 ohms and load capacitance of 15 pF at an ambient temperature of 25 C and V_{CC} = 5 V.

1.3 54/74L LOW POWER TTL

Figure 1-3 shows the schematic of a Low Power TTL NAND gate. The figure shown is a schematic of one of four circuits of either the 54L00 or the 74L00 Quad 2-Input NAND gate. Circuit operation is identical to the 54/7400 Standard TTL gate. Power has been reduced at the expense of decreased speed.

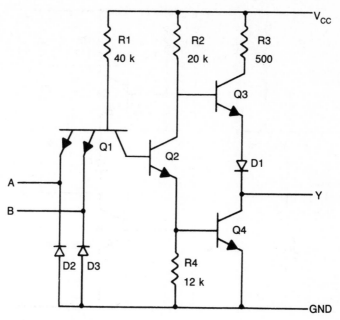

Fig. 1-3. Schematic of 54/74L00 NAND gate.

Note the increase in resistor values. In particular, R1 is increased from 4 k to 40 k. I_{IL} is decreased to 0.18 mA maximum.

The output voltage V_{OL} is 0.3 V maximum (0.15 V typical) when sinking 2 mA. V_{OH} is 2.4 V minimum (3.3 V typical) with minimum V_{CC} and sourcing 0.1 mA. I_{CC} is 2.04 mA maximum (for all four gates; 1.16 mA typical) when the output is LOW and 0.8 mA maximum (0.44 mA typical) when the output is HIGH. The propagation delay is 60 nS maximum (35 nS typical) when the output is changing from LOW to HIGH and 60 nS maximum (31 nS typical) when changing from HIGH to LOW with a load resistance of 4 k ohms and load capacitance of 50 pF at an ambient temperature of 25 C and V_{CC} = 5 V.

1.4 54/74H HIGH POWER TTL

Figure 1-4 shows the schematic of a High Power TTL NAND gate. The figure shown is a schematic of one of four circuits of either the 54H00 or the 74H00 Quad 2-Input NAND gate. The circuit design is nearly identical to the 54/7400 Standard TTL gate. The Q3-D1 combination is replaced by Q3, Q5, and R5. The speed is improved at the expense of increased power. Note the reduction in resistor values. In particular, R1 is reduced from 4 k to 2.8 k. I_{IL} is increased to 2 mA maximum.

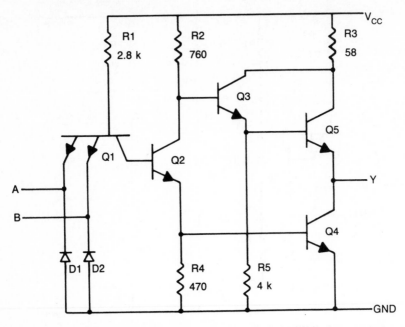

Fig. 1-4. Schematic of 54/74H00 NAND gate.

The output voltage V_{OL} is 0.4 V maximum (0.2 V typical) when sinking 20 mA. V_{OH} is 2.4 V minimum (3.5 V typical) with minimum V_{CC} and sourcing 0.5 mA. I_{CC} is 40 mA maximum (for all four gates; 26 mA typical) when the output is LOW and 16.8 mA maximum (10 mA typical) when the output is HIGH. The propagation delay is 10 nS maximum (5.9 nS typical) when the output is changing from LOW to HIGH and 10 nS maximum (6.2 nS typical) when changing from HIGH to LOW with a load resistance of 280 ohms and load capacitance of 25 pF at an ambient temperature of 25 C and V_{CC} = 5 V.

1.5 54/74S SCHOTTKY TTL

Figure 1-5 shows the schematic of a Schottky TTL NAND gate. The figure shown is a schematic of one of four circuits of either the 54S00 or the 74S00 Quad 2-Input NAND gate. The circuit is nearly identical to the 54/74H00 High Power TTL gate. The speed is improved by using Schottky transistors in place of all transistors except Q5, where the use of a Schottky Q3 makes a Schottky Q5 unnecessary. (Note the different symbol. The Schottky transistor is denoted by an ''s'' type base instead of a straight line.)

A Schottky transistor is a standard NPN transistor with a Schottky diode connected from base to collector. The Schottky diode is a metal-semiconductor

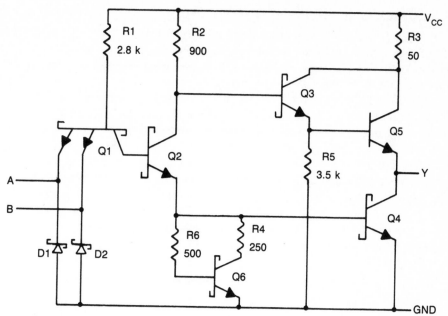

Fig. 1-5. Schematic of 54/74S00 NAND gate.

diode as opposed to a junction diode. The Schottky diode has about half the forward voltage of a junction diode for the same current—0.4 V instead of 0.7 V as a rule of thumb. Also, the Schottky diode is faster than a junction diode. When a Schottky diode is placed across the base-collector junction of an NPN transistor, it prevents the transistor from going into full saturation, i.e. the collector-emitter voltage is clamped to about 0.3 V instead of 0.1 V. Therefore, collector voltage swing is reduced. More important, excess base current goes through the Schottky instead of into the base of the transistor. As a result, the switching speed of the transistor is improved. The 54/74S00 is twice as fast as the 54/74H00 for approximately the same power.

The output voltage V_{OL} is 0.5 V maximum when sinking 20 mA. The 54S00 V_{OH} is 2.5 V minimum (3.4 V typical) with minimum V_{CC} and sourcing 0.5 mA. The 74S00 V_{OH} is 2.7 V minimum (3.4 V typical) with minimum V_{CC} and sourcing 1 mA. I_{CC} is 36 mA maximum (for all four gates; 20 mA typical) when the output is LOW and 16 mA maximum (10 mA typical) when the output is HIGH. The propagation delay is 5 nS maximum (3 nS typical) when the output is changing from LOW to HIGH and 4.5 nS maximum (3 nS typical) when changing from HIGH to LOW with a load resistance of 280 ohms and load capacitance of 15 pF at an ambient temperature of 25 C and $V_{CC} = 5$ V.

1.6 54/74LS LOW POWER SCHOTTKY TTL

Figure 1-6 shows the schematic of a Low Power Schottky TTL NAND gate. The figure shown is a schematic of one of four circuits of either the 54LS00 or the 74LS00 Quad 2-Input NAND gate. Resistor values have been increased to reduce power at the expense of speed.

The 54/74LS00 V_{OL} is 0.4 V maximum (0.25 V typical) when sinking 4 mA. The 74LS00 V_{OH} is 0.5 V maximum (0.35 V typical) when sinking 8 mA. The 54LS00 V_{OH} is 2.5 V minimum (3.4 V typical) with minimum V_{CC} and sourcing 0.4 mA. The 74LS00 V_{OH} is 2.7 V minimum (3.4 V typical) with minimum V_{CC} and sourcing 0.4 mA. I_{CC} is 4.4 mA maximum (for all four gates; 2.4 mA typical) when the output is LOW and 1.6 mA maximum (0.8 mA typical) when the output is HIGH. The propagation delay is 15 nS maximum (9 nS typical) when the output is changing from LOW to HIGH and 15 nS maximum (10 nS typical) when changing from HIGH to LOW with a load resistance of 2 k ohms and load capacitance of 15 pF at an ambient temperature of 25 C and V_{CC} = 5 V.

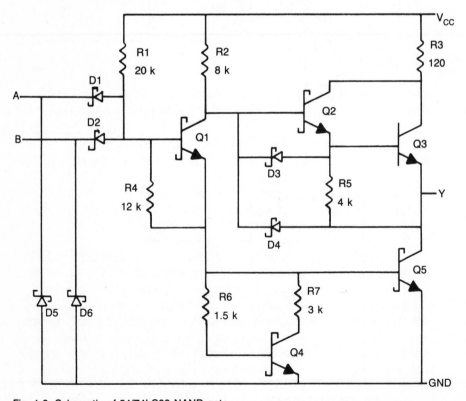

Fig. 1-6. Schematic of 54/74LS00 NAND gate.

1.7 54/74ALS ADVANCED LOW POWER SCHOTTKY TTL

Figure 1-7 shows the schematic of an Advanced Low Power Schottky TTL NAND gate. The figure shown is a schematic of one of four circuits of either the 54ALS00 or the 74ALS00 Quad 2-Input NAND gate. Notice the use of PNP input transistors. Not only is the circuit design different from the previous families, the basic fabrication process is different. The ALS process uses oxide isolation between transistors (the previous families use junction isolation), smaller geometries, a thinner epitaxial layer, and ion implantation. The result: even faster transistors, and, therefore, reduced propagation delay for logic functions. A detailed description of Fig. 1-7 may be found in the Texas Instruments *ALS/AS Logic Data Book.*

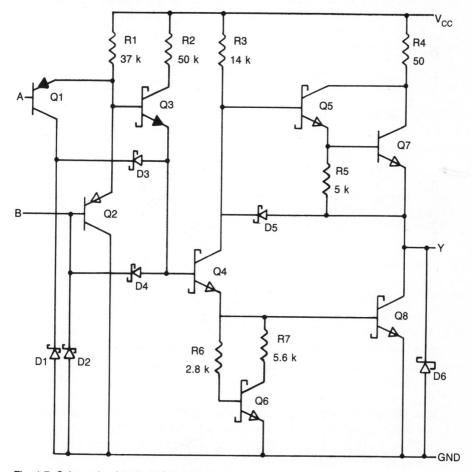

Fig. 1-7. Schematic of 54/74ALS00 NAND gate.

The 54/74ALS00 V_{OL} is 0.4 V maximum (0.25 V typical) when sinking 4 mA. The 74ALS00 V_{OH} is 0.5 V maximum (0.35 V typical) when sinking 8 mA. V_{OH} is 2.5 V minimum with minimum V_{CC} and sourcing 0.4 mA. I_{CC} is 3 mA maximum (for all four gates; 1.5 mA typical) when the output is LOW and 0.85 mA maximum (0.5 mA typical) when the output is HIGH.

54ALS00 propagation delay is 16 nS maximum (3 nS minimum) when the output is changing from LOW to HIGH and 13 nS maximum (2 nS minimum) when changing from HIGH to LOW with a load resistance of 500 ohms and load capacitance of 50 pF over the operating temperature and voltage range. For the same conditions, 74ALS00 propagation delay is 11 nS maximum (3 nS minimum) when the output is changing from LOW to HIGH and 8 nS maximum (2 nS minimum) when changing from HIGH to LOW. Note that previous TTL families specified delay only at 25 C and V_{CC} = 5 V. For this condition, the 54/74ALS00 is an average 1.65 times faster than 54/74LS00, even though 54/74ALS00 is specified for worse load conditions than 54/74LS00:

Quad NAND Gate	Typical Delays at 25 C and 5 V	
	L $\longrightarrow$ H	H $\longrightarrow$ L
54/74LS00 driving 2 k and 15 pF:	9 nS	10 nS
54/74ALS00 driving 500 ohms and 50 pF:	7 nS	5 nS
Improvement factor (ratio):	1.3	2.0

This much improvement is not apparent from Tables 1-1 and 1-2. As has been mentioned, the data in these tables is over the operating temperature range unless otherwise noted. Note 2 states that DELAY is at 25 C and 5 V and is applicable to the previously discussed 54/74 families, but not to 54/74ALS and some of the other logic families to be discussed. Therefore, be careful when you are using these tables to compare the speeds of logic families.

1.8 54/74AS ADVANCED SCHOTTKY TTL

Figure 1-8 shows the schematic of an Advanced Schottky TTL NAND gate. The figure shown is a schematic of one of four circuits of either the 54AS00 or the 74AS00 Quad 2-Input NAND gate. A detailed description of Fig. 1-8 may be found in the Texas Instruments *ALS/AS Logic Data Book*.

The 54/74AS00 V_{OL} is 0.5 V maximum (0.35 V typical) when sinking 20 mA. V_{OH} is 2.5 V minimum with minimum V_{CC} and sourcing 2 mA. I_{CC} is 17.4 mA maximum (for all four gates; 10.8 mA typical) when the output is LOW and 3.2 mA maximum (2 mA typical) when the output is HIGH.

54AS00 propagation delay is 5 nS maximum (1 nS minimum) when the output is changing either from LOW to HIGH or from HIGH to LOW with a load resistance of 50 ohms and load capacitance of 50 pF over the operating temperature

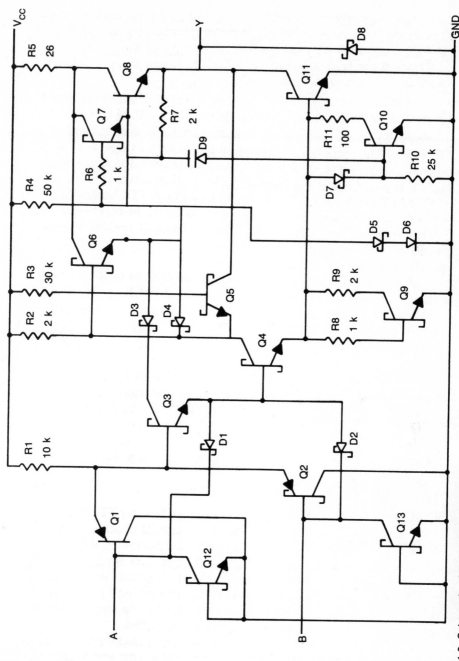

Fig. 1-8. Schematic of 54/74AS00 NAND gate.

and voltage range. For the same conditions, 74AS00 propagation delay is 4.5 nS maximum (1 nS minimum) when the output is changing from LOW to HIGH and 4 nS maximum (1 nS minimum) when changing from HIGH to LOW.

The most significant improvement in 54/74AS00 over the 54/74S00 is I_{CC} reduction: 17.4 mA, down from 36 mA.

1.9 54/74F FAIRCHILD ADVANCED SCHOTTKY TTL (FAST)

Figure 1-9 shows the schematic of the Fairchild Advanced Schottky TTL NAND gate. The figure shown is a schematic of one of four circuits of either the 54F00 or the 74F00 Quad 2-Input NAND gate. A detailed description of Fig. 1-9 may be found in the Fairchild *FAST Data Book*.

The 54/74F00 V_{OL} is 0.5 V maximum (0.30 V typical) when sinking 20 mA. 54F00 V_{OH} is 2.5 V minimum with minimum V_{CC} and sourcing 1 mA. 74F00 V_{OH} is 2.7 V minimum with minimum V_{CC} and sourcing 1 mA. I_{CC} is 10.2 mA maximum (for all four gates; 6.8 mA typical) when the output is LOW and 2.8 mA maximum (1.9 mA typical) when the output is HIGH.

54F00 propagation delay is 7 nS maximum (2 nS minimum) when the output is changing from LOW to HIGH and 6.5 nS maximum (1.5 nS minimum) when

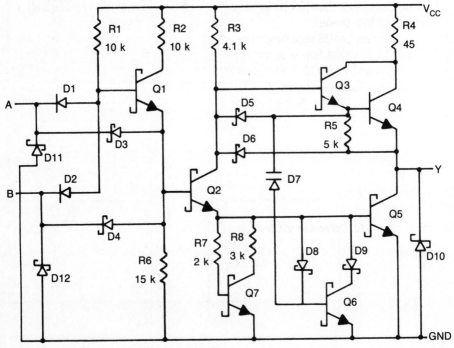

Fig. 1-9. Schematic of 54/74F00 NAND gate.

the output is changing from HIGH to LOW with a load resistance of 500 ohms and load capacitance of 50 pF over the operating temperature and voltage range. For the same conditions, 74F00 propagation delay is 5.3 nS maximum (1.5 nS minimum) when the output is changing from LOW to HIGH and 6 nS maximum (2.4 nS minimum) when changing from HIGH to LOW.

The most significant improvement in 54/74F is I_{CC} reduction:

Quad NAND Gate	**Max I_{cc}**
54/74S00	36 mA
54/74AS00	17.4 mA
54/74F00	10.2 mA

1.10 4000A SERIES CMOS

The schematics of the basic CMOS inverter, NAND gate, and NOR gate are shown in Figs. 1-10, 1-11, and 1-12, respectively. These schematics apply to all CMOS logic families: the differences in the CMOS logic families are in the fabrication processes, not in the circuit design. These schematics demonstrate the topological simplicity of CMOS, which requires considerably less silicon area than bipolar logic. The result is very high density of gates per chip and low power.

The first CMOS logic family was the 4000 "A" Series from RCA. See Tables 1-1 and 1-2. 4000A Series operates from 3 to 12 V with data sheet limits specified at both 5 and 10 V (15 V for quiescent current and input current limits). The input threshold ranges from 30% to 70% of the power supply voltage V_{DD}. The maximum V_{NL} (Input Noise Immunity Voltage, LOW; corresponds to V_{IL}) is a

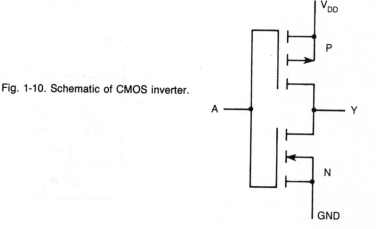

Fig. 1-10. Schematic of CMOS inverter.

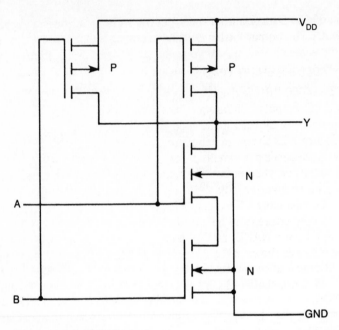

Fig. 1-11. Schematic of CMOS NAND gate.

minimum of 30% of V_{DD}, or 1.5 V for V_{DD} = 5 V. The minimum V_{NH} (Input Noise Immunity Voltage, HIGH; corresponds to V_{IH}) is a maximum of 70% of V_{DD}, 3.5 V for V_{DD} 5 V. Input leakage current (I_{IL}, I_{IH}) is + or − 1 μA.

As for output characteristics, 4000A CMOS swings almost to the voltage rails when driving light loads (4.95 V minimum for logic HIGH state, 0.05 V maximum for logic LOW state; V_{DD} = 5 V and I_{OH} or I_{OL} less than 1 μA). At V_{OH} = 2.5 V the output can source a minimum of 0.24 mA at 85 C (industrial temperature grade devices) or 0.35 mA at 125 C (military temperature grade devices). At V_{OL} = 0.5 V the output can sink a minimum of 0.24 mA at 85 C or 0.28 mA at 125 C.

Quiescent current I_{DD} for a type 4000A Dual 3-Input NOR Gate Plus Inverter is 3 μA maximum at 125 C and 15 μA at 85 C. These numbers are not backwards. Military grade devices have tighter limits.

Propagation delay at 5 V and 25 C for a type 4000A NOR gate industrial grade is 80 nS maximum (35 nS typical) when the output is changing from HIGH to LOW and 120 nS maximum (35 nS typical) when the output is changing from LOW to HIGH. The output load is 15 pF.

Propagation delay at 5 V and 25 C for a type 4000A NOR gate military grade is 50 nS maximum (35 nS typical) when the output is changing from HIGH to

LOW and 95 nS maximum (35 nS typical) when the output is changing from LOW to HIGH. The output load is 15 pF.

1.11 4000B SERIES CMOS

The 4000 "B" Series is a high voltage version of the "A" Series and also buffers all outputs. Buffering is used to make the output "on" impedance independent of all valid input logic conditions.

Figure 1-12 shows an unbuffered NOR gate. The output "on" impedance will vary, depending on whether one or both N-channel devices are ON (for logic LOW output) or whether both P-channel devices are ON (for logic HIGH output). Only with an inverter (Fig. 1-10) can the output "on" resistance for all logic inputs be guaranteed. To create a buffered NOR gate from an unbuffered NOR gate, two inverters must be added to the output. Or, a buffered NOR gate can be made from a NAND gate by adding an inverter to the output and to each of the inputs as shown in Fig. 1-13. More information on buffered and unbuffered CMOS gates can be found in RCA application note ICAN-6558, "Understanding Buffered and Unbuffered CMOS Characteristics," in the RCA *CMOS Data Book*.

V_{NH}, V_{NL}, I_{IH}, I_{IL}, V_{OH}, V_{OL} of the 4000B Series are the same as the 4000A

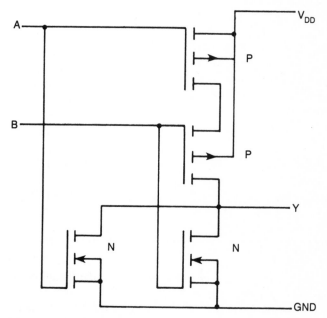

Fig. 1-12. Schematic of CMOS NOR gate.

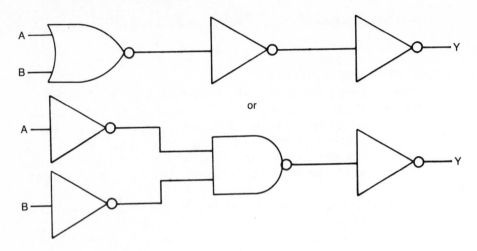

Fig. 1-13. Logic diagrams of a buffered NOR gate.

Series. At V_{OH} = 2.5 V the output can source a minimum of 0.42 mA at 85 C (industrial temperature grade devices) or 0.36 mA at 125 C (military temperature grade devices). At V_{OL} = 0.5 V the output can sink a minimum of 0.42 mA at 85 C or 0.36 mA at 125 C.

Quiescent current I_{DD} for a type 4000B Dual 3-Input NOR Gate Plus Inverter is 7.5 μA maximum at 125 C and at 85 C. In other words, the military and industrial temperature grade devices have the same limits.

Propagation delay at 5 V and 25 C for a type 4000B NOR gate industrial or military grade is 250 nS maximum (125 nS typical) when the output is changing from HIGH to LOW or when the output is changing from LOW to HIGH. The output load is 200 k ohms and 50 pF.

1.12 4000UB SERIES CMOS

The 4000 "UB" Series is a high voltage version of the "A" Series (or an unbuffered version of the "B" Series). V_{NL} maximum is a minimum of 20% of V_{DD}, or 1 V for V_{DD} = 5 V. V_{NH} minimum is a maximum of 80% of V_{DD}, or 4 V for V_{DD} = 5 V. The output characteristics are the same as the "B" Series. Quiescent current I_{DD} for a type 4000UB Dual 3-Input NOR Gate Plus Inverter is the same as the 4000B.

Propagation delay at 5 V and 25 C for a type 4000UB NOR gate industrial or military grade is 120 nS maximum (60 nS typical) when the output is changing from HIGH to LOW or when the output is changing from LOW to HIGH. The output load is 200 k ohms and 50 pF.

1.13 54/74C CMOS

National Semiconductor was the first manufacturer to provide pin-for-pin replacements in CMOS for the 54/74 logic functions. The result: the 54/74C CMOS logic family.

Input characteristics are the same as 4000A and 4000B Series CMOS. Output levels V_{OH} and V_{OL} are specified at 10 μA (instead of less than 1 μA for 4000 Series) and are 4.5 V and 0.5 V, respectively, at V_{DD} = 5 V. However, at an I_{OH} of 0.36 mA, V_{OH} is 2.4 V maximum. At an I_{OL} of 0.36 mA, V_{OL} is 0.4 V minimum. This means that 54/74C logic functions can drive 54/74L logic functions. Typical I_{DD} for the 54/74C00 Quad 2-Input NAND Gate is 0.01 μA at V_{DD} = 15 V.

54/74C00 propagation delay for the output going HIGH or LOW is 90 nS maximum (50 nS typical) at V_{DD} = 5 V and an ambient temperature of 25 C. The output load is 50 pF.

1.14 54/74HC HIGH SPEED CMOS

In the early 1980s, National, Motorola, RCA, and Texas Instruments all came out with high speed CMOS versions of the basic 54/74 logic functions. 54/74HC is fabricated using silicon-gate CMOS technology. Previous CMOS logic families were fabricated using metal-gate CMOS.

Simplified cross-section drawings of a metal-gate and a silicon-gate N-channel MOS transistor are shown in Fig. 1-14. Metal-gate CMOS uses metal over a thin oxide to form the gate between the source and drain areas. Silicon-gate uses polycrystalline silicon (or polysilicon, or poly) over a thin oxide to form the gate.

Notice in Fig. 1-14A that the thin-oxide region overlaps the drain and source areas for the metal-gate process. This is necessary in order to guarantee that with mask misalignment that the P-area between the source and drain is covered with the thin gate oxide. In Fig. 1-14B, the poly is formed first, then used as a mask in the formation of the drain and source areas. Gate coverage is, therefore, guaranteed. The process is said to be self-aligned. If all other process rules were the same, this difference alone would allow for the creation of at least slightly smaller transistors. This reduces parasitic capacitance and reduces delay time.

All other process rules are not the same however. In the earlier metal-gate 4000 Series CMOS process, the distance between the source and drain areas, or the gate length, was 7 microns. In the newer 54/74HC silicon-gate process, the gate length is 3.5 microns. This is the main reason for the speed improvement between metal-gate and silicon-gate.

54/74HC operates over a V_{DD} range of 2 to 6 V. Minimum V_{IH} is 3.15 V

Ⓐ Metal-gate transistor

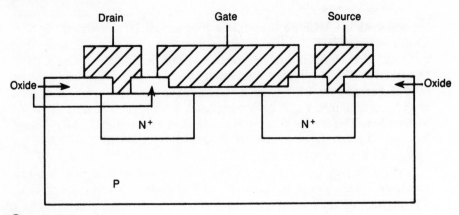

Ⓑ Silicon-gate transistor

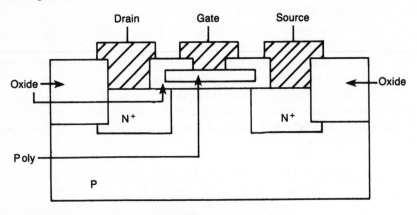

Fig. 1-14. Metal-gate and silicon-gate CMOS transistor structures.

at V_{DD} = 4.5 V. V_{IL} is 0.9 maximum at V_{DD} = 4.5 V. Input current, I_{IH} or I_{IL}, is + or − 1 μA for V_{DD} = 6 V for the input at either zero or 6 V.

54HC V_{OH} is 3.7 V minimum sourcing an I_{OH} of 4 mA at V_{DD} = 4.5 V. 74HC V_{OH} is 3.84 V minimum for the same conditions.

54HC V_{OL} is 0.4 V maximum sinking an I_{OL} of 4 mA at V_{DD} = 4.5 V. 74HC V_{OL} is 0.33 V maximum for the same conditions.

54HC00 I_{DD} is 40 μA maximum at V_{DD} = 6 V. 74HC00 I_{DD} is 20 μA maximum.

54HC00 propagation delay is 27 nS maximum over the operating temperature range while driving 50 pF at V_{DD} = 4.5 V. 74HC00 delay is 23 nS for the same conditions. 54/74HC00 delay at 25 C and 4.5 V is 18 nS maximum, 9 nS typical.

1.15 54/74HCT HIGH SPEED CMOS

54/74HCT is basically a process variation of 54/74HC. The main difference is that the input thresholds (V_{IH}, V_{IL}) and the output levels (V_{OH}, V_{OL}) are compatible with the bipolar TTL logic families. This means that you could pull a 74 LS00 out of an existing board and plug in a 74HC00 if your system could work with the slightly slower 74HC00. Or more likely, you can mix 54/74HCT with the bipolar 54/74 families, using the HCT parts wherever possible to keep the power dissipation as low as possible. HCT parts are slightly slower than the HC versions. See Tables 1-1 and 1-2.

1.16 54/74AC FAIRCHILD ADVANCED CMOS TECHNOLOGY (FACT)

54/74AC is the latest, and the fastest, CMOS logic family. Fairchild's 54/74AC Advanced CMOS Technology (FACT) family outperforms all logic families shown in Tables 1-1 and 1-2 except 54/74S and 54/74AS. FACT has the best combination of high speed, low power, and high output drive of any logic family. Unfortunately, at the time this is being written (July 1987), there are relatively few part types available. However, expect the catalog of FACT parts to fill out in the near future.

Input characteristics are the same as 54/74HC except V_{IL} is slightly higher at 1.35 V maximum. V_{OH} is 3.7 V minimum at I_{OH} = 24 mA at V_{DD} = 4.5 V. V_{OL} is 0.4 V minimum at I_{OL} = 24 mA at V_{DD} = 4.5 V. 54AC00 I_{DD} is 0.1 mA maximum at V_{DD} = 5.5 V. 74AC00 I_{DD} is 0.05 mA at V_{DD} = 5.5 V.

54AC00 propagation delay is 8.5 nS maximum (LOW to HIGH; 8 nS maximum, HIGH to LOW) over the operating temperature range at V_{DD} = 4.5 V driving 50 pF. 74AC00 delay is 8.5 nS maximum (LOW to HIGH; 7.5 nS maximum, HIGH to LOW) for the same conditions. 54/74AC00 delay at 25 C and 4.5 V is 5 nS typical LOW to HIGH and 4 nS typical HIGH to LOW.

1.17 54/74ACT FAIRCHILD ADVANCED CMOS TECHNOLOGY (FACT)

54/74ACT is a process variation of 54/74AC. Like HCT, ACT input thresholds and output voltage levels are compatible with the bipolar TTL families. ACT speed is slightly slower than AC. At the time this is being written, the 54/74ACT00 does not exist. However, for comparison purposes, I have estimated that the 54/74ACT00 will be 4 nS slower worst case than the AC version. This estimate is based on a comparison of the 54/74ACT240 and 241 to the AC versions of the 240 and 241.

1.18 OUTPUT STRUCTURES

In the above discussions of logic families, the output characteristics are based on the *standard output*, which was shown in the schematics. The standard output has both a pull-up transistor and a pull-down transistor. For CMOS families there may be one or more pull-up transistors in series or in parallel, and there may be one or more pull-down transistors in series or in parallel. See Figs. 1-10 through 1-12.

The standard, or *totem-pole*, output for the 54/74 Standard TTL logic family is shown in Fig. 1-2 (a single NAND gate). The pull-up transistor is Q3. The pull-down transistor is Q4. The other bipolar families are basically the same.

There are two other types of output structures: *open-collector* (or open-drain for CMOS), and *3-state* (TRI-STATE® is a registered trademark of National Semiconductor).

The open-collector output does not have a pull-up transistor. The open-collector version of the NAND gate shown in Fig. 1-2 has R3, Q3, and D1 removed. Open-collector versions of logic functions may be used either to interface to high-voltage loads on to interface easily to CMOS logic families.

The 3-state output is the same as the standard output except that additional circuitry has been added so that both the pull-up and the pull-down transistor may be turned OFF using an external output control line. When both the pull-up and the pull-down transistor are OFF, this is called the *high impedance* state, or HI-Z. The three states are then HIGH, LOW, and HI-Z. The advantage of logic functions with 3-state outputs is that multiple logic functions may to tied to a single line. The most common application is in microprocessor applications where many 8-bit wide logic functions are tied to a common data bus. The 3-state control lines of each logic function are used to activate only one logic function at a time on the bus. The requirement is that the system design must insure that only one logic function is driving the bus at one time, otherwise unwanted bus contention will occur.

Chapter 2

Gates

Gates and flip-flops are the fundamental building blocks of digital systems. In these days of VLSI (Very Large Scale Integration)—of 32-bit microprocessors and 50,000-gate gate arrays— it's hard to believe that back in the 1960s mainframe computers were built using gates and flip-flops (and core memory). Now, gates and flip-flops and other SSI (Small Scale Integration) circuits are the "glue" logic of complex microprocessor-based systems, including personal computers and digital signal processors.

Chapter 3 covers flip-flops. In this chapter, I present logic diagrams, function tables, descriptions, and selection guides for the following types of gates:

☐ Inverters
☐ NAND Gates
☐ NOR Gates
☐ AND Gates
☐ OR Gates
☐ Exclusive-OR and Exclusive-NOR Gates
☐ Schmitt-Trigger Gates
☐ AND-OR-INVERT Gates

2.1 INVERTERS

The logic diagram and function table for an inverter is shown in Fig. 2-1. When the input is LOW, the output is HIGH and vice versa. Tables 2-1 through

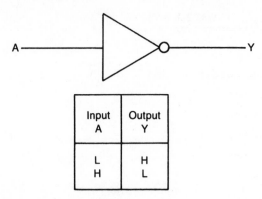

Fig. 2-1. Logic diagram and function table for inverter.

2-4 list the maximum power, maximum propagation delay, and 100-piece price for inverters from the 54/74 families and 4000 Series families.

Maximum V_{OH} for type '05 is 5.5 V (6 V for HCT). The complementary pairs in the 4007 may be wired as two separate inverters, for a total of three.

Table 2-1. Inverters, 54 Family.

TYPE	DESCRIPTION	MAX POWER (mW)	MAX DELAY (nS)	PRICE ($)
5404	Hex Inverters	181.50	22.0	1.03
54ALS04	Hex Inverters	23.10	14.0	0.84
54C04	Hex Inverters	0.23	90.0	1.30
54F04	Hex Inverters	84.15	7.0	1.16
54HC04	Hex Inverters	0.24	29.0	0.57
54HCT04	Hex Inverters	0.22	30.0	0.64
54LS04	Hex Inverters	36.30	15.0	0.56
54S04	Hex Inverters	297.00	5.0	1.22
5405	Hex Inverters with Open-Collector Outputs	181.50	55.0	1.06
54ALS05	Hex Inverters with Open-Collector Outputs	23.10	84.0	0.84
54HC05	Hex Inverters with Open-Drain Outputs	0.24	35.0	1.00
54HCT05	Hex Inverters with Open-Drain Outputs	0.22	33.0	1.05
54LS05	Hex Inverters with Open-Collector Outputs	36.30	32.0	0.56
54S05	Hex Inverters with Open-Collector Outputs	297.00	7.5	1.29

Table 2-2. Inverters, 74 Family.

TYPE	DESCRIPTION	MAX POWER (mW)	MAX DELAY (nS)	PRICE ($)
7404	Hex Inverters	173.25	22.0	0.26
74ALS04	Hex Inverters	23.10	11.0	0.34
74AS04	Hex Inverters	144.65	5.0	0.51
74C04	Hex Inverters	0.23	90.0	0.33
74F04	Hex Inverters	80.33	6.0	0.26
74H04	Hex Inverters	304.50	10.0	3.29
74HC04	Hex Inverters	0.12	31.0	0.38
74HCT04	Hex Inverters	0.11	25.0	0.33
74L04	Hex Inverters	16.07	60.0	0.90
74LS04	Hex Inverters	34.65	15.0	0.23
74S04	Hex Inverters	283.50	5.0	0.29
7405	Hex Inverters with Open-Collector Outputs	173.25	55.0	0.26
74ALS05	Hex Inverters with Open-Collector Outputs	23.10	54.0	0.34
74H05	Hex Inverters with Open-Collector Outputs	304.50	15.0	3.29
74HC05	Hex Inverters with Open-Drain Outputs	0.12	29.0	0.38
74HCT05	Hex Inverters with Open-Drain Outputs	0.11	28.0	0.59
74LS05	Hex Inverters with Open-Collector Outputs	34.65	32.0	0.23
74S05	Hex Inverters with Open-Collector Outputs	283.50	7.5	0.29

Table 2-3. Inverters, 4000 Series, Industrial Temperature Range.

TYPE	DESCRIPTION	MAX POWER (mW)	MAX DELAY (nS)	PRICE ($)
4007A	Dual Complementary Pair plus Inverter	0.07	75.0	0.33
4007UB	Dual Complementary Pair plus Inverter	0.04	110.0	0.28
4069UB	Hex Inverter	0.04	110.0	0.28
4572UB	Hex Gate (4 Inverters, 2-Input NAND Gate, 2-Input NOR Gate)	0.02	360.0	0.64

Table 2-4. Inverters, 4000 Series, Military Temperature Range.

TYPE	DESCRIPTION	MAX POWER (mW)	MAX DELAY (nS)	PRICE ($)
4007A	Dual Complementary Pair plus Inverter	0.02	60.0	0.78
4007UB	Dual Complementary Pair plus Inverter	0.04	110.0	0.50
4069UB	Hex Inverter	0.04	110.0	0.50
4572UB	Hex Gate (4 Inverters, 2-Input NAND Gate, 2-Input NOR Gate)	0.01	360.0	0.83

In these tables and those in the remainder of this chapter and in Chapters 2 through 7, the data for propagation delay (and other timing parameters in other chapters) is not for the same conditions for all logic families, as was mentioned in Chapter 1. To repeat, delay data is at 25 C and V_{CC} = 5 V for all logic families except 54/74AC, 'ACT, 'ALS, 'AS, 'F, 'HC, and 'HCT (7 of the 16 logic families), where delay data is over the operating power supply voltage and temperature range (see Tables 1-1 and 1-2 in Chapter 1).

2.2 NAND GATES

The logic diagram and function table for a 2-input NAND gate is shown in Fig. 2-2. When any input is LOW, the output is HIGH; the output is LOW only

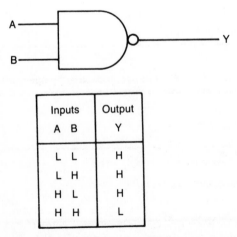

Inputs A B	Output Y
L L	H
L H	H
H L	H
H H	L

Fig. 2-2. Logic diagram and function table for NAND gate.

if both inputs are HIGH. Tables 2-5 through 2-8 list the maximum power, maximum propagation delay, and 100-piece price for NAND gates from the 54/74 families and 4000 Series families.

The only difference between the '01 and the '03 is the pinout. Maximum V_{OH} for open-collector types is 5.5 V.

Table 2-5. NAND Gates, 54 Family.

TYPE	DESCRIPTION	MAX POWER (mW)	MAX DELAY (nS)	PRICE ($)
5400	Quad 2-Input NAND Gates	121.00	22.0	1.00
54AC00	Quad 2-Input NAND Gates	0.55	8.5	2.65
54ALS00	Quad 2-Input NAND Gates	16.50	16.0	0.84
54C00	Quad 2-Input NAND Gates	0.23	90.0	2.14
54F00	Quad 2-Input NAND Gates	56.10	7.0	1.16
54HC00	Quad 2-Input NAND Gates	0.24	27.0	0.57
54HCT00	Quad 2-Input NAND Gates	0.22	30.0	0.64
54L00	Quad 2-Input NAND Gates	11.22	60.0	8.30
54LS00	Quad 2-Input NAND Gates	24.20	15.0	0.56
54S00	Quad 2-Input NAND Gates	198.00	5.0	1.22
5401	Quad 2-Input NAND Gates with Open-Collector Outputs	121.00	55.0	1.00
54ALS01	Quad 2-Input NAND Gates with Open-Collector Outputs	16.50	66.0	0.84
54LS01	Quad 2-Input NAND Gates with Open-Collector Outputs	24.20	32.0	0.56
5403	Quad 2-Input NAND Gates with Open-Collector Outputs	121.00	45.0	0.97
54ALS03	Quad 2-Input NAND Gates with Open-Collector Outputs	16.50	59.0	0.84
54HC03	Quad 2-Input NAND Gates with Open-Collector Outputs	0.24	36.0	0.66
54LS03	Quad 2-Input NAND Gates with Open-Collector Outputs	24.20	32.0	0.56
54S03	Quad 2-Input NAND Gates with Open-Collector Outputs	198.00	7.5	1.22
5410	Triple 3-Input NAND Gates	90.75	22.0	1.00
54ALS10	Triple 3-Input NAND Gates	12.10	16.0	0.84

TYPE	DESCRIPTION	MAX POWER (mW)	MAX DELAY (nS)	PRICE ($)
54C10	Triple 3-Input NAND Gates	0.23	100.0	2.14
54F10	Triple 3-Input NAND Gates	42.35	7.0	1.16
54HC10	Triple 3-Input NAND Gates	0.24	30.0	0.57
54HCT10	Triple 3-Input NAND Gates	0.22	36.0	0.64
54L10	Triple 3-Input NAND Gates	8.42	60.0	5.23
54LS10	Triple 3-Input NAND Gates	18.15	15.0	0.56
54S10	Triple 3-Input NAND Gates	148.50	5.0	1.22
5412	Triple 3-Input NAND Gates with Open-Collector Outputs	90.75	45.0	1.36
54ALS12	Triple 3-Input NAND Gates with Open-Collector Outputs	12.10	59.0	0.84
54LS12	Triple 3-Input NAND Gates with Open-Collector Outputs	18.15	32.0	0.56
5420	Dual 4-Input NAND Gates	60.50	22.0	1.02
54ALS20	Dual 4-Input NAND Gates	8.25	18.0	0.84
54F20	Dual 4-Input NAND Gates	28.05	7.0	1.16
54HC20	Dual 4-Input NAND Gates	0.24	33.0	0.57
54HCT20	Dual 4-Input NAND Gates	0.22	42.0	0.64
54LS20	Dual 4-Input NAND Gates	12.10	15.0	0.56
54S20	Dual 4-Input NAND Gates	99.00	5.0	1.22
54ALS22	Dual 4-Input NAND Gates with Open-Collector Outputs	8.25	65.0	0.84
54LS22	Dual 4-Input NAND Gates with Open-Collector Outputs	12.10	32.0	0.56
54S22	Dual 4-Input NAND Gates with Open-Collector Outputs	99.00	7.5	1.29
5430	8-Input NAND Gate	33.00	22.0	1.00
54ALS30	8-Input NAND Gate	4.95	15.0	0.84
54C30	8-Input NAND Gate	0.23	180.0	2.14
54HC30	8-Input NAND Gate	0.24	39.0	0.57
54HCT30	8-Input NAND Gate	0.22	45.0	0.64
54LS30	8-Input NAND Gate	6.05	20.0	0.56
54S30	8-Input NAND Gate	55.00	7.0	1.22

TYPE	DESCRIPTION	MAX POWER (mW)	MAX DELAY (nS)	PRICE ($)
54ALS133	13-Input NAND Gate	4.40	47.0	0.90
54HC133	13-Input NAND Gate	0.24	45.0	0.79
54LS133	13-Input NAND Gate	6.05	59.0	0.78
54S133	13-Input NAND Gate	55.00	7.0	1.36
54S134	12-Input NAND Gate with 3-State Output	137.50	7.5	1.37

Table 2-6. NAND Gates, 74 Family.

TYPE	DESCRIPTION	MAX POWER (mW)	MAX DELAY (nS)	PRICE ($)
7400	Quad 2-Input NAND Gates	115.50	22.0	0.26
74AC00	Quad 2-Input NAND Gates	0.28	8.5	0.33
74ALS00	Quad 2-Input NAND Gates	16.50	11.0	0.34
74AS00	Quad 2-Input NAND Gates	95.70	4.5	0.50
74C00	Quad 2-Input NAND Gates	0.23	900.0	0.26
74F00	Quad 2-Input NAND Gates	53.55	6.0	0.26
74H00	Quad 2-Input NAND Gates	210.00	10.0	3.29
74HC00	Quad 2-Input NAND Gates	0.12	23.0	0.38
74HCT00	Quad 2-Input NAND Gates	0.11	25.0	0.33
74L00	Quad 2-Input NAND Gates	10.71	60.0	0.83
74LS00	Quad 2-Input NAND Gates	23.10	15.0	0.23
74S00	Quad 2-Input NAND Gates	189.00	5.0	0.29
7401	Quad 2-Input NAND Gates with Open-Collector Outputs	115.50	55.0	0.26
74ALS01	Quad 2-Input NAND Gates with Open-Collector Outputs	16.50	54.0	0.34
74H01	Quad 2-Input NAND Gates with Open-Collector Outputs	210.00	15.0	3.29
74LS01	Quad 2-Input NAND Gates with Open-Collector Outputs	23.10	32.0	0.25
7403	Quad 2-Input NAND Gates with Open-Collector Outputs	115.50	45.0	0.26

TYPE	DESCRIPTION	MAX POWER (mW)	MAX DELAY (nS)	PRICE ($)
74ALS03	Quad 2-Input NAND Gates with Open-Collector Outputs	16.50	50.0	0.34
74HC03	Quad 2-Input NAND Gates with Open-Drain Outputs	0.12	23.0	0.38
74LS03	Quad 2-Input NAND Gates with Open-Collector Outputs	23.10	32.0	0.23
74S03	Quad 2-Input NAND Gates with Open-Collector Outputs	189.00	7.5	0.29
7410	Triple 3-Input NAND Gates	86.62	22.0	0.26
74ALS10	Triple 3-Input NAND Gates	12.10	11.0	0.34
74AS10	Triple 3-Input NAND Gates	71.50	4.5	0.50
74C10	Triple 3-Input NAND Gates	0.23	100.0	0.26
74F10	Triple 3-Input NAND Gates	40.43	6.0	0.26
74H10	Triple 3-Input NAND Gates	157.50	10.0	3.29
74HC10	Triple 3-Input NAND Gates	0.12	25.0	0.38
74HCT10	Triple 3-Input NAND Gates	0.11	30.0	0.33
74L10	Triple 3-Input NAND Gates	8.03	60.0	0.83
74LS10	Triple 3-Input NAND Gates	17.32	15.0	0.23
74S10	Triple 3-Input NAND Gates	141.75	5.0	0.29
7412	Triple 3-Input NAND Gates with Open-Collector Outputs	86.62	45.0	0.41
74ALS12	Triple 3-Input NAND Gates with Open-Collector Outputs	12.10	54.0	0.34
74LS12	Triple 3-Input NAND Gates with Open-Collector Outputs	17.32	32.0	0.23
7420	Dual 4-Input NAND Gates	57.75	22.0	0.26
74ALS20	Dual 4-Input NAND Gates	8.25	11.0	0.34
74AS20	Dual 4-Input NAND Gates	47.85	5.0	0.50
74C20	Dual 4-Input NAND Gates	0.23	115.0	0.26
74F20	Dual 4-Input NAND Gates	26.77	6.0	0.26
74H20	Dual 4-Input NAND Gates	105.00	10.0	3.29

TYPE	DESCRIPTION	MAX POWER (mW)	MAX DELAY (nS)	PRICE ($)
74HC20	Dual 4-Input NAND Gates	0.12	25.0	0.38
74HCT20	Dual 4-Input NAND Gates	0.11	35.0	0.33
74L20	Dual 4-Input NAND Gates	5.36	60.0	0.83
74LS20	Dual 4-Input NAND Gates	11.55	15.0	0.23
74S20	Dual 4-Input NAND Gates	94.50	5.0	0.29
7422	Dual 4-Input NAND Gates with Open-Collector Outputs	57.75	45.0	0.41
74ALS22	Dual 4-Input NAND Gates with Open-Collector Outputs	8.25	45.0	0.34
74H22	Dual 4-Input NAND Gates with Open-Collector Outputs	105.00	15.0	3.29
74LS22	Dual 4-Input NAND Gates with Open-Collector Outputs	11.55	32.0	0.25
74S22	Dual 4-Input NAND Gates with Open-Collector Outputs	94.50	7.5	0.41
7430	8-Input NAND Gate	31.50	22.0	0.26
74ALS30	8-Input NAND Gate	4.95	12.0	0.34
74AS30	8-Input NAND Gate	26.95	5.0	0.50
74C30	8-Input NAND Gate	0.23	180.0	0.26
74H30	8-Input NAND Gate	52.50	12.0	3.29
74HC30	8-Input NAND Gate	0.12	33.0	0.38
74HCT30	8-Input NAND Gate	0.11	38.0	0.33
74LS30	8-Input NAND Gate	5.78	20.0	0.23
74S30	8-Input NAND Gate	52.50	7.0	0.29
74ALS133	13-Input NAND Gate	4.40	25.0	0.43
74HC133	13-Input NAND Gate	0.12	38.0	0.42
74LS133	13-Input NAND Gate	5.78	59.0	0.26
74S133	13-Input NAND Gate	52.50	7.0	0.29
74S134	12-Input NAND Gate with 3-State Output	131.25	7.5	0.58
74ALS8003	Dual 2-Input NAND Gates	8.25	11.0	0.44

Table 2-7. NAND Gates, 4000 Series, Industrial Temperature Range.

TYPE	DESCRIPTION	MAX POWER (mW)	MAX DELAY (nS)	PRICE ($)
4011A	Quad 2-Input NAND Gates	0.07	100.0	0.33
4011B	Quad 2-Input NAND Gates	0.04	250.0	0.28
4011UB	Quad 2-Input NAND Gates	0.04	120.0	0.28
4012A	Dual 4-Input NAND Gates	0.07	200.0	0.45
4012B	Dual 4-Input NAND Gates	0.04	250.0	0.28
4012UB	Dual 4-Input NAND Gates	0.04	120.0	0.28
4023A	Triple 3-Input NAND Gates	0.07	100.0	0.40
4023B	Triple 3-Input NAND Gates	0.04	250.0	0.28
4023UB	Triple 3-Input NAND Gates	0.04	120.0	0.28
4068B	8-Input NAND/AND Gate	0.04	300.0	0.28

Table 2-8. NAND Gates, 4000 Series, Military Temperature Range.

TYPE	DESCRIPTION	MAX POWER (mW)	MAX DELAY (nS)	PRICE ($)
4011A	Quad 2-Input NAND Gates	0.02	75.0	0.78
4011B	Quad 2-Input NAND Gates	0.04	250.0	0.50
4011UB	Quad 2-Input NAND Gates	0.04	120.0	0.50
4012A	Dual 4-Input NAND Gates	0.02	150.0	2.50
4012B	Dual 4-Input NAND Gates	0.04	250.0	0.50
4012UB	Dual 4-Input NAND Gates	0.04	120.0	0.50
4023A	Triple 3-Input NAND Gates	0.02	75.0	0.78
4023B	Triple 3-Input NAND Gates	0.04	250.0	0.50
4023UB	Triple 3-Input NAND Gates	0.04	120.0	0.50
4068B	8-Input NAND/AND Gate	0.04	300.0	0.50

2.3 NOR GATES

The logic diagram and function table for a 2-input NOR gate is shown in Fig. 2-3. When any input is HIGH, the output is LOW; the output is HIGH only if both inputs are LOW. Tables 2-9 through 2-12 list the maximum power, maximum propagation delay, and 100-piece price for NOR gates from the 54/74 families and 4000 Series families.

The '23 is expandable to a dual 8-input NOR gate using the '60 Dual 4-Input Expander circuit. The 54/74HC4002 is a pin-for-pin high speed replacement for the 4002 metal-gate CMOS device.

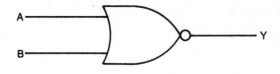

Inputs		Output
A	B	Y
L	L	H
L	H	L
H	L	L
H	H	L

Fig. 2-3. Logic diagram and function table for NOR gate.

Table 2-9. NOR Gates, 54 Family.

TYPE	DESCRIPTION	MAX POWER (mW)	MAX DELAY (nS)	PRICE ($)
5402	Quad 2-Input NOR Gates	148.50	22.0	1.00
54ALS02	Quad 2-Input NOR Gates	22.00	18.0	0.84
54C02	Quad 2-Input NOR Gates	0.23	90.0	2.14
54F02	Quad 2-Input NOR Gates	71.50	7.5	1.16
54HC02	Quad 2-Input NOR Gates	0.24	27.0	0.57
54HCT02	Quad 2-Input NOR Gates	0.22	33.0	0.64

TYPE	DESCRIPTION	MAX POWER (mW)	MAX DELAY (nS)	PRICE ($)
54L02	Quad 2-Input NOR Gates	14.30	60.0	8.30
54LS02	Quad 2-Input NOR Gates	29.70	15.0	0.56
54S02	Quad 2-Input NOR Gates	247.50	5.5	1.22
5423	Dual 4-Input NOR Gates with Strobe	104.50	22.0	1.00
5425	Dual 4-Input NOR Gates with Strobe	104.50	22.0	1.00
5427	Triple 3-Input NOR Gates	143.00	15.0	1.00
54ALS27	Triple 3-Input NOR Gates	22.00	26.0	0.84
54HC27	Triple 3-Input NOR Gates	0.24	30.0	0.57
54HCT27	Triple 3-Input NOR Gates	0.22	36.0	0.64
54LS27	Triple 3-Input NOR Gates	37.40	15.0	0.56
54HC36	Quad 2-Input NOR Gates	0.24	30.0	0.79
54LS260	Dual 5-Input NOR Gates	30.25	15.0	0.78
54S260	Dual 5-Input NOR Gates	247.50	6.0	1.22
54HC4002	Dual 4-Input NOR Gates	0.24	33.0	0.66

Table 2-10. NOR Gates, 74 Family.

TYPE	DESCRIPTION	MAX POWER (mW)	MAX DELAY (nS)	PRICE ($)
7402	Quad 2-Input NOR Gates	141.75	22.0	0.26
74ALS02	Quad 2-Input NOR Gates	22.00	12.0	0.34
74AS02	Quad 2-Input NOR Gates	110.55	4.5	0.50
74C02	Quad 2-Input NOR Gates	0.23	90.0	0.26
74F02	Quad 2-Input NOR Gates	68.25	6.5	0.26
74HC02	Quad 2-Input NOR Gates	0.12	23.0	0.38
74HCT02	Quad 2-Input NOR Gates	0.11	28.0	0.33
74L02	Quad 2-Input NOR Gates	13.65	60.0	0.83
74LS02	Quad 2-Input NOR Gates	28.35	15.0	0.23
74S02	Quad 2-Input NOR Gates	236.25	5.5	0.29

TYPE	DESCRIPTION	MAX POWER (mW)	MAX DELAY (nS)	PRICE ($)
7423	Dual 4-Input NOR Gates with Strobe	99.75	22.0	0.41
7425	Dual 4-Input NOR Gates with Strobe	99.75	22.0	0.29
7427	Triple 3-Input NOR Gates	136.50	15.0	0.29
74ALS27	Triple 3-Input NOR Gates	22.00	15.0	0.34
74AS27	Triple 3-Input NOR Gates	94.05	5.5	0.51
74HC27	Triple 3-Input NOR Gates	0.12	25.0	0.38
74HCT27	Triple 3-Input NOR Gates	0.11	30.0	0.33
74LS27	Triple 3-Input NOR Gates	35.70	15.0	0.23
74HC36	Quad 2-Input NOR Gates	0.12	25.0	0.38
74LS260	Dual 5-Input NOR Gates	28.88	15.0	0.26
74S260	Dual 5-Input NOR Gates	236.25	6.0	0.70
74HC4002	Dual 4-Input NOR Gates	0.12	28.0	0.38

Table 2-11. NOR Gates, 4000 Series, Industrial Temperature Range.

TYPE	DESCRIPTION	MAX POWER (mW)	MAX DELAY (nS)	PRICE ($)
4000A	Dual 3-Input NOR Gates plus Inverter	0.07	120.0	0.45
4000B	Dual 3-Input NOR Gates plus Inverter	0.04	250.0	0.28
4000UB	Dual 3-Input NOR Gates plus Inverter	0.04	120.0	0.28
4001A	Quad 2-Input NOR Gates	0.07	120.0	0.33
4001B	Quad 2-Input NOR Gates	0.04	250.0	0.28
4001UB	Quad 2-Input NOR Gates	0.04	120.0	0.28
4002A	Dual 4-Input NOR Gates	0.07	120.0	0.40
4002B	Dual 4-Input NOR Gates	0.04	250.0	0.28
4002UB	Dual 4-Input NOR Gates	0.04	120.0	0.28
4025A	Triple 3-Input NOR Gates	0.07	120.0	0.40
4025B	Triple 3-Input NOR Gates	0.04	250.0	0.28
4025UB	Triple 3-Input NOR Gates	0.04	120.0	0.28

Table 2-12. NOR Gates, 4000 Series, Military Temperature Range.

TYPE	DESCRIPTION	MAX POWER (mW)	MAX DELAY (nS)	PRICE ($)
4000A	Dual 3-Input NOR Gates plus Inverter	0.02	95.0	2.50
4000B	Dual 3-Input NOR Gates plus Inverter	0.04	250.0	0.50
4000UB	Dual 3-Input NOR Gates plus Inverter	0.04	120.0	0.50
4001A	Quad 2-Input NOR Gates	0.02	95.0	0.78
4001B	Quad 2-Input NOR Gates	0.04	250.0	0.50
4001UB	Quad 2-Input NOR Gates	0.04	120.0	0.50
4002A	Dual 4-Input NOR Gates	0.02	95.0	0.78
4002B	Dual 4-Input NOR Gates	0.04	250.0	0.50
4002UB	Dual 4-Input NOR Gates	0.04	120.0	0.50
4025A	Triple 3-Input NOR Gates	0.02	120.0	0.78
4025B	Triple 3-Input NOR Gates	0.04	250.0	0.50
4025UB	Triple 3-Input NOR Gates	0.04	120.0	0.50

2.4 AND GATES

The logic diagram and function table for a 2-input AND gate is shown in Fig. 2-4. When any input is LOW, the output is LOW; the output is HIGH only

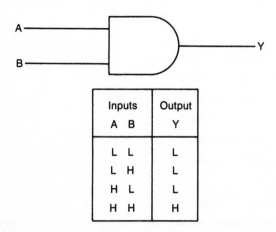

Fig. 2-4. Logic diagram and function table for AND gate.

if both inputs are HIGH. Tables 2-13 through 2-16 list the maximum power, maximum propagation delay, and 100-piece price for AND gates from the 54/74 families and the 4000 Series families.

Maximum V_{OH} for the '09 and '15 is 5.5 V. See Tables 2-7 and 2-8 for type 4068 8-Input NAND/AND Gate.

Table 2-13. AND Gates, 54 Family.

TYPE	DESCRIPTION	MAX POWER (mW)	MAX DELAY (nS)	PRICE ($)
5408	Quad 2-Input AND Gates	181.50	27.0	1.06
54ALS08	Quad 2-Input AND Gates	22.00	18.0	0.84
54C08	Quad 2-Input AND Gates	0.23	140.0	2.14
54F08	Quad 2-Input AND Gates	70.95	7.5	1.16
54HC08	Quad 2-Input AND Gates	0.24	27.0	0.57
54HCT08	Quad 2-Input AND Gates	0.22	41.0	0.64
54LS08	Quad 2-Input AND Gates	48.40	20.0	0.56
54S08	Quad 2-Input AND Gates	313.50	7.5	1.22
5409	Quad 2-Input AND Gates with Open-Collector Outputs	181.50	32.0	1.06
54ALS09	Quad 2-Input AND Gates with Open-Collector Outputs	22.00	69.0	0.84
54HC09	Quad 2-Input AND Gates with Open-Drain Outputs	0.24	36.0	0.79
54LS09	Quad 2-Input AND Gates with Open-Collector Outputs	48.40	35.0	0.56
54S09	Quad 2-Input AND Gates with Open-Collector Outputs	313.50	10.0	1.22
54ALS11	Triple 3-Input AND Gates	16.50	17.0	0.84
54F11	Triple 3-Input AND Gates	53.35	7.5	1.16
54HC11	Triple 3-Input AND Gates	0.24	33.0	0.57
54HCT11	Triple 3-Input AND Gates	0.22	42.0	0.64
54LS11	Triple 3-Input AND Gates	36.30	20.0	0.56
54S11	Triple 3-Input AND Gates	231.00	7.5	1.22
54ALS15	Triple 3-Input AND Gates with Open-Collector Outputs	16.50	59.0	0.84
54LS15	Triple 3-Input AND Gates with Open-Collector Outputs	36.30	35.0	0.56
54S15	Triple 3-Input AND Gates with Open-Collector Outputs	231.00	9.0	1.29

TYPE	DESCRIPTION	MAX POWER (mW)	MAX DELAY (nS)	PRICE ($)
54ALS21	Dual 4-Input AND Gates	11.00	18.0	0.84
54HC21	Dual 4-Input AND Gates	0.24	33.0	0.66
54LS21	Dual 4-Input AND Gates	24.20	20.0	0.56

Table 2-14. AND Gates, 74 Family.

TYPE	DESCRIPTION	MAX POWER (mW)	MAX DELAY (nS)	PRICE ($)
7408	Quad 2-Input AND Gates	173.25	27.0	0.26
74ALS08	Quad 2-Input AND Gates	22.00	14.0	0.34
74AS08	Quad 2-Input AND Gates	132.00	5.5	0.51
74C08	Quad 2-Input AND Gates	0.23	140.0	0.26
74F08	Quad 2-Input AND Gates	67.73	6.6	0.26
74HC08	Quad 2-Input AND Gates	0.12	25.0	0.38
74HCT08	Quad 2-Input AND Gates	0.11	34.0	0.33
74LS08	Quad 2-Input AND Gates	46.20	20.0	0.23
74S08	Quad 2-Input AND Gates	299.25	7.5	0.29
7409	Quad 2-Input AND Gates with Open-Collector Outputs	173.25	32.0	0.26
74ALS09	Quad 2-Input AND Gates with Open-Collector Outputs	22.00	54.0	0.34
74HC09	Quad 2-Input AND Gates with Open-Drain Outputs	0.12	31.0	0.38
74LS09	Quad 2-Input AND Gates with Open-Collector Outputs	46.20	35.0	0.23
74S09	Quad 2-Input AND Gates with Open-Collector Outputs	299.25	10.0	0.35
7411	Triple 3-Input AND Gates	126.00	27.0	0.26
74ALS11	Triple 3-Input AND Gates	16.50	13.0	0.34
74AS11	Triple 3-Input AND Gates	99.00	6.0	0.50
74F11	Triple 3-Input AND Gates	50.92	6.6	0.26
74H11	Triple 3-Input AND Gates	252.00	12.0	3.29
74HC11	Triple 3-Input AND Gates	0.12	28.0	0.38
74HCT11	Triple 3-Input AND Gates	0.11	35.0	0.33

TYPE	DESCRIPTION	MAX POWER (mW)	MAX DELAY (nS)	PRICE ($)
74LS11	Triple 3-Input AND Gates	34.65	20.0	0.23
74S11	Triple 3-Input AND Gates	220.50	7.5	0.29
74ALS15	Triple 3-Input AND Gates with Open-Collector Outputs	16.50	45.0	0.34
74H15	Triple 3-Input AND Gates with Open-Collector Outputs	252.00	18.0	3.29
74LS15	Triple 3-Input AND Gates with Open-Collector Outputs	34.65	35.0	0.23
74S15	Triple 3-Input AND Gates with Open-Collector Outputs	220.50	9.0	0.41
74ALS21	Dual 4-Input AND Gates	11.00	15.0	0.34
74AS21	Dual 4-Input AND Gates	66.00	6.0	0.51
74H21	Dual 4-Input AND Gates	168.00	12.0	3.29
74HC21	Dual 4-Input AND Gates	0.12	28.0	0.38
74LS21	Dual 4-Input AND Gates	23.10	20.0	0.23

Table 2-15. AND Gates, 4000 Series, Industrial Temperature Range.

TYPE	DESCRIPTION	MAX POWER (mW)	MAX DELAY (nS)	PRICE ($)
4073B	Triple 3-Input AND Gates	0.04	250.0	0.28
4081B	Quad 2-Input AND Gates	0.04	250.0	0.28
4082B	Dual 4-Input AND Gates	0.04	250.0	0.28

Table 2-16. AND Gates, 4000 Series, Military Temperature Range.

TYPE	DESCRIPTION	MAX POWER (mW)	MAX DELAY (nS)	PRICE ($)
4073B	Triple 3-Input AND Gates	0.04	250.0	0.50
4081B	Quad 2-Input AND Gates	0.04	250.0	0.50
4082B	Dual 4-Input AND Gates	0.04	250.0	0.50

2.5 OR GATES

The logic diagram and function table for a 2-input OR gate is shown in Fig. 2-5. When any input is HIGH, the output is HIGH; the output is LOW only if both inputs are LOW. Tables 2-17 through 2-20 list the maximum power, maximum propagation delay, and 100-piece price for OR gates from the 54/74 families and 4000 Series families.

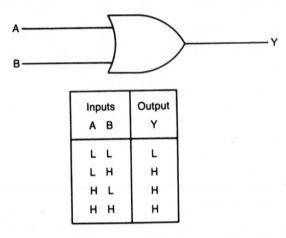

Fig. 2-5. Logic diagram and function table for OR gate.

Table 2-17. OR Gates, 54 Family.

TYPE	DESCRIPTION	MAX POWER (mW)	MAX DELAY (nS)	PRICE ($)
5432	Quad 2-Input OR Gates	209.00	22.0	1.06
54ALS32	Quad 2-Input OR Gates	26.95	18.0	0.84
54C32	Quad 2-Input OR Gates	0.23	150.0	2.14
54F32	Quad 2-Input OR Gates	85.25	7.5	1.16
54HC32	Quad 2-Input OR Gates	0.24	27.0	0.57
54HCT32	Quad 2-Input OR Gates	0.22	36.0	0.64
54LS32	Quad 2-Input OR Gates	53.90	22.0	0.56
54S32	Quad 2-Input OR Gates	374.00	7.0	1.32
54HC4075	Triple 3-Input OR Gates	0.24	30.0	0.57

Table 2-18. OR Gates, 74 Family.

TYPE	DESCRIPTION	MAX POWER (mW)	MAX DELAY (nS)	PRICE ($)
7432	Quad 2-Input OR Gates	199.50	22.0	0.29
74ALS32	Quad 2-Input OR Gates	26.95	14.0	0.34
74AS32	Quad 2-Input OR Gates	146.30	5.8	0.50
74C32	Quad 2-Input OR Gates	0.23	150.0	0.26
74F32	Quad 2-Input OR Gates	81.38	6.6	0.26
74HC32	Quad 2-Input OR Gates	0.12	23.0	0.38
74HCT32	Quad 2-Input OR Gates	0.11	30.0	0.33
74LS32	Quad 2-Input OR Gates	51.45	22.0	0.23
74S32	Quad 2-Input OR Gates	357.00	7.0	0.29
74HC4075	Triple 3-Input OR Gates	0.12	25.0	0.38

Table 2-19. OR Gates, 4000 Series, Industrial Temperature Range.

TYPE	DESCRIPTION	MAX POWER (mW)	MAX DELAY (nS)	PRICE ($)
4071B	Quad 2-Input OR Gates	0.04	250.0	0.28
4072B	Dual 4-Input OR Gates	0.04	250.0	0.28
4075B	Triple 3-Input OR Gates	0.04	250.0	0.28

Table 2-20. OR Gates, 4000 Series, Military Temperature Range.

TYPE	DESCRIPTION	MAX POWER (mW)	MAX DELAY (nS)	PRICE ($)
4071B	Quad 2-Input OR Gates	0.04	250.0	0.50
4072B	Dual 4-Input OR Gates	0.04	250.0	0.50
4075B	Triple 3-Input OR Gates	0.04	250.0	0.50

2.6 EXCLUSIVE-OR AND EXCLUSIVE-NOR GATES

The logic diagram and function table for an Exclusive-OR gate is shown in Fig. 2-6. When one input is HIGH and the other input is LOW, then the output is HIGH; the output is LOW if both inputs are LOW or both inputs are HIGH.

The logic diagram and function table for an Exclusive-NOR gate is shown in Fig. 2-7. When one input is HIGH and the other input is LOW, then the output is LOW; the output is HIGH if both inputs are LOW or both inputs are HIGH.

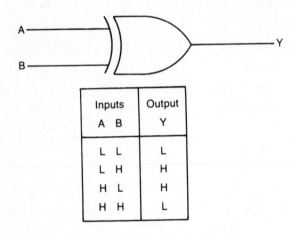

Inputs A B	Output Y
L L	L
L H	H
H L	H
H H	L

Fig. 2-6. Logic diagram and function table for Exclusive-OR gate.

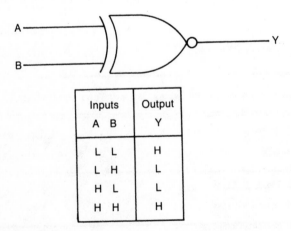

Inputs A B	Output Y
L L	H
L H	L
H L	L
H H	H

Fig. 2-7. Logic diagram and function table for Exclusive-NOR gate.

Tables 2-21 through 2-24 list the maximum power, maximum propagation delay, and 100-piece price for the following Exclusive-OR, -NOR, -OR/NOR device types from the 54/74 families and 4000 Series families.

Table 2-21. Exclusive-OR, -NOR, -OR/NOR Gates, 54 Family.

TYPE	DESCRIPTION	MAX POWER (mW)	MAX DELAY (nS)	PRICE ($)
5486	Quad 2-Input Exclusive-OR Gate	275.00	30.0	1.19
54C86	Quad 2-Input Exclusive-OR Gate	0.23	185.0	1.30
54F86	Quad 2-Input Exclusive-OR Gate	154.00	8.5	1.68
54HC86	Quad 2-Input Exclusive-OR Gate	0.24	36.0	0.74
54HCT86	Quad 2-Input Exclusive-OR Gate	0.22	48.0	0.69
54LS86	Quad 2-Input Exclusive-OR Gate	55.00	30.0	0.60
54S86	Quad 2-Input Exclusive-OR Gate	412.50	10.5	1.72
54S135	Quad Exclusive-OR/NOR Gates	544.50	15.0	2.12
54136	Quad 2-Input Exclusive-OR Gates with Open-Collector Outputs	275.00	55.0	1.63
54LS136	Quad 2-Input Exclusive-OR Gates with Open-Collector Outputs	55.00	30.0	0.60
54HC266	Quad 2-Input Exclusive-NOR Gates with Open-Drain Outputs	0.24	38.0	1.02
54LS266	Quad 2-Input Exclusive-NOR Gates with Open-Collector Outputs	71.50	30.0	0.60
54HC386	Quad 2-Input Exclusive-OR Gates	0.24	30.0	1.02
54LS386	Quad 2-Input Exclusive-OR Gates	55.00	30.0	0.66
54HC7266	Quad 2-Input Exclusive-NOR Gates	0.24	30.0	0.83

Table 2-22. Exclusive-OR, -NOR, -OR/NOR Gates, 74 Family.

TYPE	DESCRIPTION	MAX POWER (mW)	MAX DELAY (nS)	PRICE ($)
7486	Quad 2-Input Exclusive-OR Gate	262.50	30.0	0.33
74ALS86	Quad 2-Input Exclusive-OR Gate	32.45	17.0	0.45
74C86	Quad 2-Input Exclusive-OR Gate	0.23	185.0	0.33

TYPE	DESCRIPTION	MAX POWER (mW)	MAX DELAY (nS)	PRICE ($)
74F86	Quad 2-Input Exclusive-OR Gate	147.00	8.0	0.46
74HC86	Quad 2-Input Exclusive-OR Gate	0.12	30.0	0.41
74HCT86	Quad 2-Input Exclusive-OR Gate	0.11	40.0	0.41
74LS86	Quad 2-Input Exclusive-OR Gate	52.50	30.0	0.26
74S86	Quad 2-Input Exclusive-OR Gate	393.75	10.5	0.49
74S135	Quad Exclusive-OR/NOR Gates	519.75	15.0	1.00
74136	Quad 2-Input Exclusive-OR Gates with Open-Collector Outputs	262.50	55.0	0.58
74ALS136	Quad 2-Input Exclusive-OR Gates with Open-Collector Outputs	32.45	50.0	0.57
74LS136	Quad 2-Input Exclusive-OR Gates with Open-Collector Outputs	52.50	30.0	0.26
74HC266	Quad 2-Input Exclusive-NOR Gates with Open-Drain Outputs	0.12	31.0	0.58
74LS266	Quad 2-Input Exclusive-NOR Gates with Open-Collector Outputs	68.25	30.0	0.26
74HC386	Quad 2-Input Exclusive-OR Gates	0.12	25.0	0.58
74LS386	Quad 2-Input Exclusive-OR Gates	52.50	30.0	0.31
74ALS810	Quad 2-Input Exclusive-NOR Gates	41.25	20.0	0.57
74ALS811	Quad 2-Input Exclusive-NOR Gates with Open Collector Outputs	41.25	55.0	0.57

Table 2-23. Exclusive-OR, -NOR Gates, 4000 Series, Industrial Temperature Range.

TYPE	DESCRIPTION	MAX POWER (mW)	MAX DELAY (nS)	PRICE ($)
4030A	Quad Exclusive-OR Gates	0.35	300.0	0.41
4030B	Quad Exclusive-OR Gates	0.15	280.0	0.56
4070B	Quad Exclusive-OR Gates	0.15	280.0	0.28
4077B	Quad Exclusive-NOR Gates	0.15	280.0	0.28

Table 2-24. Exclusive-OR, -NOR Gates, 4000 Series, Military Temperature Range.

TYPE	DESCRIPTION	MAX POWER (mW)	MAX DELAY (nS)	PRICE ($)
4030A	Quad Exclusive-OR Gates	0.15	200.0	0.89
4030B	Quad Exclusive-OR Gates	0.15	280.0	1.26
4070B	Quad Exclusive-OR Gates	0.15	280.0	0.50
4077B	Quad Exclusive-NOR Gates	0.15	280.0	0.50

All types have four gates per package. The '386 has a different pinout than the '86. The '811 has a different pinout than the '266. The '7266 is the standard output, or totem-pole output, version of the '266. Maximum V_{OH} for open-collector types is 5.5 V (6 V for open-drain). The 4030 is identical to the 4070, except for price.

2.7 SCHMITT-TRIGGER GATES

The logic diagram and transfer function for a Schmitt-Trigger Inverter is shown in Fig. 2-8. While standard inverters and gates have only one input threshold voltage that causes the output to switch, Schmitt-Trigger inverters and gates have two different input threshold voltages: one threshold for when the input is changing from LOW to HIGH and a different threshold for when the input is changing from HIGH to LOW.

Assume the input is LOW (zero volts) and the output is HIGH (3.4 V typical). As the input voltage is increased, the output does not change until the input reaches 1.7 V. Then the output snaps to the LOW state (0.2 V typical) and stays LOW for further increases in input voltage. If the input starts in the HIGH state and is reduced toward zero, the output will stay LOW until the input reaches 0.9 V. Then the output will snap to the HIGH state.

The difference between the high threshold (V_T+, 1.7 V) and the low threshold (V_T-, 0.9 V) is called *hysteresis*. In the above discussion, the values for V_T+ and V_T- were for the 54/7414 Schmitt-Trigger Inverter. The minimum V_T+ is 1.5 V and the maximum V_T- is 1.1 V. Therefore, the minimum hysteresis is 1.5 V minus 1.1 V, or 0.4 V.

Tables 2-25 through 2-28 list the maximum power, minimum hysteresis, maximum propagation delay, and 100-piece price for Schmitt-Trigger inverters and gates from the 54/74 families and 4000 Series families.

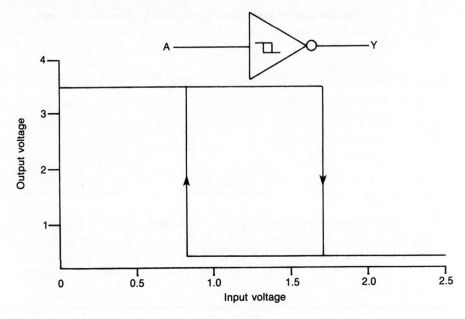

Fig. 2-8. Logic diagram and transfer function for Schmitt- Trigger inverter.

Table 2-25. Schmitt-Trigger Gates, 54 Family.

TYPE	DESCRIPTION	MAX POWER (mW)	MIN HYS (V)	MAX DELAY (nS)	PRICE ($)
5413	Dual 4-Input Schmitt-Trigger NAND Gates	176.00	0.4	27.0	1.73
54LS13	Dual 4-Input Schmitt-Trigger NAND Gates	38.50	0.4	27.0	0.60
5414	Hex Schmitt-Trigger Inverters	330.00	0.4	22.0	2.57
54C14	Hex Schmitt-Trigger Inverters	0.23	1.0	400.0	3.98
54HC14	Hex Schmitt-Trigger Inverters	0.24	0.4	38.0	1.52
54LS14	Hex Schmitt-Trigger Inverters	115.50	0.4	22.0	0.98
54132	Quad 2-Input Schmitt-Trigger NAND Gates	220.00	0.4	22.0	1.99
54HC132	Quad 2-Input Schmitt-Trigger NAND Gates	0.24	0.4	38.0	1.52
54LS132	Quad 2-Input Schmitt-Trigger NAND Gates	77.00	0.4	22.0	1.04
54S132	Quad 2-Input Schmitt-Trigger NAND Gates	374.00	0.2	13.0	3.43
54C914	Hex Schmitt-Trigger with Extended Input Voltage	4.50	1.0	400.0	5.67

Table 2-26. Schmitt-Trigger Gates, 74 Family.

TYPE	DESCRIPTION	MAX POWER (mW)	MIN HYS (V)	MAX DELAY (nS)	PRICE ($)
7413	Dual 4-Input Schmitt-Trigger NAND Gates	168.00	0.4	27.0	0.42
74LS13	Dual 4-Input Schmitt-Trigger NAND Gates	36.75	0.4	27.0	0.23
7414	Hex Schmitt-Trigger Inverters	315.00	0.4	22.0	0.29
74C14	Hex Schmitt-Trigger Inverters	0.23	1.0	400.0	0.63
74HC14	Hex Schmitt-Trigger Inverters	0.12	0.2	22.0	0.58
74LS14	Hex Schmitt-Trigger Inverters	110.25	0.4	22.0	0.26
74LS19	Hex Schmitt-Trigger Inverters	157.50	0.4	30.0	0.48
74LS24	Quad 2-Input Schmitt-Trigger NAND Gates	105.00	0.4	20.0	1.02
74132	Quad 2-Input Schmitt-Trigger NAND Gates	210.00	0.4	22.0	0.47
74HC132	Quad 2-Input Schmitt-Trigger NAND Gates	0.12	0.2	31.0	0.68
74LS132	Quad 2-Input Schmitt-Trigger NAND Gates	73.50	0.4	22.0	0.36
74S132	Quad 2-Input Schmitt-Trigger NAND Gates	357.00	0.2	13.0	0.57
74C914	Hex Schmitt-Trigger with Extended Input Voltage	4.50	1.0	400.0	1.46

Table 2-27. Schmitt-Trigger Gates, 4000 Series, Industrial Temperature Range.

TYPE	DESCRIPTION	MAX POWER (mW)	MIN HYS (V)	MAX DELAY (nS)	PRICE ($)
4093B	Quad 2-Input NAND Schmitt-Triggers	0.15	0.9	380.0	0.45
40106B	Hex Schmitt-Triggers	0.15	0.3	280.0	0.58

Table 2-28. Schmitt-Trigger Gates, 4000 Series, Military Temperature Range.

TYPE	DESCRIPTION	MAX POWER (mW)	MIN HYS (V)	MAX DELAY (nS)	PRICE ($)
4093B	Quad 2-Input NAND Schmitt-Triggers	0.15	0.9	380.0	0.96
40106B	Hex Schmitt-Triggers	0.15	0.3	280.0	1.32

2.8 AND-OR-INVERT GATES

The logic diagram for a 2-wide 2-input AND-OR-INVERT gate is shown in Fig. 2-9. For the gate shown, if inputs A and B are HIGH, or if inputs C and D are HIGH, then the output is LOW; otherwise the output is HIGH. Tables 2-29 through 2-32 list the maximum power, maximum propagation delay, and 100-piece price for AND-OR-INVERT gates from the 54/74 families and 4000 Series families. The "2-wide" or "4-wide" refers to either 2 or 4 AND gates, respectively. The "2-input" or "4-input" refers to either 2 or 4 inputs per AND gate.

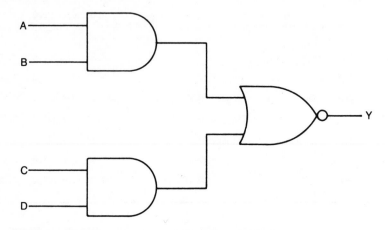

Fig. 2-9. Logic diagram of 2-wide 2-input AND-OR-INVERT gate.

Table 2-29. AND-OR-INVERT Gates, 54 Family.

TYPE	DESCRIPTION	MAX POWER (mW)	MAX DELAY (nS)	PRICE ($)
5450	Dual Expandable 2-Wide 2-Input AND-OR-INVERT Gates	77.00	22.0	1.00
5451	Dual 2-Wide 2-Input AND-OR-INVERT Gates	77.00	22.0	1.00
54HC51	Dual 2-Wide 2-Input AND-OR-INVERT Gates	0.24	42.0	0.79
54LS51	Dual 2-Wide 2-Input AND-OR-INVERT Gates	15.40	20.0	0.56
54S51	Dual 2-Wide 2-Input AND-OR-INVERT Gates	121.00	5.5	1.22
5453	Expandable 4-Wide AND-OR-INVERT Gate	52.25	22.0	1.00
5454	4-Wide 2-Input AND-OR-INVERT Gate	52.25	22.0	1.00

TYPE	DESCRIPTION	MAX POWER (mW)	MAX DELAY (nS)	PRICE ($)
54LS54	4-Wide 2-Input AND-OR-INVERT Gate	11.00	20.0	0.56
54LS55	2-Wide 4-Input AND-OR-INVERT Gate	7.15	11.0	0.64
54F64	4-Wide AND-OR-INVERT Gate	25.85	8.5	1.16
54S64	4-Wide AND-OR-INVERT Gate	88.00	5.5	1.37
54S65	4-Wide AND-OR-INVERT Gate with Open-Collector Output	88.00	8.5	1.37

Table 2-30. AND-OR-INVERT Gates, 74 Family.

TYPE	DESCRIPTION	MAX POWER (mW)	MAX DELAY (nS)	PRICE ($)
7450	Dual Expandable 2-Wide 2-Input AND-OR-INVERT Gates	73.50	22.0	0.23
74H50	Dual Expandable 2-Wide 2-Input AND-OR-INVERT Gates	126.00	11.0	3.29
7451	Dual 2-Wide 2-Input AND-OR-INVERT Gates	73.50	22.0	0.26
74H51	Dual 2-Wide 2-Input AND-OR-INVERT Gates	126.00	11.0	3.29
74HC51	Dual 2-Wide 2-Input AND-OR-INVERT Gates	0.12	35.0	0.38
74LS51	Dual 2-Wide 2-Input AND-OR-INVERT Gates	14.70	20.0	0.23
74S51	Dual 2-Wide 2-Input AND-OR-INVERT Gates	115.50	5.5	0.29
7453	Expandable 4-Wide AND-OR-INVERT Gate	49.88	22.0	0.72
74H53	Expandable 4-Wide AND-OR-INVERT Gate	73.50	11.0	3.29
7454	4-Wide 2-Input AND-OR-INVERT Gate	49.88	22.0	0.76
74H54	4-Wide 2-Input AND-OR-INVERT Gate	73.50	11.0	3.29
74LS54	4-Wide 2-Input AND-OR-INVERT Gate	10.50	20.0	0.23
74H55	2-Wide 4-Input AND-OR-INVERT Gate	63.00	11.0	3.29
74LS55	2-Wide 4-Input AND-OR-INVERT Gate	6.83	20.0	0.23
74F64	4-Wide AND-OR-INVERT Gate	24.68	7.5	0.26
74S64	4-Wide AND-OR-INVERT Gate	84.00	5.5	0.29
74S65	4-Wide AND-OR-INVERT Gate with Open-Collector Output	84.00	8.5	0.40

Table 2-31. AND-OR-INVERT Gates, 4000 Series, Industrial Temperature Range.

TYPE	DESCRIPTION	MAX POWER (mW)	MAX DELAY (nS)	PRICE ($)
4085B	Dual 2-Wide 2-Input AND-OR-INVERT Gates	0.15	620.0	0.78
4086B	Expandable 4-Wide 2-Input AND-OR-INVERT Gate	0.15	620.0	0.78

Table 2-32. AND-OR-INVERT Gates, 4000 Series, Military Temperature Range.

TYPE	DESCRIPTION	MAX POWER (mW)	MAX DELAY (nS)	PRICE ($)
4085B	Dual 2-Wide 2-Input AND-OR-INVERT Gates	0.15	620.0	1.32
4086B	Expandable 4-Wide 2-Input AND-OR-INVERT Gate	0.15	620.0	1.32

Be careful. Many of these devices violate the basic part-numbering system: the 54/7451 and 54/74S51 are different from the 54/74HC51 and 54/74LS51. The standard TTL part and the S part have two 2-wide 2-input gates, but the HC and LS parts have one 2-wide 3-input gate and one 2-wide 2-input gate. Circuits with different numbers of either inputs or outputs should not have the same basic part number.

The 54/7453 is a 4-wide 2-input gate. The 54/74H53 is 4-wide but has three 2-input AND gates and one 3-input AND gate. The arrangement is called a 2-2-3-2-input AND-OR-INVERT gate.

The 54/7454 is 4-wide 2-input. The 'H54 is 4-wide, 2-2-3-2-input. The 'LS54 is 4-wide, 2-3-3-2-input.

The 74H55 is expandable, the 'LS55 is not expandable.

The '64 and '65 are 4-wide, 4-2-3-2-input.

Expandable gates may be expanded using the '60 dual expander.

Chapter 3

Flip-Flops, Latches, and Multivibrators

In this chapter, I will present logic diagrams, function tables, descriptions, and selection guides for the following logic functions:

☐ D-Type Flip-Flops
☐ J-K Flip-Flops
☐ Latches
☐ Monostable Multivibrators

3.1 D-TYPE FLIP-FLOPS

The logic symbol and function table for a D-type flip-flop is shown in Fig. 3-1. The D-type flip-flop has four inputs and two outputs. The inputs are PRESET (PRE), CLEAR (CLR), CLOCK (CLK), and DATA (D). The outputs are Q and $\overline{Q}$ (pronounced "Q bar" or "Q not" or "Q inverted"; "NOT" is the Boolean algebra term for the inversion logic function).

When PRESET is LOW and CLEAR is HIGH then the Q output is HIGH and the $\overline{Q}$ output is LOW, regardless of the voltage levels on the CLOCK and DATA inputs ("X" in the table means "don't care"). When the PRESET is returned to the HIGH level after being LOW, Q will remain HIGH and $\overline{Q}$ will remain LOW. This is the flip-flop "set" condition, or state.

When PRESET is HIGH and CLEAR is LOW then the Q output is LOW and the $\overline{Q}$ output is HIGH, regardless of the voltage levels on the CLOCK and DATA inputs. When the CLEAR is returned to the HIGH level after being LOW, Q will

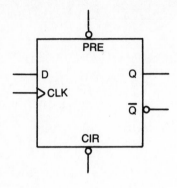

Fig. 3-1. Logic symbol and function table for D-type flip-flop.

Inputs				Outputs	
PRE	CLR	CLK	D	Q	$\overline{Q}$
L	H	X	X	H	L
H	L	X	X	L	H
L	L	X	X	H	H
H	H	↑	H	H	L
H	H	↑	L	L	H
H	H	L	X	Q_o	$\overline{Q}_o$

remain LOW and $\overline{Q}$ will remain HIGH. This is the flip-flop "reset" state.

When PRESET is LOW and CLEAR is LOW then the Q output is HIGH and the $\overline{Q}$ output is HIGH, regardless of the voltage levels on the CLOCK and DATA inputs. This is not a stable state: when either the PRESET or the CLEAR is returned HIGH, the outputs will go to the states defined for either one of the input conditions described in the previous paragraphs.

When PRESET and CLEAR are both HIGH (or, *inactive*), then the voltage level on the DATA input is transferred to the Q output when the CLOCK input changes from LOW to HIGH (up arrow in the function table). The inversion of the DATA input level is transferred to the $\overline{Q}$ output. If DATA is HIGH, then Q will go HIGH and $\overline{Q}$ will go LOW on the rising edge of the CLOCK input. If DATA is LOW, then Q will go LOW and $\overline{Q}$ will go HIGH. When the CLOCK input return to the LOW level, then Q and $\overline{Q}$ will remain in the states in which they were when the CLOCK was HIGH, regardless of the state of the DATA input.

The DATA input must be stable just prior to and just after the rising edge of the CLOCK. This is shown in Fig. 3-2 for the case when DATA is HIGH during the CLOCK transition. The time that the DATA input must be stable prior to

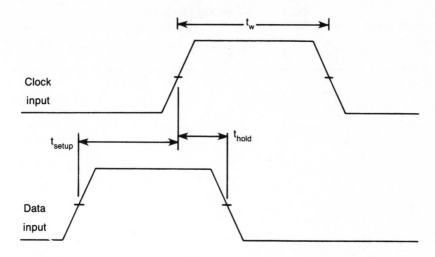

Fig. 3-2. Voltage waveforms for setup and hold times and clock pulse duration.

the rising edge of the CLOCK is called the *setup time*. The time that the DATA input must be stable after the rising edge of the CLOCK is called the *hold time*. Both of these times are specified as minimums in the data sheets for flip-flops and are considered required operating conditions. If the minimum setup and hold times are not met then operation of the flip-flop is not guaranteed.

Another operating condition is the CLOCK pulse duration, or pulse width, designated by t_w in Fig. 3-2. Both minimum clock HIGH time and clock LOW time are specified in data sheets. In the figure, the LOW time is not shown. Clock LOW time is the minimum time between pulses. The clock period is defined as the sum of the clock HIGH and LOW times. The clock frequency is 1 divided by the clock period.

Tables 3-1 through 3-4 list the maximum power, maximum clock frequency, minimum setup time, minimum hold time, and 100-piece price for D-type flip-flops from the 54/74 families and 4000 Series families.

Type '374 features 3-state outputs with high drive capability.

Types '377, '378, and '379 are similar to the '273, '174, and '175, respectively, except that the '377, '378, and '379 feature a common clock enable instead of a common clear.

Type '534 is functionally equivalent to the '374 except that the '534 has inverted outputs ($\overline{Q}$ outputs instead of Q outputs).

Type '564 is a bus-structured pinout version of the '534: input are on one side of the package, outputs on the other.

Type '574 is a bus-structured pinout version of the '374.

Type '575 is '574 with synchronous clear input: when CLEAR is LOW,

Table 3-1. D-Type Flip-Flops, 54 Family.

TYPE	DESCRIPTION	MAX POWER (mW)	FMAX (MHz)	MIN SETUP (nS)	MIN HOLD (nS)	PRICE ($)
5474	Dual Positive-Edge-Triggered D-Type Flip-Flops with Preset and Clear	82.50	15.0	20.0	5.0	1.19
54AC74	Dual Positive-Edge-Triggered D-Type Flip-Flops with Preset and Clear	0.55	100.0	3.5	0.0	3.72
54ALS74	Dual Positive-Edge-Triggered D-Type Flip-Flops with Preset and Clear	22.00	30.0	16.0	2.0	1.06
54AS74	Dual Positive-Edge-Triggered D-Type Flip-Flops with Preset and Clear	88.00	90.0	4.5	0.0	1.73
54C74	Dual Positive-Edge-Triggered D-Type Flip-Flops with Preset and Clear	0.90	2.0	100.0	0.0	2.85
54F74	Dual Positive-Edge-Triggered D-Type Flip-Flops with Preset and Clear	88.00	80.0	4.0	2.0	1.44
54HC74	Dual Positive-Edge-Triggered D-Type Flip-Flops with Preset and Clear	0.48	20.0	30.0	3.0	0.82
54HCT74	Dual Positive-Edge-Triggered D-Type Flip-Flops with Preset and Clear	0.44	16.0	30.0	3.0	0.69
54L74	Dual Positive-Edge-Triggered D-Type Flip-Flops with Preset and Clear	16.50	2.5	50.0	15.0	7.83
54LS74	Dual Positive-Edge-Triggered D-Type Flip-Flops with Preset and Clear	44.00	25.0	20.0	5.0	0.60
54S74	Dual Positive-Edge-Triggered D-Type Flip-Flops with Preset and Clear	137.50	75.0	3.0	2.0	1.72
54174	Hex D-Type Flip-Flops with Clear	357.50	25.0	20.0	5.0	2.09
54ALS174	Hex D-Type Flip-Flops with Clear	104.50	40.0	15.0	0.0	1.80
54C174	Hex D-Type Flip-Flops with Clear	4.50	2.0	75.0	0.0	3.00
54F174	Hex D-Type Flip-Flops with Clear	247.50	80.0	4.0	0.0	3.22
54HC174	Hex D-Type Flip-Flops with Clear	0.96	20.0	24.0	5.0	1.29
54HCT174	Hex D-Type Flip-Flops with Clear	0.88	17.0	30.0	5.0	1.15
54LS174	Hex D-Type Flip-Flops with Clear	143.00	30.0	20.0	5.0	1.06
54S174	Hex D-Type Flip-Flops with Clear	792.00	75.0	5.0	3.0	3.29
54175	Quad D-Type Flip-Flops with Clear	247.50	25.0	20.0	5.0	2.12
54ALS175	Quad D-Type Flip-Flops with Clear	77.00	40.0	15.0	0.0	1.80
54C175	Quad D-Type Flip-Flops with Clear	4.50	2.0	100.0	0.0	3.00
54F175	Quad D-Type Flip-Flops with Clear	187.00	100.0	3.0	1.0	3.22
54HC175	Quad D-Type Flip-Flops with Clear	0.48	20.0	30.0	5.0	1.07

TYPE	DESCRIPTION	MAX POWER (mW)	FMAX (MHz)	MIN SETUP (nS)	MIN HOLD (nS)	PRICE ($)
54HCT175	Quad D-Type Flip-Flops with Clear	0.88	16.0	30.0	5.0	1.15
54LS175	Quad D-Type Flip-Flops with Clear	99.00	30.0	20.0	5.0	1.06
54S175	Quad D-Type Flip-Flops with Clear	528.00	75.0	5.0	3.0	3.29
54ALS273	Octal D-Type Flip-Flop with Clear	159.50	30.0	10.0	0.0	3.22
54HC273	Octal D-Type Flip-Flop with Clear	0.96	20.0	30.0	3.0	2.25
54HCT273	Octal D-Type Flip-Flop with Clear	0.88	16.0	30.0	3.0	2.06
54LS273	Octal D-Type Flip-Flop with Clear	148.50	30.0	20.0	5.0	2.07
54ALS374	Octal 3-State Positive-Edge-Triggered D-Type Flip-Flops	170.50	30.0	10.0	4.0	3.36
54AS374	Octal 3-State Positive-Edge-Triggered D-Type Flip-Flops	704.00	100.0	3.0	3.0	5.95
54C374	Octal 3-State Positive-Edge-Triggered D-Type Flip-Flops	4.50	3.5	140.0	0.0	7.71
54F374	Octal 3-State Positive-Edge-Triggered D-Type Flip-Flops	473.00	60.0	2.5	2.5	5.04
54HC374	Octal 3-State Positive-Edge-Triggered D-Type Flip-Flops	0.96	20.0	30.0	5.0	3.09
54HCT374	Octal 3-State Positive-Edge-Triggered D-Type Flip-Flops	0.88	20.0	30.0	5.0	2.48
54LS374	Octal 3-State Positive-Edge-Triggered D-Type Flip-Flops	220.00	35.0	20.0	0.0	2.62
54S374	Octal 3-State Positive-Edge-Triggered D-Type Flip-Flops	880.00	75.0	5.0	2.0	5.06
54HC377	Octal D-Type Flip-Flops with Enable	0.96	20.0	18.0	3.0	3.02
54HCT377	Octal D-Type Flip-Flops with Enable	0.88	16.0	18.0	3.0	2.39
54LS377	Octal D-Type Flip-Flops with Enable	154.00	30.0	20.0	5.0	2.07
54F378	Hex D-Type Flip-Flops with Enable	247.50	80.0	4.0	0.0	3.94
54HC378	Hex D-Type Flip-Flops with Enable	0.96	16.0	30.0	0.0	1.64
54LS378	Hex D-Type Flip-Flops with Enable	121.00	30.0	20.0	5.0	1.28
54F379	Quad D-Type Flip-Flops with Enable	220.00	100.0	3.0	1.0	3.94
54HC379	Quad D-Type Flip-Flops with Enable	0.48	16.0	30.0	0.0	1.64
54LS379	Quad D-Type Flip-Flops with Enable	82.50	30.0	20.0	5.0	1.28
54F534	Octal 3-State Inverting Positive-Edge-Triggered D-Type Flip-Flops	473.00	60.0	2.5	2.5	5.38

TYPE	DESCRIPTION	MAX POWER (mW)	FMAX (MHz)	MIN SETUP (nS)	MIN HOLD (nS)	PRICE ($)
54HC534	Octal 3-State Inverting	0.96	20.0	24.0	3.0	3.56
	Positive-Edge-Triggered D-Type Flip-Flops					
54HCT534	Octal 3-State Inverting Positive-Edge-Triggered D-Type Flip-Flops	0.88	16.0	30.0	3.0	2.48
54HC564	Octal D-Type Flip-Flops	0.96	20.0	24.0	3.0	3.88
54ALS574	Octal 3-State Positive-Edge-Triggered D-Type Flip-Flops	148.50	28.0	15.0	4.0	3.36
54HC574	Octal 3-State Positive-Edge-Triggered D-Type Flip-Flops	0.96	20.0	30.0	5.0	3.88
54HCT574	Octal 3-State Positive-Edge-Triggered D-Type Flip-Flops	0.88	20.0	30.0	5.0	3.30
54ALS576	Octal 3-State Inverting Positive-Edge-Triggered D-Type Flip-Flops	148.50	25.0	15.0	4.0	3.36
54ALS874	Dual 3-State 4-Bit Positive-Edge-Triggered D-Type Flip-Flops	170.50	25.0	15.0	4.0	4.35

Table 3-2. D-Type Flip-Flops, 74 Family.

TYPE	DESCRIPTION	MAX POWER (mW)	FMAX (MHz)	MIN SETUP (nS)	MIN HOLD (nS)	PRICE ($)
7474	Dual Positive-Edge-Triggered D-Type Flip-Flops with Preset and Clear	78.75	15.0	20.0	5.0	0.33
74AC74	Dual Positive-Edge-Triggered D-Type Flip-Flops with Preset and Clear	0.28	100.0	3.0	0.0	0.44
74ALS74	Dual Positive-Edge-Triggered D-Type Flip-Flops with Preset and Clear	22.00	34.0	15.0	0.0	0.43
74AS74	Dual Positive-Edge-Triggered D-Type Flip-Flops with Preset and Clear	88.00	105.0	4.5	0.0	0.54
74C74	Dual Positive-Edge-Triggered D-Type Flip-Flops with Preset and Clear	0.90	2.0	100.0	0.0	0.60
74F74	Dual Positive-Edge-Triggered D-Type Flip-Flops with Preset and Clear	84.00	100.0	3.0	1.0	0.36

TYPE	DESCRIPTION	MAX POWER (mW)	FMAX (MHz)	MIN SETUP (nS)	MIN HOLD (nS)	PRICE ($)
74H74	Dual Positive-Edge-Triggered D-Type Flip-Flops with Preset and Clear	131.25	35.0	15.0	5.0	3.29
74HC74	Dual Positive-Edge-Triggered D-Type Flip-Flops with Preset and Clear	0.24	25.0	25.0	3.0	0.41
74HCT74	Dual Positive-Edge-Triggered D-Type Flip-Flops with Preset and Clear	0.22	20.0	25.0	3.0	0.41
74L74	Dual Positive-Edge-Triggered D-Type Flip-Flops with Preset and Clear	15.75	2.5	50.0	15.0	1.35
74LS74	Dual Positive-Edge-Triggered D-Type Flip-Flops with Preset and Clear	42.00	25.0	20.0	5.0	0.26
74S74	Dual Positive-Edge-Triggered D-Type Flip-Flops with Preset and Clear	131.25	75.0	3.0	2.0	0.40
74174	Hex D-Type Flip-Flops with Clear	341.25	25.0	20.0	5.0	0.43
74ALS174	Hex D-Type Flip-Flops with Clear	104.50	50.0	10.0	0.0	0.66
74AS174	Hex D-Type Flip-Flops with Clear	247.50	100.0	3.0	1.0	1.49
74C174	Hex D-Type Flip-Flops with Clear	4.50	2.0	75.0	0.0	0.87
74F174	Hex D-Type Flip-Flops with Clear	236.25	80.0	4.0	0.0	0.86
74HC174	Hex D-Type Flip-Flops with Clear	0.48	24.0	20.0	5.0	0.58
74HCT174	Hex D-Type Flip-Flops with Clear	0.44	20.0	25.0	5.0	0.64
74LS174	Hex D-Type Flip-Flops with Clear	136.50	30.0	20.0	5.0	0.36
74S174	Hex D-Type Flip-Flops with Clear	756.00	75.0	5.0	3.0	0.60
74175	Quad D-Type Flip-Flops with Clear	236.25	25.0	20.0	5.0	0.43
74ALS175	Quad D-Type Flip-Flops with Clear	77.00	50.0	10.0	0.0	0.66
74AS175	Quad D-Type Flip-Flops with Clear	187.00	100.0	3.0	1.0	1.49
74C175	Quad D-Type Flip-Flops with Clear	4.50	2.0	100.0	0.0	0.96
74F175	Quad D-Type Flip-Flops with Clear	178.50	100.0	3.0	1.0	0.86
74HC175	Quad D-Type Flip-Flops with Clear	0.24	25.0	25.0	5.0	0.63
74HCT175	Quad D-Type Flip-Flops with Clear	0.44	20.0	25.0	5.0	0.64
74LS175	Quad D-Type Flip-Flops with Clear	94.50	30.0	20.0	5.0	0.36
74S175	Quad D-Type Flip-Flops with Clear	504.00	75.0	5.0	3.0	0.60
74273	Octal D-Type Flip-Flop with Clear	493.50	30.0	20.0	5.0	2.20
74ALS273	Octal D-Type Flip-Flop with Clear	159.50	35.0	10.0	0.0	1.36

TYPE	DESCRIPTION	MAX POWER (mW)	FMAX (MHz)	MIN SETUP (nS)	MIN HOLD (nS)	PRICE ($)
74HC273	Octal D-Type Flip-Flop with Clear	0.48	25.0	25.0	3.0	1.14
74HCT273	Octal D-Type Flip-Flop with Clear	0.44	20.0	25.0	3.0	1.14
74LS273	Octal D-Type Flip-Flop with Clear	141.75	30.0	20.0	5.0	0.60
74AC374	Octal 3-State Positive-Edge-Triggered D-Type Flip-Flops	0.28	100.0	5.0	0.0	1.27
74ALS374	Octal 3-State Positive-Edge-Triggered D-Type Flip-Flops	170.50	35.0	10.0	0.0	1.28
74AS374	Octal 3-State Positive-Edge-Triggered D-Type Flip-Flops	704.00	125.0	2.0	2.0	2.63
74C374	Octal 3-State Positive-Edge-Triggered D-Type Flip-Flops	4.50	3.5	140.0	0.0	1.80
74F374	Octal 3-State Positive-Edge-Triggered D-Type Flip-Flops	451.50	70.0	2.0	2.0	1.14
74HC374	Octal 3-State Positive-Edge-Triggered D-Type Flip-Flops	0.48	25.0	25.0	5.0	0.99
74HCT374	Octal 3-State Positive-Edge-Triggered D-Type Flip-Flops	0.44	25.0	25.0	5.0	1.16
74LS374	Octal 3-State Positive-Edge-Triggered D-Type Flip-Flops	210.00	35.0	20.0	0.0	0.60
74S374	Octal 3-State Positive-Edge-Triggered D-Type Flip-Flops	840.00	75.0	5.0	2.0	2.25
74HC377	Octal D-Type Flip-Flops with Enable	0.48	25.0	15.0	3.0	1.06
74HCT377	Octal D-Type Flip-Flops with Enable	0.44	20.0	15.0	3.0	1.06
74LS377	Octal D-Type Flip-Flops with Enable	147.00	30.0	20.0	5.0	0.60
74F378	Hex D-Type Flip-Flops with Enable	236.25	80.0	4.0	0.0	1.14
74HC378	Hex D-Type Flip-Flops with Enable	0.48	20.0	25.0	0.0	1.63
74LS378	Hex D-Type Flip-Flops with Enable	115.50	30.0	20.0	5.0	0.69
74F379	Quad D-Type Flip-Flops with Enable	210.00	100.0	3.0	1.0	1.14
74HC379	Quad D-Type Flip-Flops with Enable	0.24	20.0	25.0	0.0	1.68
74LS379	Quad D-Type Flip-Flops with Enable	78.75	30.0	20.0	5.0	0.69
74ALS534	Octal 3-State Inverting Positive-Edge-Triggered D-Type Flip-Flops	170.50	35.0	10.0	0.0	1.44
74AS534	Octal 3-State Inverting Positive-Edge-Triggered D-Type Flip-Flops	704.00	125.0	2.0	2.0	2.63

TYPE	DESCRIPTION	MAX POWER (mW)	FMAX (MHz)	MIN SETUP (nS)	MIN HOLD (nS)	PRICE ($)
74F534	Octal 3-State Inverting Positive-Edge-Triggered D-Type Flip-Flops	451.50	70.0	2.0	2.0	1.29
74HC534	Octal 3-State Inverting Positive-Edge-Triggered D-Type Flip-Flops	0.48	25.0	20.0	3.0	1.59
74HCT534	Octal 3-State Inverting Positive-Edge-Triggered D-Type Flip-Flops	0.44	20.0	25.0	3.0	1.57
74LS534	Octal 3-State Inverting Positive-Edge-Triggered D-Type Flip-Flops	236.25	70.0	2.0	2.0	0.79
74ALS564	Octal 3-State Inverting Positive-Edge-Triggered D-Type Flip-Flops	148.50	30.0	15.0	0.0	1.44
74HC564	Octal 3-State Inverting Positive-Edge-Triggered D-Type Flip-Flops	0.48	25.0	20.0	3.0	1.40
74HCT564	Octal 3-State Inverting Positive-Edge-Triggered D-Type Flip-Flops	0.44	20.0	25.0	3.0	1.78
74ALS574	Octal 3-State Positive-Edge-Triggered D-Type Flip-Flops	148.50	30.0	15.0	0.0	1.34
74AS574	Octal 3-State Positive-Edge-Triggered D-Type Flip-Flops	737.00	125.0	2.0	2.0	2.61
74HC574	Octal 3-State Positive-Edge-Triggered D-Type Flip-Flops	0.48	25.0	25.0	5.0	1.40
74HCT574	Octal 3-State Positive-Edge-Triggered D-Type Flip-Flops	0.44	25.0	25.0	5.0	1.78
74LS574	Octal 3-State Positive-Edge-Triggered D-Type Flip-Flops	236.25	100.0	2.0	2.0	1.00
74ALS575	Octal 3-State Positive-Edge-Triggered D-Type Flip-Flops	148.50	30.0	15.0	0.0	2.02
74AS575	Octal 3-State Positive-Edge-Triggered D-Type Flip-Flops	781.00	125.0	2.0	2.0	3.17
74ALS576	Octal 3-State Inverting Positive-Edge-Triggered D-Type Flip-Flops	148.50	30.0	15.0	0.0	1.44
74AS576	Octal 3-State Inverting Positive-Edge-Triggered D-Type Flip-Flops	742.50	125.0	2.0	2.0	2.61

TYPE	DESCRIPTION	MAX POWER (mW)	FMAX (MHz)	MIN SETUP (nS)	MIN HOLD (nS)	PRICE ($)
74ALS577	Octal 3-State Inverting Positive-Edge-Triggered D-Type Flip-Flops	148.50	30.0	15.0	0.0	2.02
74AS577	Octal 3-State Inverting Positive-Edge-Triggered D-Type Flip-Flops	781.00	125.0	2.0	2.0	3.17
74ALS874	Dual 3-State 4-Bit Positive-Edge-Triggered D-Type Flip-Flops	170.50	30.0	15.0	0.0	1.58
74AS874	Dual 3-State 4-Bit Positive-Edge-Triggered D-Type Flip-Flops	880.00	125.0	2.0	1.0	2.91
74ALS876	Dual 3-State 4-Bit Inverting Positive-Edge-Triggered D-Type Flip-Flops	170.50	30.0	15.0	0.0	1.58
74AS876	Dual 3-State 4-Bit Inverting Positive-Edge-Triggered D-Type Flip-Flops	880.00	125.0	2.0	1.0	2.91
74ALS879	Dual 3-State 4-Bit Inverting Positive-Edge-Triggered D-Type Flip-Flops	170.50	25.0	15.0	4.0	1.76
74AS879	Dual 3-State 4-Bit Inverting Positive-Edge-Triggered D-Type Flip-Flops	880.00	125.0	2.0	2.0	3.17

Table 3-3. D-Type Flip-Flops, 4000 Series, Industrial Temperature Range.

TYPE	DESCRIPTION	MAX POWER (mW)	FMAX (MHz)	MIN SETUP (nS)	MIN HOLD (nS)	PRICE ($)
4013A	Dual D-Type Flip-Flops	0.70	1.0	500.0	0.0	0.71
4013B	Dual D-Type Flip-Flops	0.15	3.5	40.0	0.0	0.41
40174B	Hex D-Type Flip-Flops	0.15	3.5	40.0	80.0	0.68
40175B	Quad D-Type Flip-Flops	0.15	2.0	120.0	80.0	0.68

all eight Q outputs go LOW on the next rising edge of the CLOCK, regardless of the level on the DATA input.

Types '576 and '577 are inverted output versions of the '574 and '575 respectively.

Table 3-4. D-Type Flip-Flops, 4000 Series, Military Temperature Range.

TYPE	DESCRIPTION	MAX POWER (mW)	FMAX (MHz)	MIN SETUP (nS)	MIN HOLD (nS)	PRICE ($)
4013A	Dual D-Type Flip-Flops	0.30	2.5	200.0	0.0	1.16
4013B	Dual D-Type Flip-Flops	0.15	3.5	40.0	0.0	0.89
40174B	Hex D-Type Flip-Flops	0.15	3.5	40.0	80.0	1.24
40175B	Quad D-Type Flip-Flops	0.15	2.0	120.0	80.0	1.24

Types '874 and '876 have high-drive capability (same as '374).

Type '879 is the same as '876 except the '879 has a synchronous clear ('876 has asynchronous, or non-clocked, clear).

Types 40174 and 40175 are 4000 Series CMOS versions of 54/74 family types '174 and '175 respectively.

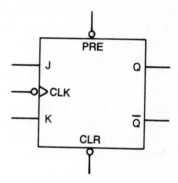

Fig. 3-3. Logic symbol and function table for negative-edge-triggered J-K flip-flop.

Inputs					Outputs	
PRE	CIR	CLK	J	K	Q	$\overline{Q}$
L	H	X	X	X	H	L
H	L	X	X	X	L	H
L	L	X	X	X	H	H
H	H	↓	L	L	Q_o	$\overline{Q}_o$
H	H	↓	H	L	H	L
H	H	↓	L	H	L	H
H	H	↓	H	H	Toggle	
H	H	H	X	X	Q_o	$\overline{Q}_o$

3.2 J-K FLIP-FLOPS

The logic symbol and function table for a negative-edge-triggered J-K flip-flop is shown in Fig. 3-3. The J-K flip-flop has five inputs and two outputs. The inputs are PRESET (PRE), CLEAR (CLR), CLOCK (CLK), J and K. The outputs are Q and $\overline{Q}$.

Preset and clear operation is the same as for the D-type flip-flop. When the preset and clear inputs are both HIGH the J-K flip-flop operation is as follows:

If the J input is LOW and the K input is HIGH, then the Q output will go LOW and the $\overline{Q}$ output will go HIGH on the next HIGH-to-LOW transition of the clock (denoted by a down arrow in the function table).

If the J input is HIGH and the K input is LOW, then the Q output will go HIGH and the $\overline{Q}$ output will go LOW on the next HIGH-to-LOW transition of the clock.

If the J and K inputs are both LOW, then the Q and $\overline{Q}$ outputs will remain in their previous state on the next HIGH-to-LOW transition of the clock.

If the J and K inputs are both HIGH, then the Q and $\overline{Q}$ outputs will toggle, or change to the opposite state, on the next HIGH-to-LOW transition of the clock.

For all of the above four conditions, the J and K inputs must be stable for a minimum of one setup time prior to the negative edge of the clock.

While the clock is HIGH, the outputs will remain unchanged, regardless of the levels on the J and K inputs.

The above functional description is for a negative-edge-triggered J-K flip-flop. The description is the same for positive-edge-triggered J-K flip-flops except that the outputs change on the LOW-to-HIGH transition of the clock. Also, there is another type of J-K flip-flop called a *master-slave* J-K flip-flop. This type of flip-flop has two sections—a master flip-flop and a slave flip-flop. The clock waveform and function table for the master-slave J-K flip-flop is shown in Fig. 3-4. The operation is as follows:

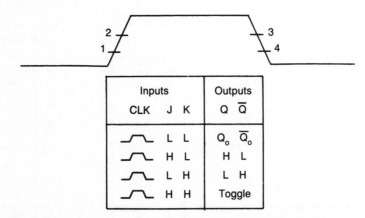

Inputs			Outputs	
CLK	J	K	Q	$\overline{Q}$
⎍	L	L	Q_o	$\overline{Q}_o$
⎍	H	L	H	L
⎍	L	H	L	H
⎍	H	H	Toggle	

Fig. 3-4. Clock waveform and function table for master-slave J-K flip-flop.

When the clock input rises to voltage level 1, the slave is isolated from the master. At level 2, the data on the J and K inputs is entered into the master.

When the clock input falls to voltage level 3, the J and K inputs are disabled. At level 4, the data in the master is transferred to the slave and appears on the Q and $\overline{Q}$ outputs.

While the clock is HIGH, the J and K inputs must be stable.

Tables 3-5 through 3-8 list the maximum power, maximum clock frequency, minimum setup time, minimum hold time, and 100-piece price for J-K flip-flops from the 54/74 families and 4000 Series families.

Type '70 has three ANDed J inputs (J1, J2, $\overline{J3}$) and three ANDed K inputs (K1, K2, $\overline{K3}$).

Type '71 has AND-OR inputs. J = (J1A″ • J1B) + (J2A″ J2B). ″ • ″ = AND; ″ + ″ = OR J2 J3). Same equation for JTB + (J2A• J2B).

Type '72 has ANDed inputs. J = (J1•J2•J3). Same equation for K.

The 54/7473, 54/74H73, and 54/74L73 are master-slave types. The C, HC and LS versions are negative-edge triggered.

The 54/7476 and 54/74H76 are master-slave types. The C, HC and LS versions are negative-edge triggered.

The 54/74H78 is a master-slave type. HC and LS are negative-edge triggered.

Table 3-5. J-K Flip-Flops, 54 Family.

TYPE	DESCRIPTION	MAX POWER (mW)	FMAX (MHz)	MIN SETUP (nS)	MIN HOLD (nS)	PRICE ($)
5470	AND-Gated Positive-Edge-Triggered J-K Flip-Flop with Preset and Clear	143.00	20.0	20.0	5.0	1.27
5473	Dual Master-Slave J-K Flip-Flops with Clear	110.00	15.0	0.0	0.0	1.19
54HC73	Dual Negative-Edge-Triggered J-K Flip-Flops with Clear	0.48	25.0	20.0	0.0	0.94
54L73	Dual Master-Slave J-K Flip-Flops with Clear	15.84	2.5	0.0	0.0	7.83
54LS73	Dual Negative-Edge-Triggered J-K Flip-Flops with Clear	33.00	30.0	20.0	0.0	0.60
5476	Dual Master-Slave J-K Flip-Flops with Preset and Clear	110.00	15.0	0.0	0.0	1.19
54C76	Dual Negative-Edge-Triggered J-K Flip-Flops with Preset and Clear	0.90	2.5	175.0	0.0	2.85
54HC76	Dual Negative-Edge-Triggered J-K Flip-Flops with Preset and Clear	0.48	21.0	45.0	0.0	1.29
54LS76	Dual Negative-Edge-Triggered J-K Flip-Flops with Preset and Clear	33.00	30.0	20.0	0.0	0.60

TYPE	DESCRIPTION	MAX POWER (mW)	FMAX (MHz)	MIN SETUP (nS)	MIN HOLD (nS)	PRICE ($)
54LS78	Dual J-K Flip-Flops with Preset, Common Clear, and Common Clock	33.00	30.0	20.0	0.0	0.60
54107	Dual Master-Slave J-K Flip-Flops with Clear	110.00	15.0	0.0	0.0	1.27
54C107	Dual Negative-Edge-Triggered J-K Flip-Flops with Clear	0.90	2.5	175.0	0.0	2.85
54HC107	Dual Negative-Edge-Triggered J-K Flip-Flops with Clear	0.48	21.0	30.0	0.0	0.82
54LS107	Dual Negative-Edge-Triggered J-K Flip-Flops with Clear	33.00	30.0	20.0	0.0	0.60
54109	Dual Positive-Edge-Triggered J-K Flip-Flops with Preset and Clear	82.50	25.0	10.0	6.0	1.22
54AC109	Dual Positive-Edge-Triggered J-K Flip-Flops with Preset and Clear	0.55	50.0	6.5	0.0	3.86
54ALS109	Dual Positive-Edge-Triggered J-K Flip-Flops with Preset and Clear	22.00	30.0	15.0	0.0	1.06
54F109	Dual Positive-Edge-Triggered J-K Flip-Flops with Preset and Clear	93.50	70.0	3.0	1.0	1.68
54HC109	Dual Positive-Edge-Triggered J-K Flip-Flops with Preset and Clear	0.48	20.0	27.0	5.0	0.82
54HCT109	Dual Positive-Edge-Triggered J-K Flip-Flops with Preset and Clear	0.44	18.0	27.0	3.0	0.69
54LS109	Dual Positive-Edge-Triggered J-K Flip-Flops with Preset and Clear	44.00	25.0	35.0	5.0	0.60
54111	Dual Master-Slave J-K Flip-Flip with Data Lockout	112.75	20.0	0.0	30.0	1.73
54ALS112	Dual Negative-Edge-Triggered J-K Flip-Flops with Preset and Clear	24.75	25.0	25.0	0.0	1.06
54HC112	Dual Negative-Edge-Triggered J-K Flip-Flops with Preset and Clear	0.48	17.0	30.0	0.0	0.94
54LS112	Dual Negative-Edge-Triggered J-K Flip-Flops with Preset and Clear	33.00	30.0	20.0	0.0	0.90
54S112	Dual Negative-Edge-Triggered J-K Flip-Flops with Preset and Clear	137.50	80.0	3.0	0.0	1.72
54ALS113	Dual Negative-Edge-Triggered J-K Flip-Flops with Preset	24.75	25.0	25.0	0.0	1.06
54HC113	Dual Negative-Edge-Triggered J-K Flip-Flops with Preset	0.48	21.0	30.0	0.0	1.00
54LS113	Dual Negative-Edge-Triggered J-K Flip-Flops with Preset	33.00	30.0	20.0	0.0	0.90

TYPE	DESCRIPTION	MAX POWER (mW)	FMAX (MHz)	MIN SETUP (nS)	MIN HOLD (nS)	PRICE ($)
54S113	Dual Negative-Edge-Triggered J-K Flip-Flops with Preset	137.50	80.0	3.0	0.0	1.72
54ALS114	Dual J-K Flip-Flops with Preset, Common Clear, and Common Clock	24.75	25.0	25.0	0.0	1.06
54HC114	Dual J-K Flip-Flops with Preset, Common Clear, and Common Clock	0.48	17.0	30.0	0.0	1.00
54LS114	Dual J-K Flip-Flops with Preset, Common Clear, and Common Clock	33.00	30.0	20.0	0.0	0.90
54S114	Dual J-K Flip-Flops with Preset, Common Clear, and Common Clock	137.50	80.0	3.0	0.0	1.79
54376	Quad J-K Flip-Flops	407.00	30.0	0.0	20.0	5.49

Table 3-6. J-K Flip-Flops, 74 Family.

TYPE	DESCRIPTION	MAX POWER (mW)	FMAX (MHz)	MIN SETUP (nS)	MIN HOLD (nS)	PRICE ($)
7470	AND-Gated Positive-Edge-Triggered J-K Flip-Flop with Preset and Clear	136.50	20.0	20.0	5.0	0.43
74H71	AND-OR-Gated Master-Slave J-K Flip-Flip with Preset	157.50	25.0	0.0	0.0	3.29
7472	AND-Gated Master-Slave J-K Flip-Flop with Preset and Clear	105.00	15.0	0.0	0.0	0.86
74H72	AND-Gated Master-Slave J-K Flip-Flop with Preset and Clear	131.25	25.0	0.0	0.0	3.29
74L72	AND-Gated Master-Slave J-K Flip-Flop with Preset and Clear	7.56	2.5	0.0	0.0	1.05
7473	Dual Master-Slave J-K Flip-Flops with Clear	105.00	15.0	0.0	0.0	0.33
74C73	Dual Negative-Edge-Triggered J-K Flip-Flops with Clear	0.90	2.5	175.0	0.0	0.60
74H73	Dual Master-Slave J-K Flip-Flops with Clear	131.25	25.0	0.0	0.0	3.29
74HC73	Dual Negative-Edge-Triggered J-K Flip-Flops with Clear	0.24	25.0	20.0	0.0	0.41
74L73	Dual Master-Slave J-K Flip-Flops with Clear	15.12	2.5	0.0	0.0	1.35
• 74LS73	Dual Negative-Edge-Triggered J-K Flip-Flops with Clear	31.50	30.0	20.0	0.0	0.34

TYPE	DESCRIPTION	MAX POWER (mW)	FMAX (MHz)	MIN SETUP (nS)	MIN HOLD (nS)	PRICE ($)
7476	Dual Master-Slave J-K Flip-Flops with Preset and Clear	105.00	15.0	0.0	0.0	0.33
74C76	Dual Negative-Edge-Triggered J-K Flip-Flops with Preset and Clear	0.90	2.5	175.0	0.0	0.60
74H76	Dual Master-Slave J-K Flip-Flops with Preset and Clear	131.25	25.0	0.0	0.0	3.29
74HC76	Dual Negative-Edge-Triggered J-K Flip-Flops with Preset and Clear	0.24	25.0	38.0	0.0	0.63
74LS76	Dual Negative-Edge-Triggered J-K Flip-Flops with Preset and Clear	31.50	30.0	20.0	0.0	0.35
74H78	Dual J-K Flip-Flops with Preset, Common Clear, and Common Clock	131.25	25.0	0.0	0.0	3.85
74HC78	Dual J-K Flip-Flops with Preset, Common Clear, and Common Clock	0.24	25.0	20.0	0.0	0.63
74LS78	Dual J-K Flip-Flops with Preset, Common Clear, and Common Clock	31.50	30.0	20.0	0.0	0.35
74H101	AND-OR-Gated Negative-Edge-Triggered J-K Flip-Flop with Preset	199.50	40.0	13.0	0.0	3.29
74H102	AND-Gated Negative-Edge-Triggered J-K Flip-Flop with Preset and Clear	199.50	40.0	13.0	0.0	3.29
74H103	Dual Negative-Edge-Triggered J-K Flip-Flop with Clear	199.50	40.0	13.0	0.0	3.29
74H106	Dual Negative-Edge-Triggered J-K Flip-Flops with Preset and Clear	199.50	40.0	13.0	0.0	3.29
74107	Dual Master-Slave J-K Flip-Flops with Clear	105.00	15.0	0.0	0.0	0.39
74C107	Dual Negative-Edge-Triggered J-K Flip-Flops with Clear	0.90	2.5	175.0	0.0	1.26
74HC107	Dual Negative-Edge-Triggered J-K Flip-Flops with Clear	0.24	25.0	25.0	0.0	0.41
74LS107	Dual Negative-Edge-Triggered J-K Flip-Flops with Clear	31.50	30.0	20.0	0.0	0.32
74H108	Dual J-K Flip-Flops with Preset, Common Clear, and Common Clock	199.50	40.0	13.0	0.0	3.29
74109	Dual Positive-Edge-Triggered J-K Flip-Flops with Preset and Clear	78.75	25.0	10.0	6.0	0.39
74AC109	Dual Positive-Edge-Triggered J-K Flip-Flops with Preset and Clear	0.28	50.0	6.5	0.0	0.44

TYPE	DESCRIPTION	MAX POWER (mW)	FMAX (MHz)	MIN SETUP (nS)	MIN HOLD (nS)	PRICE ($)
74ALS109	Dual Positive-Edge-Triggered J-K Flip-Flops with Preset and Clear	22.00	34.0	15.0	0.0	0.43
74AS109	Dual Positive-Edge-Triggered J-K Flip-Flops with Preset and Clear	93.50	105.0	5.5	0.0	0.60
74F109	Dual Positive-Edge-Triggered J-K Flip-Flops with Preset and Clear	89.25	90.0	3.0	1.0	0.46
74HC109	Dual Positive-Edge-Triggered J-K Flip-Flops with Preset and Clear	0.24	25.0	23.0	5.0	0.41
74HCT109	Dual Positive-Edge-Triggered J-K Flip-Flops with Preset and Clear	0.22	22.0	23.0	3.0	0.41
74LS109	Dual Positive-Edge-Triggered J-K Flip-Flops with Preset and Clear	42.00	25.0	35.0	5.0	0.26
74S109	Dual Positive-Edge-Triggered J-K Flip-Flops with Preset and Clear	273.00	75.0	6.0	0.0	1.12
74111	Dual Master-Slave J-K Flip-Flip with Data Lockout	107.62	20.0	0.0	30.0	1.40
74ALS112	Dual Negative-Edge-Triggered J-K Flip-Flops with Preset and Clear	24.75	30.0	22.0	0.0	0.45
74F112	Dual Negative-Edge-Triggered J-K Flip-Flops with Preset and Clear	99.75	100.0	5.0	0.0	1.14
74HC112	Dual Negative-Edge-Triggered J-K Flip-Flops with Preset and Clear	0.24	20.0	25.0	0.0	0.53
74LS112	Dual Negative-Edge-Triggered J-K Flip-Flops with Preset and Clear	31.50	30.0	20.0	0.0	0.32
74S112	Dual Negative-Edge-Triggered J-K Flip-Flops with Preset and Clear	131.25	80.0	3.0	0.0	0.50
74ALS113	Dual Negative-Edge-Triggered J-K Flip-Flops with Preset	24.75	30.0	22.0	0.0	0.45
74F113	Dual Negative-Edge-Triggered J-K Flip-Flops with Preset	99.75	100.0	5.0	0.0	1.14
74HC113	Dual Negative-Edge-Triggered J-K Flip-Flops with Preset	0.24	25.0	25.0	0.0	0.53
74LS113	Dual Negative-Edge-Triggered J-K Flip-Flops with Preset	31.50	30.0	20.0	0.0	0.33
74S113	Dual Negative-Edge-Triggered J-K Flip-Flops with Preset	131.25	80.0	3.0	0.0	0.51
74ALS114	Dual J-K Flip-Flops with Preset, Common Clear, and Common Clock	24.75	30.0	22.0	0.0	0.45
74F114	Dual J-K Flip-Flops with Preset, Common Clear, and Common Clock	99.75	90.0	5.0	0.0	1.14

TYPE	DESCRIPTION	MAX POWER (mW)	FMAX (MHz)	MIN SETUP (nS)	MIN HOLD (nS)	PRICE ($)
74HC114	Dual J-K Flip-Flops with Preset, Common Clear, and Common Clock	0.24	20.0	25.0	0.0	0.53
74LS114	Dual J-K Flip-Flops with Preset, Common Clear, and Common Clock	31.50	30.0	20.0	0.0	0.33
74S114	Dual J-K Flip-Flops with Preset, Common Clear, and Common Clock	131.25	80.0	3.0	0.0	0.66
74276	Quad J-K Flip-Flops	425.25	35.0	3.0	10.0	2.50
74376	Quad J-K Flip-Flops	388.50	30.0	0.0	20.0	1.40

Table 3-7. J-K Flip-Flops, 4000 Series, Industrial Temperature Range.

TYPE	DESCRIPTION	MAX POWER (mW)	FMAX (MHz)	MIN SETUP (nS)	MIN HOLD (nS)	PRICE ($)
4027A	Dual J-K Master-Slave Flip-Flops	0.70	1.0	200.0	0.0	0.78
4027B	Dual J-K Master-Slave Flip-Flops	0.15	3.5	200.0	0.0	0.45
4095B	Gated J-K Master-Slave Flip-Flop	0.15	3.5	400.0	0.0	0.78
4096B	Gated J-K Master-Slave Flip-Flop (Inverting and Non-Inverting Inputs)	0.15	3.5	400.0	0.0	0.69

Table 3-8. J-K Flip-Flops, 4000 Series, Military Temperature Range.

TYPE	DESCRIPTION	MAX POWER (mW)	FMAX (MHz)	MIN SETUP (nS)	MIN HOLD (nS)	PRICE ($)
4027A	Dual J-K Master-Slave Flip-Flops	0.30	1.5	150.0	0.0	1.34
4027B	Dual J-K Master-Slave Flip-Flops	0.15	3.5	200.0	0.0	0.89
4095B	Gated J-K Master-Slave Flip-Flop	0.15	3.5	400.0	0.0	1.28
4096B	Gated J-K Master-Slave Flip-Flop (Inverting and Non-Inverting Inputs)	0.15	3.5	400.0	0.0	1.24

Type '101 has AND-OR inputs. Same equations as type '71.

Type '102 has AND inputs. Same equations as type '72.

The 54/74107 is a master-slave type. C, HC, and LS are negative-edge triggered.

Type '109 has $\overline{K}$ inputs.

Type '111 has data lockout feature. J and K inputs can receive data only during a 30 nS period maximum following the rising edge of the clock.

Type '276 has $\overline{K}$ inputs, separate clocks, common clear and common preclear.

Type '376 has $\overline{K}$ inputs, common clock, and common clear.

The 4095 and 4096 have AND inputs. 4095 has three noninverted J inputs and three non-inverted K inputs. 4096 has two noninverted and one inverted J inputs; and two noninverted and one inverted K input.

3.3 LATCHES

The logic symbol and function table for a D-type transparent latch is shown in Fig. 3-5. The latch shown has two inputs and two outputs. The inputs are DATA and ENABLE. The outputs are Q and $\overline{Q}$.

The operation of the latch is very simple. While the enable is HIGH, the outputs following the data input. In this mode the latch is said to be *transparent*. When the enable goes LOW, the output states are latched and will stay latched until the enable line goes HIGH again. For example, if DATA is HIGH just before

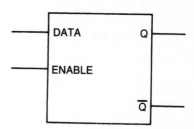

Fig. 3-5. Logic symbol and function table for a latch.

Inputs		Outputs	
DATA	ENABLE	Q	$\overline{Q}$
L	H	L	H
H	H	H	L
X	L	Q_o	$\overline{Q}_o$

(one setup time) ENABLE goes LOW, then Q will be latched in the HIGH state and $\overline{Q}$ will be latched in the LOW state as long as ENABLE is LOW.

While flip-flops are generally used as building blocks for counters, the latch is used for temporary storage, such as an address latch or input/output port (data latch) in a microprocessor system. Latches are available in 4-, 8-, 9-, or 10-bit versions, which means that there are 4, 8, 9, or 10 latches per package, usually with common latch enable lines and a common clear, or reset, line.

Tables 3-9 through 3-12 list the maximum power, maximum delay from the data input to either Q or $\overline{Q}$, minimum setup time, minimum hold time, and 100-piece price for latches from the 54/74 families and 4000 Series families.

Table 3-9. Latches, 54 Family.

TYPE	DESCRIPTION	MAX POWER (mW)	MAX DELAY (nS)	MIN SETUP (nS)	MIN HOLD (nS)	PRICE ($)
5475	4–Bit Bistable Latch	291.50	40.0	20.0	5.0	1.60
54HC75	4–Bit Bistable Latch	0.48	39.0	18.0	3.0	0.94
54HCT75	4–Bit Bistable Latch	0.44	48.0	18.0	3.0	0.69
54LS75	4–Bit Bistable Latch	66.00	27.0	20.0	5.0	0.86
54LS77	4–Bit Bistable Latch	71.50	19.0	20.0	5.0	1.10
54100	8–Bit Bistable Latch	583.00	30.0	20.0	5.0	6.08
54116	Dual 4–Bit Latches with Clear	550.00	18.0	14.0	8.0	4.12
54LS256	Dual 4–Bit Addressable Latch	137.50	30.0	20.0	0.0	1.82
54HC259	8–Bit Addressable Latch	0.96	39.0	23.0	5.0	2.26
54LS259	8–Bit Addressable Latch	198.00	30.0	20.0	0.0	1.29
54ALS373	Octal 3–State Transparent D–Type Latches	148.50	19.0	10.0	7.0	3.22
54AS373	Octal 3–State Transparent D–Type Latches	550.00	8.0	2.0	3.0	5.95
54C373	Octal 3–State Transparent D–Type Latches	4.50	300.0	140.0	0.0	7.71
54F373	Octal 3–State Transparent D–Type Latches	302.50	8.5	2.0	3.0	5.04
54HC373	Octal 3–State Transparent D–Type Latches	0.96	45.0	15.0	5.0	3.09
54HCT373	Octal 3–State Transparent D–Type Latches	0.88	53.0	15.0	5.0	2.48
54LS373	Octal 3–State Transparent D–Type Latches	220.00	18.0	5.0	20.0	2.62
54S373	Octal 3–State Transparent D–Type Latches	1045.00	12.0	0.0	10.0	5.06
54LS375	4–Bit Bistable Latch	66.00	27.0	20.0	0.0	0.86
54F412	Multimode Octal Latch	330.00	11.5	2.0	10.0	14.80

TYPE	DESCRIPTION	MAX POWER (mW)	MAX DELAY (nS)	MIN SETUP (nS)	MIN HOLD (nS)	PRICE ($)
54F533	Octal 3-State Inverting Transparent D-Type Latches	335.50	12.0	2.0	3.0	5.38
54HC533	Octal 3-State Inverting Transparent D-Type Latches	0.96	53.0	15.0	5.0	3.56
54HCT533	Octal 3-State Inverting Transparent D-Type Latches	0.88	53.0	15.0	5.0	2.48
54ALS563	Octal 3-State Inverting Transparent D-Type Latches	148.50	21.0	10.0	10.0	3.36
54F563	Octal 3-State Inverting Transparent D-Type Latches	302.50	7.0	2.0	3.0	14.09
54HC563	Octal 3-State Inverting Transparent D-Type Latches	0.96	53.0	15.0	5.0	3.73
54HCT563	Octal 3-State Inverting Transparent D-Type Latches	0.88	53.0	15.0	5.0	3.30
54ALS573	Octal 3-State Transparent D-Type Latches	148.50	15.0	10.0	7.0	3.36
54F573	Octal 3-State Transparent D-Type Latches	302.50	8.0	3.0	3.0	14.09
54HC573	Octal 3-State Transparent D-Type Latches	0.96	53.0	15.0	5.0	3.88
54HCT573	Octal 3-State Transparent D-Type Latches	0.88	53.0	15.0	5.0	3.30
54ALS580	Octal 3-State Inverting D-Type Latches	148.50	21.0	10.0	10.0	3.36
54LS793	8-Bit Latch with Readback	660.00	18.0	15.0	10.0	6.68
54ALS873	Dual 3-State 4-Bit Transparent D-Type Latches	170.50	17.0	10.0	7.0	4.35
54HC4724	8-Bit Addressable Latch	0.96	39.0	23.0	5.0	4.46

Table 3-10. Latches, 74 Family.

TYPE	DESCRIPTION	MAX POWER (mW)	MAX DELAY (nS)	MIN SETUP (nS)	MIN HOLD (nS)	PRICE ($)
7475	4-Bit Bistable Latch	278.25	40.0	20.0	5.0	0.37
74HC75	4-Bit Bistable Latch	0.24	33.0	15.0	3.0	0.41
74HCT75	4-Bit Bistable Latch	0.22	40.0	15.0	3.0	0.41
74LS75	4-Bit Bistable Latch	63.00	27.0	20.0	5.0	0.36
74HC77	4-Bit Bistable Latch	0.24	30.0	25.0	5.0	0.63

TYPE	DESCRIPTION	MAX POWER (mW)	MAX DELAY (nS)	MIN SETUP (nS)	MIN HOLD (nS)	PRICE ($)
74LS77	4-Bit Bistable Latch	63.00	19.0	20.0	5.0	0.56
74100	8-Bit Bistable Latch	556.50	30.0	20.0	5.0	3.32
74116	Dual 4-Bit Latches with Clear	525.00	18.0	14.0	8.0	1.42
74LS256	Dual 4-Bit Addressable Latch	131.25	30.0	20.0	0.0	0.69
74259	8-Bit Addressable Latch	472.50	24.0	15.0	0.0	2.20
74HC259	8-Bit Addressable Latch	0.48	33.0	19.0	5.0	1.02
74LS259	8-Bit Addressable Latch	189.00	30.0	20.0	0.0	0.69
74AC373	Octal 3-State Transparent D-Type Latches	0.28	11.0	4.5	0.0	1.27
74ALS373	Octal 3-State Transparent D-Type Latches	148.50	16.0	10.0	7.0	1.28
74AS373	Octal 3-State Transparent D-Type Latches	550.00	6.0	2.0	3.0	2.63
74C373	Octal 3-State Transparent D-Type Latches	4.50	300.0	140.0	0.0	1.80
74F373	Octal 3-State Transparent D-Type Latches	288.75	8.0	2.0	3.0	1.14
74HC373	Octal 3-State Transparent D-Type Latches	0.48	38.0	13.0	5.0	1.16
74HCT373	Octal 3-State Transparent D-Type Latches	0.44	44.0	13.0	5.0	1.16
74LS373	Octal 3-State Transparent D-Type Latches	210.00	18.0	5.0	20.0	0.60
74S373	Octal 3-State Transparent D-Type Latches	997.50	12.0	0.0	10.0	2.25
74HC375	4-Bit Bistable Latch	0.24	30.0	25.0	5.0	0.58
74LS375	4-Bit Bistable Latch	63.00	27.0	20.0	0.0	0.36
74F412	Multimode Octal Latch	315.00	9.5	1.0	9.0	3.22
74S412	Multimode Octal Latch	682.50	2.0	15.0	20.0	7.00
74F432	Inverting Multimode Octal Latch	341.25	12.0	0.0	12.5	3.22
74ALS533	Octal 3-State Inverting Transparent D-Type Latches	154.00	19.0	15.0	7.0	1.44
74AS533	Octal 3-State Inverting Transparent D-Type Latches	605.00	7.5	2.0	3.0	2.63
74F533	Octal 3-State Inverting Transparent D-Type Latches	320.25	10.0	2.0	3.0	1.29
74HC533	Octal 3-State Inverting Transparent D-Type Latches	0.48	44.0	13.0	5.0	1.16
74HCT533	Octal 3-State Inverting Transparent D-Type Latches	0.44	44.0	13.0	5.0	1.57
74LS533	Octal 3-State Inverting Transparent D-Type Latches	210.00	20.0	0.0	10.0	0.79

TYPE	DESCRIPTION	MAX POWER (mW)	MAX DELAY (nS)	MIN SETUP (nS)	MIN HOLD (nS)	PRICE ($)
74ALS563	Octal 3-State Inverting Transparent D-Type Latches	148.50	18.0	10.0	10.0	1.36
74F563	Octal 3-State Inverting Transparent D-Type Latches	288.75	7.0	2.0	3.0	2.79
74HC563	Octal 3-State Inverting Transparent D-Type Latches	0.48	44.0	13.0	5.0	1.40
74HCT563	Octal 3-State Inverting Transparent D-Type Latches	0.44	44.0	13.0	5.0	1.78
74LS563	Octal 3-State Inverting Transparent D-Type Latches	210.00	20.0	0.0	10.0	1.57
74ALS573	Octal 3-State Transparent D-Type Latches	148.50	14.0	10.0	7.0	1.34
74AS573	Octal 3-State Transparent D-Type Latches	583.00	6.0	2.0	3.0	2.61
74F573	Octal 3-State Transparent D-Type Latches	288.75	8.0	3.0	3.0	2.79
74HC573	Octal 3-State Transparent D-Type Latches	0.48	44.0	13.0	5.0	1.40
74HCT573	Octal 3-State Transparent D-Type Latches	0.44	44.0	13.0	5.0	1.78
74LS573	Octal 3-State Transparent D-Type Latches	210.00	20.0	0.0	10.0	1.00
74ALS580	Octal 3-State Inverting D-Type Latches	148.50	18.0	10.0	10.0	1.36
74AS580	Octal 3-State Inverting D-Type Latches	632.50	7.5	2.0	3.0	2.61
74ALS666	8-Bit D-Type Read-Back Latches with 3-State Outputs	401.50	18.0	10.0	5.0	5.88
74ALS667	8-Bit Invering D-Type Read-Back Latches with 3-State Outputs	434.50	20.0	10.0	5.0	5.88
74LS793	8-Bit Latch with Readback	630.00	18.0	15.0	10.0	2.34
74ALS841	10-Bit Bus Interface D-Type Latches with 3-State Outputs	341.00	13.0	10.0	5.0	3.19
74AS841	10-Bit Bus Interface D-Type Latches with 3-State Outputs	517.00	9.0	2.5	2.5	3.17
74ALS842	10-Bit Inverting Bus Interface D-Type Latches with 3-State Outputs	407.00	18.0	10.0	5.0	3.17
74AS842	10-Bit Inverting Bus Interface D-Type Latches with 3-State Outputs	533.50	9.0	2.5	2.5	3.17
74AS843	9-Bit Bus Interface D-Type Latches with 3-State Outputs	506.00	9.0	2.5	2.5	3.17
74AS844	9-Bit Inverting Bus Interface D-Type Latches with 3-State Outputs	522.50	10.0	2.5	2.5	3.17
74AS845	8-Bit Bus Interface D-Type Latches with 3-State Outputs	467.50	9.0	2.5	2.5	3.17

TYPE	DESCRIPTION	MAX POWER (mW)	MAX DELAY (nS)	MIN SETUP (nS)	MIN HOLD (nS)	PRICE ($)
74AS846	8-Bit Inverting Bus Interface D-Type Latches with 3-State Outputs	478.50	10.0	2.5	2.5	3.17
74ALS873	Dual 3-State 4-Bit Transparent D-Type Latches	170.50	14.0	10.0	7.0	1.58
74AS873	Dual 3-State 4-Bit Transparent D-Type Latches	709.50	6.0	2.0	3.0	2.91
74ALS880	Dual 3-State 4-Bit Inverting Transparent D-Type Latches	170.50	20.0	10.0	10.0	1.68
74AS880	Dual 3-State 4-Bit Inverting Transparent D-Type Latches	753.50	9.5	2.0	1.0	2.91
74ALS990	8-Bit D-Type Read-Back Latches with 3-State Outputs	385.00	24.0	10.0	5.0	3.36
74ALS991	8-Bit Inverting D-Type Read-Back Latches with 3-state Outputs	412.50	20.0	10.0	5.0	3.36
74HC4724	8-Bit Addressable Latch	0.48	33.0	19.0	5.0	1.80

Table 3-11. Latches, 4000 Series, Industrial Temperature Range.

TYPE	DESCRIPTION	MAX POWER (mW)	MAX DELAY (nS)	MIN SETUP (nS)	MIN HOLD (nS)	PRICE ($)
4042A	Quad Clocked D-Type Latch	0.70	600.0	50.0	300.0	1.06
4042B	Quad Clocked D-Type Latch	0.15	300.0	50.0	120.0	0.66
4099B	8-Bit Addressable Latch	0.75	400.0	100.0	150.0	1.16
4508B	Dual 4-Bit Latch	0.75	210.0	50.0	0.0	3.75
4723B	Dual 4-Bit Addressable Latch	0.75	400.0	80.0	120.0	1.24
4724B	8-Bit Addressable Latch	0.75	400.0	100.0	150.0	1.32

Type '75 has Q and $\overline{Q}$ outputs and two enables, one enable per pair of latches. Type '77 has only Q outputs. Type '100 has Q outputs and one common enable.

Types '256, '259, and '4724 are *addressable* latches. These types have a single DATA input and two or three address lines. The address lines are used to select only one latch at a time when storing data. All latch outputs are available.

Table 3-12. Latches, 4000 Series, Military Temperature Range.

TYPE	DESCRIPTION	MAX POWER (mW)	MAX DELAY (nS)	MIN SETUP (nS)	MIN HOLD (nS)	PRICE ($)
4042A	Quad Clocked D–Type Latch	0.30	500.0	50.0	350.0	1.96
4042B	Quad Clocked D–Type Latch	0.15	300.0	50.0	120.0	1.19
4099B	8–Bit Addressable Latch	0.75	400.0	100.0	150.0	2.15
4508B	Dual 4–Bit Latch	0.75	210.0	50.0	0.0	5.36
4723B	Dual 4–Bit Addressable Latch	0.75	400.0	80.0	120.0	2.80
4724B	8–Bit Addressable Latch	0.75	400.0	100.0	150.0	1.85

Type '373 features 3-state outputs with high drive capability.

Type '375 is the same as '75 except for the pinout.

Type '412 includes a status flip-flop which may be used to provide busy or interrupt commands in a microprocessor system. The '412 has 3-state outputs with high drive capability.

The 74F432 is a 74F412 with inverting outputs.

Type '533 is a '373 with inverting outputs. See '373 for drive capability. Type '563 is a bus-structured version of the '533. The '573 is a bus-structured version of the '373. As far as I can tell, the '580 is identical to the '563.

Types '666 and '667 are designed to be 8-bit output ports with the additional capability of "reading-back" the output data onto the input data bus. The Q output goes through a 3-state buffer back to the D input. In the read-back mode the D input is an output with only standard drive capability (see Tables 1-1 and 1-2, Chapter 1). The Q outputs have high drive capability.

The '990 and '991 are standard output versions of the '666 and '667 in 20-pin packages. The '666/667 is in a 24-pin package has two output control lines, a clear, and preclear.

The '793 is a read-back latch with high drive capability for both the D and Q outputs.

3.4 MONOSTABLE MULTIVIBRATORS

The logic symbol and waveform diagram for a monostable multivibrator, or *one-shot* is shown in Fig. 3-6. The figure shows only one trigger input. In practice, one-shot ICs have multiple trigger inputs to provide flexibility in system applications.

In the absence of a trigger input pulse, the Q output is LOW and the $\overline{Q}$ output

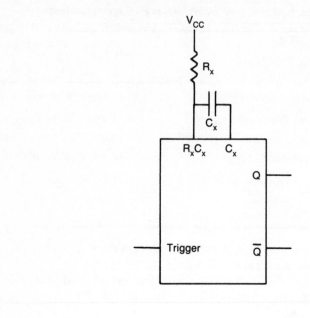

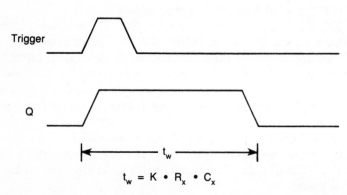

Fig. 3-6. Logic symbol and waveform diagram for monostable multivibrator.

is HIGH. On the rising edge of the trigger input pulse, Q goes HIGH and stays HIGH for a period of time t_w determined by the values of the external resistor R_x and capacitor C_x and also the internal circuit design of the IC (the K factor in the equation shown for the pulse width t_w).

Maximum output pulse width is established by the external resistor and capacitor values. Data sheets for one-shot IC's specify maximum values for R_x and C_x as recommended operating conditions. The minimum output pulse is obtained when no external resistor and capacitor is used.

A *retriggerable* one-shot may be retriggered while the output is HIGH. The output is then equal to t_w plus the time between the rising edges of the trigger pulses. For one-shots that are not retriggerable, the one-shot cannot be triggered again until the output is LOW.

Tables 3-13 through 3-16 list the maximum power, minimum output pulse width, and 100-piece price for monostable multivibrators from the 54/74 families and 4000 Series families.

The '122 and '123 have a clear input that may be used to cause the output to go LOW early. The clear input can also be used to trigger the one-shot, depending on the condition of the other trigger inputs. The '422 and '423 are identical to the '122 and '123 except that the clear input cannot be used to trigger the one-shot.

Table 3-13. Monostable Multivibrators, 54 Family.

TYPE	DESCRIPTION	MAX POWER (mW)	MIN PULSE (nS)	PRICE ($)
54121	Monostable Multivibrator with Schmitt-Trigger Input	220.00	50	1.06
54122	Retriggerable Monostable Multivibrator with Clear	198.00	65	1.29
54LS122	Retriggerable Monostable Multivibrator with Clear	110.00	200	0.89
54123	Dual Retriggerable Monostable Multivibrators with Clear	363.00	65	1.99
54HC123	Dual Retriggerable Monostable Multivibrators with Clear	0.96	400	2.18
54LS123	Dual Retriggerable Monostable Multivibrators with Clear	110.00	200	1.50
54221	Dual Monostable Multivibrators with Schmitt-Trigger Input	440.00	50	3.36
54C221	Dual Monostable Multivibrators with Schmitt-Trigger Input	4.50	900	5.24
54HC221	Dual Monostable Multivibrators with Schmitt-Trigger Input	0.96	140	2.18
54HCT221	Dual Monostable Multivibrators with Schmitt-Trigger Input	0.88	140	1.96
54LS221	Dual Monostable Multivibrators with Schmitt-Trigger Input	148.50	70	1.54
54HC423	Dual Retriggerable Monostable Multivibrators	0.96	400	2.18
54HC4538	Dual Retriggerable Monostable Multivibrator	2.40	185	2.89
54HCT4538	Dual Retriggerable Monostable Multivibrator	0.88	185	2.48

Table 3-14. Monostable Multivibrators, 74 Family.

TYPE	DESCRIPTION	MAX POWER (mW)	MIN PULSE (nS)	PRICE ($)
74121	Monostable Multivibrator with Schmitt-Trigger Input	210.00	50	0.36
74122	Retriggerable Monostable Multivibrator with Clear	189.00	65	0.62
74LS122	Retriggerable Monostable Multivibrator with Clear	105.00	200	0.43
74123	Dual Retriggerable Monostable Multivibrators with Clear	346.50	65	0.43
74HC123	Dual Retriggerable Monostable Multivibrators with Clear	0.48	400	0.74
74LS123	Dual Retriggerable Monostable Multivibrators with Clear	105.00	200	0.58
74221	Dual Monostable Multivibrators with Schmitt-Trigger Input	420.00	50	0.90
74C221	Dual Monostable Multivibrators with Schmitt-Trigger Input	4.50	900	1.45
74HC221	Dual Monostable Multivibrators with Schmitt-Trigger Input	0.48	140	0.96
74HCT221	Dual Monostable Multivibrators with Schmitt-Trigger Input	0.44	140	0.96
74LS221	Dual Monostable Multivibrators with Schmitt-Trigger Input	141.75	70	0.74
74LS422	Retriggerable Monostable Multivibrator	57.75	200	1.02
74HC423	Dual Retriggerable Monostable Multivibrators	0.48	400	0.63
74LS423	Dual Retriggerable Monostable Multivibrators	105.00	200	0.63
74HC4538	Dual Retriggerable Monostable Multivibrator	1.50	185	1.07
74HCT4538	Dual Retriggerable Monostable Multivibrator	0.44	185	1.07

Table 3-15. Monostable Multivibrators, 4000 Series, Industrial Temperature Range.

TYPE	DESCRIPTION	MAX POWER (mW)	MIN PULSE (nS)	PRICE ($)
4047A	Monostable/Astable Multivibrator	3.50	25000	1.78
4047B	Monostable/Astable Multivibrator	0.15	2000	0.84

TYPE	DESCRIPTION	MAX POWER (mW)	MIN PULSE (nS)	PRICE ($)
4098B	Dual Monostable Multivibrators	0.15	500	0.86
4528B	Dual Monostable Multivibrator	0.75	550	0.71
4538B	Dual Precision Monostable Multivibrators	0.75	20000	1.07

Table 3-16. Monostable Multivibrators, 4000 Series, Military Temperature Range.

TYPE	DESCRIPTION	MAX POWER (mW)	MIN PULSE (nS)	PRICE ($)
4047A	Monostable/Astable Multivibrator	1.50	25000	3.73
4047B	Monostable/Astable Multivibrator	0.15	2000	2.31
4098B	Dual Monostable Multivibrators	0.15	500	2.06
4528B	Dual Monostable Multivibrator	0.75	550	1.50
4538B	Dual Precision Monostable Multivibrators	0.75	20000	2.24

Chapter 4

Buffers and Transceivers

A *buffer* is designed to drive larger loads than a standard gate. A variety of buffers are available as standard ICs: inverting and noninverting buffers (single input, single output), NAND buffers, NOR buffers, AND buffers, and OR buffers. Buffers are also sometimes called *drivers*, although the term *driver* is sometimes used to designate a circuit that has more drive capability than a buffer. Most buffers have 3-state outputs for use in bus-oriented systems, but there are some types with open-collector outputs.

The logic diagram for the 3-state buffer is shown in Fig. 4-1. When G is HIGH, the output Y is the same logic level as the input A. When G is LOW the Y output is high impedance, or high-Z.

A *transceiver* is also used in bus-oriented systems and is used to pass digital signals in both directions. Most transceivers are 3-state in both directions, but there are some types with open-collector outputs. Basically, a transceiver is two 3-state buffers in parallel, the output of each buffer connected to the input of the other buffer. The logic diagram and function table for the basic transceiver is shown in Fig. 4-2.

A transceiver may also include latches or flip-flops. Buffers and transceivers are characterized by their high current capabilities: both I_{OH} and I_{OL} are considerably higher than for gates.

4.1 BUFFERS

Tables 4-1 and 4-2 list dual, triple, and quad buffers for 54/74 families. The

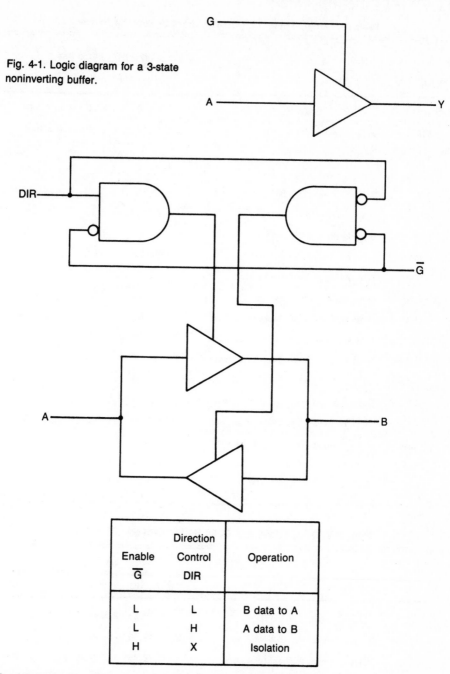

Fig. 4-1. Logic diagram for a 3-state noninverting buffer.

Enable $\overline{G}$	Direction Control DIR	Operation
L	L	B data to A
L	H	A data to B
H	X	Isolation

Fig. 4-2. Logic diagram and function table for a noninverting transceiver.

Table 4-1. Dual, Triple, and Quad Buffers/Drivers, 54 Family.

TYPE	DESCRIPTION	MAX POWER (mW)	MAX IOH (mA)	MAX IOL (mA)	MAX DELAY (nS)	PRICE ($)
5428	Quad 2-Input NOR Buffers	313.50	2.4	48.0	18.0	1.82
54ALS28	Quad 2-Input NOR Buffers	49.50	1.0	12.0	16.0	0.90
54LS28	Quad 2-Input NOR Buffers	75.90	1.2	12.0	24.0	0.56
5437	Quad 2-Input NAND Buffers	297.00	1.2	48.0	22.0	1.06
54ALS37	Quad 2-Input NAND Buffers	42.90	1.0	12.0	17.0	0.90
54LS37	Quad 2-Input NAND Buffers	66.00	1.2	12.0	24.0	0.57
54S37	Quad 2-Input NAND Buffers	440.00	3.0	60.0	6.5	1.72
5440	Dual 4-Input NAND Buffers	148.50	1.2	48.0	22.0	1.00
54LS40	Dual 4-Input NAND Buffers	33.00	1.2	12.0	24.0	0.56
54S40	Dual 4-Input NAND Buffers	242.00	3.0	60.0	6.5	1.22
54125	Quad Buffers with 3-State Outputs	297.00	2.0	16.0	18.0	1.00
54HC125	Quad Buffers with 3-State Outputs	0.96	6.0	6.0	36.0	0.79
54LS125	Quad Buffers with 3-State Outputs	121.00	1.0	12.0	18.0	0.56
54126	Quad Buffers with 3-State Outputs	341.00	2.0	16.0	18.0	1.00
54HC126	Quad Buffers with 3-State Outputs	0.96	6.0	6.0	36.0	0.79
54LS126	Quad Buffers with 3-State Outputs	121.00	1.0	12.0	18.0	0.56
54128	Quad 2-Input NOR Line Drivers	313.50	29.0	48.0	18.0	5.12
54S140	Dual 4-Input NAND 50-Ohm Line Drivers	242.00	40.0	60.0	6.5	1.83
54ALS1010	Triple 3-Input NAND Buffers	31.90	1.0	12.0	12.0	0.90

Table 4-2. Dual, Triple, and Quad Buffers/Drivers, 74 Family.

TYPE	DESCRIPTION	MAX POWER (mW)	MAX IOH (mA)	MAX IOL (mA)	MAX DELAY (nS)	PRICE ($)
7428	Quad 2-Input NOR Buffers	299.25	2.4	48.0	18.0	0.42
74ALS28	Quad 2-Input NOR Buffers	49.50	2.6	24.0	8.0	0.40
74LS28	Quad 2-Input NOR Buffers	72.45	1.2	24.0	24.0	0.23

TYPE	DESCRIPTION	MAX POWER (mW)	MAX IOH (mA)	MAX IOL (mA)	MAX DELAY (nS)	PRICE ($)
7437	Quad 2-Input NAND Buffers	283.50	1.2	48.0	22.0	0.29
74ALS37	Quad 2-Input NAND Buffers	42.90	2.6	24.0	8.0	0.42
74LS37	Quad 2-Input NAND Buffers	63.00	1.2	24.0	24.0	0.23
74S37	Quad 2-Input NAND Buffers	420.00	3.0	60.0	6.5	0.90
7440	Dual 4-Input NAND Buffers	141.75	1.2	48.0	22.0	0.26
74ALS40	Dual 4-Input NAND Buffers	21.45	2.6	24.0	8.0	0.40
74H40	Dual 4-Input NAND Buffers	210.00	1.5	60.0	12.0	3.29
74LS40	Dual 4-Input NAND Buffers	31.50	1.2	24.0	24.0	0.23
74S40	Dual 4-Input NAND Buffers	231.00	3.0	60.0	6.5	0.29
74125	Quad Buffers with 3-State Outputs	283.50	5.2	16.0	18.0	0.44
74HC125	Quad Buffers with 3-State Outputs	0.48	6.0	6.0	30.0	0.43
74LS125	Quad Buffers with 3-State Outputs	115.50	2.6	24.0	18.0	0.26
74126	Quad Buffers with 3-State Outputs	325.50	5.2	16.0	18.0	0.62
74HC126	Quad Buffers with 3-State Outputs	0.48	6.0	6.0	30.0	0.43
74LS126	Quad Buffers with 3-State Outputs	115.50	2.6	24.0	18.0	0.26
74128	Quad 2-Input NOR Line Drivers	299.25	42.4	48.0	18.0	0.66
74S140	Dual 4-Input NAND 50-Ohm Line Drivers	231.00	40.0	60.0	6.5	0.50
74425	Quad Bus Buffers with 3-State Outputs	283.50	5.2	16.0	18.0	1.48
74ALS1000	Quad 2-Input NAND Buffers	42.90	2.6	24.0	8.0	0.40
74AS1000	Quad 2-Input NAND Buffers	104.50	48.0	48.0	4.0	0.75
74ALS1002	Quad 2-Input NOR Buffers	49.50	2.6	24.0	8.0	0.40
74ALS1008	Quad 2-Input AND Buffers	51.15	2.6	24.0	9.0	0.40
74AS1008	Quad 2-Input AND Buffers	121.00	48.0	48.0	6.0	0.75
74ALS1010	Triple 3-Input NAND Buffers	31.90	2.6	24.0	8.0	0.40
74ALS1011	Triple 3-Input AND Buffers	38.50	2.6	24.0	10.0	0.40
74ALS1020	Dual 4-Input NAND Buffers	21.45	2.6	24.0	8.0	0.40
74ALS1032	Quad 2-Input OR Buffers	58.30	2.6	24.0	12.0	0.40
74AS1032	Quad 2-Input OR Buffers	132.00	48.0	48.0	6.3	0.75
74AS1036	Quad 2-Input NOR Buffers	126.50	48.0	48.0	4.3	0.75

TYPE	DESCRIPTION	MAX POWER (mW)	MAX IOH (mA)	MAX IOL (mA)	MAX DELAY (nS)	PRICE ($)
54365	Hex 3-State Buffers/Bus Drivers	467.50	2.0	32.0	22.0	1.66
54HC365	Hex 3-State Buffers/Bus Drivers	0.96	6.0	6.0	33.0	1.07
54HCT365	Hex 3-State Buffers/Bus Drivers	0.88	6.0	6.0	38.0	0.89
54LS365	Hex 3-State Buffers/Bus Drivers	132.00	1.0	12.0	22.0	0.77
54366	Hex 3-State Inverting Buffers/Bus Drivers	423.50	2.0	32.0	17.0	1.66
54HC366	Hex 3-State Inverting Buffers/Bus Drivers	0.96	6.0	6.0	38.0	1.07
54HCT366	Hex 3-State Inverting Buffers/Bus Drivers	0.88	6.0	6.0	45.0	0.89
54LS366	Hex 3-State Inverting Buffers/Bus Drivers	115.50	1.0	12.0	18.0	0.77
54367	Hex 3-State Buffers/Bus Drivers	467.50	2.0	32.0	22.0	1.66
54HC367	Hex 3-State Buffers/Bus Drivers	0.96	6.0	6.0	33.0	1.07
54HCT367	Hex 3-State Buffers/Bus Drivers	0.88	6.0	6.0	38.0	0.89
54LS367	Hex 3-State Buffers/Bus Drivers	132.00	1.0	12.0	22.0	0.77
54368	Hex 3-State Inverting Buffers/Bus Drivers	423.50	2.0	32.0	17.0	1.66
54HC368	Hex 3-State Inverting Buffers/Bus Drivers	0.96	6.0	6.0	38.0	1.07
54HCT368	Hex 3-State Inverting Buffers/Bus Drivers	0.88	6.0	6.0	45.0	0.89
54LS368	Hex 3-State Inverting Buffers/Bus Drivers	115.50	1.0	12.0	18.0	0.77
54ALS804	Hex 2-Input NAND Line Drivers	66.00	12.0	12.0	9.0	2.80
54AS804	Hex 2-Input NAND Line Drivers	148.50	40.0	40.0	5.0	7.11
54ALS805	Hex 2-Input NOR Line Drivers	77.00	12.0	12.0	9.0	2.80
54ALS808	Hex 2-Input AND Line Drivers	88.00	12.0	12.0	11.0	2.80
54ALS832	Hex 2-Input OR Line Drivers	88.00	12.0	12.0	11.0	2.80
54AS832	Hex 2-Input OR Line Drivers	198.00	40.0	40.0	6.3	7.11
54C901	Hex Inverting TTL Buffers	0.23	0.8	2.6	70.0	2.85
54C902	Hex Non-Inverting TTL Buffers	0.23	0.8	3.2	90.0	2.85
54ALS1034	Hex Non-Inverting Buffers	77.00	12.0	12.0	13.0	0.90

'125 outputs are enabled when the enable $\overline{G}$ is LOW ($\overline{G}$ is *active LOW*). The '126 outputs are enabled when the enable G is HIGH (G is *active HIGH*). The '425 is identical to the '125. The '1000, '1002, '1008, '1010, '1011, '1020, and '1032 are buffer versions of the '00, '02, '08, '10, '11, '20, and '32.

Tables 4-3 and 4-4 list hex buffers/drivers for the 54/74 families. '365 and '366 have common enables. '367 and '368 have one enable for four buffers and another enable for the other two. The '1004 is the buffer version of the '04.

Tables 4-5 and 4-6 list octal buffers/drivers for the 54/74 families. The '230 has four inverting outputs with common $\overline{G}$ enable and four noninverting outputs with common G enable. The '231 has two sets of four inverting buffers, one set with $\overline{G}$ enable, one with G enable.

Table 4-4. Hex Buffers/Drivers, 74 Family.

TYPE	DESCRIPTION	MAX POWER (mW)	MAX IOH (mA)	MAX IOL (mA)	MAX DELAY (nS)	PRICE ($)
74365	Hex 3-State Buffers/Bus Drivers	446.25	5.2	32.0	22.0	0.51
74HC365	Hex 3-State Buffers/Bus Drivers	0.48	6.0	6.0	28.0	0.58
74HCT365	Hex 3-State Buffers/Bus Drivers	0.44	6.0	6.0	31.0	0.48
74LS365	Hex 3-State Buffers/Bus Drivers	126.00	2.6	24.0	22.0	0.36
74366	Hex 3-State Inverting Buffers/Bus Drivers	404.25	5.2	32.0	17.0	0.66
74HC366	Hex 3-State Inverting Buffers/Bus Drivers	0.48	6.0	6.0	31.0	0.58
74HCT366	Hex 3-State Inverting Buffers/Bus Drivers	0.44	6.0	6.0	38.0	0.48
74LS366	Hex 3-State Inverting Buffers/Bus Drivers	110.25	2.6	24.0	18.0	0.36
74367	Hex 3-State Buffers/Bus Drivers	446.25	5.2	32.0	22.0	0.51
74HC367	Hex 3-State Buffers/Bus Drivers	0.48	6.0	6.0	28.0	0.58
74HCT367	Hex 3-State Buffers/Bus Drivers	0.44	6.0	6.0	31.0	0.48
74LS367	Hex 3-State Buffers/Bus Drivers	126.00	2.6	24.0	22.0	0.36
74368	Hex 3-State Inverting Buffers/Bus Drivers	404.25	5.2	32.0	17.0	0.51

TYPE	DESCRIPTION	MAX POWER (mW)	MAX IOH (mA)	MAX IOL (mA)	MAX DELAY (nS)	PRICE ($)
74HC368	Hex 3-State Inverting Buffers/Bus Drivers	0.48	6.0	6.0	31.0	0.58
74HCT368	Hex 3-State Inverting Buffers/Bus Drivers	0.44	6.0	6.0	38.0	0.48
74LS368	Hex 3-State Inverting Buffers/Bus Drivers	110.25	2.6	24.0	18.0	0.36
74ALS804	Hex 2-Input NAND Line Drivers	66.00	15.0	24.0	8.0	1.26
74AS804	Hex 2-Input NAND Line Drivers	148.50	48.0	48.0	4.0	1.75
74HC804	Hex 2-Input NAND Line Drivers	0.48	6.0	6.0	46.0	2.72
74ALS805	Hex 2-Input NOR Line Drivers	77.00	15.0	24.0	8.0	1.26
74AS805	Hex 2-Input NOR Line Drivers	176.00	48.0	48.0	4.0	1.75
74HC805	Hex 2-Input NOR Line Drivers	0.48	6.0	6.0	45.0	2.72
74ALS808	Hex 2-Input AND Line Drivers	88.00	15.0	24.0	9.0	1.26
74AS808	Hex 2-Input AND Line Drivers	176.00	48.0	48.0	6.0	1.75
74HC808	Hex 2-Input AND Line Drivers	0.48	6.0	6.0	25.0	2.00
74ALS832	Hex 2-Input OR Line Drivers	88.00	15.0	24.0	9.0	1.26
74AS832	Hex 2-Input OR Line Drivers	198.00	48.0	48.0	6.3	1.75
74HC832	Hex 2-Input OR Line Drivers	0.48	6.0	6.0	25.0	2.00
74C901	Hex Inverting TTL Buffers	0.23	0.8	2.6	70.0	0.47
74C902	Hex Non-Inverting TTL Buffers	0.23	0.8	3.2	90.0	0.47
74C903	Hex Inverting PMOS Buffers	0.23	0.8	2.6	70.0	0.47
74C904	Hex Non-Inverting PMOS Buffers	0.23	0.8	3.2	90.0	0.47
74ALS1004	Hex Inverting Buffers	66.00	15.0	24.0	7.0	0.40
74AS1004	Hex Inverting Buffers	154.00	15.0	48.0	4.0	0.75
74ALS1034	Hex Non-Inverting Buffers	77.00	15.0	24.0	8.0	0.40
74AS1034	Hex Non-Inverting Buffers	181.50	15.0	48.0	4.0	0.75

The '240: two sets of four inverting buffers, each with common $\overline{G}$ enable. Schmitt-trigger buffer and enable inputs.

The '241: two sets of four noninverting buffers, one with common $\overline{G}$ enable,

Table 4-5. Octal Buffers/Drivers, 54 Family.

TYPE	DESCRIPTION	MAX POWER (mW)	MAX IOH (mA)	MAX IOL (mA)	MAX DELAY (nS)	PRICE ($)
54AC240	Octal 3-State Inverting Buffers/Line Drivers/Line Receivers	0.55	24.0	24.0	11.0	11.44
54ACT240	Octal 3-State Inverting Buffers/Line Drivers/Line Receivers	0.88	24.0	24.0	14.5	11.44
54ALS240	Octal 3-State Inverting Buffers/Line Drivers/Line Receivers	137.50	12.0	12.0	22.0	3.22
54AS240	Octal 3-State Inverting Buffers/Line Drivers/Line Receivers	412.50	12.0	48.0	7.0	5.41
54F240	Octal 3-State Inverting Buffers/Line Drivers/Line Receivers	412.50	15.0	48.0	9.0	4.74
54HC240	Octal 3-State Inverting Buffers/Line Drivers/Line Receivers	0.96	6.0	6.0	30.0	3.00
54HCT240	Octal 3-State Inverting Buffers/Line Drivers/Line Receivers	0.88	6.0	6.0	37.0	2.39
54LS240	Octal 3-State Inverting Buffers/Line Drivers/Line Receivers	275.00	12.0	12.0	18.0	2.07
54S240	Octal 3-State Inverting Buffers/Line Drivers/Line Receivers	825.00	12.0	48.0	7.0	4.62
54AC241	Octal 3-State Buffers/Line Drivers/Line Receivers	0.55	24.0	24.0	11.0	11.44
54ACT241	Octal 3-State Buffers/Line Drivers/Line Receivers	0.88	24.0	24.0	14.5	11.44
54ALS241	Octal 3-State Buffers/Line Drivers/Line Receivers	176.00	12.0	12.0	31.0	3.22
54AS241	Octal 3-State Buffers/Line Drivers/Line Receivers	495.00	12.0	48.0	9.0	5.41
54F241	Octal 3-State Buffers/Line Drivers/Line Receivers	495.00	15.0	48.0	9.0	4.74
54HC241	Octal 3-State Buffers/Line Drivers/Line Receivers	0.96	6.0	6.0	34.0	3.00
54HCT241	Octal 3-State Buffers/Line Drivers/Line Receivers	0.88	6.0	6.0	39.0	2.39
54LS241	Octal 3-State Buffers/Line Drivers/Line Receivers	297.00	12.0	12.0	18.0	2.07
54S241	Octal 3-State Buffers/Line Drivers/Line Receivers	990.00	12.0	48.0	7.0	4.62
54AC244	Octal 3-State Buffers/Line Drivers/Line Receivers	0.55	24.0	24.0	11.0	11.44

TYPE	DESCRIPTION	MAX POWER (mW)	MAX IOH (mA)	MAX IOL (mA)	MAX DELAY (nS)	PRICE ($)
54ACT244	Octal 3-State Buffers/Line Drivers/Line Receivers	0.88	24.0	24.0	14.5	11.44
54ALS244	Octal 3-State Buffers/Line Drivers/Line Receivers	148.50	12.0	12.0	18.0	3.22
54C244	Octal 3-State Buffers/Line Drivers/Line Receivers	4.50	2.2	2.2	70.0	7.14
54F244	Octal 3-State Buffers/Line Drivers/Line Receivers	495.00	15.0	48.0	9.0	4.74
54HC244	Octal 3-State Buffers/Line Drivers/Line Receivers	0.96	6.0	6.0	34.0	3.00
54HCT244	Octal 3-State Buffers/Line Drivers/Line Receivers	0.88	6.0	6.0	42.0	2.07
54LS244	Octal 3-State Buffers/Line Drivers/Line Receivers	297.00	12.0	12.0	18.0	2.07
54S244	Octal 3-State Buffers/Line Drivers/Line Receivers	990.00	12.0	48.0	7.0	4.62
54HC540	Octal 3-State Inverting Buffer	0.96	6.0	6.0	33.0	3.18
54HCT540	Octal 3-State Inverting Buffer	0.88	6.0	6.0	36.0	2.23
54LS540	Octal 3-State Inverting Buffer	286.00	12.0	12.0	15.0	1.93
54HC541	Octal 3-State Buffer	0.96	6.0	6.0	35.0	3.18
54HCT541	Octal 3-State Buffer	0.88	6.0	6.0	42.0	2.23
54LS541	Octal 3-State Buffer	302.50	12.0	12.0	18.0	1.93
54S940	Octal 3-State Inverting Buffers/Line Receivers/Line Drivers	797.50	12.0	48.0	7.0	5.00
54C941	Octal 3-State Buffers/Line Receivers/Line Drivers	4.50	2.2	2.2	140.0	4.42
54S941	Octal 3-State Buffers/Line Receivers/Line Drivers	797.50	12.0	48.0	9.0	5.00
54ALS1244	Octal 3-State Bus Driver/Receivers	137.50	12.0	8.0	21.0	2.92

Table 4-6. Octal Buffers/Drivers, 74 Family.

TYPE	DESCRIPTION	MAX POWER (mW)	MAX IOH (mA)	MAX IOL (mA)	MAX DELAY (nS)	PRICE ($)
74AS230	Octal 3-State True and Inverting Bus Drivers/Receivers	478.50	15.0	64.0	6.5	2.39

TYPE	DESCRIPTION	MAX POWER (mW)	MAX IOH (mA)	MAX IOL (mA)	MAX DELAY (nS)	PRICE ($)
74AS231	Octal 3-State Inverting Bus Drivers/Receivers	451.00	15.0	64.0	6.5	2.50
74AC240	Octal 3-State Inverting Buffers/Line Drivers/Line Receivers	0.28	24.0	24.0	10.5	1.27
74ACT240	Octal 3-State Inverting Buffers/Line Drivers/Line Receivers	0.44	24.0	24.0	13.5	1.27
74ALS240	Octal 3-State Inverting Buffers/Line Drivers/Line Receivers	137.50	15.0	24.0	9.0	1.20
74AS240	Octal 3-State Inverting Buffers/Line Drivers/Line Receivers	412.50	15.0	64.0	6.5	2.39
74C240	Octal 3-State Inverting Buffers/Line Drivers/Line Receivers	4.50	2.2	2.2	90.0	1.53
74F240	Octal 3-State Inverting Buffers/Line Drivers/Line Receivers	393.75	15.0	64.0	8.0	1.03
74HC240	Octal 3-State Inverting Buffers/Line Drivers/Line Receivers	0.48	6.0	6.0	25.0	0.99
74HCT240	Octal 3-State Inverting Buffers/Line Drivers/Line Receivers	0.44	6.0	6.0	28.0	1.06
74LS240	Octal 3-State Inverting Buffers/Line Drivers/Line Receivers	262.50	2.6	24.0	18.0	0.60
74S240	Octal 3-State Inverting Buffers/Line Drivers/Line Receivers	787.50	15.0	64.0	7.0	1.78
74AC241	Octal 3-State Buffers/Line Drivers/Line Receivers	0.28	24.0	24.0	10.5	1.27
74ACT241	Octal 3-State Buffers/Line Drivers/Line Receivers	0.44	24.0	24.0	13.5	1.27
74ALS241	Octal 3-State Buffers/Line Drivers/Line Receivers	165.00	15.0	24.0	11.0	1.20
74AS241	Octal 3-State Buffers/Line Drivers/Line Receivers	495.00	15.0	64.0	6.2	2.39
74F241	Octal 3-State Buffers/Line Drivers/Line Receivers	472.50	15.0	64.0	8.0	1.03
74HC241	Octal 3-State Buffers/Line Drivers/Line Receivers	0.48	6.0	6.0	28.0	0.99
74HCT241	Octal 3-State Buffers/Line Drivers/Line Receivers	0.44	6.0	6.0	33.0	0.99
74LS241	Octal 3-State Buffers/Line Drivers/Line Receivers	283.50	2.6	24.0	18.0	0.60
74S241	Octal 3-State Buffers/Line Drivers/Line Receivers	945.00	15.0	64.0	9.0	1.78

TYPE	DESCRIPTION	MAX POWER (mW)	MAX IOH (mA)	MAX IOL (mA)	MAX DELAY (nS)	PRICE ($)
74AC244	Octal 3-State Buffers/Line Drivers/Line Receivers	0.28	24.0	24.0	10.5	1.27
74ACT244	Octal 3-State Buffers/Line Drivers/Line Receivers	0.44	24.0	24.0	13.5	1.27
74ALS244	Octal 3-State Buffers/Line Drivers/Line Receivers	148.50	15.0	24.0	10.0	1.20
74AS244	Octal 3-State Buffers/Line Drivers/Line Receivers	495.00	15.0	64.0	6.2	2.39
74C244	Octal 3-State Buffers/Line Drivers/Line Receivers	4.50	2.2	2.2	70.0	1.53
74F244	Octal 3-State Buffers/Line Drivers/Line Receivers	472.50	15.0	64.0	8.0	1.03
74HC244	Octal 3-State Buffers/Line Drivers/Line Receivers	0.48	6.0	6.0	28.0	1.06
74HCT244	Octal 3-State Buffers/Line Drivers/Line Receivers	0.44	6.0	6.0	33.0	1.06
74LS244	Octal 3-State Buffers/Line Drivers/Line Receivers	283.50	2.6	24.0	18.0	0.60
74S244	Octal 3-State Buffers/Line Drivers/Line Receivers	945.00	15.0	64.0	9.0	2.02
74ALS465	Octal 3-State Buffers/Bus Drivers	181.50	15.0	24.0	13.0	1.28
74LS465	Octal 3-State Buffers/Bus Drivers	194.25	2.6	24.0	18.0	1.15
74ALS466	Octal 3-State Inverting Buffers/Bus Drivers	148.50	15.0	24.0	12.0	1.28
74LS466	Octal 3-State Inverting Buffers/Bus Drivers	147.00	2.6	24.0	15.0	1.15
74ALS467	Octal 3-State Buffers/Bus Drivers	181.50	15.0	24.0	13.0	1.28
74LS467	Octal 3-State Buffers/Bus Drivers	194.25	2.6	24.0	18.0	2.30
74ALS468	Octal 3-State Inverting Buffers/Bus Drivers	148.50	15.0	24.0	12.0	1.28
74LS468	Octal 3-State Inverting Buffers/Bus Drivers	147.00	2.6	24.0	15.0	2.30
74HC540	Octal 3-State Inverting Buffer	0.48	6.0	6.0	28.0	1.03
74HCT540	Octal 3-State Inverting Buffer	0.44	6.0	6.0	30.0	1.02
74LS540	Octal 3-State Inverting Buffer	273.00	2.6	24.0	15.0	0.79
74HC541	Octal 3-State Buffer	0.48	6.0	6.0	29.0	1.02
74HCT541	Octal 3-State Buffer	0.44	6.0	6.0	35.0	1.02

TYPE	DESCRIPTION	MAX POWER (mW)	MAX IOH (mA)	MAX IOL (mA)	MAX DELAY (nS)	PRICE ($)
74LS541	Octal 3-State Buffer	288.75	2.6	24.0	18.0	0.90
74LS795	Octal 3-State Buffers	136.50	2.6	16.0	22.0	1.02
74LS796	Octal 3-State Inverting Buffers	110.25	2.6	16.0	17.0	1.02
74LS797	Octal 3-State Buffers	135.50	2.6	16.0	22.0	1.02
74LS798	Octal 3-State Inverting Buffers	110.25	2.6	16.0	17.0	1.02
74S940	Octal 3-State Inverting Buffers/Line Receivers/Line Drivers	787.50	15.0	2.2	140.0	2.17
	Drivers/Receivers					
74ALS1241	Octal 3-State Bus Drivers/Receivers	93.50	15.0	16.0	12.0	1.36
74ALS1244	Octal 3-State Bus Driver/Receivers	110.00	15.0	16.0	14.0	1.36
74C941	Octal 3-State Buffers/Line Receivers/Line Drivers	4.50	2.2	2.2	140.0	1.53
74S941	Octal 3-State Buffers/Line Receivers/Line Drivers	945.00	15.0	64.0	9.0	2.17
74ALS1240	Octal 3-State Inverting Bus	71.50	15.0	16.0	13.0	1.33

one with common G enable. Schmitt-trigger buffer and enable inputs.

The '244: two sets of four noninverting buffers, each with common $\overline{G}$ enable. Schmitt-trigger buffer and enable inputs.

The '465: one set of eight noninverting buffers with common enables, $\overline{G}1$ and $\overline{G}2$.

The '466: one set of eight inverting buffers with common enables, $\overline{G}1$ and $\overline{G}2$.

The '467: two sets of four noninverting buffers, each with common $\overline{G}$ enable.

The '468: two sets of four inverting buffers, each with common $\overline{G}$ enable.

The '540: one set of eight inverting buffers with common enables, $\overline{G}1$ and $\overline{G}2$. Bus-structured pinout: inputs on one side, outputs on the other.

The '541: one set of eight noninverting buffers with common enables, $\overline{G}1$ and $\overline{G}2$. Bus-structured pinout.

The '795, '796, '797, and '798 have same function and pinout as '465 through '468, but have lower I_{OL} and power and are slightly slower.

The '940: one set of eight inverting buffers. Schmitt-trigger buffer and enable inputs. '941: inverting version of '940.

The '1240, '1241, and '1244 are low power versions of the '240, 241, and '244.

Tables 4-7 and 4-8 list maximum power, maximum V_{OH}, maximum I_{OL}, and maximum delay for 54/74 family open-collector (or open-drain) buffers. Tables 4-9 and 4-10 list 4000 Series CMOS buffers.

Table 4-7. Open-Collector/Open-Drain Buffers/Drivers, 54 Family.

TYPE	DESCRIPTION	MAX POWER (mW)	MAX VOH (V)	MAX IOL (mA)	MAX DELAY (nS)	PRICE ($)
5406	Hex Inverting Buffers/Drivers with High-Voltage Open-Collector Outputs	280.50	30.0	30.0	23.0	1.79
5407	Hex Buffers/Drivers with High-Voltage Open-Collector Outputs	225.50	30.0	30.0	30.0	1.79
5416	Hex Inverting Buffers/Drivers with High-Voltage Open-Collector Outputs	280.50	15.0	30.0	23.0	1.79
5417	Hex Buffers/Drivers with High-Voltage Open-Collector Outputs	165.00	15.0	30.0	30.0	1.79
5433	Quad 2-Input NOR Buffers with Open-Collector Outputs	313.50	5.5	48.0	24.0	1.82
54ALS33	Quad 2-Input NOR Buffers with Open-Collector Outputs	49.50	5.5	12.0	59.0	0.90
54LS33	Quad 2-Input NOR Buffers with Open-Collector Outputs	75.90	5.5	12.0	32.0	0.57
5438	Quad 2-Input NAND Buffers with Open-Collector Outputs	297.00	5.5	48.0	22.0	1.06
54ALS38	Quad 2-Input NAND Buffers with Open-Collector Outputs	42.90	5.5	12.0	59.0	0.90
54LS38	Quad 2-Input NAND Buffers with Open-Collector Outputs	66.00	5.5	12.0	32.0	0.57
54S38	Quad 2-Input NAND Buffers with Open-Collector Outputs	440.00	5.5	60.0	10.0	1.72
54C906	Hex Open Drain N-Channel Buffers	0.23	18.0	2.1	150.0	2.85
54C907	Hex Open Drain P-Channel Buffers	0.23	18.0	2.1	150.0	2.85

Table 4-8. Open-Collector/Open-Drain Buffers/Drivers, 74 Family.

TYPE	DESCRIPTION	MAX POWER (mW)	MAX VOH (V)	MAX IOL (mA)	MAX DELAY (nS)	PRICE ($)
7406	Hex Inverting Buffers/Drivers with High-Voltage Open-Collector Outputs	267.75	30.0	40.0	23.0	0.29
7407	Hex Buffers/Drivers with High-Voltage Open-Collector Outputs	215.25	30.0	40.0	30.0	0.29
7416	Hex Inverting Buffers/Drivers with High-Voltage Open-Collector Outputs	267.75	15.0	40.0	23.0	0.29
7417	Hex Buffers/Drivers with High-Voltage Open-Collector Outputs	157.50	15.0	40.0	30.0	0.29
7433	Quad 2-Input NOR Buffers with Open-Collector Outputs	299.25	5.5	48.0	24.0	0.42
74ALS33	Quad 2-Input NOR Buffers with Open-Collector Outputs	49.50	5.5	24.0	33.0	0.40
74LS33	Quad 2-Input NOR Buffers with Open-Collector Outputs	72.45	5.5	24.0	32.0	0.25
7438	Quad 2-Input NAND Buffers with Open-Collector Outputs	283.50	5.5	48.0	22.0	0.29
74ALS38	Quad 2-Input NAND Buffers with Open-Collector Outputs	42.90	5.5	24.0	33.0	0.40
74LS38	Quad 2-Input NAND Buffers with Open-Collector Outputs	63.00	5.5	24.0	32.0	0.23
74S38	Quad 2-Input NAND Buffers with Open-Collector Outputs	420.00	5.5	60.0	10.0	0.90
7439	Quad 2-Input NAND Buffers with Open-Collector Outputs	283.50	5.5	60.0	22.0	0.66
74AS756	Octal Inverting Buffers/Line Drivers with Open-Collector Outputs	440.00	5.5	64.0	19.0	2.50
74AS757	Octal Buffers/Line Drivers with Open-Collector Outputs	522.50	5.5	64.0	18.5	2.50
74AS760	Octal Buffers/Line Drivers with Open-Collector Outputs	517.00	5.5	64.0	18.5	2.50
74AS762	Octal Buffers/Line Drivers with Open-Collector Outputs	478.50	5.5	64.0	19.0	2.50
74AS763	Octal Inverting Buffers/Line Drivers with Open-Collector Outputs	451.00	5.5	64.0	19.0	2.50
74C906	Hex Open Drain N-Channel Buffers	0.23	18.0	2.1	150.0	0.47

TYPE	DESCRIPTION	MAX POWER (mW)	MAX VOH (V)	MAX IOL (mA)	MAX DELAY (nS)	PRICE ($)
74C907	Hex Open Drain P-Channel Buffers	0.23	18.0	2.1	150.0	0.47
74ALS1003	Quad 2-Input NAND Buffers with Open Collector Outputs	42.90	5.5	24.0	33.0	0.40
74ALS1005	Hex Inverting Buffers with Open Collector Outputs	66.00	5.5	24.0	30.0	0.40
74ALS1035	Hex Non-Inverting Buffers with Open-Collector Outputs	77.00	5.5	24.0	30.0	0.40

Table 4-9. Buffers, 4000 Series, Industrial Temperature Range.

TYPE	DESCRIPTION	MAX POWER (mW)	MAX IOH (mA)	MAX IOL (mA)	MAX DELAY (nS)	PRICE ($)
4009A	Hex Inverting Buffers/Converters	0.21	1.0	2.4	100.0	0.54
4009UB	Hex Inverting Buffers/Converters	0.15	0.7	2.1	140.0	0.84
4010A	Hex Buffers/Converters	0.21	1.0	2.4	100.0	0.54
4010B	Hex Buffers/Converters	0.15	0.7	2.1	200.0	0.84
4041A	Quad True/Complement Buffer	0.15	0.6	0.7	150.0	1.16
4041UB	Quad True/Complement Buffer	0.15	5.3	1.3	120.0	1.19
4049A	Hex Inverting Buffers/Converters	0.21	1.0	2.5	80.0	0.41
4049UB	Hex Inverting Buffers/Converters	0.15	1.9	2.1	120.0	0.41
4050A	Hex Buffers/Converters	0.21	1.0	2.5	140.0	0.71
4050B	Hex Buffers/Converters	0.15	1.9	2.1	140.0	0.41
4502B	Strobed Hex Inverter/Buffer with 3-State Outputs	0.15	1.3	2.5	270.0	0.89
4503B	Hex Buffer with 3-State Outputs	0.15	3.4	1.4	150.0	0.63

Table 4-10. Buffers, 4000 Series, Military Temperature Range.

TYPE	DESCRIPTION	MAX POWER (mW)	MAX IOH (mA)	MAX IOL (mA)	MAX DELAY (nS)	PRICE ($)
4009A	Hex Inverting Buffers/Converters	0.10	0.9	2.1	80.0	2.08

TYPE	DESCRIPTION	MAX POWER (mW)	MAX VOH (V)	MAX IOL (mA)	MAX DELAY (nS)	PRICE ($)
4009UB	Hex Inverting Buffers/Converters	0.15	0.6	1.8	140.0	1.19
4010B	Hex Buffers/Converters	0.15	0.6	1.8	200.0	1.19
4041A	Quad True/Complement Buffer	0.30	1.0	1.2	125.0	3.31
4041UB	Quad True/Complement Buffer	0.15	4.6	1.2	120.0	1.73
4049A	Hex Inverting Buffers/Converters	0.10	0.9	2.1	80.0	1.19
4049UB	Hex Inverting Buffers/Converters	0.15	1.6	1.8	120.0	0.89
4050A	Hex Buffers/Converters	0.10	0.9	2.1	140.0	1.19
4050B	Hex Buffers/Converters	0.15	1.6	1.8	140.0	0.89
4502B	Strobed Hex Inverter/Buffer with 3-State Outputs	0.15	1.1	2.1	270.0	1.40
4503B	Hex Buffer with 3-State Outputs	0.15	3.0	1.3	150.0	1.04

4.2 TRANSCEIVERS

Tables 4-11 and 4-12 list maximum power, maximum I_{OH}, maximum I_{OL} and maximum A-to-B or B-to-A delay for 54/74 family transceivers. Delay data for transceivers with D-type flip-flops is clock to output delay.

The '245: Direction (DIR) and enable ($\overline{G}$) controls.

The '442: Tridirectional, noninverting.

The '444: Tridirectional, inverting and noninverting.

The '543: Two sets of back-to-back D-type latches with 3-state outputs. I_{OL} in the tables is for A outputs. 54F543 B outputs can sink 48 mA. 74F543 can sink 64 mA. I_{OH} in the tables is for the B outputs. The A outputs can source 3 mA.

The '544: Same as the '543 except that the '544 inverts data in both directions.

The '545: A outputs can source 3 mA. B outputs can sink 48 mA for 54F version and 64 mA for 74F version.

The '546: D-type flip-flops.

The '547: D-type latches.

The '550: D-type flip-flops.

The '551: D-type flip-flops. Data is inverted in both directions.

The '552: D-type flip-flops.

The '566: D-type flip-flops. Data is inverted in both directions.

The '567: D-type latches. Data is inverted in both directions.

The '620 and '623: Separate enables for A-to-B and B-to-A 3-state control (GAB and $\overline{GBA}$).

Table 4-11. Transceivers, 54 Family.

TYPE	DESCRIPTION	MAX POWER (mW)	MAX IOH (mA)	MAX IOL (mA)	MAX DELAY (nS)	PRICE ($)
54S226	4-Bit Parallel Latched Bus Transceivers	1017.50	6.5	15.0	30.0	14.80
54ALS242	Quad 3-State Inverting Bus Transceivers	148.50	12.0	12.0	15.0	3.65
54HC242	Quad 3-State Inverting Bus Transceivers	0.96	6.0	6.0	30.0	2.10
54HCT242	Quad 3-State Inverting Bus Transceivers	0.88	6.0	6.0	45.0	2.18
54LS242	Quad 3-State Inverting Bus Transceivers	275.00	12.0	12.0	18.0	1.89
54ALS243	Quad 3-State Bus Transceivers	203.50	12.0	12.0	15.0	3.65
54F243	Quad 3-State Bus Transceivers	495.00	3.0	48.0	8.5	4.46
54HC243	Quad 3-State Bus Transceivers	0.96	6.0	6.0	30.0	2.10
54HCT243	Quad 3-State Bus Transceivers	0.88	6.0	6.0	45.0	2.18
54LS243	Quad 3-State Bus Transceivers	297.00	12.0	12.0	18.0	1.89
54ALS245	Octal 3-State Bus Transceivers	346.50	12.0	12.0	19.0	4.20
54F245	Octal 3-State Bus Transceivers	660.00	3.0	20.0	6.0	12.87
54HC245	Octal 3-State Bus Transceivers	0.96	6.0	6.0	32.0	3.58
54HCT245	Octal 3-State Bus Transceivers	0.88	6.0	6.0	33.0	3.18
54LS245	Octal 3-State Bus Transceivers	522.50	12.0	12.0	12.0	2.76
54LS442	Quad 3-State Bus Transceivers	522.50	12.0	12.0	20.0	6.31
54F544	Octal Registered Transceiver	715.00	1.0	20.0	9.5	23.17
54F545	Octal Transceiver	660.00	1.0	20.0	7.0	14.80
54LS546	8-Bit Bus Register Transceiver	990.00	1.0	24.0	26.0	6.95
54LS566	8-Bit Inverting Bus Register Transceiver	990.00	1.0	24.0	26.0	6.95
54LS567	8-Bit Inverting Bus Latch Transceiver	990.00	1.0	24.0	29.0	6.95
54HC620	Octal 3-State Inverting Bus Transceivers	0.96	6.0	6.0	32.0	4.76
54HC623	Octal 3-State Bus Transceivers	0.96	6.0	6.0	32.0	4.76
54LS623	Octal 3-State Bus Transceivers	522.50	12.0	12.0	15.0	2.77
54ALS640	Octal 3-State Inverting Bus Transceivers	264.00	12.0	12.0	14.0	4.20
54HC640	Octal 3-State Inverting Bus Transceivers	0.96	6.0	6.0	32.0	3.12
54HCT640	Octal 3-State Inverting Bus Transceivers	0.88	6.0	6.0	32.0	3.27
54LS640	Octal 3-State Inverting Bus Transceivers	522.50	12.0	12.0	15.0	2.90

TYPE	DESCRIPTION	MAX POWER (mW)	MAX IOH (mA)	MAX IOL (mA)	MAX DELAY (nS)	PRICE ($)
54HC643	Octal 3-State True/Inverting Bus Transceivers	0.96	6.0	6.0	33.0	3.12
54HCT643	Octal 3-State True/Inverting Bus Transceivers	0.88	6.0	6.0	32.0	3.27
54LS643	Octal 3-State True/Inverting Bus Transceivers	522.50	12.0	12.0	15.0	3.22
54ALS645	Octal 3-State Bus Transceivers	346.50	12.0	12.0	19.0	4.20
54HC645	Octal 3-State Bus Transceivers	0.96	6.0	6.0	32.0	4.40
54LS645	Octal 3-State Bus Transceivers	522.50	12.0	12.0	15.0	2.77
54HC646	Octal 3-State Bus Transceivers/Registers	0.96	6.0	6.0	72.0	6.98
54HCT646	Octal 3-State Bus Transceivers/Registers	0.88	6.0	6.0	81.0	6.27
54LS646	Octal 3-State Bus Transceivers/Registers	907.50	12.0	12.0	20.0	6.95
54HC648	Octal 3-State Inverting Bus Transceivers/Registers	0.96	6.0	6.0	72.0	6.98
54HCT648	Octal 3-State Inverting Bus Transceivers/Registers	0.88	6.0	6.0	81.0	6.27
54LS648	Octal 3-State Inverting Bus Transceivers/Registers	907.50	12.0	12.0	25.0	6.95
54LS651	Octal 3-State Inverting Bus Transceivers/Registers	907.50	12.0	12.0	30.0	6.95
54LS652	Octal 3-State Bus Transceivers/Registers	907.50	12.0	12.0	20.0	6.95
54ALS1245	Octal 3-State Bus Transceivers	220.00	12.0	8.0	19.0	3.15

Table 4-12. Transceivers, 74 Family.

TYPE	DESCRIPTION	MAX POWER (mW)	MAX IOH (mA)	MAX IOL (mA)	MAX DELAY (nS)	PRICE ($)
74S226	4-Bit Parallel Latched Bus Transceivers	971.25	10.3	15.0	30.0	6.00
74ALS242	Quad 3-State Inverting Bus Transceivers	121.00	15.0	24.0	11.0	1.20
74AS242	Quad 3-State Inverting Bus Transceivers	330.00	15.0	64.0	6.5	2.39
74HC242	Quad 3-State Inverting Bus Transceivers	0.48	6.0	6.0	25.0	0.91
74HCT242	Quad 3-State Inverting Bus Transceivers	0.44	6.0	6.0	38.0	0.91
74LS242	Quad 3-State Inverting Bus Transceivers	262.50	15.0	24.0	18.0	0.88

TYPE	DESCRIPTION	MAX POWER (mW)	MAX IOH (mA)	MAX IOL (mA)	MAX DELAY (nS)	PRICE ($)
74ALS243	Quad 3-State Bus Transceivers	176.00	15.0	24.0	11.0	1.20
74AS243	Quad 3-State Bus Transceivers	407.00	15.0	64.0	7.5	2.39
74F243	Quad 3-State Bus Transceivers	472.50	3.0	64.0	6.5	1.36
74HC243	Quad 3-State Bus Transceivers	0.48	6.0	6.0	25.0	0.91
74HCT243	Quad 3-State Bus Transceivers	0.44	6.0	6.0	38.0	0.91
74LS243	Quad 3-State Bus Transceivers	283.50	15.0	24.0	18.0	0.88
74ALS245	Octal 3-State Bus Transceivers	319.00	15.0	24.0	10.0	1.28
74F245	Octal 3-State Bus Transceivers	630.00	3.0	24.0	7.0	2.15
74HC245	Octal 3-State Bus Transceivers	0.48	6.0	6.0	26.0	1.22
74HCT245	Octal 3-State Bus Transceivers	0.44	6.0	6.0	28.0	1.22
74LS245	Octal 3-State Bus Transceivers	498.75	15.0	24.0	12.0	0.74
74LS442	Quad 3-State Bus Transceivers	498.75	15.0	24.0	20.0	3.71
74LS444	Quad 3-State Bus Transceivers	498.75	15.0	24.0	20.0	7.42
74LS449	Quad 3-State Bus Transceivers with Individual Direction Controls	420.00	15.0	24.0	17.0	7.42
74F543	Octal Registered Transceiver	656.25	1.0	24.0	8.5	4.29
74F544	Octal Registered Transceiver	682.50	1.0	24.0	10.5	4.29
74F545	Octal Transceiver	630.00	1.0	24.0	7.0	4.43
74LS546	8-Bit Bus Register Transceiver	945.00	2.6	32.0	21.0	3.57
74LS547	8-Bit Bus Latch Transceiver	945.00	2.6	32.0	18.0	3.57
74F550	Octal Registered Transceiver	997.50	3.0	24.0	9.0	5.59
74F551	Octal Registered Transceiver	997.50	3.0	24.0	9.0	5.59
74F552	Octal Registered Transceiver with Parity and Flags	866.25	3.0	24.0	9.5	5.75
74LS566	8-Bit Inverting Bus Register Transceiver	945.00	2.6	32.0	21.0	3.57
74LS567	8-Bit Inverting Bus Latch Transceiver	945.00	2.6	32.0	23.0	3.57
74F588	GPIB Compatable Octal Transceiver	708.75	3.0	24.0	7.5	4.69
74ALS620	Octal 3-State Inverting Bus Transceivers	258.50	15.0	24.0	10.0	1.60
74AS620	Octal 3-State Inverting Bus Transceivers	671.00	15.0	64.0	7.0	3.75
74HC620	Octal 3-State Inverting Bus Transceivers	0.48	6.0	6.0	26.0	1.92
74HCT620	Octal 3-State Inverting Bus Transceivers	0.44	6.0	6.0	26.0	1.92

TYPE	DESCRIPTION	MAX POWER (mW)	MAX IOH (mA)	MAX IOL (mA)	MAX DELAY (nS)	PRICE ($)
74LS620	Octal 3-State Inverting Bus Transceivers	498.75	15.0	24.0	15.0	1.44
74ALS623	Octal 3-State Bus Transceivers	302.50	15.0	24.0	13.0	1.66
74AS623	Octal 3-State Bus Transceivers	1039.50	15.0	64.0	9.0	3.75
74HC623	Octal 3-State Bus Transceivers	0.48	6.0	6.0	26.0	1.92
74HCT623	Octal 3-State Bus Transceivers	0.44	6.0	6.0	26.0	1.92
74LS623	Octal 3-State Bus Transceivers	498.75	15.0	24.0	15.0	1.44
74ALS638	Octal Inverting Bus Transceivers	225.50	15.0	24.0	30.0	1.88
74AS638	Octal Inverting Bus Transceivers	671.00	15.0	64.0	20.0	3.75
74LS638	Octal Inverting Bus Transceivers	498.75	15.0	24.0	25.0	3.26
74ALS639	Octal Bus Transceivers	297.00	15.0	24.0	30.0	1.88
74AS639	Octal Bus Transceivers	847.00	15.0	64.0	22.0	3.75
74LS639	Octal Bus Transceivers	498.75	15.0	24.0	25.0	3.26
74ALS640	Octal 3-State Inverting Bus Transceivers	236.50	15.0	24.0	11.0	1.60
74AS640	Octal 3-State Inverting Bus Transceivers	676.50	15.0	64.0	7.0	3.75
74HC640	Octal 3-State Inverting Bus Transceivers	0.48	6.0	6.0	26.0	1.40
74HCT640	Octal 3-State Inverting Bus Transceivers	0.44	6.0	6.0	26.0	1.63
74LS640	Octal 3-State Inverting Bus Transceivers	498.75	15.0	24.0	15.0	1.44
74ALS643	Octal 3-State True/Inverting Bus Transceivers	264.00	15.0	24.0	13.0	1.60
74AS643	Octal 3-State True/Inverting Bus Transceivers	786.50	15.0	64.0	10.0	3.75
74HC643	Octal 3-State True/Inverting Bus Transceivers	0.48	6.0	6.0	28.0	1.40
74HCT643	Octal 3-State True/Inverting Bus Transceivers	0.44	6.0	6.0	26.0	1.63
74LS643	Octal 3-State True/Inverting Bus Transceivers	498.75	15.0	24.0	15.0	1.44
74ALS645	Octal 3-State Bus Transceivers	319.00	15.0	24.0	10.0	1.52
74AS645	Octal 3-State Bus Transceivers	819.50	15.0	64.0	9.5	3.60
74HC645	Octal 3-State Bus Transceivers	0.48	6.0	6.0	26.0	1.92
74HCT645	Octal 3-State Bus Transceivers	0.44	6.0	6.0	28.0	1.92
74LS645	Octal 3-State Bus Transceivers	498.75	15.0	24.0	15.0	1.02

TYPE	DESCRIPTION	MAX POWER (mW)	MAX IOH (mA)	MAX IOL (mA)	MAX DELAY (nS)	PRICE ($)
74ALS646	Octal 3-State Bus Transceivers/Registers	484.00	15.0	24.0	30.0	5.68
74AS646	Octal 3-State Bus Transceivers/Registers	1160.50	15.0	48.0	9.0	5.10
74HC646	Octal 3-State Bus Transceivers/Registers	0.48	6.0	6.0	60.0	4.13
74HCT646	Octal 3-State Bus Transceivers/Registers	0.44	6.0	6.0	68.0	4.19
74LS646	Octal 3-State Bus Transceivers/Registers	866.25	15.0	24.0	20.0	4.31
74ALS648	Octal 3-State Inverting Bus Transceivers/Registers	484.00	15.0	24.0	33.0	5.67
74AS648	Octal 3-State Inverting Bus Transceivers/Registers	1072.50	15.0	48.0	9.0	5.10
74HC648	Octal 3-State Inverting Bus Transceivers/Registers	0.48	6.0	6.0	60.0	4.13
74HCT648	Octal 3-State Inverting Bus Transceivers/Registers	0.44	6.0	6.0	68.0	4.19
74LS648	Octal 3-State Inverting Bus Transceivers/Registers	945.00	15.0	24.0	25.0	4.31
74ALS651	Octal 3-State Inverting Bus Transceivers/Registers	451.00	15.0	24.0	32.0	5.67
74AS651	Octal 3-State Inverting Bus Transceivers/Registers	1072.50	15.0	48.0	9.0	5.10
74HC651	Octal 3-State Inverting Bus Transceivers/Registers	0.48	6.0	6.0	45.0	4.24
74HCT651	Octal 3-State Inverting Bus Transceivers/Registers	0.44	6.0	6.0	45.0	4.24
74LS651	Octal 3-State Inverting Bus Transceivers/Registers	866.25	15.0	24.0	20.0	4.31
74ALS652	Octal 3-State Bus Transceivers/Registers	484.00	15.0	24.0	30.0	5.68
74AS652	Octal 3-State Bus Transceivers/Registers	1160.50	15.0	48.0	9.0	5.10
74HC652	Octal 3-State Bus Transceivers/Registers	0.48	6.0	6.0	45.0	3.94
74HCT652	Octal 3-State Bus Transceivers/Registers	0.44	6.0	6.0	45.0	4.24
74LS652	Octal 3-State Bus Transceivers/Registers	945.00	15.0	25.0	20.0	4.31
74HC658	Octal Bus Transceivers with Parity	0.48	6.0	6.0	38.0	3.34
74HC659	Octal Bus Transceivers with Parity	0.48	6.0	6.0	35.0	3.34
74HCT659	Octal Bus Transceivers with Parity	0.44	6.0	6.0	35.0	3.34

TYPE	DESCRIPTION	MAX POWER (mW)	MAX IOH (mA)	MAX IOL (mA)	MAX DELAY (nS)	PRICE ($)
74HC664	Octal Bus Transceivers with Parity	0.48	6.0	6.0	38.0	3.34
74HC665	Octal Bus Transceivers with Parity	0.48	6.0	6.0	35.0	3.34
74HCT665	Octal Bus Transceivers with Parity	0.44	6.0	6.0	50.0	3.34
74ALS1242	Quad 3-State Inverting Bus Transceivers	77.00	15.0	16.0	12.0	1.17
74ALS1243	Quad 3-State Bus Transceivers	93.50	15.0	16.0	12.0	1.20
74ALS1245	Octal 3-State Bus Transceivers	198.00	15.0	16.0	13.0	1.60
74ALS1640	Octal 3-State Inverting Bus Transceivers	176.00	15.0	16.0	15.0	1.58
74ALS1645	Octal 3-State Bus Transceivers	198.00	15.0	16.0	13.0	1.60

The '638 and '639: Direction (DIR) and enable ($\overline{G}$) controls.

The '640: DIR and $\overline{G}$ controls. Data is inverted in both directions.

The '643: DIR and $\overline{G}$ controls. Data is inverted in the A-to-B direction.

The '645: DIR and $\overline{G}$ controls. Noninverting.

The '646 and '648: D-type flip-flops. DIR and $\overline{G}$ controls.

The '651 and '652: D-type flip-flops. GAB and $\overline{GBA}$ controls.

The '658: GAB and $\overline{GBA}$ controls. Inverting.

The '659: GAB and $\overline{GBA}$ controls. Noninverting.

The '664: DIR and $\overline{G}$ controls. Inverting.

The '665: DIR and $\overline{G}$ controls. Noninverting.

The 'ALS242, 'ALS1243, and 'ALS1245 are low power versions of 'ALS242, 'ALS243, and 'ALS245, respectively.

The 'ALS1640 and 'ALS1645 are low power versions of 'ALS640 and 'ALS645, respectively.

Tables 4-13 and 4-14 list maximum power, maximum V_{OH}, maximum I_{OL}, and maximum delay for 54/74 family open-collector transceivers.

Table 4-13. Open-Collector Transceivers, 54 Family.

TYPE	DESCRIPTION	MAX POWER (mW)	MAX VOH (V)	MAX IOL (mA)	MAX DELAY (nS)	PRICE ($)
54LS641	Octal Bus Transceivers with Open Collector Outputs	522.50	5.5	12.0	25.0	2.77
54LS642	Octal Inverting Bus Transceivers with Open Collector Outputs	522.50	5.5	12.0	25.0	2.77

TYPE	DESCRIPTION	MAX POWER (mW)	MAX VOH (V)	MAX IOL (mA)	MAX DELAY (nS)	PRICE ($)
54LS644	Octal True/Inverting Bus Transceivers with Open Collector Outputs	522.50	5.5	12.0	25.0	2.77
54LS647	Octal Bus Transceivers/Registers with Open Collector Outputs	825.00	5.5	12.0	27.0	6.95
54LS649	Octal Inverting Bus Transceivers/Registers with Open Collector Outputs	825.00	5.5	12.0	30.0	6.95
54LS653	Octal Inverting Bus Transceivers/Registers with Open Collector Outputs	907.50	5.5	12.0	32.0	6.95
54LS654	Octal Bus Transceivers/Registers with Open Collector Outputs	907.50	5.5	12.0	30.0	6.95

Table 4-14. Open-Collector Transceivers, 74 Family.

TYPE	DESCRIPTION	MAX POWER (mW)	MAX VOH (V)	MAX IOL (mA)	MAX DELAY (nS)	PRICE ($)
74ALS621	Octal Bus Transceivers with Open Collector Outputs	264.00	5.5	24.0	33.0	1.66
74AS621	Octal Bus Transceivers with Open Collector Outputs	1039.50	5.5	64.0	24.0	3.75
74LS621	Octal Bus Transceivers with Open Collector Outputs	472.50	5.5	24.0	25.0	1.44
74ALS622	Octal Bus Transceivers with Open Collector Outputs	154.00	5.5	24.0	35.0	1.66
74AS622	Octal Bus Transceivers with Open Collector Outputs	566.50	5.5	64.0	24.5	3.75
74LS622	Octal Bus Transceivers with Open Collector Outputs	472.50	5.5	24.0	25.0	1.44
74ALS641	Octal Bus Transceivers with Open Collector Outputs	258.50	5.5	24.0	25.0	1.60
74AS641	Octal Bus Transceivers with Open Collector Outputs	748.00	5.5	64.0	21.0	3.75
74LS641	Octal Bus Transceivers with Open Collector Outputs	498.75	5.5	24.0	25.0	1.44
74ALS642	Octal Inverting Bus Transceivers with Open Collector Outputs	154.00	5.5	24.0	30.0	1.60
74AS642	Octal Inverting Bus Transceivers with	572.00	5.5	64.0	24.0	3.75

TYPE	DESCRIPTION	MAX POWER (mW)	MAX VOH (V)	MAX IOL (mA)	MAX DELAY (nS)	PRICE ($)
	Open Collector Outputs					
74LS642	Octal Inverting Bus Transceivers with Open Collector Outputs	498.75	5.5	24.0	25.0	1.44
74ALS644	Octal True/Inverting Bus Transceivers with Open Collector Outputs	220.00	5.5	24.0	30.0	1.60
74AS644	Octal True/Inverting Bus Transceivers with Open Collector Outputs	682.00	5.5	64.0	24.0	3.75
74LS644	Octal True/Inverting Bus Transceivers with Open Collector Outputs	498.75	5.5	24.0	25.0	1.44
74ALS647	Octal Bus Transceivers/Registers with Open Collector Outputs	357.50	5.5	24.0	58.0	5.63
74LS647	Octal Bus Transceivers/Registers with Open Collector Outputs	787.50	5.5	24.0	27.0	4.31
74ALS649	Octal Inverting Bus Transceivers/Registers with Open Collector Outputs	385.00	5.5	24.0	62.0	5.68
74LS649	Octal Inverting Bus Transceivers/Registers with Open Collector Outputs	787.50	5.5	24.0	30.0	4.31
74LS653	Octal Inverting Bus Transceivers/Registers with Open Collector Outputs	866.25	5.5	24.0	32.0	4.31
74LS654	Octal Bus Transceivers/Registers with Open Collector Outputs	945.00	5.5	24.0	30.0	4.31
74AS758	Quad Inverting Bus Transceivers with Open-Collector Outputs	330.00	5.5	64.0	19.5	2.25
74AS759	Quad Bus Transceivers with Open-Collector Outputs	407.00	5.5	64.0	20.0	2.25

The '621 and '622: Separate enables for A-to-B and B-to-A 3-state control (GAB and $\overline{\text{GBA}}$). '621 is noninverting; '622 is inverting.

The '641: DIR and $\overline{\text{G}}$ controls. Noninverting.

The '642: DIR and $\overline{\text{G}}$ controls. Inverting.

The '644: DIR and $\overline{\text{G}}$ controls. Data is inverted in the A-to-B direction.

The '647 and '649: D-type flip-flops. DIR and $\overline{\text{G}}$ controls.

The '653 and '654: D-type flip-flops. GAB and $\overline{\text{GBA}}$ controls.

The '758: GAB and $\overline{\text{GBA}}$ controls. Inverting.

The '759: GAB and $\overline{\text{GBA}}$ controls. Noninverting.

Chapter 5

Decoders, Encoders,
and Data Selectors

This chapter presents functional descriptions and selection guides for decoders, encoders, and data selectors.

5.1 DECODERS

Figure 5-1 shows the logic symbol and function table for a 2-line to 4-line decoder, or demultiplexer. There are four output lines, one for each of the four possible combinations voltage levels on the two inputs A and B. Hence, the data on the input lines is *decoded* and one of four output lines is brought LOW with all other outputs remaining HIGH.

Figure 5-2 shows the logic symbol and function table for a 3-line to 8-line decoder. There are eight output lines, one for each of the eight possible combinations of voltage levels on the three inputs A, B, and C.

Figure 5-3 shows the logic symbol for a 4-line to 16-line decoder.

Figure 5-4 shows the logic symbol for a BCD to decimal decoder. BCD stands for binary-coded-decimal. Figure 5-4 also shows the decimal equivalents for the possible voltage level combinations on the BCD input lines (lines A, B, C, and D). The BCD decoder is a special version of the 4 to 16 line decoder where six of the possible 16 input conditions are not decoded. All outputs are HIGH for these six input conditions which are as follows:

D C B A   D C B A
H L H L (10)   H H L H (13)

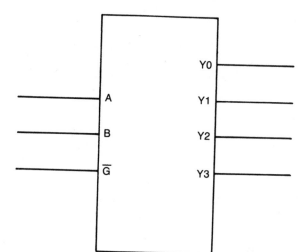

Fig. 5-1. Logic symbol and function table for a 2 to 4 line decoder.

Inputs			Outputs			
$\overline{G}$	A	B	Y0	Y1	Y2	Y3
H	X	X	H	H	H	H
L	L	L	L	H	H	H
L	H	L	H	L	H	H
L	L	H	H	H	L	H
L	H	H	H	H	H	L

H L H H (11)   H H H L (14)
H H L L (12)   H H H H (15)

Figure 5-5 shows the logic symbol for a BCD to 7-segment decoder. This logic function is used to drive 7-segment displays. The locations of the segments (designated a through g) is shown in Fig. 5-6A and the 16 possible displays are shown in Fig. 5-6B.

Tables 5-1 through 5-4 list the maximum power, maximum delay, and 100-piece price for decoders from the 54/74 families and the 4000 Series CMOS families.

The '131 has D-type flip-flops on the select inputs (also called the *address inputs*). The '137 has latches on the select inputs.

The '237 has active HIGH outputs (all outputs normally LOW; decoded output

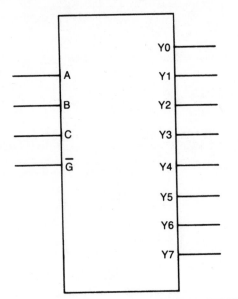

Fig. 5-2. Logic symbol and function table for a 3 to 8 line decoder.

Inputs				Outputs							
$\overline{G}$	A	B	C	Y0	Y1	Y2	Y3	Y4	Y5	Y6	Y7
H	X	X	X	H	H	H	H	H	H	H	H
L	L	L	L	L	H	H	H	H	H	H	H
L	H	L	L	H	L	H	H	H	H	H	H
L	L	H	L	H	H	L	H	H	H	H	H
L	H	H	L	H	H	H	L	H	H	H	H
L	L	L	H	H	H	H	H	L	H	H	H
L	H	L	H	H	H	H	H	H	L	H	H
L	L	H	H	H	H	H	H	H	H	L	H
L	H	H	H	H	H	H	H	H	H	H	L

is HIGH). The '237 is a '137 with inverted outputs.

The '238 has active HIGH outputs. The '238 is a '138 with inverted outputs.
The '239 has active HIGH outputs. The '239 is a '139 with inverted outputs.
The '537, '538, and '539 have 3-state outputs.

5.2 DECODER/DRIVERS

Tables 5-5 through 5-8 list the maximum power, maximum I_{OL}, maximum

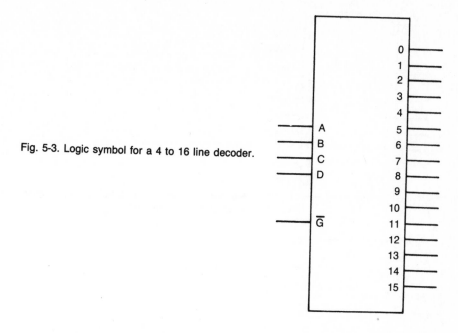

Fig. 5-3. Logic symbol for a 4 to 16 line decoder.

V_{OH}, and 100-piece price for decoder/drivers from the 54/74 families and the 4000 Series CMOS families.

The '247, '248, and '249 are identical to the '47, '48, and '49 except in the formation of the 6 and 9. The '247 through '249 turn on the "a" segment for the 6 and the "d" segment for the 9. See Fig. 5-6.

The '347 is a low voltage version of the '47.

The '447 is a low voltage version of the '247.

5.3 ENCODERS

Figure 5-7 shows the logic symbol and function table for a 8-line decimal to 3-line octal priority encoder. The 3-line output code corresponds to the highest priority input with a LOW voltage on it. Input 0 is the lowest priority input; input 7 is the highest. For example, a LOW on input 7 produces a LOW on each of the three outputs A, B, and C. In this example, even if there is a LOW on other inputs, the outputs will still all be LOW if input 7 is LOW.

Figure 5-8 shows the logic symbol for a 10-line decimal to 4-line BCD priority encoder. Operation is the same as the 8 to 3 line encoder but extended to 10 inputs.

Tables 5-9 through 5-12 list the maximum power, maximum delay and 100-piece price for encoders from the 54/74 families and the 4000 Series CMOS families.

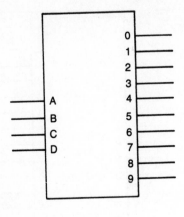

Fig. 5-4. Logic symbol and decimal equivalents of a BCD to decimal decoder.

BCD Inputs				Decimal Equivalent
D	C	B	A	
L	L	L	L	0
L	L	L	H	1
L	L	H	L	2
L	L	H	H	3
L	H	L	L	4
L	H	L	H	5
L	H	H	L	6
L	H	H	H	7
H	L	L	L	8
H	L	L	H	9

5.4 DATA SELECTORS/MULTIPLEXERS

Figure 5-9 shows the logic symbol and function table for a 2-line to 1-line data selector. HIGH or LOW data on the A input is transferred to the Y output when the select input $\overline{A}/B$ is LOW. HIGH or LOW data on the B input is transferred to the Y output when the select input A/B is HIGH.

Figure 5-10 shows the logic symbol and function table for a 4-line to 1-line data selector. There are two select inputs, A and B, and four data inputs, C0 through C3.

Figure 5-11 shows the logic symbol for the 8-line to 1-line data selector.

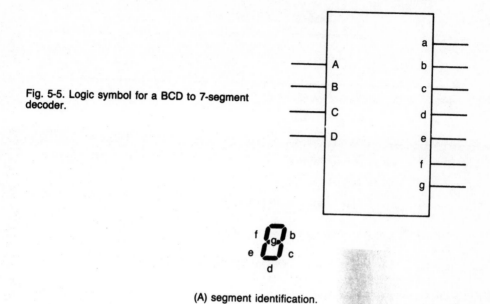

(A) segment identification.

Fig. 5-5. Logic symbol for a BCD to 7-segment decoder.

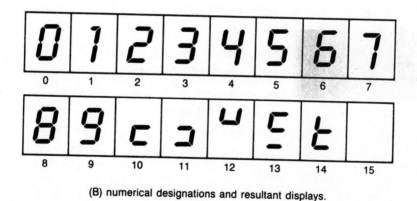

(B) numerical designations and resultant displays.

Fig. 5-6. Segment identification, numerical designators and resultant displays.

There are three select inputs, A through C, and eight data inputs, D0 through D7.

Figure 5-12 shows the logic symbol for the 16-line to 1-line data selector. There are four select inputs, A through D, and 16 data inputs, E0 through E15.

Data selectors have various names. For examples, an 8-line to 1-line data selector may be called any one of the following names:

Table 5-1. Decoders, 54 Family.

TYPE	DESCRIPTION	MAX POWER (mW)	MAX DELAY (nS)	PRICE ($)
5442	BCD to Decimal Decoder	308.00	30.0	1.99
54C42	BCD to Decimal Decoder	4.50	300.0	4.05
54HC42	BCD to Decimal Decoder	0.96	45.0	1.24
54HCT42	BCD to Decimal Decoder	0.88	56.0	1.09
54LS42	BCD to Decimal Decoder	71.50	30.0	0.94
54HC137	3 to 8 Line Decoder/Demultiplexer with Address Latches	0.96	72.0	1.49
54HCT137	3 to 8 Line Decoder/Demultiplexer with Address Latches	0.88	57.0	1.24
54LS137	3 to 8 Line Decoder/Demultiplexer with Address Latches	99.00	38.0	1.63
54ALS138	3 to 8 Line Decoder/Demultiplexer	55.00	28.0	1.84
54F138	3 to 8 Line Decoder/Demultiplexer	110.00	12.0	2.02
54HC138	3 to 8 Line Decoder/Demultiplexer	0.96	60.0	1.04
54HCT138	3 to 8 Line Decoder/Demultiplexer	0.88	60.0	0.97
54LS138	3 to 8 Line Decoder/Demultiplexer	55.00	41.0	0.94
54S138	3 to 8 Line Decoder/Demultiplexer	495.00	12.0	3.12
54F139	Dual 2 to 4 Line Decoders/Demultiplexers	110.00	12.0	2.02
54HC139	Dual 2 to 4 Line Decoders/Demultiplexers	0.96	64.0	1.04
54HCT139	Dual 2 to 4 Line Decoders/Demultiplexers	0.44	53.0	1.12
54LS139	Dual 2 to 4 Line Decoders/Demultiplexers	60.50	38.0	0.94
54S139	Dual 2 to 4 Line Decoders/Demultiplexers	495.00	12.0	3.12
54154	4 to 16 Line Decoder/Demultiplexer	308.00	36.0	5.93
54C154	4 to 16 Line Decoder/Demultiplexer	4.50	400.0	11.34
54HC154	4 to 16 Line Decoder/Demultiplexer	0.96	53.0	4.70
54HCT154	4 to 16 Line Decoder/Demultiplexer	0.88	53.0	4.21
54155	Dual 2 to 4 Line Decoders/Demultiplexers	220.00	32.0	2.49
54LS155	Dual 2 to 4 Line Decoders/Demultiplexers	55.00	30.0	1.20
54156	Dual 2 to 4 Line Decoders/Demultiplexers with Open-Collector Outputs	220.00	34.0	2.49

TYPE	DESCRIPTION	MAX POWER (mW)	MAX DELAY (nS)	PRICE ($)
54LS156	Dual 2 to 4 Line Decoders/Demultiplexers with Open-Collector Outputs	55.00	51.0	1.20
54HC237	3 to 8 Line Decoder/Demultiplexer with Address Latches	0.96	70.0	1.49
54HCT237	3 to 8 Line Decoder/Demultiplexer with Address Latches	0.88	57.0	1.24
54HC238	3 to 8 Line Decoder/Demultiplexer	0.96	45.0	1.04
54HCT238	3 to 8 Line Decoder/Demultiplexer	0.88	53.0	0.97
54F547	3 to 8 Line Decoder/Demultiplexer with Address Latches	137.50	12.0	14.30
54F548	3 to 8 Line Decoder/Demultiplexer with Acknowledge	115.50	12.0	21.09
54HC4514	4 to 16 Line Decoder with Address Latch	0.96	83.0	4.39
54HCT4514	4 to 16 Line Decoder with Address Latch	0.88	90.0	3.96
54HC4515	4 to 16 Line Inverting Decoder with Address Latch	0.96	83.0	4.39
54HCT4515	4 to 16 Line Inverting Decoder with Address Latch	0.88	90.0	3.96

Table 5-2. Decoders, 74 Family.

TYPE	DESCRIPTION	MAX POWER (mW)	MAX DELAY (nS)	PRICE ($)
7442	BCD to Decimal Decoder	294.00	30.0	0.42
74C42	BCD to Decimal Decoder	4.50	300.0	0.98
74HC42	BCD to Decimal Decoder	0.48	38.0	0.50
74HCT42	BCD to Decimal Decoder	0.44	46.0	0.50
74LS42	BCD to Decimal Decoder	68.25	30.0	0.36
74ALS131	3 to 8 Line Decoder/Demultiplexer with Address Latches	60.50	25.0	0.66
74ALS137	3 to 8 Line Decoder/Demultiplexer with Address Latches	60.50	20.0	0.62
74HC137	3 to 8 Line Decoder/Demultiplexer with Address Latches	0.48	48.0	0.54
74HCT137	3 to 8 Line Decoder/Demultiplexer with Address Latches	0.44	48.0	0.54

TYPE	DESCRIPTION	MAX POWER (mW)	MAX DELAY (nS)	PRICE ($)
74LS137	3 to 8 Line Decoder/Demultiplexer with Address Latches	94.50	38.0	0.33
74AC138	3 to 8 Line Decoder/Demultiplexer	0.28	15.0	0.69
74ALS138	3 to 8 Line Decoder/Demultiplexer	55.00	22.0	0.62
74F138	3 to 8 Line Decoder/Demultiplexer	105.00	9.0	0.60
74HC138	3 to 8 Line Decoder/Demultiplexer	0.48	38.0	0.54
74HCT138	3 to 8 Line Decoder/Demultiplexer	0.44	44.0	0.54
74LS138	3 to 8 Line Decoder/Demultiplexer	52.50	41.0	0.36
74S138	3 to 8 Line Decoder/Demultiplexer	472.50	12.0	0.60
74AC139	Dual 2 to 4 Line Decoders/Demultiplexers	0.28	14.5	0.69
74F139	Dual 2 to 4 Line Decoders/Demultiplexers	105.00	9.0	0.60
74HC139	Dual 2 to 4 Line Decoders/Demultiplexers	0.48	40.0	0.54
74HCT139	Dual 2 to 4 Line Decoders/Demultiplexers	0.22	44.0	0.54
74LS139	Dual 2 to 4 Line Decoders/Demultiplexers	57.75	38.0	0.36
74S139	Dual 2 to 4 Line Decoders/Demultiplexers	472.50	12.0	0.60
74154	4 to 16 Line Decoder/Demultiplexer	294.00	36.0	1.12
74C154	4 to 16 Line Decoder/Demultiplexer	4.50	400.0	3.80
74HC154	4 to 16 Line Decoder/Demultiplexer	0.48	44.0	1.65
74HCT154	4 to 16 Line Decoder/Demultiplexer	0.44	44.0	1.65
74LS154	4 to 16 Line Decoder/Demultiplexer	73.50	30.0	0.93
74155	Dual 2 to 4 Line Decoders/Demultiplexers	210.00	32.0	0.41
74LS155	Dual 2 to 4 Line Decoders/Demultiplexers	52.50	30.0	0.39
74156	Dual 2 to 4 Line Decoders/Demultiplexers with Open-Collector Outputs	210.00	34.0	0.70
74LS156	Dual 2 to 4 Line Decoders/Demultiplexers with Open-Collector Outputs	52.50	51.0	0.39
74159	4 to 16 Line Decoder/Demultiplexer with Open-Collector Outputs	294.00	36.0	1.50
74HC237	3 to 8 Line Decoder/Demultiplexer with Address Latches	0.48	48.0	0.79
74HCT237	3 to 8 Line Decoder/Demultiplexer with Address Latches	0.44	48.0	0.79
74HC238	3 to 8 Line Decoder/Demultiplexer	0.48	45.0	0.63

TYPE	DESCRIPTION	MAX POWER (mW)	MAX DELAY (nS)	PRICE ($)
74HCT238	3 to 8 Line Decoder/Demultiplexer	0.44	45.0	0.63
74HC239	Dual 2 to 4 Line Decoders/Demultiplexers	0.48	38.0	0.94
74F537	1 of 10 Decoder	346.50	17.0	3.72
74F538	1 of 8 Decoder	294.00	17.0	3.72
74F539	Dual 1 of 4 Decoders	315.00	19.5	3.72
74F547	3 to 8 Line Decoder/Demultiplexer with Address Latches	131.25	13.0	4.65
74F548	3 to 8 Line Decoder/Demultiplexer with Acknowledge	110.25	11.5	3.93
74HC4514	4 to 16 Line Decoder with Address Latch	0.48	69.0	2.81
74HCT4514	4 to 16 Line Decoder with Address Latch	0.44	75.0	2.82
74HC4515	4 to 16 Line Inverting Decoder with Address Latch	0.48	69.0	2.82
74HCT4515	4 to 16 Line Inverting Decoder with Address Latch	0.44	75.0	2.82

Table 5-3. Decoders, 4000 Series, Industrial Temperature Range.

TYPE	DESCRIPTION	MAX POWER (mW)	MAX DELAY (nS)	PRICE ($)
4028A	BCD to Decimal Decoder	3.50	700.0	1.01
4028B	BCD to Decimal Decoder	0.75	350.0	0.71
4514B	4-Bit Latch/4-to-16 Line Decoder (Output High on Select)	0.75	970.0	1.90
4515B	4-Bit Latch/4-to-16 Line Decoder (Output Low on Select)	0.75	970.0	1.90
4555B	Dual Binary 1-of-4 Decoders (Outputs High on Select)	0.75	440.0	0.59
4556B	Dual Binary 1-of-4 Decoders (Outputs Low on Select)	0.75	440.0	0.59

☐ 1-of-8 line data selector/multiplexer
☐ 8-input multiplexer
☐ 8-to-1 multiplexer
☐ 8-channel data selector/multiplexer

Table 5-4. Decoders, 4000 Series, Military Temperature Range.

TYPE	DESCRIPTION	MAX POWER (mW)	MAX DELAY (nS)	PRICE ($)
4028A	BCD to Decimal Decoder	1.50	700.0	2.15
4028B	BCD to Decimal Decoder	0.75	350.0	1.25
4514B	4-Bit Latch/4-to-16 Line Decoder (Output High on Select)	0.75	970.0	3.60
4515B	4-Bit Latch/4-to-16 Line Decoder (Output Low on Select)	0.75	970.0	3.60
4555B	Dual Binary 1-of-4 Decoders (Outputs High on Select)	0.75	440.0	1.26
4556B	Dual Binary 1-of-4 Decoders (Outputs Low on Select)	0.75	440.0	1.26

Table 5-5. Decoder/Drivers, 54 Family.

TYPE	DESCRIPTION	MAX POWER (mW)	MAX IOL (mA)	MAX VOH (V)	PRICE ($)
5441	BCD to Decimal Decoder/Driver (NIXIE Driver)	198.00	7.0	70.0	7.10
5445	BCD to Decimal Decoder/Driver	385.00	20.0	30.0	3.26
5446	BCD to 7-Segment Decoder/Driver with Open-Collector Outputs	566.50	40.0	30.0	3.69
5447	BCD to 7-Segment Decoder/Driver with Open-Collector Outputs	566.50	40.0	15.0	3.69
54LS47	BCD to 7-Segment Decoder/Driver with Open-Collector Outputs	71.50	12.0	15.0	1.49
5448	BCD to 7-Segment Decoder/Driver with Internal Pull-Up Resistor Outputs	495.00	6.4	5.5	2.75
54C48	BCD to 7-Segment Decoder/Driver with Internal Pull-Up Resistor Outputs	4.50	1.7	4.5	5.50
54LS48	BCD to 7-Segment Decoder/Driver with Internal Pull-Up Resistor Outputs	209.00	2.0	5.5	1.49
54LS49	BCD to 7-Segment Decoder/Driver with Open-Collector Outputs	82.50	4.0	5.5	1.49
54145	BCD to Decimal Decoder/Driver	341.00	80.0	15.0	3.30
54LS145	BCD to Decimal Decoder/Driver	71.50	12.0	15.0	0.94

TYPE	DESCRIPTION	MAX POWER (mW)	MAX IOL (mA)	MAX VOH (V)	PRICE ($)
54LS247	BCD to 7 Segment Decoder/Driver with Open-Collector Outputs	71.50	12.0	15.0	1.49
54LS248	BCD to 7 Segment Decoder/Driver	209.00	2.0	5.5	1.49
54LS249	BCD to 7 Segment Decoder/Driver with Open-Collector Outputs	82.50	4.0	5.5	1.49
54LS347	BCD to 7-Segment Decoder/Driver	71.50	1.6	7.0	1.29
54LS447	BCD to 7-Segment Decoder/Driver	71.50	12.0	7.0	2.17

Table 5-6. Decoder/Drivers, 74 Family.

TYPE	DESCRIPTION	MAX POWER (mW)	MAX IOL (mA)	MAX VOH (V)	PRICE ($)
7441	BCD to Decimal Decoder/Driver (NIXIE Driver)	189.00	7.0	70.0	0.93
7445	BCD to Decimal Decoder/Driver	367.50	20.0	30.0	0.73
7446	BCD to 7-Segment Decoder/Driver with Open-Collector Outputs	540.75	40.0	30.0	0.78
7447	BCD to 7-Segment Decoder/Driver with Open-Collector Outputs	540.75	40.0	15.0	0.67
74LS47	BCD to 7-Segment Decoder/Driver with Open-Collector Outputs	68.25	24.0	15.0	0.50
7448	BCD to 7-Segment Decoder/Driver with Internal Pull-Up Resistor Outputs	472.50	6.4	5.5	1.92
74C48	BCD to 7-Segment Decoder/Driver with Internal Pull-Up Resistor Outputs	4.50	1.7	4.5	1.47
74LS48	BCD to 7-Segment Decoder/Driver with Internal Pull-Up Resistor Outputs	199.50	3.2	5.5	0.50
74LS49	BCD to 7-Segment Decoder/Driver with Open-Collector Outputs	78.75	8.0	5.5	0.80
74141	BCD to Decimal Decoder/Driver	131.25	7.0	60.0	1.00
74143	4-Bit Counter/Latch/7-Segment Decoder/Driver	488.25	15.0	7.0	4.20
74144	4-Bit Counter/Latch/7-Segment Decoder/Driver	488.25	25.0	15.0	8.00
74145	BCD to Decimal Decoder/Driver	367.50	80.0	15.0	0.63
74LS145	BCD to Decimal Decoder/Driver	68.25	80.0	15.0	0.58
74247	BCD to 7 Segment Decoder/Driver with Open-Collector Outputs	540.75	40.0	15.0	3.00

TYPE	DESCRIPTION	MAX POWER (mW)	MAX IOL (mA)	MAX VOH (V)	PRICE ($)
74LS247	BCD to 7 Segment Decoder/Driver with Open-Collector Outputs	68.25	24.0	15.0	0.69
74LS248	BCD to 7 Segment Decoder/Driver	199.50	6.0	5.5	0.69
74LS249	BCD to 7 Segment Decoder/Driver with Open-Collector Outputs	78.75	8.0	5.5	0.69
74LS347	BCD to 7-Segment Decoder/Driver	68.25	24.0	7.0	0.50
74LS447	BCD to 7-Segment Decoder/Driver	68.25	24.0	15.0	0.64

Table 5-7. Decoder/Drivers, 4000 Series, Industrial Temperature Range.

TYPE	DESCRIPTION	MAX POWER (mW)	MAX IOL (mA)	MAX IOH (mA)	PRICE ($)
4054B	4-Segment Decoder/Driver	0.75	2.4	1.2	1.75
4055B	BCD to 7-Segment Decoder/Driver	0.75	2.4	1.2	1.45
4056B	BCD to 7-Segment Decoder/Driver with Strobed Latch Function	0.75	2.4	1.2	1.75
4511B	BCD to 7-Segment Latch/Decoder/Driver	0.75	2.8	25.0	0.79
4543B	BCD to 7-Segment Latch/Decoder/Driver	0.75	2.8	2.2	0.99
40110B	Decade Up/Down Counter/Latch/Decoder Driver	0.75	5.6	25.0	2.11

Table 5-8. Decoder/Drivers, 4000 Series, Military Temperature Range.

TYPE	DESCRIPTION	MAX POWER (mW)	MAX IOL (mA)	MAX IOH (mA)	PRICE ($)
4054B	4-Segment Decoder/Driver	0.75	2.0	1.1	2.48
4055B	BCD to 7-Segment Decoder/Driver	0.75	2.0	1.1	2.18
4056B	BCD to 7-Segment Decoder/Driver with Strobed Latch Function	0.75	2.0	1.1	2.48
4511B	BCD to 7-Segment Latch/Decoder/Driver	0.75	2.4	25.0	1.78
4543B	BCD to 7-Segment Latch/Decoder/Driver	0.75	2.4	1.9	1.68
40110B	Decade Up/Down Counter/Latch/Decoder Driver	0.75	4.8	25.0	2.97

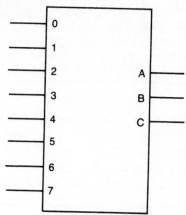

Fig. 5-7. Logic symbol and function table for an 8 to 3 line priority encoder.

Inputs								Outputs		
0	1	2	3	4	5	6	7	A	B	C
X	X	X	X	X	X	X	L	L	L	L
X	X	X	X	X	X	L	H	H	L	L
X	X	X	X	X	L	H	H	L	H	L
X	X	X	X	L	H	H	H	H	H	L
X	X	X	L	H	H	H	H	L	L	H
X	X	L	H	H	H	H	H	H	L	H
X	L	H	H	H	H	H	H	L	H	H
L	H	H	H	H	H	H	H	H	H	H

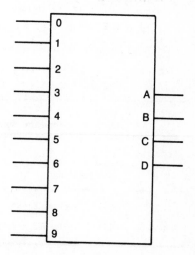

Fig. 5-8. Logic symbol for a 10-line decimal to 4-line BCD priority encoder.

Table 5-9. Encoders, 54 Family.

TYPE	DESCRIPTION	MAX POWER (mW)	MAX DELAY (nS)	PRICE ($)
54HC147	10-Line Decimal to 4-Line BCD Priority Encoder	0.96	57.0	1.90
54LS147	10-Line Decimal to 4-Line BCD Priority Encoder	110.00	18.0	2.69
54148	8-Line Decimal to 3-Line Octal Priority Encoder	330.00	15.0	1.99
54LS148	8-Line Decimal to 3-Line Octal Priority Encoder	110.00	25.0	1.80
54LS348	8 to 3 Line Priority Encoder with 3-State Outputs	137.50	30.0	2.16

Table 5-10. Encoders, 74 Family.

TYPE	DESCRIPTION	MAX POWER (mW)	MAX DELAY (nS)	PRICE ($)
74147	10-Line Decimal to 4-Line BCD Priority Encoder	367.50	14.0	1.64
74HC147	10-Line Decimal to 4-Line BCD Priority Encoder	0.48	48.0	0.90
74LS147	10-Line Decimal to 4-Line BCD Priority Encoder	105.00	18.0	1.16
74148	8-Line Decimal to 3-Line Octal Priority Encoder	315.00	15.0	0.85
74F148	8-Line Decimal to 3-Line Octal Priority Encoder	183.75	12.0	0.80
74HC148	8-Line Decimal to 3-Line Octal Priority Encoder	0.48	45.0	0.90
74LS148	8-Line Decimal to 3-Line Octal Priority Encoder	105.00	25.0	0.76
74LS348	8 to 3 Line Priority Encoder with 3-State Outputs	131.25	30.0	0.88
74LS748	8 to 3 Line Priority Encoder	105.00	25.0	0.80
74LS848	3-State 8 to 3 Line Priority Encoder	131.25	30.0	0.92

Table 5-11. Encoders, 4000 Series, Industrial Temperature Range.

TYPE	DESCRIPTION	MAX POWER (mW)	MAX DELAY (nS)	PRICE ($)
4532B	8-Bit Priority Encoder	0.75	440.0	0.83
40147B	10 to 4 Line BCD Priority Encoder	0.15	900.0	1.50

Table 5-12. Encoders, 4000 Series, Military Temperature Range.

TYPE	DESCRIPTION	MAX POWER (mW)	MAX DELAY (nS)	PRICE ($)
4532B	8-Bit Priority Encoder	0.75	440.0	2.01
40147B	10 to 4 Line BCD Priority Encoder	0.15	900.0	2.10

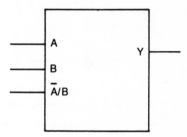

Fig. 5-9. Logic symbol and function table for a 2 to 1 line data selector.

Select Input $\overline{A}/B$	Data Inputs A B	Output Y
L	L X	L
L	H X	H
H	X L	L
H	X H	H

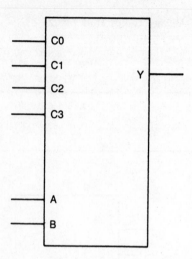

Fig. 5-10. Logic symbol and function table for a 4 to 1 line data selector.

Select Inputs		Data Inputs				Output Y
A	B	C0	C1	C2	C3	Y
L	L	L	X	X	X	L
L	L	H	X	X	X	H
H	L	X	L	X	X	L
H	L	X	H	X	X	H
L	H	X	X	L	X	L
L	H	X	X	H	X	H
H	H	X	X	X	L	L
H	H	X	X	X	H	H

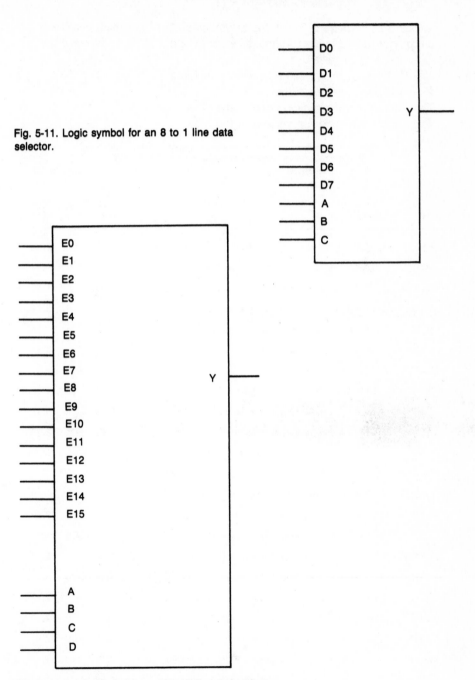

Fig. 5-11. Logic symbol for an 8 to 1 line data selector.

Fig. 5-12. Logic symbol for a 16 to 1 line data selector.

Tables 5-13 through 5-16 list the maximum power, maximum delay and 100-piece price for data selectors/multiplexers from the 54/74 families and the 4000 Series CMOS families.

The '151 has inverting and noninverting outputs.

The '152 has inverting output.

The '352 is the inverting version of the '153.

The '353 is the inverting version of the '253.

Table 5-13. Data Selectors/Multiplexers, 54 Family.

TYPE	DESCRIPTION	MAX POWER (mW)	MAX DELAY (nS)	PRICE ($)
54150	1 of 16 Line Data Selector/Multiplexer	374.00	20.0	5.86
54151	1 of 8 Line Data Selector/Multiplexer	264.00	14.0	1.90
54ALS151	1 of 8 Line Data Selector/Multiplexer	66.00	23.0	1.46
54C151	1 of 8 Line Data Selector/Multiplexer	4.50	270.0	8.24
54F151	1 of 8 Line Data Selector/Multiplexer	115.50	7.5	2.02
54HC151	1 of 8 Line Data Selector/Multiplexer	0.96	51.0	0.96
54HCT151	1 of 8 Line Data Selector/Multiplexer	0.88	60.0	1.01
54LS151	1 of 8 Line Data Selector/Multiplexer	55.00	21.0	0.94
54S151	1 of 8 Line Data Selector/Multiplexer	385.00	7.0	3.12
54HC152	1 of 8 Line Data Selector/Multiplexer	0.96	39.0	1.77
54153	Dual 4 to 1 Line Data Selectors/Multiplexers	236.50	23.0	1.90
54AC153	Dual 4 to 1 Line Data Selectors/Multiplexers	0.55	18.5	3.93
54ALS153	Dual 4 to 1 Line Data Selectors/Multiplexers	77.00	18.0	1.46
54F153	Dual 4 to 1 Line Data Selectors/Multiplexers	110.00	9.0	2.02
54HC153	Dual 4 to 1 Line Data Selectors/Multiplexers	0.96	42.0	1.11
54LS153	Dual 4 to 1 Line Data Selectors/Multiplexers	55.00	26.0	0.94
54S153	Dual 4 to 1 Line Data Selectors/Multiplexers	385.00	9.0	3.12
54157	Quad 2 to 1 Line Data Selectors/Multiplexers	264.00	14.0	1.90
54C157	Quad 2 to 1 Line Data Selectors/Multiplexers	0.90	250.0	7.60
54F157	Quad 2 to 1 Line Data Selectors/Multiplexers	126.50	10.0	2.02
54HC157	Quad 2 to 1 Line Data Selectors/Multiplexers	0.96	38.0	1.11
54HCT157	Quad 2 to 1 Line Data Selectors/Multiplexers	0.88	45.0	1.01

TYPE	DESCRIPTION	MAX POWER (mW)	MAX DELAY (nS)	PRICE ($)
54LS157	Quad 2 to 1 Line Data Selectors/Multiplexers	88.00	14.0	0.94
54S157	Quad 2 to 1 Line Data Selectors/Multiplexers	429.00	7.5	3.12
54F158	Quad 2 to 1 Line Inverting Data Selectors/Multiplexers	82.50	8.5	2.02
54HC158	Quad 2 to 1 Line Inverting Data Selectors/Multiplexers	0.96	38.0	0.96
54HCT158	Quad 2 to 1 Line Inverting Data Selectors/Multiplexers	0.88	45.0	1.01
54LS158	Quad 2 to 1 Line Inverting Data Selectors/Multiplexers	60.50	15.0	0.94
54S158	Quad 2 to 1 Line Inverting Data Selectors/Multiplexers	445.50	6.0	3.12
54251	3-State 1 of 8 Line Data Selector/Multiplexer	341.00	15.0	2.95
54ALS251	3-State 1 of 8 Line Data Selector/Multiplexer	77.00	25.0	1.69
54F251	3-State 1 of 8 Line Data Selector/Multiplexer	132.00	8.0	2.02
54HC251	3-State 1 of 8 Line Data Selector/Multiplexer	0.96	53.0	0.96
54HCT251	3-State 1 of 8 Line Data Selector/Multiplexer	0.88	53.0	1.01
54LS251	3-State 1 of 8 Line Data Selector/Multiplexer	66.00	15.0	0.94
54S251	3-State 1 of 8 Line Data Selector/Multiplexer	467.50	7.0	2.79
54AC253	Dual 3-State 1 of 4 Line Data Selectors/Multiplexers	0.55	21.0	4.86
54ALS253	Dual 3-State 1 of 4 Line Data Selectors/Multiplexers	77.00	18.0	1.69
54F253	Dual 3-State 1 of 4 Line Data Selectors/Multiplexers	126.50	9.0	2.02
54HC253	Dual 3-State 1 of 4 Line Data Selectors/Multiplexers	0.96	53.0	0.96
54HCT253	Dual 3-State 1 of 4 Line Data Selectors/Multiplexers	0.88	60.0	1.01
54LS253	Dual 3-State 1 of 4 Line Data Selectors/Multiplexers	77.00	25.0	0.94
54S253	Dual 3-State 1 of 4 Line Data Selectors/Multiplexers	385.00	9.0	3.14
54ALS257	Quad 3-State 2 to 1 Line Data Selectors/Multiplexers	77.00	14.0	1.69
54F257	Quad 3-State 2 to 1 Line Data Selectors/Multiplexers	126.50	8.0	2.02

TYPE	DESCRIPTION	MAX POWER (mW)	MAX DELAY (nS)	PRICE ($)
54HC257	Quad 3-State 2 to 1 Line Data Selectors/Multiplexers	0.96	48.0	0.96
54HCT257	Quad 3-State 2 to 1 Line Data Selectors/Multiplexers	0.88	53.0	1.01
54LS257	Quad 3-State 2 to 1 Line Data Selectors/Multiplexers	104.50	15.0	0.94
54S257	Quad 3-State 2 to 1 Line Data Selectors/Multiplexers	544.50	7.5	3.15
54ALS258	Quad 3-State 2 to 1 Line Inverting Data Selectors/Multiplexers	71.50	12.0	1.69
54F258	Quad 3-State 2 to 1 Line Inverting Data Selectors/Multiplexers	126.50	7.5	2.02
54HC258	Quad 3-State 2 to 1 Line Inverting Data Selectors/Multiplexers	0.96	30.0	0.96
54LS258	Quad 3-State 2 to 1 Line Inverting Data Selectors/Multiplexers	88.00	17.0	0.94
54S258	Quad 3-State 2 to 1 Line Inverting Data Selectors/Multiplexers	478.50	6.0	3.15
54298	Quad 2 to 1 Line Data Selectors/Multiplexers with Storage	357.50	32.0	2.55
54HC298	Quad 2 to 1 Line Data Selectors/Multiplexers with Storage	0.96	38.0	2.15
54LS298	Quad 2 to 1 Line Data Selectors/Multiplexers with Storage	115.50	32.0	1.28
54ALS352	Dual 1 of 4 Line Inverting Data Selectors/Multiplexers	55.00	24.0	1.69
54F352	Dual 1 of 4 Line Inverting Data Selectors/Multiplexers	110.00	9.0	2.02
54HC352	Dual 1 of 4 Line Inverting Data Selectors/Multiplexers	0.96	53.0	1.74
54LS352	Dual 1 of 4 Line Inverting Data Selectors/Multiplexers	55.00	26.0	1.63
54ALS353	Dual 3-State 1 of 4 Line Data Selectors/Multiplexers	71.50	24.0	1.69
54F353	Dual 3-State 1 of 4 Line Data Selectors/Multiplexers	126.50	9.0	2.02
54HC353	Dual 3-State 1 of 4 Line Data Selectors/Multiplexers	0.96	53.0	1.74
54LS353	Dual 3-State 1 of 4 Line Data	77.00	25.0	1.92

TYPE	DESCRIPTION	MAX POWER (mW)	MAX DELAY (nS)	PRICE ($)
	Selectors/Multiplexers			
54HC354	3-State 8 to 1 Line Data Selector/Multiplexer/Register	0.96	77.0	4.62
54HCT354	3-State 8 to 1 Line Data Selector/Multiplexer/Register	0.88	77.0	3.71
54HC356	3-State 8 to 1 Line Data Selector/Multiplexer/Register	0.96	77.0	4.62
54HCT356	3-State 8 to 1 Line Data Selector/Multiplexer/Register	0.88	77.0	3.71
54LS356	3-State 8 to 1 Line Data Selector/Multiplexer/Register	253.00	36.0	4.49
54F398	Quad 2-Input Multiplexers with Storage	209.00	11.5	14.09
54LS398	Quad 2-Input Multiplexers with Storage	71.50	32.0	3.03
54F399	Quad 2-Input Multiplexers with Storage	187.00	11.5	6.01
54LS399	Quad 2-Input Multiplexers with Storage	71.50	32.0	1.68
54LS450	16 to 1 Multiplexer	550.00	45.0	6.43
54LS451	Dual 8 to 1 Multiplexer	550.00	40.0	6.43
54LS453	Quad 4 to 1 Multiplexer	550.00	45.0	6.43

Table 5-14. Data Selectors/Multiplexers, 74 Family.

TYPE	DESCRIPTION	MAX POWER (mW)	MAX DELAY (nS)	PRICE ($)
74150	1 of 16 Line Data Selector/Multiplexer	357.00	20.0	1.16
74C150	1 of 16 Line Data Selector/Multiplexer	4.50	600.0	3.80
74151	1 of 8 Line Data Selector/Multiplexer	252.00	14.0	0.39
74ALS151	1 of 8 Line Data Selector/Multiplexer	66.00	15.0	0.62
74AS151	1 of 8 Line Data Selector/Multiplexer	165.00	6.5	1.20
74C151	1 of 8 Line Data Selector/Multiplexer	4.50	270.0	2.54
74F151	1 of 8 Line Data Selector/Multiplexer	110.25	6.5	0.60
74HC151	1 of 8 Line Data Selector/Multiplexer	0.48	43.0	0.54
74HCT151	1 of 8 Line Data Selector/Multiplexer	0.44	50.0	0.54

TYPE	DESCRIPTION	MAX POWER (mW)	MAX DELAY (nS)	PRICE ($)
74LS151	1 of 8 Line Data Selector/Multiplexer	52.50	21.0	0.36
74S151	1 of 8 Line Data Selector/Multiplexer	367.50	7.0	0.60
74HC152	1 of 8 Line Data Selector/Multiplexer	0.48	33.0	0.75
74153	Dual 4 to 1 Line Data Selectors/Multiplexers	225.75	23.0	0.41
74AC153	Dual 4 to 1 Line Data Selectors/Multiplexers	0.28	17.0	0.69
74ALS153	Dual 4 to 1 Line Data Selectors/Multiplexers	77.00	15.0	0.62
74AS153	Dual 4 to 1 Line Data Selectors/Multiplexers	181.50	8.0	1.20
74F153	Dual 4 to 1 Line Data Selectors/Multiplexers	105.00	8.0	0.60
74HC153	Dual 4 to 1 Line Data Selectors/Multiplexers	0.48	35.0	0.54
74LS153	Dual 4 to 1 Line Data Selectors/Multiplexers	52.50	26.0	0.36
74S153	Dual 4 to 1 Line Data Selectors/Multiplexers	367.50	9.0	0.60
74157	Quad 2 to 1 Line Data Selectors/Multiplexers	252.00	14.0	0.41
74AS157	Quad 2 to 1 Line Data Selectors/Multiplexers	154.00	6.0	1.10
74C157	Quad 2 to 1 Line Data Selectors/Multiplexers	0.90	250.0	2.28
74F157	Quad 2 to 1 Line Data Selectors/Multiplexers	120.75	8.0	0.60
74HC157	Quad 2 to 1 Line Data Selectors/Multiplexers	0.48	31.0	0.54
74HCT157	Quad 2 to 1 Line Data Selectors/Multiplexers	0.44	38.0	0.54
74LS157	Quad 2 to 1 Line Data Selectors/Multiplexers	84.00	14.0	0.36
74S157	Quad 2 to 1 Line Data Selectors/Multiplexers	409.50	7.5	0.60
74AS158	Quad 2 to 1 Line Inverting Data Selectors/Multiplexers	123.75	5.0	1.10
74F158	Quad 2 to 1 Line Inverting Data Selectors/Multiplexers	78.75	7.0	0.60
74HC158	Quad 2 to 1 Line Inverting Data Selectors/Multiplexers	0.48	31.0	0.72
74HCT158	Quad 2 to 1 Line Inverting Data Selectors/Multiplexers	0.44	38.0	0.54
74LS158	Quad 2 to 1 Line Inverting Data Selectors/Multiplexers	57.75	15.0	0.36
74S158	Quad 2 to 1 Line Inverting Data Selectors/Multiplexers	425.25	6.0	0.60
74AS250	1 of 16 Line Data Selector/Multiplexer	275.00	8.0	2.17
74251	3-State 1 of 8 Line Data Selector/Multiplexer	325.50	15.0	1.00

TYPE	DESCRIPTION	MAX POWER (mW)	MAX DELAY (nS)	PRICE ($)
74ALS251	3-State 1 of 8 Line Data Selector/Multiplexer	77.00	15.0	0.72
74F251	3-State 1 of 8 Line Data Selector/Multiplexer	126.00	7.0	0.58
74HC251	3-State 1 of 8 Line Data Selector/Multiplexer	0.48	44.0	0.58
74HCT251	3-State 1 of 8 Line Data Selector/Multiplexer	0.44	44.0	0.58
74LS251	3-State 1 of 8 Line Data Selector/Multiplexer	63.00	15.0	0.36
74S251	3-State 1 of 8 Line Data Selector/Multiplexer	446.25	7.0	1.01
74AC253	Dual 3-State 1 of 4 Line Data Selectors/Multiplexers	0.28	19.5	0.69
74ALS253	Dual 3-State 1 of 4 Line Data Selectors/Multiplexers	77.00	14.0	0.72
74AS253	Dual 3-State 1 of 4 Line Data Selectors/Multiplexers	181.50	8.0	1.30
74F253	Dual 3-State 1 of 4 Line Data Selectors/Multiplexers	120.75	8.0	0.58
74HC253	Dual 3-State 1 of 4 Line Data Selectors/Multiplexers	0.48	44.0	0.58
74HCT253	Dual 3-State 1 of 4 Line Data Selectors/Multiplexers	0.44	50.0	0.58
74LS253	Dual 3-State 1 of 4 Line Data Selectors/Multiplexers	73.50	25.0	0.36
74S253	Dual 3-State 1 of 4 Line Data Selectors/Multiplexers	446.25	9.0	0.60
74ALS257	Quad 3-State 2 to 1 Line Data Selectors/Multiplexers	77.00	12.0	0.72
74AS257	Quad 3-State 2 to 1 Line Data Selectors/Multiplexers	175.45	6.0	1.17
74F257	Quad 3-State 2 to 1 Line Data Selectors/Multiplexers	120.75	7.0	0.58
74HC257	Quad 3-State 2 to 1 Line Data Selectors/Multiplexers	0.48	40.0	0.54
74HCT257	Quad 3-State 2 to 1 Line Data Selectors/Multiplexers	0.44	44.0	0.54
74LS257	Quad 3-State 2 to 1 Line Data Selectors/Multiplexers	99.75	15.0	0.36
74S257	Quad 3-State 2 to 1 Line Data Selectors/Multiplexers	519.75	7.0	0.60
74ALS258	Quad 3-State 2 to 1 Line Inverting Data	71.50	8.0	0.72

TYPE	DESCRIPTION	MAX POWER (mW)	MAX DELAY (nS)	PRICE ($)
	Selectors/Multiplexers			
74AS258	Quad 3-State 2 to 1 Line Inverting Data Selectors/Multiplexers	138.60	5.0	1.07
74F258	Quad 3-State 2 to 1 Line Inverting Data Selectors/Multiplexers	120.75	6.0	0.58
74HC258	Quad 3-State 2 to 1 Line Inverting Data Selectors/Multiplexers	0.48	25.0	0.54
74LS258	Quad 3-State 2 to 1 Line Inverting Data Selectors/Multiplexers	84.00	17.0	0.36
74S258	Quad 3-State 2 to 1 Line Inverting Data Selectors/Multiplexers	456.75	6.0	0.60
74298	Quad 2 to 1 Line Data Selectors/Multiplexers with Storage	341.25	32.0	1.08
74AS298	Quad 2 to 1 Line Data Selectors/Multiplexers with Storage	198.00	11.0	1.15
74HC298	Quad 2 to 1 Line Data Selectors/Multiplexers with Storage	0.48	31.0	1.09
74LS298	Quad 2 to 1 Line Data Selectors/Multiplexers with Storage	110.25	32.0	0.69
74ALS352	Dual 1 of 4 Line Inverting Data Selectors/Multiplexers	55.00	18.0	0.72
74AS352	Dual 1 of 4 Line Inverting Data Selectors/Multiplexers	154.00	6.5	1.30
74F352	Dual 1 of 4 Line Inverting Data Selectors/Multiplexers	105.00	8.0	0.58
74HC352	Dual 1 of 4 Line Inverting Data Selectors/Multiplexers	0.48	44.0	0.89
74LS352	Dual 1 of 4 Line Inverting Data Selectors/Multiplexers	52.50	26.0	0.57
74ALS353	Dual 3-State 1 of 4 Line Data Selectors/Multiplexers	71.50	18.0	0.72
74AS353	Dual 3-State 1 of 4 Line Data Selectors/Multiplexers	170.50	12.0	1.30
74F353	Dual 3-State 1 of 4 Line Data Selectors/Multiplexers	120.75	8.0	0.58
74HC353	Dual 3-State 1 of 4 Line Data Selectors/Multiplexers	0.48	44.0	0.97

TYPE	DESCRIPTION	MAX POWER (mW)	MAX DELAY (nS)	PRICE ($)
74LS353	Dual 3-State 1 of 4 Line Data Selectors/Multiplexers	73.50	25.0	0.57
74HC354	3-State 8 to 1 Line Data Selector/Multiplexer/Register	0.48	64.0	0.83
74HCT354	3-State 8 to 1 Line Data Selector/Multiplexer/Register	0.44	64.0	2.48
74LS354	3-State 8 to 1 Line Data Selector/Multiplexer/Register	241.50	36.0	2.48
74LS355	Open-Collector 8 to 1 Line Data Selector/Multiplexer/Register	241.50	41.0	4.96
74HC356	3-State 8 to 1 Line Data Selector/Multiplexer/Register	0.48	64.0	0.83
74HCT356	3-State 8 to 1 Line Data Selector/Multiplexer/Register	0.44	64.0	2.48
74LS356	3-State 8 to 1 Line Data Selector/Multiplexer/Register	241.50	36.0	2.48
74LS357	Open-Collector 8 to 1 Line Data Selector/Multiplexer/Register	241.50	48.0	4.96
74F398	Quad 2-Input Multiplexers with Storage	199.50	10.0	1.14
74LS398	Quad 2-Input Multiplexers with Storage	68.25	32.0	1.10
74F399	Quad 2-Input Multiplexers with Storage	178.50	10.0	1.14
74LS399	Quad 2-Input Multiplexers with Storage	68.25	32.0	0.94
74LS450	16 to 1 Multiplexer	525.00	40.0	3.42
74LS453	Quad 4 to 1 Multiplexer	525.00	40.0	3.42
74AS850	1 of 16 Data Selector/Multiplexer with 3-State Outputs	467.50	8.0	4.33
74AS851	1 of 16 Data Selector/Multiplexer with 3-State Outputs	473.00	8.0	4.33
74ALS857	Hex 2 to 1 Line Multiplexers with 3-State Outputs	198.00	25.0	1.95
74AS857	Hex 2 to 1 Line Multiplexers with 3-State Outputs	962.50	12.0	2.75

Table 5-15. Data Selectors/Multiplexers, 4000 Series, Industrial Temperature Range.

TYPE	DESCRIPTION	MAX POWER (mW)	MAX DELAY (nS)	PRICE ($)
4512B	8-Channel Data Selector	0.75	360.0	0.69
4539B	Dual 4-Channel Data Selector/Multiplexer	0.75	420.0	0.72
40257B	Quad 2 to 1 Line Data Selector/Multiplexer	0.15	300.0	1.39

Table 5-16. Data Selectors/Multiplexers, 4000 Series, Military Temperature Range.

TYPE	DESCRIPTION	MAX POWER (mW)	MAX DELAY (nS)	PRICE ($)
4512B	8-Channel Data Selector	0.75	360.0	1.35
4539B	Dual 4-Channel Data Selector/Multiplexer	0.75	420.0	1.37
40257B	Quad 2 to 1 Line Data Selector/Multiplexer	0.15	300.0	1.98

Chapter 6

Counters and Shift Registers

This chapter presents functional descriptions and selection guides for counters and shift registers from the 54/74 families and the 4000 Series CMOS families.

6.1 COUNTERS

Figure 6-1 shows the logic diagram and waveforms for a 1-bit divide-by-2 binary counter. The figure shows a D-type flip-flop with the $\overline{Q}$ output tied back to the D input. The Q output changes state on each rising edge of the clock. The Q output is a square wave with a frequency equal to one-half the clock frequency. This same function can be performed using a J-K flip-flop with the J and K inputs tied to a fixed HIGH level.

Figure 6-2 shows the logic diagram and count sequence of a 4-bit binary ripple counter. The counter is called a *ripple* counter because the output of the first flip-flop is tied to the clock input of the second flip-flop, and so forth. The frequency of the QA output is one-half the clock frequency; QB is one-fourth; QC is one-eighth; and QD is one-sixteenth. Or, said another way: QA is the divide-by-2 output; QB is the divide-by-4 output; QC is the divide-by-8 output; and QD is the divide-by-16 output. With the appropriate external logic, it is possible to decode any count between 0 and 15. Using a 4 line to 16 line decoder (see Chapter 5), all counts between 0 and 15 may be decoded.

Figure 6-3 shows the logic diagram of a synchronous 4-bit binary counter. It is called a *synchronous* counter because each flip-flop is simultaneously clocked (or not-clocked, depending on the previous output states). Because the second

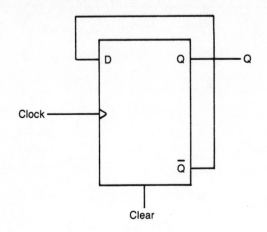

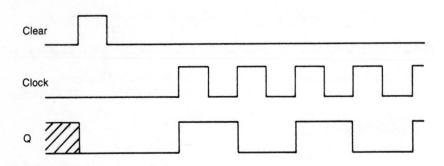

Fig. 6-1. Divide-by-2 binary counter logic diagram and waveforms.

flip-flop doesn't have to wait on the first flip-flop to change (and so forth), the synchronous counter is faster than the ripple counter.

The 4-bit binary counter has 16 possible states. With the addition of a few gates it is possible to create a counter with 10 states. Such a counter divides by 10 and is called a *decade counter*. Figure 6-4 shows the logic diagram of a 4-bit synchronous decade counter.

Counter ICs are available in 4-, 7-, 8-, 12-, and 14-bit lengths. Longer counters may be formed by cascading. For example, a 16-bit counter can be formed by connecting the output of one 8-bit counter to the input of another 8-bit counter.

As has been mentioned, counters may be ripple or synchronous. Some counters count *up*, as in Fig. 6-2. Some count *down*. A 4-bit down counter, for example, would have the following count sequence:

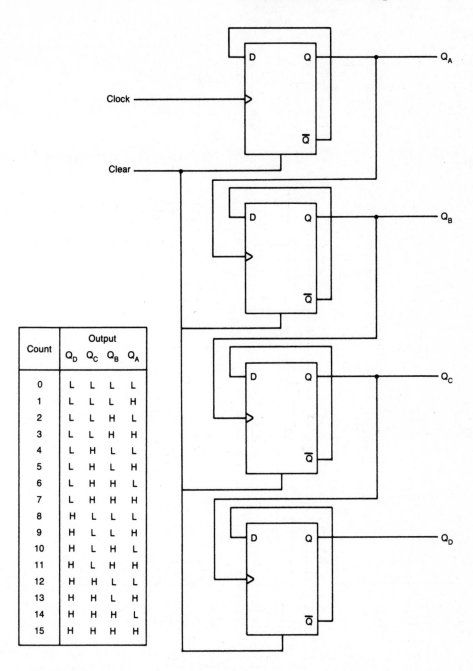

Count	Output			
	Q_D	Q_C	Q_B	Q_A
0	L	L	L	L
1	L	L	L	H
2	L	L	H	L
3	L	L	H	H
4	L	H	L	L
5	L	H	L	H
6	L	H	H	L
7	L	H	H	H
8	H	L	L	L
9	H	L	L	H
10	H	L	H	L
11	H	L	H	H
12	H	H	L	L
13	H	H	L	H
14	H	H	H	L
15	H	H	H	H

Fig. 6-2. Logic diagram and count sequence of a 4-bit binary ripple counter.

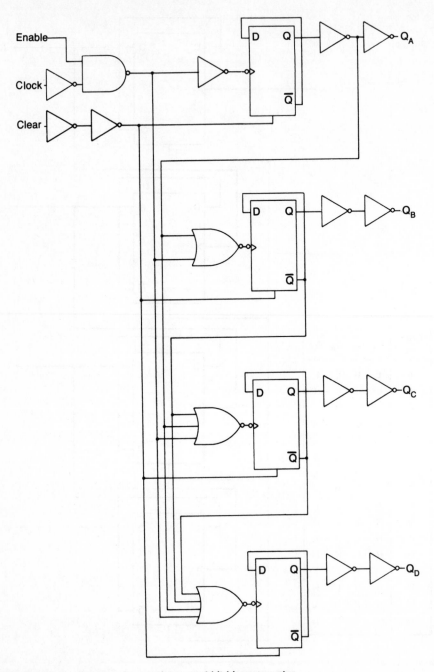

Fig. 6-3. Logic diagram of a synchronous 4-bit binary counter.

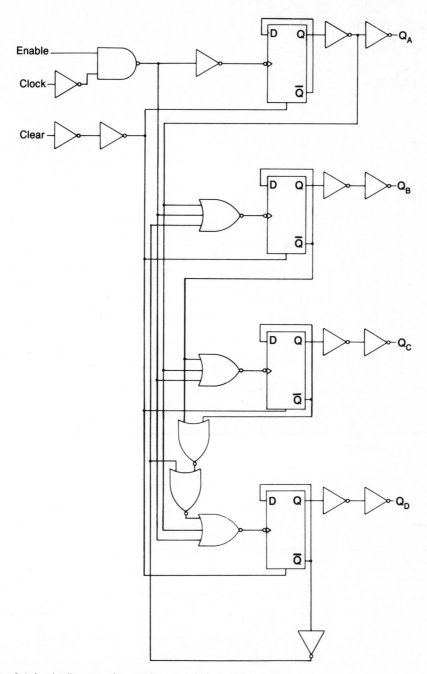

Fig. 6-4. Logic diagram of a synchronous 4-bit decade counter.

Count	QD	QC	QB	QA
0	H	H	H	H
1	H	H	H	L
2	H	H	L	H
3	H	H	L	L
•	•	•	•	•
•	•	•	•	•
•	•	•	•	•
14	L	L	L	H
15	L	L	L	L

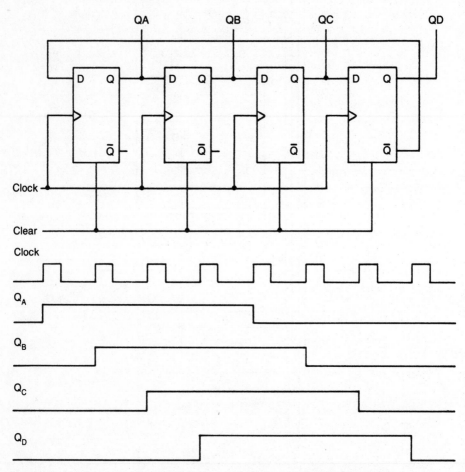

Fig. 6-5. Logic diagram and waveforms for a 4-bit divide-by-8 Johnson counter.

There are also *up/down* counters, which obviously may count in either direction.

A *presettable* counter has parallel data inputs and may be initialized to any count within the range of the counter. A *divide-by-N* counter is a programmable counter. The number of counter states is determined by the data inputs. A presettable down counter may be converted to a divide-by-N counter by adding external logic to automatically load the data on the data inputs when the count reaches zero.

Another type of popular counter is the *Johnson* counter. The logic diagram and waveforms for a 4-bit divide-by-8 Johnson counter is shown in Fig. 6-5. All outputs have the same frequency (not so for binary and BCD decade counters) but are phase-shifted one clock period with respect to each other. The number of unique states is exactly twice the number of flip-flops. A 5-bit, or 5-stage, Johnson counter has 10 states, with the frequency of each output equal to one-tenth the clock frequency. With additional logic, a Johnson counter can be designed to divide by any number up to two times the number of flip-flops.

6.1.1 Divide-by-N and Binary Counters

Tables 6-1 and 6-2 list the maximum power, maximum clock frequency, and 100-piece price for binary counters from the 54 and 74 families. Comments:

Table 6-1. Binary Counters, 54 Family.

TYPE	DESCRIPTION	MAX POWER (mW)	MAX FREQ (MHz)	PRICE ($)
5493	4-Bit Binary Counter	214.50	32.0	1.56
54L93	4-Bit Binary Counter	30.25	3.0	14.60
54LS93	4-Bit Binary Counter	82.50	32.0	0.96
54161	Synchronous 4-Bit Binary Counter with Asynchronous Clear	555.50	25.0	2.12
54ALS161	Synchronous 4-Bit Binary Counter with Asynchronous Clear	115.50	22.0	2.19
54C161	Synchronous 4-Bit Binary Counter with Asynchronous Clear	4.50	2.0	3.20
54F161	Synchronous 4-Bit Binary Counter with Asynchronous Clear	302.50	75.0	6.01
54HC161	Synchronous 4-Bit Binary Counter with Asynchronous Clear	0.96	13.0	1.39
54HCT161	Synchronous 4-Bit Binary Counter with Asynchronous Clear	0.22	13.0	1.37

TYPE	DESCRIPTION	MAX POWER (mW)	MAX FREQ (MHz)	PRICE ($)
54LS161	Synchronous 4-Bit Binary Counter with Asynchronous Clear	176.00	25.0	1.20
54163	Synchronous 4-Bit Binary Counter with Synchronous Clear	555.50	25.0	2.12
54ALS163	Synchronous 4-Bit Binary Counter with Synchronous Clear	88.00	22.0	3.15
54C163	Synchronous 4-Bit Binary Counter with Synchronous Clear	4.50	2.0	3.20
54F163	Synchronous 4-Bit Binary Counter with Synchronous Clear	302.50	75.0	6.01
54HC163	Synchronous 4-Bit Binary Counter with Synchronous Clear	0.96	13.0	1.60
54HCT163	Synchronous 4-Bit Binary Counter with Synchronous Clear	0.22	13.0	1.37
54LS163	Synchronous 4-Bit Binary Counter with Synchronous Clear	176.00	25.0	1.20
54S163	Synchronous 4-Bit Binary Counter with Synchronous Clear	880.00	40.0	3.36
54ALS169	Synchronous 4-Bit Up/Down Binary Counter	137.50	22.0	1.96
54LS169	Synchronous 4-Bit Up/Down Binary Counter	247.50	20.0	1.79
54S169	Synchronous 4-Bit Up/Down Binary Counter	880.00	40.0	4.68
54191	Synchronous 4-Bit Up/Down Binary Counter with Mode Control	577.50	20.0	2.55
54F191	Synchronous 4-Bit Up/Down Binary Counter with Mode Control	302.50	75.0	8.44
54HC191	Synchronous 4-Bit Up/Down Binary Counter with Mode Control	0.96	13.0	1.68
54HCT191	Synchronous 4-Bit Up/Down Binary Counter with Mode Control	0.88	13.0	1.68
54LS191	Synchronous 4-Bit Up/Down Binary Counter with Mode Control	192.50	20.0	1.38
54193	Synchronous 4-Bit Up/Down Binary Counter with Dual Clock	561.00	25.0	2.63
54ALS193	Synchronous 4-Bit Up/Down Binary Counter with Dual Clock	121.00	20.0	2.25
54C193	Synchronous 4-Bit Up/Down Binary Counter with Dual Clock	4.50	2.5	3.20
54F193	Synchronous 4-Bit Up/Down Binary Counter with Dual Clock	302.50	75.0	10.87

TYPE	DESCRIPTION	MAX POWER (mW)	MAX FREQ (MHz)	PRICE ($)
54HC193	Synchronous 4-Bit Up/Down Binary Counter with Dual Clock	0.96	13.0	1.68
54HCT193	Synchronous 4-Bit Up/Down Binary Counter with Dual Clock	0.88	13.0	1.47
54LS193	Synchronous 4-Bit Up/Down Binary Counter with Dual Clock	187.00	25.0	1.46
54197	Presettable Binary Counter	324.50	50.0	2.75
54LS197	Presettable Binary Counter	148.50	30.0	1.20
54S197	Presettable Binary Counter	660.00	100.0	4.08
54293	4-Bit Binary Counter	214.50	32.0	3.26
54LS293	4-Bit Binary Counter	82.50	32.0	1.34
54393	Dual 4-Bit Binary Counters	352.00	25.0	4.98
54HC393	Dual 4-Bit Binary Counters	0.96	20.0	1.73
54HCT393	Dual 4-Bit Binary Counters	0.88	18.0	1.49
54LS393	Dual 4-Bit Binary Counters	143.00	25.0	1.74
54LS461	8-Bit Counter	990.00	10.5	17.95
54LS469	8-Bit Up/Down Counter	990.00	10.5	17.95
54LS491	10-Bit Counter	990.00	10.5	17.95
54ALS569	Synchronous 4-Bit Binary Up/Down Binary Counter with 3-State Outputs	176.00	22.0	3.65
54LS569	Synchronous 4-Bit Binary Up/Down Binary Counter with 3-State Outputs	236.50	25.0	6.12
54LS590	8-Bit Binary Counter with Output Registers	357.50	20.0	7.71
54LS592	8-Bit Binary Counter with Input Registers	330.00	20.0	7.71
54LS669	Synchronous 4-Bit Up/Down Binary Counter	187.00	25.0	1.60
54LS691	Synchronous Binary Counter with Output Register	385.00	20.0	4.20
54LS697	Synchronous Up/Down Binary Counter with Output Register	385.00	20.0	4.20
54LS699	Synchronous Up/Down Binary Counter with Output Register	385.00	20.0	4.20
54AS869	Synchronous 8-Bit Up/Down Counter	990.00	40.0	14.41
54HC4020	14-Stage Binary Counter	0.96	20.0	1.73
54HCT4020	14-Stage Binary Counter	0.88	16.0	1.57

TYPE	DESCRIPTION	MAX POWER (mW)	MAX FREQ (MHz)	PRICE ($)
54HC4024	7-Stage Binary Counter	0.96	20.0	1.70
54HCT4024	7-Stage Binary Counter	0.88	16.0	1.47
54HC4040	12-Stage Binary Counter	0.96	20.0	1.73
54HCT4040	12-Stage Binary Counter	0.88	16.0	1.57
54HC4060	14-Stage Binary Counter	0.96	20.0	1.50
54HCT4060	14-Stage Binary Counter	0.88	20.0	1.57
54HC4520	Dual 4-Bit Binary Counter	0.96	17.0	2.44
54HCT4520	Dual 4-Bit Binary Counter	0.88	17.0	2.19
54HC40103	8-Bit Binary Down Counter	0.96	25.0	3.05
54HCT40103	8-Bit Binary Down Counter	0.88	25.0	2.76

Table 6-2. Binary Counters, 74 Family.

TYPE	DESCRIPTION	MAX POWER (mW)	MAX FREQ (MHz)	PRICE ($)
74LS69	Dual 4-Bit Binary Counter	283.50	25.0	1.58
7493	4-Bit Binary Counter	204.75	32.0	0.40
74C93	4-Bit Binary Counter	4.50	2.0	0.89
74L93	4-Bit Binary Counter	28.88	3.0	3.45
74LS93	4-Bit Binary Counter	78.75	32.0	0.36
74161	Synchronous 4-Bit Binary Counter with Asynchronous Clear	530.25	25.0	0.54
74ALS161	Synchronous 4-Bit Binary Counter with Asynchronous Clear	115.50	40.0	0.78
74AS161	Synchronous 4-Bit Binary Counter with Asynchronous Clear	291.50	75.0	2.30
74C161	Synchronous 4-Bit Binary Counter with Asynchronous Clear	4.50	2.0	0.99
74F161	Synchronous 4-Bit Binary Counter with Asynchronous Clear	288.75	90.0	1.43
74HC161	Synchronous 4-Bit Binary Counter with Asynchronous Clear	0.48	16.0	0.73

TYPE	DESCRIPTION	MAX POWER (mW)	MAX FREQ (MHz)	PRICE ($)
74HCT161	Synchronous 4-Bit Binary Counter with Asynchronous Clear	0.11	16.0	0.73
74LS161	Synchronous 4-Bit Binary Counter with Asynchronous Clear	168.00	25.0	0.39
74S161	Synchronous 4-Bit Binary Counter with Asynchronous Clear	840.00	40.0	2.33
74163	Synchronous 4-Bit Binary Counter with Synchronous Clear	530.25	25.0	0.54
74ALS163	Synchronous 4-Bit Binary Counter with Synchronous Clear	115.50	40.0	0.78
74AS163	Synchronous 4-Bit Binary Counter with Synchronous Clear	291.50	75.0	2.30
74C163	Synchronous 4-Bit Binary Counter with Synchronous Clear	4.50	2.0	0.99
74F163	Synchronous 4-Bit Binary Counter with Synchronous Clear	288.75	90.0	1.43
74HC163	Synchronous 4-Bit Binary Counter with Synchronous Clear	0.48	16.0	0.73
74HCT163	Synchronous 4-Bit Binary Counter with Synchronous Clear	0.11	16.0	0.73
74LS163	Synchronous 4-Bit Binary Counter with Synchronous Clear	168.00	25.0	0.39
74S163	Synchronous 4-Bit Binary Counter with Synchronous Clear	840.00	40.0	2.33
74ALS169	Synchronous 4-Bit Up/Down Binary Counter	137.50	40.0	0.78
74AS169	Synchronous 4-Bit Up/Down Binary Counter	346.50	75.0	2.30
74F169	Synchronous 4-Bit Up/Down Binary Counter	273.00	90.0	2.82
74LS169	Synchronous 4-Bit Up/Down Binary Counter	236.25	20.0	0.74
74S169	Synchronous 4-Bit Up/Down Binary Counter	840.00	40.0	4.50
74177	Presettable Binary Counter	252.00	35.0	0.96
74191	Synchronous 4-Bit Up/Down Binary Counter with Mode Control	551.25	20.0	0.63
74ALS191	Synchronous 4-Bit Up/Down Binary Counter with Mode Control	121.00	30.0	0.87
74F191	Synchronous 4-Bit Up/Down Binary Counter with Mode Control	288.75	90.0	2.80

TYPE	DESCRIPTION	MAX POWER (mW)	MAX FREQ (MHz)	PRICE ($)
74HC191	Synchronous 4-Bit Up/Down Binary Counter with Mode Control	0.48	16.0	0.79
74HCT191	Synchronous 4-Bit Up/Down Binary Counter with Mode Control	0.44	16.0	0.79
74LS191	Synchronous 4-Bit Up/Down Binary Counter with Mode Control	183.75	20.0	0.66
74193	Synchronous 4-Bit Up/Down Binary Counter with Dual Clock	535.50	25.0	0.67
74ALS193	Synchronous 4-Bit Up/Down Binary Counter with Dual Clock	121.00	30.0	0.87
74C193	Synchronous 4-Bit Up/Down Binary Counter with Dual Clock	4.50	2.5	1.32
74F193	Synchronous 4-Bit Up/Down Binary Counter with Dual Clock	288.75	90.0	2.72
74HC193	Synchronous 4-Bit Up/Down Binary Counter with Dual Clock	0.48	16.0	0.79
74HCT193	Synchronous 4-Bit Up/Down Binary Counter with Dual Clock	0.44	16.0	0.79
74LS193	Synchronous 4-Bit Up/Down Binary Counter with Dual Clock	178.50	25.0	0.50
74197	Presettable Binary Counter	309.75	50.0	0.69
74LS197	Presettable Binary Counter	141.75	30.0	0.50
74S197	Presettable Binary Counter	630.00	100.0	2.72
74293	4-Bit Binary Counter	204.75	32.0	1.08
74LS293	4-Bit Binary Counter	78.75	32.0	0.50
74393	Dual 4-Bit Binary Counters	336.00	25.0	1.66
74HC393	Dual 4-Bit Binary Counters	0.48	24.0	0.91
74HCT393	Dual 4-Bit Binary Counters	0.44	22.0	0.91
74LS393	Dual 4-Bit Binary Counters	136.50	25.0	0.50
74LS461	8-Bit Counter	945.00	12.5	3.84
74LS469	8-Bit Up/Down Counter	945.00	12.5	3.84
74LS491	10-Bit Counter	945.00	12.5	3.84
74F525	16 Stage Programmable Counter/Divider	708.75	45.0	7.72
74ALS561	Synchronous 4-Bit Binary Counter with 3-State Outputs	198.00	30.0	2.18

TYPE	DESCRIPTION	MAX POWER (mW)	MAX FREQ (MHz)	PRICE ($)
74ALS569	Synchronous 4-Bit Binary Up/Down Binary Counter with 3-State Outputs	176.00	30.0	2.18
74F569	Synchronous 4-Bit Binary Up/Down Binary Counter with 3-State Outputs	351.75	90.0	3.20
74LS569	Synchronous 4-Bit Binary Up/Down Binary Counter with 3-State Outputs	225.75	25.0	1.60
74HC590	8-Bit Binary Counter with Output Registers	0.48	16.0	2.51
74LS590	8-Bit Binary Counter with Output Registers	341.25	20.0	4.54
74LS591	8-Bit Binary Counter with Output Registers	341.25	20.0	9.08
74LS592	8-Bit Binary Counter with Input Registers	315.00	20.0	4.54
74LS593	8-Bit Binary Counter with Input Registers	446.25	20.0	5.78
74LS669	Synchronous 4-Bit Up/Down Binary Counter	178.50	25.0	0.74
74LS691	Synchronous Binary Counter with Output Register	367.50	20.0	4.96
74LS693	Synchronous Binary Counter with Output Register	367.50	20.0	4.96
74LS697	Synchronous Up/Down Binary Counter with Output Register	367.50	20.0	2.48
74LS699	Synchronous Up/Down Binary Counter with Output Register	367.50	20.0	2.48
74LS718	Programmable Binary Counter	168.00	8.0	5.24
74AS867	Synchronous 8-Bit Up/Down Counter with Asynchronous Clear	1072.50	50.0	5.25
74AS869	Synchronous 8-Bit Up/Down Counter with Synchronous Clear	990.00	45.0	5.25
74HC4020	14-Stage Binary Counter	0.48	25.0	1.04
74HCT4020	14-Stage Binary Counter	0.44	20.0	1.04
74HC4024	7-Stage Binary Counter	0.48	24.0	0.85
74HCT4024	7-Stage Binary Counter	0.44	20.0	0.84
74HC4040	12-Stage Binary Counter	0.48	25.0	1.04
74HCT4040	12-Stage Binary Counter	0.44	20.0	1.04
74HC4060	14-Stage Binary Counter	0.48	25.0	0.90
74HCT4060	14-Stage Binary Counter	0.44	25.0	0.97
74HC4061	14-Stage Binary Counter	0.12	22.0	1.12
74HC4520	Dual 4-Bit Binary Counter	0.48	20.0	1.07

TYPE	DESCRIPTION	MAX POWER (mW)	MAX FREQ (MHz)	PRICE ($)
74HCT4520	Dual 4-Bit Binary Counter	0.44	20.0	1.07
74HC40103	8-Bit Binary Down Counter	0.48	25.0	1.68
74HCT40103	8-Bit Binary Down Counter	0.44	25.0	1.68

The 74LS69. Ripple clock. I_{OL} maximum 16 mA. One of the two counters has divide-by-2 and divide-by-8 sections. Asynchronous clear.

The '93. Ripple clock. Divide-by-2 and divide-by-8 sections. Asynchronous gated clear.

The '161, '163. Presettable. Ripple carry out for N-bit cascading. Two count enable inputs.

The '169. Presettable. Ripple carry. Two count enable inputs. Same pinout as '161, '163, except up/down control line replaces clear line.

The '177. Ripple clock. Divide-by-2 and divide-by-8 sections. Asynchronous clear.

The '191. Presettable. Ripple carry output. Maximum/minimum count output. Count enable. Single up/down control line.

The '193. Presettable. Both borrow and carry outputs for cascading N-bit up/down counters. Two clocks: one for up counting, one for down.

The '197. Faster, higher power version of '177.

The '293. Different pinout version of the '193.

The '393. Dual version of the '93.

The '461. Presettable. Synchronous clock. Clear, load, hold and increment operations. 3-state outputs. Carry in, carry out for cascading.

The '469. Up/down version of '461.

The '491. Presettable. Synchronous clock. Set, load, hold, count up, count down operations. 3-state outputs. Carry in.

The '561. Presettable. Both synchronous and asynchronous clear. Both synchronous and asynchronous load. Ripple carry out and clocked carry out. Two count enables.

The '569. Up/down version of '561. Asynchronous load control line replaced with up/down control line.

The '590. Synchronous clock. Direct (asynchronous) clear. Ripple carry out. Count clock enable. 3-state outputs.

The '591. Open-collector output version of '590.

The '592. Synchronous clock. Parallel register inputs. No parallel outputs. Ripple carry out only. Direct load and clear. Clock enable.

The '593. Synchronous clock. Parallel register input pins shared with 3-state counter outputs (pins are bi-directional). Ripple carry out. Direct load and clear. Two clock enables. Two output enables.

The '669. Redesigned version of the '169.

The '691. Presettable. Multiplexed 3-state outputs to read either the counter or the output register. Direct clear. Two clock enables. Ripple carry out. Synchronous load.

The '693. '691 with synchronous clear.

The '697. Up/down version of '691. Register clear line is replaced by up/down control line. Direct clear for counter.

The '699. '697 with synchronous clear for counter.

The '718. 4-bit divide-by-N ripple counter. Cascadable.

The '867, '869. Presettable. Ripple carry out. Two clock enables.

The '4020. Ripple clock. QB and QC outputs not brought out to pins.

The '4024. Ripple clock.

The '4040. Ripple clock.

The '4060. Ripple clock. Includes oscillator section. May use either external crystal or resistor/capacitor (RC) to set clock frequency. Outputs not available: QA, QB, QC, QK. A HIGH on the clear disables the clock and resets all outputs LOW.

'4061. Same as '4060 except that a HIGH on the clear does not disable the clock.

'4520. Synchronous clock.

'40103. Presettable. Synchronous or asynchronous load. Cascadable in synchronous or ripple mode.

Tables 6-3 and 6-4 list the maximum power, maximum clock frequency, and 100-piece price for binary and divide-by-N counters from the 4000 Series CMOS families. Comments:

Table 6-3. Divide-by-N and Binary Counters, 4000 Series, Industrial Temperature Range.

TYPE	DESCRIPTION	MAX POWER (mW)	MAX FREQ (MHz)	PRICE ($)
4018A	Presettable Divide-by-N Counter	3.50	0.6	1.12
4018B	Presettable Divide-by-N Counter	0.75	3.0	0.73
4020A	14-Bit Ripple-Carry Binary Counter/Divider	3.50	1.5	1.45
4020B	14-Bit Ripple-Carry Binary Counter/Divider	0.75	3.5	0.74
4022B	Divide-by-8 Counter/Divider with 8 Decoded Outputs	0.75	2.5	0.74
4024A	7-Bit Ripple-Carry Binary Counter/Divider	3.50	1.0	1.06

TYPE	DESCRIPTION	MAX POWER (mW)	MAX FREQ (MHz)	PRICE ($)
4024B	7-Bit Ripple-Carry Binary Counter/Divider	0.75	3.5	0.66
4029A	4-Bit Binary or BCD Decade Presettable Up/Down Counter	3.50	1.0	1.40
4029B	4-Bit Binary or BCD Decade Presettable Up/Down Counter	0.75	2.0	0.83
4040A	12-Bit Ripple-Carry Binary Counter/Divider	3.50	1.5	1.45
4040B	12-Bit Ripple-Carry Binary Counter/Divider	0.75	3.5	0.83
4045B	21-Bit Counter	0.75	5.0	1.63
4059A	Programmable Divide-by-N Counter	3.50	1.5	3.38
4060A	14-Bit Ripple-Carry Binary Counter/Divider and Oscillator	3.50	0.9	1.67
4060B	14-Bit Ripple-Carry Binary Counter/Divider and Oscillator	0.75	3.5	0.97
4516B	Presettable Binary Up/Down Counter	0.75	2.0	0.78
4520B	Dual Binary Up Counters	0.75	1.5	0.71
4526B	Programmable Divide-by-N 4-Bit Binary Counter	0.75	1.5	0.87
40103B	Presettable 8-Bit Binary Synchronous Down Counter	0.75	0.7	1.68
40161B	Synchronous Binary Counter with Asynchronous Clear	0.75	2.0	0.83
40163B	Synchronous Binary Counter with Synchronous Clear	0.75	2.0	0.83
40193B	Presettable 4-Bit Binary Up/Down Counter	0.75	2.0	0.88

Table 6-4. Divide-by-N and Binary Counters, 4000 Series, Military Temperature Range.

TYPE	DESCRIPTION	MAX POWER (mW)	MAX FREQ (MHz)	PRICE ($)
4018A	Presettable Divide-by-N Counter	1.50	1.0	2.03
4018B	Presettable Divide-by-N Counter	0.75	3.0	1.42
4020A	14-Bit Ripple-Carry Binary Counter/Divider	4.50	1.5	2.56
4020B	14-Bit Ripple-Carry Binary Counter/Divider	0.75	3.5	1.40
4022A	Divide-by-8 Counter/Divider with 8 Decoded Outputs	1.50	1.0	4.52
4022B	Divide-by-8 Counter/Divider with 8 Decoded Outputs	0.75	2.5	1.40
4024A	7-Bit Ripple-Carry Binary Counter/Divider	1.50	1.5	1.85

TYPE	DESCRIPTION	MAX POWER (mW)	MAX FREQ (MHz)	PRICE ($)
4024B	7-Bit Ripple-Carry Binary Counter/Divider	0.75	3.5	1.12
4029A	4-Bit Binary or BCD Decade Presettable Up/Down Counter	1.50	1.5	5.16
4029B	4-Bit Binary or BCD Decade Presettable Up/Down Counter	0.75	2.0	1.40
4040A	12-Bit Ripple-Carry Binary Counter/Divider	4.50	1.5	2.41
4040B	12-Bit Ripple-Carry Binary Counter/Divider	0.75	3.5	1.35
4045A	21-Bit Counter	4.50	4.4	11.50
4045B	21-Bit Counter	0.75	5.0	2.48
4059A	Programmable Divide-by-N Counter	1.50	1.5	4.73
4060A	14-Bit Ripple-Carry Binary Counter/Divider and Oscillator	4.50	1.0	4.52
4060B	14-Bit Ripple-Carry Binary Counter/Divider and Oscillator	0.75	3.5	1.40
4516B	Presettable Binary Up/Down Counter	0.75	2.0	1.35
4520B	Dual Binary Up Counters	0.75	1.5	1.40
4526B	Programmable Divide-by-N 4-Bit Binary Counter	0.75	1.5	1.75
40103B	Presettable 8-Bit Binary Synchronous Down Counter	0.75	0.7	2.36
40161B	Synchronous Binary Counter with Asynchronous Clear	0.75	2.0	1.40
40163B	Synchronous Binary Counter with Synchronous Clear	0.75	2.0	1.40
40193B	Presettable 4-Bit Binary Up/Down Counter	0.75	2.0	1.82

The 4018. 5-stage Johnson counter.

The 4020. Ripple clock. QB and QC outputs not brought out to pins.

The 4022. 4-stage Johnson counter. Carry out.

The 4024. Ripple clock.

The 4029. Synchronous clock. Carry in and carry out.

The 4040. Ripple clock.

The 4045. Ripple clock. Oscillator section. RC or crystal input. No parallel outputs.

The 4059. Divide by any number from 3 to 15,999. 16 program inputs in BCD format. Single output.

The 4060. Ripple clock. Includes oscillator section. May use either external crystal or resistor/capacitor to set clock frequency. Outputs not available: QA, QB, QC, QK. A HIGH on the clear disables the clock and resets all outputs LOW.

The 4516. 4-bit. Carry in, carry out.

The 4520. Synchronous clock. Dual 4-bit.

The 4526. Synchronous clock. Down counter. Cascadable.

The 40103. Presettable. Synchronous or asynchronous load. Cascadable in synchronous or ripple mode.

The 40161, 40163. Presettable. Ripple carry out for N-bit cascading. Two count enable inputs.

The 40193. Presettable. Both borrow and carry outputs for cascading N-bit up/down counters. Two clocks: one for up counting, one for down.

6.1.2 Decade Counters

Tables 6-5 and 6-6 list the maximum power, maximum clock frequency, and 100-piece price for decade counters from the 54 and 74 families. Comments:

Table 6-5. Decade Counters, 54 Family.

TYPE	DESCRIPTION	MAX POWER (mW)	MAX FREQ (MHz)	PRICE ($)
5490	Decade Counter	231.00	32.0	1.72
54C90	Decade Counter	4.50	2.0	5.30
54LS90	Decade Counter	82.50	32.0	0.96
54C160	Synchronous 4-Bit Decade Counter with Asynchronous Clear	4.50	2.0	3.20
54F160	Synchronous 4-Bit Decade Counter with Asynchronous Clear	302.50	75.0	6.01
54HC160	Synchronous 4-Bit Decade Counter with Asynchronous Clear	0.96	13.0	1.39
54HCT160	Synchronous 4-Bit Decade Counter with Asynchronous Clear	0.22	13.0	1.37
54LS160	Synchronous 4-Bit Decade Counter with Asynchronous Clear	176.00	25.0	1.20
54162	Synchronous 4-Bit Decade Counter with Synchronous Clear	555.50	25.0	2.32
54C162	Synchronous 4-Bit Decade Counter with Synchronous Clear	4.50	2.0	3.20
54F162	Synchronous 4-Bit Decade Counter with Synchronous Clear	302.50	75.0	6.01

TYPE	DESCRIPTION	MAX POWER (mW)	MAX FREQ (MHz)	PRICE ($)
54HC162	Synchronous 4-Bit Decade Counter with Synchronous Clear	0.96	13.0	1.60
54HCT162	Synchronous 4-Bit Decade Counter with Synchronous Clear	0.22	13.0	1.37
54LS162	Synchronous 4-Bit Decade Counter with Synchronous Clear	176.00	25.0	1.20
54S162	Synchronous 4-Bit Decade Counter with Synchronous Clear	880.00	40.0	3.43
54LS168	Synchronous 4-Bit Up/Down Decade Counter	187.00	25.0	2.68
54S168	Synchronous 4-Bit Up/Down Decade Counter	880.00	40.0	4.68
54176	Presettable Decade (Bi-Quinary) Counter	264.00	35.0	2.66
54190	Synchronous Up/Down Decade Counter with Mode Control	577.50	20.0	2.75
54F190	Synchronous Up/Down Decade Counter with Mode Control	302.50	75.0	8.44
54HC190	Synchronous Up/Down Decade Counter with Mode Control	0.96	13.0	1.46
54HCT190	Synchronous Up/Down Decade Counter with Mode Control	0.88	13.0	1.68
54LS190	Synchronous Up/Down Decade Counter with Mode Control	192.50	20.0	1.38
54192	Synchronous Up/Down Decade Counter with Dual Clock	561.00	25.0	2.75
54C192	Synchronous Up/Down Decade Counter with Dual Clock	4.50	2.5	3.20
54F192	Synchronous Up/Down Decade Counter with Dual Clock	302.50	75.0	10.87
54HC192	Synchronous Up/Down Decade Counter with Dual Clock	0.96	13.0	1.68
54HCT192	Synchronous Up/Down Decade Counter with Dual Clock	0.88	13.0	1.47
54LS192	Synchronous Up/Down Decade Counter with Dual Clock	187.00	25.0	1.38
54LS196	Presettable Decade (Bi-Quinary) Counter	148.50	30.0	1.20
54S196	Presettable Decade (Bi-Quinary) Counter	660.00	100.0	3.65
54290	Decade Counter	231.00	32.0	3.26
54LS290	Decade Counter	82.50	32.0	1.32
54390	Dual Decade (Bi-Quinary) Counters	379.50	25.0	4.98
54HC390	Dual Decade (Bi-Quinary) Counters	0.96	21.0	1.73
54LS390	Dual Decade (Bi-Quinary) Counters	143.00	25.0	1.84

TYPE	DESCRIPTION	MAX POWER (mW)	MAX FREQ (MHz)	PRICE ($)
54HC490	Dual Decade Counters	0.96	21.0	3.58
54LS490	Dual Decade Counters	143.00	25.0	2.10
54LS568	Synchronous 4-Bit Decade Up/Down Binary Counter with 3-State Outputs	236.50	25.0	6.12
54LS668	Synchronous 4-Bit Up/Down Decade Counter	187.00	25.0	1.60
54LS693	Synchronous Decade Counter with Output Register	385.00	20.0	4.20
54LS696	Synchronous Up/Down Decade Counter with Output Register	385.00	20.0	4.20
54HC4017	Decade Counter/Divider with 10 Decoded Outputs	0.96	17.0	1.73
54HCT4017	Decade Counter/Divider with 10 Decoded Outputs	0.88	15.0	1.57
54HC4518	Dual BCD Counter	0.96	17.0	2.44
54HCT4518	Dual BCD Counter	0.88	17.0	2.19
54HC40102	8-Bit Synchronous BCD Down Counter	0.96	25.0	3.05
54HCT40102	8-Bit Synchronous BCD Down Counter	0.88	25.0	2.76

Table 6-6. Decade Counters, 74 Family.

TYPE	DESCRIPTION	MAX POWER (mW)	MAX FREQ (MHz)	PRICE ($)
74LS68	Dual 4-Bit Decade Counter	283.50	20.0	1.58
7490	Decade Counter	220.50	32.0	0.34
74C90	Decade Counter	4.50	2.0	0.89
74LS90	Decade Counter	78.75	32.0	0.36
74160	Synchronous 4-Bit Decade Counter with Asynchronous Clear	530.25	25.0	0.63
74ALS160	Synchronous 4-Bit Decade Counter with Asynchronous Clear	115.50	40.0	0.78
74AS160	Synchronous 4-Bit Decade Counter with Asynchronous Clear	291.50	75.0	2.30
74C160	Synchronous 4-Bit Decade Counter with Asynchronous Clear	4.50	2.0	1.06

TYPE	DESCRIPTION	MAX POWER (mW)	MAX FREQ (MHz)	PRICE ($)
74F160	Synchronous 4-Bit Decade Counter with Asynchronous Clear	288.75	90.0	1.43
74HC160	Synchronous 4-Bit Decade Counter with Asynchronous Clear	0.48	16.0	0.73
74HCT160	Synchronous 4-Bit Decade Counter with Asynchronous Clear	0.11	16.0	0.73
74LS160	Synchronous 4-Bit Decade Counter with Asynchronous Clear	168.00	25.0	0.39
74162	Synchronous 4-Bit Decade Counter with Synchronous Clear	530.25	25.0	1.56
74ALS162	Synchronous 4-Bit Decade Counter with Synchronous Clear	115.50	40.0	0.78
74AS162	Synchronous 4-Bit Decade Counter with Synchronous Clear	291.50	75.0	2.30
74C162	Synchronous 4-Bit Decade Counter with Synchronous Clear	4.50	2.0	0.99
74F162	Synchronous 4-Bit Decade Counter with Synchronous Clear	288.75	90.0	1.43
74HC162	Synchronous 4-Bit Decade Counter with Synchronous Clear	0.48	16.0	0.73
74HCT162	Synchronous 4-Bit Decade Counter with Synchronous Clear	0.11	16.0	0.73
74LS162	Synchronous 4-Bit Decade Counter with Synchronous Clear	168.00	25.0	0.39
74S162	Synchronous 4-Bit Decade Counter with Synchronous Clear	840.00	40.0	3.00
74ALS168	Synchronous 4-Bit Up/Down Decade Counter	137.50	40.0	0.78
74AS168	Synchronous 4-Bit Up/Down Decade Counter	346.50	75.0	2.30
74F168	Synchronous 4-Bit Up/Down Decade Counter	273.00	90.0	2.82
74LS168	Synchronous 4-Bit Up/Down Decade Counter	178.50	25.0	0.74
74S168	Synchronous 4-Bit Up/Down Decade Counter	840.00	40.0	9.00
74176	Presettable Decade (Bi-Quinary) Counter	252.00	35.0	0.96
74190	Synchronous Up/Down Decade Counter with Mode Control	551.25	20.0	0.86
74ALS190	Synchronous Up/Down Decade Counter with Mode Control	121.00	25.0	0.87
74F190	Synchronous Up/Down Decade Counter with Mode Control	288.75	90.0	2.80

TYPE	DESCRIPTION	MAX POWER (mW)	MAX FREQ (MHz)	PRICE ($)
74HC190	Synchronous Up/Down Decade Counter with Mode Control	0.48	16.0	0.79
74HCT190	Synchronous Up/Down Decade Counter with Mode Control	0.44	16.0	0.79
74LS190	Synchronous Up/Down Decade Counter with Mode Control	183.75	20.0	0.64
74192	Synchronous Up/Down Decade Counter with Dual Clock	535.50	25.0	0.72
74ALS192	Synchronous Up/Down Decade Counter with Dual Clock	121.00	25.0	0.87
74C192	Synchronous Up/Down Decade Counter with Dual Clock	4.50	2.5	1.32
74F192	Synchronous Up/Down Decade Counter with Dual Clock	288.75	90.0	3.29
74HC192	Synchronous Up/Down Decade Counter with Dual Clock	0.48	16.0	0.79
74HCT192	Synchronous Up/Down Decade Counter with Dual Clock	0.44	16.0	0.79
74LS192	Synchronous Up/Down Decade Counter with Dual Clock	178.50	25.0	0.50
74196	Presettable Decade (Bi-Quinary) Counter	309.75	50.0	0.96
74LS196	Presettable Decade (Bi-Quinary) Counter	141.75	30.0	0.50
74S196	Presettable Decade (Bi-Quinary) Counter	630.00	100.0	2.00
74290	Decade Counter	220.50	32.0	2.16
74LS290	Decade Counter	78.75	32.0	0.50
74390	Dual Decade (Bi-Quinary) Counters	362.25	25.0	1.38
74HC390	Dual Decade (Bi-Quinary) Counters	0.48	25.0	0.99
74LS390	Dual Decade (Bi-Quinary) Counters	136.50	25.0	0.50
74HC490	Dual Decade Counters	0.48	25.0	1.67
74LS490	Dual Decade Counters	136.50	25.0	1.64
74ALS560	Synchronous 4-Bit Decade Counter with 3-State Outputs	198.00	20.0	2.18
74ALS568	Synchronous 4-Bit Decade Up/Down Binary Counter with 3-State Outputs	176.00	20.0	2.18
74F568	Synchronous 4-Bit Decade Up/Down Binary Counter with 3-State Outputs	351.75	90.0	3.20
74LS568	Synchronous 4-Bit Decade Up/Down Binary Counter with 3-State Outputs	225.75	25.0	1.60
74LS668	Synchronous 4-Bit Up/Down Decade Counter	178.50	25.0	0.74
74LS690	Synchronous Decade Counter with Output Register	367.50	20.0	4.96

TYPE	DESCRIPTION	MAX POWER (mW)	MAX FREQ (MHz)	PRICE ($)
74LS692	Synchronous Decade Counter with Output Register	367.50	20.0	4.96
74LS696	Synchronous Up/Down Decade Counter with Output Register	367.50	20.0	4.96
74LS716	Programmable Decade Counter	168.00	8.0	5.24
74C925	4-Digit Counter with Multiplexed 7-Segment Output Driver	5.00	2.0	5.00
74C926	4-Digit Counter with Multiplexed 7-Segment Output Driver	5.00	2.0	5.00
74C927	4-Digit Counter with Multiplexed 7-Segment Output Driver	5.00	2.0	5.00
74C928	4-Digit Counter with Multiplexed 7-Segment Output Driver	5.00	2.0	5.00
74C945	4 Digit LCD Up/Down Counter/Latch/Driver	0.30	2.0	7.62
74C946	4 1/2-Digit LCD Up Counter/Latch/Driver	0.30	2.0	7.62
74C947	4 Digit LCD Up/Down Counter/Latch/Driver	0.30	2.0	7.62
74HC4017	Decade Counter/Divider with 10 Decoded Outputs	0.48	20.0	1.04
74HCT4017	Decade Counter/Divider with 10 Decoded Outputs	0.44	18.0	1.04
74HC4518	Dual BCD Counter	0.48	20.0	1.68
74HCT4518	Dual BCD Counter	0.44	20.0	1.68
74HC40102	8-Bit Synchronous BCD Down Counter	0.48	25.0	1.68
74HCT40102	8-Bit Synchronous BCD Down Counter	0.44	25.0	1.68

The 74LS68. Ripple clock. I_{OL} maximum 16 mA. One of the two counters has divide-by-2 and divide-by-5 sections. Asynchronous clear.

The '90. Ripple clock. Divide-by-2 and divide-by-5 sections. Asynchronous gated clear.

The '160, '162. Presettable. Ripple carry out for N-bit cascading. Two count enable inputs.

The '168. Presettable. Ripple carry. Two count enable inputs. Same pinout as '160, '162, except up/down control line replaces clear line.

The '176. Ripple clock. Divide-by-2 and divide-by-5 sections. Asynchronous clear.

The '190. Presettable. Ripple carry output. Maximum/minimum count output. Count enable. Single up/down control line.

The '192. Presettable. Both borrow and carry outputs for cascading N-bit up/down counters. Two clocks: one for up counting, one for down.

The '196. Faster, higher power version of '176.

The '290. Different pinout version of the '190.

The '390. Dual version of the '90.

The '490. Ripple clock. Direct clear. Set-to-9 input.

The '560. Presettable. Both synchronous and asynchronous clear. Both synchronous and asynchronous load. Ripple carry out and clocked carry out. Two count enables.

The '568. Up/down version of '560. Asynchronous load control line replaced with up/down control line.

The '668. Redesigned version of the '168.

The '690. Presettable. Multiplexed 3-state outputs to read either the counter or the output register. Direct clear. Two clock enables. Ripple carry out. Synchronous load.

The '692. '690 with synchronous clear.

The '696. Up/down version of '690. Register clear line is replaced by up/down control line. Direct clear for counter.

The '716. 4-bit divide-by-N ripple counter. Cascadable.

The '4017. 5-stage Johnson counter.

The '4518. Synchronous clock.

The '40102. Presettable. Synchronous or asynchronous load. Cascadable in synchronous or ripple mode.

Tables 6-7 and 6-8 list the maximum power, maximum clock frequency, and 100-piece price for decade counters from the 4000 Series CMOS families.

Table 6-7. Decade Counters, 4000 Series, Industrial Temperature Range.

TYPE	DESCRIPTION	MAX POWER (mW)	MAX FREQ (MHz)	PRICE ($)
4017A	Divide-by-10 Counter/Divider with 10 Decoded Outputs	3.50	0.6	1.25
4017B	Divide-by-10 Counter/Divider with 10 Decoded Outputs	0.75	2.5	0.74
4026B	Decade Counter/Divider with 7-Segment Outputs and Display Enable	0.75	2.5	2.06
4029A	4-Bit Binary or BCD Decade Presettable Up/Down Counter	3.50	1.0	1.40
4029B	4-Bit Binary or BCD Decade Presettable Up/Down Counter	0.75	2.0	0.83

TYPE	DESCRIPTION	MAX POWER (mW)	MAX FREQ (MHz)	PRICE ($)
4033B	Decade Counter/Divider with 7-Segment Outputs and Ripple Blanking	0.75	2.5	2.06
4510B	Presettable BCD Up/Down Counter	0.75	2.0	0.78
4518B	Dual BCD Up Counters	0.75	1.5	0.71
4522B	Programmable Divide-by-N 4-Bit BCD Counter	0.75	1.5	0.86
40102B	Presettable 2-Decade BCD Synchronous Down Counter	0.75	0.7	1.68
40110B	Decade Up/Down Counter/Latch/Decoder Driver	0.75	1.0	2.11
40160B	Synchronous Decade Counter with Asynchronous Clear	0.75	2.0	0.83
40162B	Synchronous Decade Counter with Synchronous Clear	0.75	2.0	0.83
40192B	Presettable 4-Bit BCD Up/Down Counter	0.75	2.0	1.20

Table 6-8. Decade Counters, 4000 Series, Military Temperature Range.

TYPE	DESCRIPTION	MAX POWER (mW)	MAX FREQ (MHz)	PRICE ($)
4017A	Divide-by-10 Counter/Divider with 10 Decoded Outputs	1.50	1.0	2.44
4017B	Divide-by-10 Counter/Divider with 10 Decoded Outputs	0.75	2.5	1.40
4026A	Decade Counter/Divider with 7-Segment Outputs and Display Enable	1.50	1.5	7.54
4026B	Decade Counter/Divider with 7-Segment Outputs and Display Enable	0.75	2.5	2.89
4029A	4-Bit Binary or BCD Decade Presettable Up/Down Counter	1.50	1.5	5.16
4029B	4-Bit Binary or BCD Decade Presettable Up/Down Counter	0.75	2.0	1.40
4033A	Decade Counter/Divider with 7-Segment Outputs and Ripple Blanking	1.50	1.5	7.54
4033B	Decade Counter/Divider with 7-Segment Outputs and Ripple Blanking	0.75	2.5	3.30
4510B	Presettable BCD Up/Down Counter	0.75	2.0	1.40
4518B	Dual BCD Up Counters	0.75	1.5	1.40

TYPE	DESCRIPTION	MAX POWER (mW)	MAX FREQ (MHz)	PRICE ($)
4522B	Programmable Divide-by-N 4-Bit BCD Counter	0.75	1.5	1.75
40102B	Presettable 2-Decade BCD Synchronous Down Counter	0.75	0.7	2.36
40110B	Decade Up/Down Counter/Latch/Decoder Driver	0.75	1.0	2.97
40160B	Synchronous Decade Counter with Asynchronous Clear	0.75	2.0	1.40
40162B	Synchronous Decade Counter with Synchronous Clear	0.75	2.0	1.40
40192B	Presettable 4-Bit BCD Up/Down Counter	0.75	2.0	1.68

Comments:

The 4017. 5-stage Johnson counter.
The 4026. 5-stage Johnson counter.
The 4029. Synchronous clock. Carry in and carry out.
The 4033. 5-stage Johnson counter.
The 4510. 4-bit. Carry in, carry out.
The 4518. Synchronous clock.
The 4522. Synchronous clock. Down counter. Cascadable.
The 40102. Presettable. Synchronous or asynchronous load. Cascadable in synchronous or ripple mode.
The 40160, 40162. Presettable. Ripple carry out for N-bit cascading. Two count enable inputs.
The 40192. Presettable. Both borrow and carry outputs for cascading N-bit up/down counters. Two clocks: one for up counting, one for down.

6.2 SHIFT REGISTERS

Figure 6-6 shows the logic diagram and waveforms for a 4-bit shift register. In the figure shown, a HIGH appears temporarily on the data input. Because the data input line is HIGH when the clock goes HIGH, then this HIGH is shifted to the QA output, which is also connected to the D input of the next flip-flop. In general, whatever data (HIGH or LOW) is on the D input of each flip-flop is shifted to the right (the Q output) on the rising edge of each input clock pulse.

The shift register in Fig. 6-6 is a serial-in, parallel-out, shift-right shift register. Shift register ICs are available in a variety of configurations: any combination of serial- and/or parallel-in; serial- or parallel-out; and right shift or left/right shift (bi-directional). The so-called *universal* shift register has serial and parallel inputs, parallel outputs and is bi-directional.

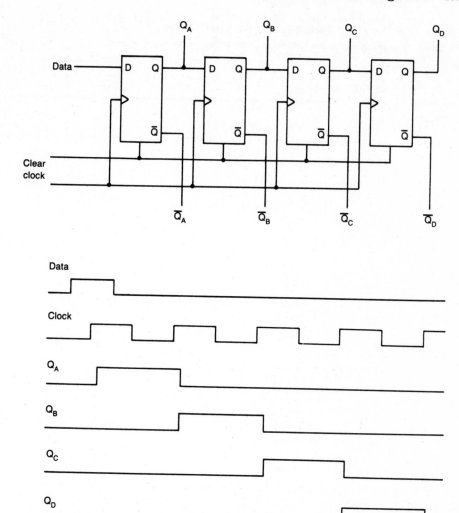

Fig. 6-6. Logic diagram and waveforms for a 4-bit shift register.

Tables 6-9 and 6-10 list the maximum power, maximum shift (clock) frequency, and 100-piece price for shift registers from the 54 and 74 families. Comments:

The '91. Serial in, serial out.

The '95. Serial and parallel in. Parallel out. Right and left shift.

The '96. Serial and parallel in. Parallel out.

The '164. Serial in, parallel out.

Table 6-9. Shift Registers, 54 Family.

TYPE	DESCRIPTION	MAX POWER (mW)	MAX FREQ (MHz)	PRICE ($)
54LS91	8-Bit Shift Register	110.00	10.0	1.76
5495	4-Bit Parallel-Access Shift Register	346.50	25.0	2.02
54L95	4-Bit Parallel-Access Shift Register	44.00	3.0	14.60
54LS95	4-Bit Parallel-Access Shift Register	115.50	25.0	1.20
5496	5-Bit Shift Register	434.50	10.0	1.99
54LS96	5-Bit Shift Register	110.00	25.0	1.20
54164	8-Bit Serial In/Parallel Out Shift Register with Asynchronous Clear	297.00	25.0	2.10
54C164	8-Bit Serial In/Parallel Out Shift Register with Asynchronous Clear	4.50	2.0	4.30
54F164	8-Bit Serial In/Parallel Out Shift Register with Asynchronous Clear	302.50	70.0	6.01
54HC164	8-Bit Serial In/Parallel Out Shift Register with Asynchronous Clear	0.96	20.0	1.39
54HCT164	8-Bit Serial In/Parallel Out Shift Register with Asynchronous Clear	0.44	18.0	1.32
54LS164	8-Bit Serial In/Parallel Out Shift Register with Asynchronous Clear	148.50	25.0	1.22
54165	8-Bit Parallel In/Serial Out Shift Register with Complementary Outputs	346.50	20.0	2.45
54C165	8-Bit Parallel In/Serial Out Shift Register with Complementary Outputs	4.50	2.5	4.30
54HC165	8-Bit Parallel In/Serial Out Shift Register with Complementary Outputs	0.96	20.0	2.10
54HCT165	8-Bit Parallel In/Serial Out Shift Register with Complementary Outputs	0.88	18.0	2.01
54LS165	8-Bit Parallel In/Serial Out Shift Register with Complementary Outputs	165.00	25.0	1.64
54166	8-Bit Parallel or Serial In/Serial Out Shift Register	698.50	25.0	2.06
54HC166	8-Bit Parallel or Serial In/Serial Out Shift Register	0.96	20.0	2.43
54HCT166	8-Bit Parallel or Serial In/Serial Out Shift Register	0.44	16.0	2.01

TYPE	DESCRIPTION	MAX POWER (mW)	MAX FREQ (MHz)	PRICE ($)
54LS166	8-Bit Parallel or Serial In/Serial Out Shift Register	176.00	25.0	1.74
54178	4-Bit Parallel-Access Shift Register	412.50	25.0	6.79
54179	4-Bit Parallel-Access Shift Register	412.50	25.0	6.79
54194	4-Bit Bidirectional Universal Shift Register	346.50	25.0	3.30
54F194	4-Bit Bidirectional Universal Shift Register	198.00	90.0	7.29
54HC194	4-Bit Bidirectional Universal Shift Register	0.96	20.0	1.34
54HCT194	4-Bit Bidirectional Universal Shift Register	0.88	17.0	1.07
54LS194	4-Bit Bidirectional Universal Shift Register	126.50	25.0	1.20
54S194	4-Bit Bidirectional Universal Shift Register	742.50	70.0	3.15
54195	4-Bit Parallel-Access Shift Register	346.50	30.0	2.32
54C195	4-Bit Parallel-Access Shift Register	4.50	2.0	3.00
54HC195	4-Bit Parallel-Access Shift Register	0.96	20.0	1.34
54HCT195	4-Bit Parallel-Access Shift Register	0.88	16.0	1.07
54LS195	4-Bit Parallel-Access Shift Register	115.50	30.0	1.20
54S195	4-Bit Parallel-Access Shift Register	599.50	70.0	3.15
54198	8-Bit Bidirectional Universal Shift Register	698.50	25.0	6.08
54199	8-Bit Bidirectional Universal Shift Register	698.50	25.0	6.08
54LS295	4-Bit Bidirectional Shift Register with 3-State Outputs	181.50	30.0	1.20
54ALS299	8-Bit Universal Shift/Storage Register with 3-State Outputs	220.00	17.0	8.12
54HC299	8-Bit Universal Shift/Storage Register with 3-State Outputs	0.96	16.0	5.02
54HCT299	8-Bit Universal Shift/Storage Register with 3-State Outputs	0.88	13.0	4.13
54LS299	8-Bit Universal Shift/Storage Register with 3-State Outputs	291.50	20.0	4.22
54S299	8-Bit Universal Shift/Storage Register with 3-State Outputs	1237.50	50.0	17.00
54F322	8-Bit Shift Register with Sign Extend	495.00	70.0	19.73
54LS322	8-Bit Shift Register with Sign Extend	330.00	20.0	3.90
54LS323	8-Bit Universal Shift/Storage Register with 3-State Outputs	291.50	25.0	3.90

TYPE	DESCRIPTION	MAX POWER (mW)	MAX FREQ (MHz)	PRICE ($)
54LS395	4-Bit Cascadable Shift Register with 3-State Outputs	187.00	30.0	1.20
54LS498	8-Bit Shift Register	990.00	10.5	17.95
54HC589	8-Bit Shift Register with Input Latches and 3-State Serial Output	0.96	30.0	3.50
54HC595	8-Bit Shift Register with Output Latches	0.96	30.0	2.95
54LS595	8-BIT Shift Register with Output Latches	357.50	20.0	7.71
54HC597	8-Bit Shift Register with Input Latches	0.96	30.0	3.50
54LS597	8-Bit Shift Register with Input Latches	291.50	20.0	7.71
54LS673	16-Bit Shift Register	440.00	20.0	10.15
54LS674	16-Bit Shift Register	220.00	20.0	6.74
54F676	16-Bit Serial/Parallel In, Serial Out Shift Register	396.00	75.0	24.02
54LS952	Dual Rank 3-State 8-Bit Positive-Edge-Triggered Shift Registers	544.50	25.0	11.70
54LS962	Dual Rank 3-State 8-Bit Positive-Edge-Triggered Shift Registers	544.50	25.0	11.70
54HC4015	Dual 4-Bit Serial In/Parallel Out Shift Register	0.96	20.0	1.96
54HCT4015	Dual 4-Bit Serial In/Parallel Out Shift Register	0.88	20.0	1.75
54HC40104	4-Bit Bidirectional Universal Shift Register with 3-State Outputs	0.96	17.0	3.12
54HCT40104	4-Bit Bidirectional Universal Shift Register with 3-State Outputs	0.88	17.0	2.79

Table 6-10. Shift Registers, 74 Family.

TYPE	DESCRIPTION	MAX POWER (mW)	MAX FREQ (MHz)	PRICE ($)
74LS91	8-Bit Shift Register	105.00	10.0	0.46
7495	4-Bit Parallel-Access Shift Register	330.75	25.0	0.40
74AS95	4-Bit Parallel-Access Shift Register	214.50	100.0	1.15
74C95	4-Bit Parallel-Access Shift Register	4.50	3.0	1.11
74L95	4-Bit Parallel-Access Shift Register	42.00	3.0	3.45

TYPE	DESCRIPTION	MAX POWER (mW)	MAX FREQ (MHz)	PRICE ($)
74LS95	4-Bit Parallel-Access Shift Register	110.25	25.0	0.36
7496	5-Bit Shift Register	414.75	10.0	0.64
74LS96	5-Bit Shift Register	105.00	25.0	0.64
74164	8-Bit Serial In/Parallel Out Shift Register with Asynchronous Clear	283.50	25.0	0.51
74C164	8-Bit Serial In/Parallel Out Shift Register with Asynchronous Clear	4.50	2.0	1.11
74F164	8-Bit Serial In/Parallel Out Shift Register with Asynchronous Clear	288.75	80.0	1.39
74HC164	8-Bit Serial In/Parallel Out Shift Register with Asynchronous Clear	0.48	24.0	0.73
74HCT164	8-Bit Serial In/Parallel Out Shift Register with Asynchronous Clear	0.22	22.0	0.73
74LS164	8-Bit Serial In/Parallel Out Shift Register with Asynchronous Clear	141.75	25.0	0.39
74165	8-Bit Parallel In/Serial Out Shift Register with Complementary Outputs	330.75	20.0	0.59
74C165	8-Bit Parallel In/Serial Out Shift Register with Complementary Outputs	4.50	2.5	1.11
74HC165	8-Bit Parallel In/Serial Out Shift Register with Complementary Outputs	0.48	24.0	0.83
74HCT165	8-Bit Parallel In/Serial Out Shift Register with Complementary Outputs	0.44	22.0	0.83
74LS165	8-Bit Parallel In/Serial Out Shift Register with Complementary Outputs	157.50	25.0	0.39
74166	8-Bit Parallel or Serial In/Serial Out Shift Register	666.75	25.0	0.70
74HC166	8-Bit Parallel or Serial In/Serial Out Shift Register	0.48	25.0	1.34
74HCT166	8-Bit Parallel or Serial In/Serial Out Shift Register	0.22	20.0	1.49
74LS166	8-Bit Parallel or Serial In/Serial Out Shift Register	168.00	25.0	1.32
74178	4-Bit Parallel-Access Shift Register	393.75	25.0	2.60
74179	4-Bit Parallel-Access Shift Register	393.75	25.0	2.60
74194	4-Bit Bidirectional Universal Shift Register	330.75	25.0	0.67
74F194	4-Bit Bidirectional Universal Shift Register	189.00	90.0	1.39

TYPE	DESCRIPTION	MAX POWER (mW)	MAX FREQ (MHz)	PRICE ($)
74HC194	4-Bit Bidirectional Universal Shift Register	0.48	24.0	0.58
74HCT194	4-Bit Bidirectional Universal Shift Register	0.44	20.0	0.58
74LS194	4-Bit Bidirectional Universal Shift Register	120.75	25.0	0.50
74S194	4-Bit Bidirectional Universal Shift Register	708.75	70.0	0.79
74195	4-Bit Parallel-Access Shift Register	330.75	30.0	0.70
74C195	4-Bit Parallel-Access Shift Register	4.50	2.0	1.16
74HC195	4-Bit Parallel-Access Shift Register	0.48	25.0	0.54
74HCT195	4-Bit Parallel-Access Shift Register	0.44	20.0	0.54
74LS195	4-Bit Parallel-Access Shift Register	110.25	30.0	0.43
74S195	4-Bit Parallel-Access Shift Register	572.25	70.0	1.47
74198	8-Bit Bidirectional Universal Shift Register	666.75	25.0	1.50
74199	8-Bit Bidirectional Universal Shift Register	666.75	25.0	1.50
74LS295	4-Bit Bidirectional Shift Register with 3-State Outputs	173.25	30.0	0.69
74ALS299	8-Bit Universal Shift/Storage Register with 3-State Outputs	220.00	30.0	3.12
74F299	8-Bit Universal Shift/Storage Register with 3-State Outputs	498.75	70.0	4.65
74HC299	8-Bit Universal Shift/Storage Register with 3-State Outputs	0.48	20.0	2.43
74HCT299	8-Bit Universal Shift/Storage Register with 3-State Outputs	0.44	16.0	2.39
74LS299	8-Bit Universal Shift/Storage Register with 3-State Outputs	278.25	20.0	2.02
74S299	8-Bit Universal Shift/Storage Register with 3-State Outputs	1181.25	50.0	5.43
74F322	8-Bit Shift Register with Sign Extend	472.50	70.0	5.25
74LS322	8-Bit Shift Register with Sign Extend	315.00	20.0	3.28
74ALS323	8-Bit Universal Shift/Storage Register with 3-State Outputs	220.00	30.0	3.12
74F323	8-Bit Universal Shift/Storage Register with 3-State Outputs	498.75	70.0	5.25
74LS323	8-Bit Universal Shift/Storage Register with 3-State Outputs	278.25	25.0	3.28

TYPE	DESCRIPTION	MAX POWER (mW)	MAX FREQ (MHz)	PRICE ($)
74LS395	4-Bit Cascadable Shift Register with 3-State Outputs	178.50	30.0	0.69
74HC589	8-Bit Shift Register with Input Latches and 3-State Serial Output	0.48	30.0	2.33
74LS594	8-Bit Shift Register with Output Registers	341.25	20.0	9.08
74HC595	8-Bit Shift Register with Output Latches	0.48	30.0	1.97
74LS595	8-Bit Shift Register with Output Latches	341.25	20.0	4.54
74HC597	8-Bit Shift Register with Input Latches	0.48	30.0	2.33
74LS597	8-Bit Shift Register with Input Latches	278.25	20.0	4.54
74LS598	8-Bit Shift Register with Input Latches	446.25	20.0	5.78
74LS599	8-Bit Shift Register with Output Latches	288.75	20.0	4.54
74F673	16-Bit Serial In, Serial/Parallel Out Shift Register	840.00	100.0	9.44
74LS673	16-Bit Serial In, Serial/Parallel Out Shift Register	420.00	20.0	3.66
74LS674	16-Bit Shift Register	210.00	20.0	3.66
74F675	16-Bit Serial In, Serial/Parallel Out Shift Register	840.00	100.0	8.58
74F676	16-Bit Serial/Parallel In, Serial Out Shift Register	378.00	90.0	11.44
74LS952	Dual Rank 3-State 8-Bit Positive-Edge-Triggered Shift Registers	519.75	25.0	2.87
74LS962	Dual Rank 3-State 8-Bit Positive-Edge-Triggered Shift Registers	519.75	25.0	2.87
74HC4015	Dual 4-Bit Serial In/Parallel Out Shift Register	0.48	24.0	1.96
74HCT4015	Dual 4-Bit Serial In/Parallel Out Shift Register	0.44	24.0	0.97
74HC40104	4-Bit Bidirectional Universal Shift Register with 3-State Outputs	0.48	20.0	1.40
74HCT40104	4-Bit Bidirectional Universal Shift Register with 3-State Outputs	0.44	20.0	1.40

The '165. Serial and parallel in. Serial out (Q and $\overline{Q}$). Clock enable. No clear.

The '166. '165 with Q output only. Has clear.

The '178. Serial and parallel in. Parallel out. Hold mode. No clear.

The '179. '178 with clear and $\overline{Q}$D output.

The '194. Left and right shift serial inputs and parallel inputs. Parallel outputs. Mode: synchronous parallel load, right shift, left shift, and hold (do nothing).

The '195. Serial and parallel in. Parallel out.

The '198. 8-bit version of '194.

The '199. 8-bit version of '195.

The '295. Serial and parallel in. Parallel out. Right and left shift. 3-state outputs.

The '299. Right and left shift serial inputs. Multiplexed inputs/outputs: parallel inputs and parallel 3-state outputs share pins. Direct clear.

The '322. Serial in. Multiplexed parallel inputs/outputs. Sign extend function repeats the data in QA flip-flop during shift. Direct clear.

The '323. '299 with synchronous clear.

The '395. Serial and parallel in. Parallel out. 3-state outputs.

The '589. Serial and latched parallel inputs. Serial 3-state output.

The '594. Serial in, parallel D-type flip-flop output register.

The '595. '594 with 3-state outputs.

The '597. Parallel in, serial out. 8-bit D-type flip-flop input register.

The '598. Serial in. Multiplexed parallel inputs/3-state outputs. 8-bit D-type flip-flop input register.

The '599. '594 with open-collector outputs.

The '673. Multiplexed serial in/3-state serial out. Parallel D-type output register.

The '674. Multiplexed serial in/3-state serial out. Parallel D-type input register.

The '675. Serial in, serial out. Multiplexed parallel in/3-state D-type output register.

The '676. Serial and parallel in. Serial out.

The '952. Multiplexed parallel in/3-state out. Serial in, serial out. Modes: load storage register A; transfer contents of register A to shift register B (B is over written); transfer B to A (A overwritten); shift B; synchronous clear.

The '962. Multiplexed parallel in/3-state out. Serial in, serial out. Modes: load storage register A; transfer contents of register A to shift register B (B is over written); transfer B to A (A overwritten); exchange A and B; shift B.

The '4015. Serial in, parallel out.

The '40104. Left and right shift serial inputs. Parallel inputs. Parallel outputs. Right and left shift, hold and clear.

Tables 6-11 and 6-12 list the maximum power, maximum shift (clock) frequency, and 100-piece price for shift registers from the 4000 Series CMOS families. Comments:

Table 6-11. Shift Registers, 4000 Series, Industrial Temperature Range.

TYPE	DESCRIPTION	MAX POWER (mW)	MAX FREQ (MHz)	PRICE ($)
4006A	18-Bit Static Shift Register	0.75	0.6	1.25
4006B	18-Bit Static Shift Register	0.75	2.5	0.74
4014B	8-Bit Static Shift Register	0.75	3.0	0.74
4015A	Dual 4-Bit Static Shift Register	3.50	0.6	1.45
4015B	Dual 4-Bit Static Shift Register	0.75	3.0	0.74
4021A	8-Bit Static Shift Register	3.50	0.6	1.16
4021B	8-Bit Static Shift Register	0.75	3.0	0.74
4031B	64-Bit Static Shift Register	0.75	2.0	2.69
4034B	8-Bit Bidirectional Serial/Parallel In, Parallel Out Shift Register	0.75	2.0	2.31
4035A	4-Bit Parallel In/Parallel Out Shift Register	3.50	1.0	1.85
4035B	4-Bit Parallel In/Parallel Out Shift Register	0.75	2.0	0.83
4094B	8-Bit Shift and Store Bus Register	0.75	1.2	0.97
4517B	Dual 64-Bit Static Shift Registers	0.75	3.0	2.06
40100B	32-Bit Static Left/Right Shift Register	0.75	1.0	2.21
40104B	4-Bit Bidirectional Universsal Shift Register	0.75	3.0	1.40
40194B	4-Bit Bidirectional Universal Shift Register	0.75	3.0	0.83

Table 6-12. Shift Registers, 4000 Series, Military Temperature Range.

TYPE	DESCRIPTION	MAX POWER (mW)	MAX FREQ (MHz)	PRICE ($)
4006A	18-Bit Static Shift Register	0.15	1.0	5.56
4006B	18-Bit Static Shift Register	0.75	2.5	1.49
4014A	8-Bit Static Shift Register	1.50	0.6	5.65

TYPE	DESCRIPTION	MAX POWER (mW)	MAX FREQ (MHz)	PRICE ($)
4014B	8-Bit Static Shift Register	0.75	3.0	1.34
4015A	Dual 4-Bit Static Shift Register	1.50	1.0	2.44
4015B	Dual 4-Bit Static Shift Register	0.75	3.0	1.42
4021A	8-Bit Static Shift Register	1.50	1.0	2.41
4021B	8-Bit Static Shift Register	0.75	3.0	1.35
4031A	64-Bit Static Shift Register	3.00	0.8	12.86
4031B	64-Bit Static Shift Register	0.75	2.0	3.76
4034A	8-Bit Bidirectional Serial/Parallel In, Parallel Out Shift Register	1.50	1.5	12.86
4034B	8-Bit Bidirectional Serial/Parallel In, Parallel Out Shift Register	0.75	2.0	4.32
4035A	4-Bit Parallel In/Parallel Out Shift Register	1.50	1.5	2.87
4035B	4-Bit Parallel In/Parallel Out Shift Register	0.75	2.0	1.35
4094B	8-Bit Shift and Store Bus Register	0.75	1.2	1.57
4517B	Dual 64-Bit Static Shift Registers	0.75	3.0	2.89
40100B	32-Bit Static Left/Right Shift Register	0.75	1.0	3.10
40104B	4-Bit Bidirectional Universsal Shift Register	0.75	3.0	1.96
40194B	4-Bit Bidirectional Universal Shift Register	0.75	3.0	1.40

The 4006. Two sections of four stages and two sections of five stages. Each section has serial in and serial out. Five-stage sections have serial out at fourth and fifth stages.

The 4014. Synchronous serial and synchronous parallel in. Outputs Q6-Q8 only.

The 4015. Serial in, parallel out.

The 4021. Synchronous serial and asynchronous parallel in. Outputs Q6-Q8 only.

The 4031. Serial in, serial out.

The 4034. Two bi-directional parallel data buses. Two bi-directional serial lines. Modes: transfer data between buses; convert serial data to parallel and output data to either bus; input parallel data from either bus and convert to serial data.

The 4035. Serial and parallel in. Parallel out.

The 4094. Serial in, serial out. Parallel 3-state output latch.

The 4517. Serial in. Outputs at stages 16, 32, 48, and 64.

The 40100. Left and right shift serial inputs. Serial out.

The 40104. Left and right shift serial inputs. Parallel inputs. Parallel 3-state outputs. Right and left shift, hold and synchronous clear.

The 40194. Left and right shift serial inputs. Parallel inputs. Parallel outputs. Right and left shift, hold and direct clear.

Chapter 7

Arithmetic Circuits

This chapter presents functional descriptions and selection guides for the following four types of arithmetic ICs:

☐ Adders
☐ Arithmetic Logic Units (ALUs)
☐ Multipliers
☐ Multiplier/Accumulators

7.1 ADDERS

Figure 7-1 shows the logic symbol and function table for the 74LS183 one-bit full adder. There are two addend inputs, A and B; a carry input, C_n; a sum output, S; and a carry output, C_{n+1}. To be consistent with function tables in the previous chapters, I have shown the inputs and outputs in terms of HIGH and LOW voltage levels. However, since the 74LS183 adds two one-bit binary numbers, I may use 0s and 1s, with 0 corresponding to LOW and 1 corresponding to HIGH.

Assume that the carry input equals 0. Then:

(1) 0 (A input) plus 0 (B input) equals 0 (S output). Carry out equals 0.
(2) 0 plus 1 equals 1. Carry out equals 0.
(3) 1 plus 0 equals 1. Carry out equals 0.
(4) 1 plus 1 equals 0 with 1 to carry. (Carry out equals 1.) Now assume that the carry input equals 1. Then:

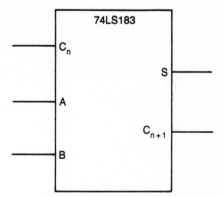

Fig. 7-1. Logic symbol and function table for the 74LS183 one-bit adder.

Inputs			Outputs	
C_n	A	B	S	C_{n+1}
L	L	L	L	L
L	L	H	H	L
L	H	L	H	L
L	H	H	L	H
H	L	L	H	L
H	L	H	L	H
H	H	L	L	H
H	H	H	H	H

(5) 1 (carry input) plus 0 (A input) plus 0 (B input) equals 1. Carry out equals 0.

(6) 1 plus 0 plus 1 equals 0 with 1 to carry.

(7) 1 plus 1 plus 0 equals 0 with 1 to carry.

(8) 1 plus 1 plus 1 equals 1 with 1 to carry.

Since the type '183 adder has a carry input and a carry output, it is possible to make multiple-bit adders using multiple '183s (the carry output is connected to the carry input of the next '183, etc.). However, since 2- and 4-bit adders are available, it is unlikely that you will use the '183 adder unless you need an odd number of bits, i.e., a 5-bit adder.

The logic symbol for the 7482 2-bit adder is shown in Fig. 7-2. A1 is bit

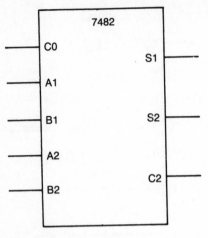

Fig. 7-2. Logic symbol for the 7482 2-bit adder.

1 of input word A. A2 is bit 2 of word A. The same naming convention applies to input word B and output word S. Bit 1 of A, B, and S is the least significant bit (LSB) and has a place value to 2^0, or 1. Bit 2 is the most significant bit (MSB) and has a place value of 2^1, or 2. The logic symbol for the 7483 4-bit adder is shown in Fig. 7-3. A1 through A4 are bits 1 through 4 of input word A. Bit 1 is the LSB; bit 4 is the MSB. The place values, arranged from MSB to LSB are as follows:

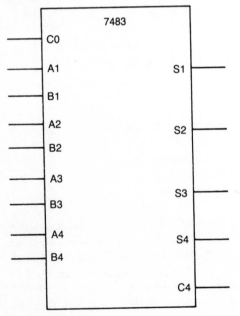

Fig. 7-3. Logic symbol for the 7483 4-bit binary adder.

$$
\begin{array}{cccc}
\textbf{MSB} & & \textbf{LSB} & \\
2^3 & 2^2 & 2^1 & 2^0 \\
& \text{or} & & \\
8 & 4 & 2 & 1
\end{array}
$$

Example:

$$1 \quad 0 \quad 0 \quad 1 \; = \; 1(8) + 0(4) + 0(2) + 1(1) = 9$$

A 4-bit adder adds numbers in the range of 0 through 15 decimal:

Decimal	Binary
0	0000
1	0001
2	0010
3	0011
4	0100
5	0101
6	0110
7	0111
8	1000
9	1001
10	1010
11	1011
12	1100
13	1101
14	1110
15	1111

Example addition:

Decimal	Binary
9	1001
+ 3	+ 0011
12	1100

Table 7-1 lists the temperature range, number of bits, maximum add time, maximum carry time, maximum power dissipation, number of pins, and 100-piece price for adders from the 54/74 families and 4000 series CMOS families.

The type '283 is electrically and functionally equivalent to the '83. Only the pinout is different.

Table 7-1. Adders.

TYPE	TEMP	BITS	MAX ADD TIME (nS)	MAX CARRY TIME (nS)	MAX POWER (mW)	PINS	PRICE ($)
5483	M	4	24.0	16.0	605.00	16	1.99
54C83	M	4	550.0	200.0	4.50	16	4.17
54LS83	M	4	24.0	22.0	214.50	16	1.28
54LS183	M	1	33.0	33.0	93.50	14	4.45
54283	M	4	24.0	16.0	605.00	16	3.60
54F283	M	4	14.0	10.5	302.50	16	5.72
54HC283	M	4	50.0	59.0	0.96	16	1.49
54LS283	M	4	24.0	22.0	187.00	16	1.20
54S283	M	4	18.0	12.0	880.00	16	4.50
54F583	M	4	16.5	8.5	330.00	16	16.52
7482	C	2	40.0	27.0	304.50	14	2.88
7483	C	4	24.0	16.0	577.50	16	0.70
74C83	I	4	550.0	200.0	4.50	16	1.38
74LS83	C	4	24.0	22.0	204.75	16	0.36
74H183	C	1	18.0	18.0	393.75	14	6.67
74LS183	C	1	33.0	33.0	89.25	14	2.34
74283	C	4	24.0	16.0	577.50	16	0.74
74F283	C	4	10.5	8.5	288.75	16	1.86
74HC283	I	4	41.0	49.0	0.48	16	0.68
74LS283	C	4	24.0	22.0	178.50	16	0.50
74S283	C	4	18.0	12.0	840.00	16	2.56
74F583	C	4	17.5	9.5	315.00	16	5.51
4008A	M	4	1300.0	175.0	1.50	16	5.65
4008B	I	4	800.0	200.0	0.75	16	0.70
4008B	M	4	800.0	200.0	0.75	16	1.24
4560B	I	4	2100.0	1500.0	0.75	16	3.14
4560B	M	4	2100.0	1500.0	0.75	16	4.08

The 54/74F583 logic symbol is the same as the type '83 shown in Fig. 7-3. However, the 'F583 is a binary-coded decimal (BCD) adder (adds numbers in the range 0-9).

The 4008 logic symbol is the same as the type 7483.

The 4560 is a BCD adder. The logic symbol is the same as the type 7483.

7.2 ARITHMETIC LOGIC UNITS (ALUs)

Figure 7-4 shows the logic symbol for the 74LS381 arithmetic logic unit. The '381 has 12 inputs and 6 outputs. The inputs: C_n, carry in; A0-A3, input operand A; B0-B3, input operand B; S0-S2, function select. The outputs: F0-F3, function output result; $\overline{P}$ and $\overline{G}$, "generate" and "propagate" signals used with an external type '182 look-ahead carry generator (see Fig. 7-5). A0 is the LSB of operand A. A3 is the MSB of operand A. The same naming convention applies to operand B and output F.

The '381 performs three arithmetic functions and three logic functions, plus preset (F = 1111) and clear (F = 0000):

S2	S1	S0	Operation
L	L	L	F = 0000
L	L	H	F = B minus A

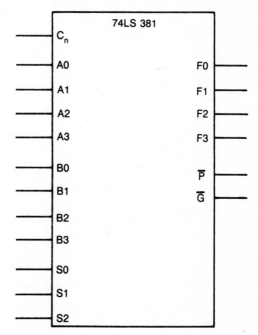

Fig. 7-4. Logic symbol for the 74LS381 arithmetic logic unit.

S2	S1	S0	Operation
L	H	L	F = A minus B
L	H	H	F = A plus B
H	L	L	F = A exclusive-OR B
H	L	H	F = A OR B
H	H	L	F = A AND B
H	H	H	F = 1111

The logic symbol for the 74LS382 is shown in Fig. 7-6. The '382 is identical to the '381 except that the $\overline{G}$ and $\overline{P}$ outputs have been replaced by the OVR and C_{n+4} outputs. C_{n+4} is the ripple carry output. OVR is the 2s complement overflow output.

The *2s complement* is a form of signed numbers. The '382 can be used to perform subtraction by means of adding two 4-bit signed numbers (3 bits plus sign bit). For 4-bit numbers, the signed number range is from $+7$ to -8 as follows:

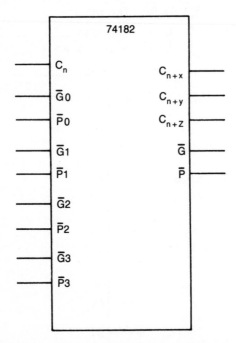

Fig. 7-5. Logic symbol for the 74182 look-ahead carry generator.

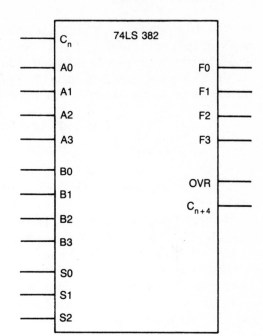

Fig. 7-6. Logic symbol for the 74LS382 arithmetic logic unit.

Signed Decimal	2s Complement
7	0111
6	0110
5	0101
4	0100
3	0011
2	0010
1	0001
0	0000
−1	1111
−2	1110
−3	1101
−4	1100
−5	1011
−6	1010
−7	1001
−8	1000

(The 2s complement of a positive number is the same as the unsigned magnitude form of the number. The 2s complement of a negative number is formed by first changing all 1s to 0s and 0s to 1s and then adding 1.)

The OVR output goes HIGH when the result of a 2s complement addition exceeds the range. For example, what happens when I subtract 7 from -4?

$$\begin{array}{cc}
\textbf{Decimal} & \textbf{2s complement} \\
-4 & 1100 \\
\underline{-7} & \underline{+1001} \\
-11 & 0101
\end{array}$$

The 2s complement answer is $+5$. This is incorrect because -11 is outside the range of the '382 and the OVR output will go HIGH.

Figure 7-7 shows the logic symbol for the 74181 ALU. The '181 can perform 16 arithmetic functions (M = LOW) and 16 logic functions (M = HIGH). The A = B output is HIGH when operand A is identical to operand B.

Figure 7-8 shows the logic symbol for the 74F582 BCD arithmetic logic unit. Pin description:

$C/\overline{B}_n$	Carry/borrow input
A0-A3	A operand input
B0-B3	B operand input
$\overline{A}/S$	Add/Subtract input
F0-F3	Function output
$C/\overline{B}_{n+4}$	Carry/borrow output
$A = B$	Comparator output
$\overline{G}$	Carry generate output
$\overline{P}$	Carry propagate output

Table 7-2 lists the temperature range, number of bits, maximum add time, maximum carry time, maximum power dissipation, number of pins, and 100-piece price for ALUs from the 54/74 families and 4000 series CMOS families.

The 74AS881 is equivalent to the '181 except that the $\overline{P}$, $\overline{G}$, and C_{n+4} output when the device is in the logic mode.

The 40181 is the 4000 series version of the 54/74181.

Table 7-3 lists the temperature range, maximum delay time, maximum power dissipation, number of pins, and 100-piece price for look-ahead carry generators from the 54/74 families and 4000 series CMOS families.

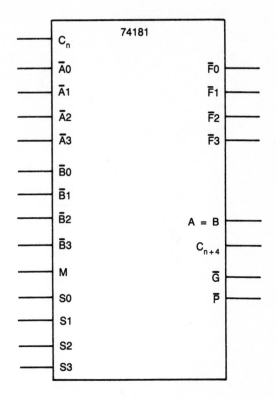

Fig. 7-7. Logic symbol for the 74181 arithmetic logic unit.

7.3 MULTIPLIERS

Table 7-4 lists the temperature range, number of bits, maximum multiply time, maximum power dissipation, number of pins, and 100-piece price for multipliers from the 54/74 families and multipliers made by Advanced Micro Devices (2900 numbers), Analog Devices (ADSP numbers) and Integrated Device Technology (IDT numbers).

Figure 7-9 shows the logic symbol for the 54/74LS261 2-bit by 4-bit multiplier. The '261 performs multiplication in 2s complement form. The two input operands are the multiplicand B0-B4 and the multiplier M0-M2. The most significant bit (B4, M2) is the sign bit. The output is a 5-bit product Q0-Q4. The C input is an output latch control.

Figure 7-10 shows a schematic for a 4-bit by 4-bit multiplier using a combination 74284 and 74285.

Figure 7-11 shows the logic symbol for the 74S557 8-bit by 8-bit multiplier. The '557 multiplies two 8-bit numbers (either unsigned or 2s complement signed)

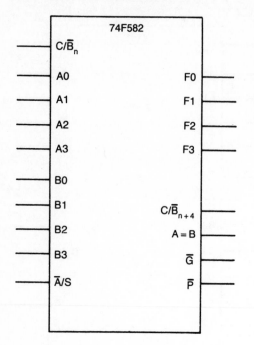

Fig. 7-8. Logic symbol for the 74F582 BCD arithmetic logic unit.

Table 7-2. Arithmetic Logic Units.

TYPE	TEMP	BITS	MAX ADD TIME (nS)	MAX CARRY TIME (nS)	MAX POWER (mW)	PINS	PRICE ($)
54181	M	4	42.0	19.0	825.00	24	6.08
54F181	M	4	10.5	8.5	357.50	24	14.43
54HC181	M	4	54.0	38.0	0.96	24	3.22
54LS181	M	4	32.0	27.0	203.50	24	2.95
54S181	M	4	16.5	10.5	1210.00	24	6.93
54LS381	M	4	30.0	27.0	357.50	20	3.92
54S381	M	4	27.0	17.0	880.00	20	5.58
54LS382	M	4	30.0	27.0	357.50	20	3.92
74181	C	4	42.0	19.0	787.50	24	1.86
74AS181	C	4	9.0	8.0	1100.00	24	6.75
74F181	C	4	11.5	9.5	341.25	24	2.86

TYPE	TEMP	BITS	MAX ADD TIME (nS)	MAX CARRY TIME (nS)	MAX POWER (mW)	PINS	PRICE ($)
74HC181	I	4	45.0	31.0	0.48	24	1.98
74LS181	C	4	32.0	27.0	194.25	24	1.72
74S181	C	4	16.5	10.5	1155.00	24	3.41
74F381	C	4	21.5	13.0	467.25	20	3.65
74LS381	C	4	30.0	27.0	341.25	20	2.31
74S381	C	4	27.0	17.0	840.00	20	4.88
74F382	C	4	21.5	10.0	425.25	20	3.86
74LS382	C	4	30.0	27.0	341.25	20	2.31
74F582	C	4	23.0	9.5	446.25	24	8.04
74AS881	C	4	8.0	9.0	1155.00	24	6.75
40181B	I	4	800.0	400.0	0.75	24	3.18
40181B	M	4	800.0	400.0	0.75	24	4.46

Table 7-3. Look Ahead Carry Generators.

TYPE	TEMP	MAX DELAY (nS)	MAX POWER (mW)	PINS	PRICE ($)
54182	M	22.0	396.00	16	3.26
54F182	M	11.0	189.00	16	4.64
54HC182	M	44.0	0.96	16	1.45
54LS182	M	30.0	88.00	16	1.90
54S182	M	10.5	599.50	16	4.00
74182	C	22.0	378.00	16	2.00
74F182	C	10.0	189.00	16	1.43
74HC182	I	37.0	0.48	16	0.66
74S182	C	10.5	572.25	16	1.40
74AS882	C	14.0	577.50	24	3.75
40182B	I	480.0	0.75	16	1.14
40182B	M	480.0	0.75	16	1.60

Table 7-4. Multipliers.

TYPE	TEMP	BIT SIZE	MAX MPY TIME (nS)	MAX POWER (mW)	PINS	PRICE ($)
54LS261	M	2 X 4	42.0	220.00	16	2.95
54284	M	4 X 4	60.0	715.00	16	7.15
54285	M	4 X 4	60.0	715.00	16	7.15
54S558	M	8 X 8	70.0	1540.00	40	81.16
74LS261	C	2 X 4	42.0	210.00	16	2.98
74284	C	4 X 4	60.0	682.50	16	2.06
74285	C	4 X 4	60.0	682.50	16	2.06
74S557	C	8 X 8	60.0	1470.00	40	30.86
74S558	C	8 X 8	60.0	1470.00	40	30.86
29516	C	16 X 16	65.0	4200.00	64	56.00
29516	M	16 X 16	75.0	4950.00	64	130.00
29516A	C	16 X 16	38.0	4200.00	64	88.00
29L516	C	16 X 16	90.0	2100.00	64	39.00
29L516	M	16 X 16	100.0	2420.00	64	100.00
29517	C	16 X 16	65.0	4200.00	64	56.00
29517	M	16 X 16	75.0	4950.00	64	128.00
29L517	C	16 X 16	90.0	2100.00	64	39.00
29L517	M	16 X 16	100.0	2420.00	64	100.00
ADSP-1012J	C	12 X 12	165.0	131.25	64	101.00
ADSP-1012K	C	12 X 12	130.0	131.25	64	119.00
ADSP-1012S	M	12 X 12	195.0	165.00	64	253.00
ADSP-1012T	M	12 X 12	150.0	165.00	64	298.00
ADSP-1016J	C	16 X 16	220.0	131.25	64	105.00
ADSP-1016K	C	16 X 16	170.0	131.25	64	125.00
ADSP-1016S	M	16 X 16	250.0	165.00	64	263.00
ADSP-1016T	M	16 X 16	200.0	165.00	64	313.00
ADSP-1024J	C	24 X 24	275.0	131.25	84	154.00

TYPE	TEMP	BIT SIZE	MAX MPY TIME (nS)	MAX POWER (mW)	PINS	PRICE ($)
ADSP-1024K	C	24 X 24	235.0	131.25	84	192.00
ADSP-1024S	M	24 X 24	325.0	165.00	84	289.00
ADSP-1024T	M	24 X 24	275.0	165.00	84	360.00
ADSP-1080J	C	8 X 8	115.0	78.75	40	37.00
ADSP-1080K	C	8 X 8	100.0	78.75	40	54.00
ADSP-1080S	M	8 X 8	130.0	110.00	40	93.00
ADSP-1080T	M	8 X 8	115.0	110.00	40	135.00
ADSP-1081J	C	8 X 8	105.0	78.75	40	37.00
ADSP-1081K	C	8 X 8	90.0	78.75	40	54.00
ADSP-1081S	M	8 X 8	120.0	110.00	40	93.00
ADSP-1081T	M	8 X 8	105.0	110.00	40	135.00
IDT7212L45	C	12 X 12	45.0	357.50	64	43.70
IDT7212L70	C	12 X 12	70.0	357.50	64	31.20
IDT7212L115	C	12 X 12	115.0	302.50	64	26.00
IDT7212L55	M	12 X 12	55.0	467.50	64	131.00
IDT7212L90	M	12 X 12	90.0	467.50	64	93.60
IDT7212L140	M	12 X 12	140.0	412.50	64	78.00
IDT7213L45	C	12 X 12	45.0	357.50	64	43.70
IDT7213L70	C	12 X 12	70.0	357.50	64	31.20
IDT7213L115	C	12 X 12	115.0	302.50	64	26.00
IDT7213L55	M	12 X 12	55.0	467.50	64	131.00
IDT7213L90	M	12 X 12	90.0	467.50	64	93.60
IDT7213L140	M	12 X 12	140.0	412.50	64	78.00
IDT7216L35	C	16 X 16	35.0	440.00	64	66.60
IDT7216L45	C	16 X 16	45.0	440.00	64	47.60
IDT7216L55	C	16 X 16	55.0	440.00	64	36.60
IDT7216L65	C	16 X 16	65.0	440.00	64	30.50
IDT7216L75	C	16 X 16	75.0	330.00	64	26.50
IDT7216L90	C	16 X 16	90.0	330.00	64	23.00

TYPE	TEMP	BIT SIZE	MAX MPY TIME (nS)	MAX POWER (mW)	PINS	PRICE ($)
IDT7216L140	C	16 X 16	140.0	330.00	64	20.00
IDT7216L40	M	16 X 16	40.0	550.00	64	212.50
IDT7216L55	M	16 X 16	55.0	550.00	64	151.80
IDT7216L65	M	16 X 16	65.0	550.00	64	116.80
IDT7216L75	M	16 X 16	75.0	550.00	64	97.30
IDT7216L90	M	16 X 16	90.0	440.00	64	84.60
IDT7216L120	M	16 X 16	120.0	440.00	64	73.60
IDT7216L185	M	16 X 16	185.0	440.00	64	64.00
IDT7217L35	C	16 X 16	35.0	440.00	64	66.60
IDT7217L45	C	16 X 16	45.0	440.00	64	47.60
IDT7217L55	C	16 X 16	55.0	440.00	64	36.60
IDT7217L65	C	16 X 16	65.0	440.00	64	30.50
IDT7217L75	C	16 X 16	75.0	330.00	64	26.50
IDT7217L90	C	16 X 16	90.0	330.00	64	23.00
IDT7217L140	C	16 X 16	140.0	330.00	64	20.00
IDT7217L40	M	16 X 16	40.0	550.00	64	212.50
IDT7217L55	M	16 X 16	55.0	550.00	64	151.80
IDT7217L65	M	16 X 16	65.0	550.00	64	116.80
IDT7217L75	M	16 X 16	75.0	550.00	64	97.30
IDT7217L90	M	16 X 16	90.0	440.00	64	84.60
IDT7217L120	M	16 X 16	120.0	440.00	64	73.60
IDT7217L185	M	16 X 16	185.0	440.00	64	64.00

and producing a 16-bit product. Pin description:

X0-X7	Multiplicand inputs
Y0-Y7	Multiplier inputs
X_M	Multiplicand sign control input
Y_M	Multiplier sign control input
R	Rounding input
G	Latch enable input

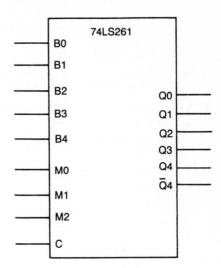

Fig. 7-9. Logic symbol for the 74LS261 2-bit by 4-bit multiplier.

$\overline{O}_E$ 3-state output enable input
S0-S15   Product outputs
$\overline{S}15$ MSB complement output

The logic symbol for the 74S558 8-bit by 8-bit multiplier is shown in Fig. 7-12. The '558 is identical to the '557 except the R and G inputs are replaced by the R_U and R_S for unsigned and signed rounding control.

Figure 7-13 shows the logic symbol for the 29516 16-bit by 16-bit multiplier. The 29516 has 16-bit D-type flip-flop registers on the X input, the Y input, and the upper and lower 16 bits of the 32-bit product P output. The registers are clocked by CLKX, CLKY, CLKM, and CLKL respectively.

The Y multiplier input is multiplexed with P0-P15 of the output product. OEL is the 3-state control for enabling P0-15 on Y input lines. OEP is the 3-state control for enabling the P output. MSPSEL is used to select either P0-P15 or P16-P31 to go to the P output.

X_M and Y_M are used to specify whether the X and Y inputs are signed or 2s complement numbers. RND provides rounding control. FA is used for output format adjust. FT makes the output registers transparent.

Figure 7-14 shows the logic symbol for the 29517 which is identical to the 29516 except that the 29517 has a single clock and three enables ENX, ENY, and ENP for the X register, Y register, and full 32-bit P register.

Figure 7-15 shows the logic symbol for the ADSP-1012 12-bit by 12-bit multiplier. The ADSP-1012 has 12-bit D-type flip-flop registers on the X input, the Y input, and the upper and lower 12 bits of the 24-bit product P output. The registers are clocked by CLK X, CLK Y, CLK M, and CLK L respectively.

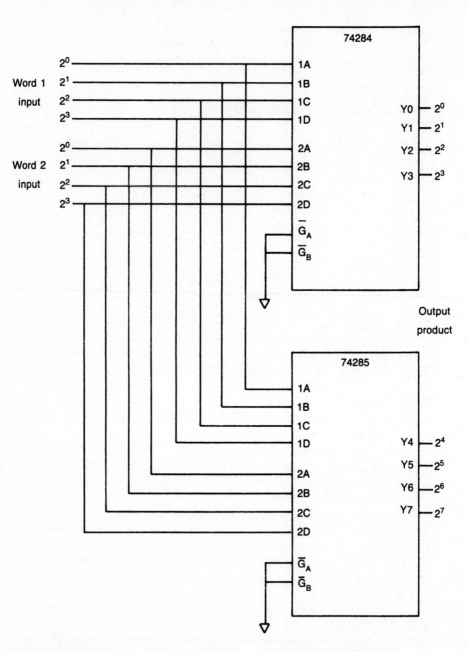

Fig. 7-10. Schematic for a 4-bit by 4-bit multiplier using the 74284 and 74285.

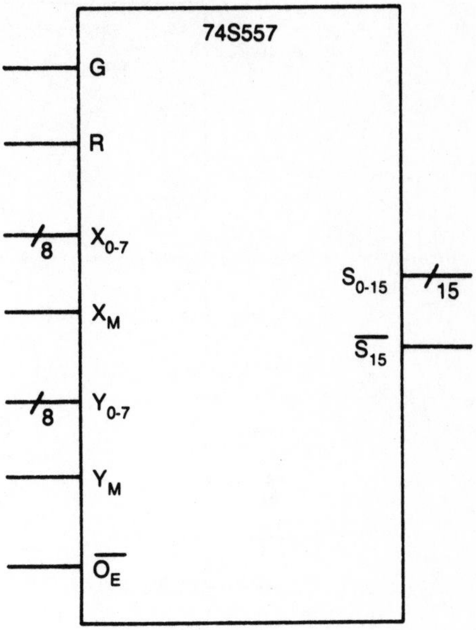

Fig. 7-11. Logic symbol for the 74S557 8-bit by 8-bit multiplier.

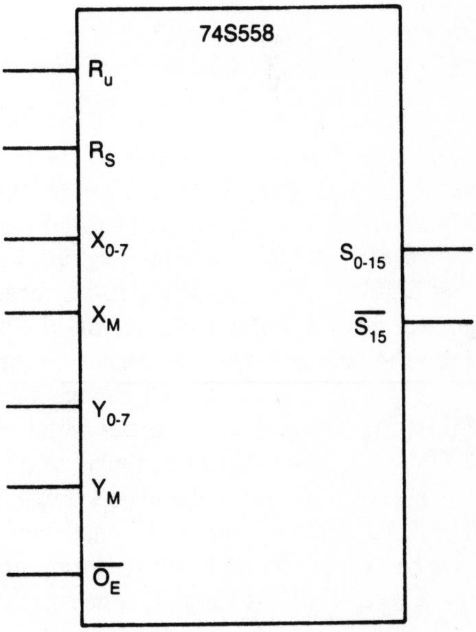

Fig. 7-12. Logic symbol for the 74S558 8-bit by 8-bit multiplier.

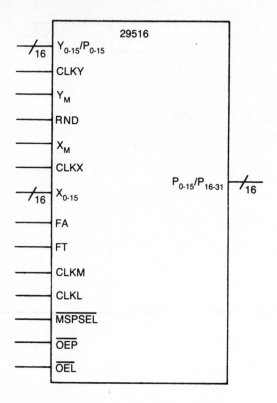

Fig. 7-13. Logic symbol for the 29516 16-bit by 16-bit multiplier.

TRIL is the 3-state output control for P0-P11. TRIM is the 3-state output control for P12-P23. TCX and TCY are used to specify whether the X and Y inputs are signed or 2s complement numbers. RND provides rounding control. FA is used for output format adjust. FT makes the output registers transparent.

Figure 7-16 shows the logic symbol for the ADSP-1016 16 × 16 multiplier. The ADSP-1016 is basically a 16-bit version of the ADSP-1012. To fit in a 64 pin package the lower 16 bits of the the product is output to the Y input pins. Note the similarity and differences to the 29516.

Figure 7-17 shows the logic symbol for the ADSP-1024 24 × 24 multiplier. SH A, SH B, and SH B shift the 48-bit output left by zero, one, or two bits. RND A and RND B control rounding on bits 21, 22, or 23, or no rounding.

Figure 7-18 shows the logic symbol for the ADSP-1080 8 × 8 multiplier. The ADSP-1080 performs 2s complement multiplication only. The ADSP-1081 (not shown) is identical, but performs unsigned multiplication only.

The IDT7212 is identical to the ADSP-1012. The IDT7213 is identical to

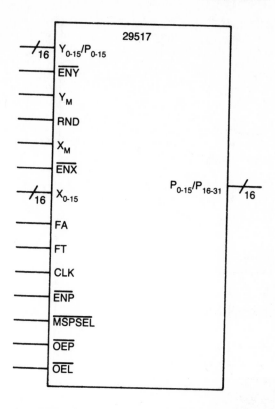

Fig. 7-14. Logic symbol for the 29517 16-bit by 16-bit multiplier.

the IDT7212 except the four clock inputs have been replaced by one clock and three enables.

The IDT7216 and IDT7217 are CMOS equivalents to the 29516 and 29517, but are available in several speed versions.

7.4 MULTIPLIER/ACCUMULATORS

Figure 7-19 shows a simplified block diagram of a 16-bit by 16-bit multiplier/accumulator (MAC) with a 35-bit output. The MAC includes:

- ☐ X and Y input registers;
- ☐ 16 by 16 multiplier with 32-bit result;
- ☐ 35-bit adder/subtractor; and a
- ☐ 35-bit output register (the accumulator)

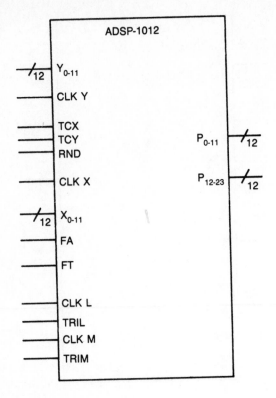

Fig. 7-15. Logic symbol for the ADSP-1012 12-bit by 12-bit CMOS multiplier.

The adder/subtractor has two inputs: the multiplier output, and the previously stored result from the 35-bit adder/subtractor. The three extra bits are provided to prevent overflow in case of accumulation beyond 32 bits.

Table 7-5 lists the temperature range, number of bits, maximum multiply/accumulate time, maximum power dissipation, number of pins, and 100-piece price for multiplier/accumulators made by Advanced Micro Devices (2900 numbers), Analog Devices (ADSP numbers) and Integrated Device Technology (IDT numbers).

Figure 7-20 shows the logic symbol for the 29510 16 × 16 MAC. Four control bits are stored when either the X or Y register is loaded: RND, which controls rounding; TC, which specifies if the inputs are in 2s complement or unsigned magnitude form; ACC, which controls if the multiplier output is added to the previous result or passed directly to the output register (the accumulator); and SUB/ADD which control subtraction or addition. In the subtraction mode,

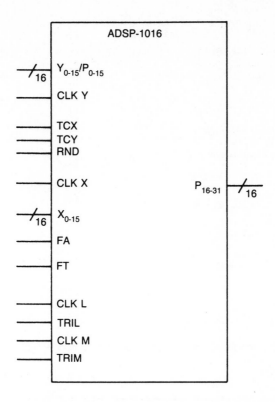

Fig. 7-16. Logic symbol for the ADSP-1016 16-bit by 16-bit CMOS multiplier.

the contents of the accumulator are subtracted from the multiplier output.

The accumulator consists of two 16-bit registers (LSP, MSP) and one 3-bit register (XTP). LSP holds P0-P15; MSP holds P16-P31; and XTP holds P32-P34. The 29510 allows preloading of the accumulator through the Y0-Y15/P0-P15, P16-P31, and P32-P34 pins. When PREL is HIGH and LE_L/OE_L is HIGH, the LSP register is loaded; when PREL is HIGH and LE_M/OE_M is HIGH, the MSP register is loaded; when PREL is HIGH and LE_X/OE_X is HIGH, the XTP register is loaded.

When PREL is LOW, the LE_L/OE_L, LE_M/OE_M, and LE_X/OE_X lines are 3-state enable lines for the LSP, MSP, and XTP register output buffers.

Figure 7-21 shows the logic symbol for the ADSP-1008 8-bit by 8-bit multiplier/accumulator. TSL, TSM, and TSX control preloading of the accumulator when PREL is HIGH and control the 3-state accumulator output buffers when PREL is LOW. Figure 7-22 shows the logic symbol for the

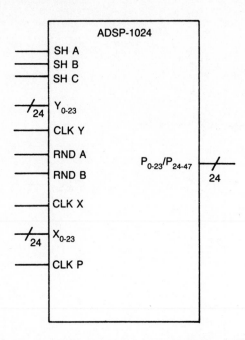

Fig. 7-17. Logic symbol for the ADSP-1024 24-bit by 24-bit CMOS multiplier.

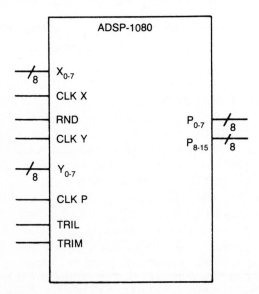

Fig. 7-18. Logic symbol for the ADSP-1080 8-bit by 8-bit CMOS multiplier.

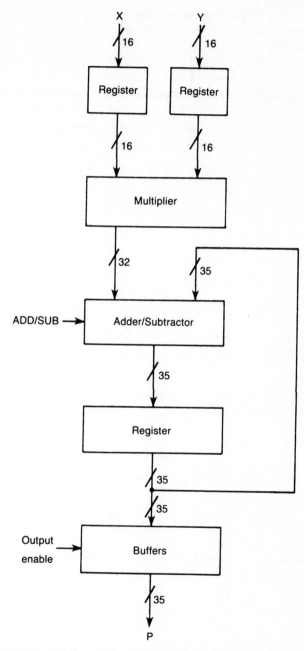

Fig. 7-19. Simplified block diagram of a 16-bit by 16-bit multiplier/accumulator with a 35-bit output.

Table 7-5. Multiplier/Accumulators.

TYPE	TEMP	BIT SIZE	MAX MAC TIME (nS)	MAX POWER (mW)	PINS	PRICE ($)
29510	C	16 X 16	80.0	4725.00	64	68.00
29510	M	16 X 16	90.0	5500.00	64	185.00
29L510	C	16 X 16	110.0	2362.50	64	58.00
29L510	M	16 X 16	120.0	2942.50	64	135.00
ADSP-1008J	C	8 X 8	160.0	78.75	48	55.00
ADSP-1008K	C	8 X 8	125.0	78.75	48	78.00
ADSP-1008S	M	8 X 8	185.0	99.00	48	138.00
ADSP-1008T	M	8 X 8	145.0	99.00	48	195.00
ADSP-1009J	C	12 X 12	195.0	131.25	64	114.00
ADSP-1009K	C	12 X 12	155.0	131.25	64	138.00
ADSP-1009S	M	12 X 12	225.0	165.00	64	285.00
ADSP-1009T	M	12 X 12	180.0	165.00	64	285.00
ADSP-1010J	C	16 X 16	240.0	131.25	64	140.00
ADSP-1010K	C	16 X 16	190.0	131.25	64	198.00
ADSP-1010S	M	16 X 16	250.0	165.00	64	350.00
ADSP-1010T	M	16 X 16	220.0	165.25	64	495.00
ADSP-1110J	C	16 X 16	240.0	131.25	28	85.00
ADSP-1110K	C	16 X 16	190.0	131.25	28	95.00
IDT7209L45	C	12 X 12	45.0	440.00	64	70.60
IDT7209L65	C	12 X 12	65.0	440.00	64	50.40
IDT7209L100	C	12 X 12	100.0	330.00	64	42.00
IDT7209L135	C	12 X 12	135.0	330.00	64	35.00
IDT7209L55	M	12 X 12	55.0	550.00	64	191.50
IDT7209L75	M	12 X 12	75.0	550.00	64	136.80
IDT7209L120	M	12 X 12	120.0	440.00	64	114.00
IDT7209L170	M	12 X 12	170.0	440.00	64	95.00
IDT7210L45	C	16 X 16	45.0	495.00	64	63.10
IDT7210L55	C	16 X 16	55.0	495.00	64	48.50

TYPE	TEMP	BIT SIZE	MAX MAC TIME (nS)	MAX POWER (mW)	PINS	PRICE ($)
IDT7210L65	C	16 X 16	65.0	495.00	64	37.30
IDT7210L75	C	16 X 16	75.0	495.00	64	31.10
IDT7210L100	C	16 X 16	100.0	385.00	64	27.00
IDT7210L165	C	16 X 16	165.0	385.00	64	22.50
IDT7210L55	M	16 X 16	55.0	605.00	64	279.90
IDT7210L65	M	16 X 16	65.0	605.00	64	215.30
IDT7210L75	M	16 X 16	75.0	605.00	64	165.60
IDT7210L85	M	16 X 16	85.0	605.00	64	138.00
IDT7210L120	M	16 X 16	120.0	495.00	64	120.00
IDT7210L200	M	16 X 16	200.0	495.00	64	100.00
IDT7243L45	C	16 X 16	45.0	495.00	64	63.10
IDT7243L55	C	16 X 16	55.0	495.00	64	48.50
IDT7243L65	C	16 X 16	65.0	495.00	64	37.30
IDT7243L75	C	16 X 16	75.0	495.00	64	31.10
IDT7243L100	C	16 X 16	100.0	385.00	64	27.00
IDT7243L165	C	16 X 16	165.0	385.00	64	22.50
IDT7243L55	M	16 X 16	55.0	605.00	64	279.90
IDT7243L65	M	16 X 16	65.0	605.00	64	215.30
IDT7243L75	M	16 X 16	75.0	605.00	64	165.60
IDT7243L85	M	16 X 16	85.0	605.00	64	138.00
IDT7243L120	M	16 X 16	120.0	495.00	64	120.00
IDT7243L200	M	16 X 16	200.0	495.00	64	100.00

ADSP-1009, the 12-bit version of the ADSP-1008. Figure 7-23 shows the logic symbol for the ADSP-1016 16 × 16 MAC.

The IDT7209 is functionally equivalent to the ADSP-1009.

The IDT7210 is functionally equivalent to the ADSP-1016.

The IDT7243 is the same as the IDT7210 except that the IDT7243 only has a 19-bit result and does not provide for preloading of the accumulator. The 19-bit result is the upper 19 bits, P16-P34.

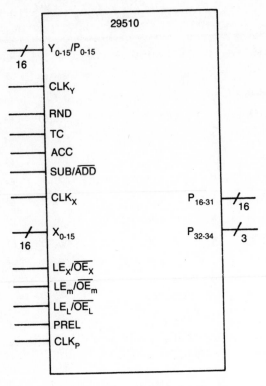

Fig. 7-20. Logic symbol for the 29510 16-bit by 16-bit multiplier/accumulator.

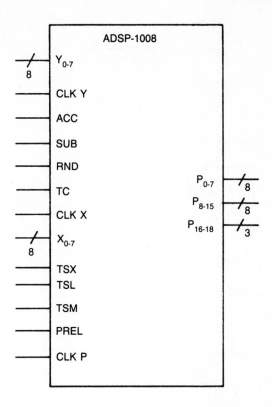

Fig. 7-21. Logic symbol for the ADSP-1008 8-bit by 8-bit multiplier/accumulator.

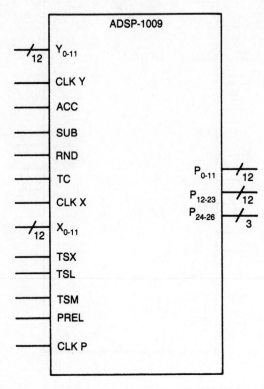

Fig. 7-22. Logic symbol for the ADSP-1009 12-bit by 12-bit multiplier/accumulator.

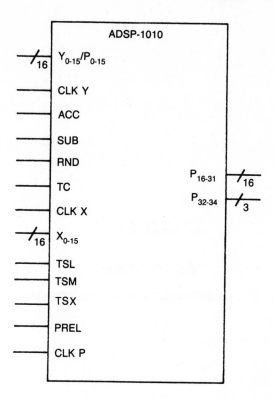

Fig. 7-23. Logic symbol for the ADSP-1010 16-bit by 16-bit multiplier/accumulator.

Chapter 8

Memories

This chapter presents functional descriptions and selection guides for the following five types of memory ICs:

☐ Static Random Access Memories (SRAMs)
☐ Dynamic Random Access Memories (DRAMs)
☐ Programmable Read Only Memories (PROMs)
☐ Registered PROMs
☐ Erasable PROMs

8.1 SRAMs

All read/write random access memories consist of four basic blocks: (1) a set of memory cells organized in an array of m columns by n rows; (2) a row address decoder; (3) a column address decoder; and (4) read/write control logic. A *static* random access memory (SRAM) has a flip-flop type memory cell. A *dynamic* random access memory (DRAM) has a memory cell that stores charge on a capacitor. DRAMs will be discussed in the next section.

Figure 8-1 shows the schematic of a bipolar static RAM cell. This cell consists of two cross-coupled double emitter NPN transistors with collector pull-up resistors. This cell has two states: either the left transistor is on and the right off; or, the right transistor is on and the left off. One state (either one) may be defined as the 1 state and the other the 0 state. The MOS version of this cell is shown in Fig. 8-2.

Figure 8-3 shows a simplified block diagram of a 16-bit by 1-bit static RAM. Each small unlabeled box represents a memory cell. The cells are connected

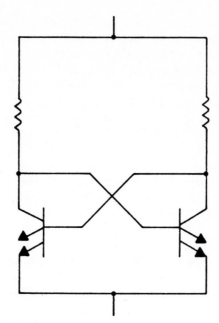

Fig. 8-1. Bipolar static RAM cell schematic.

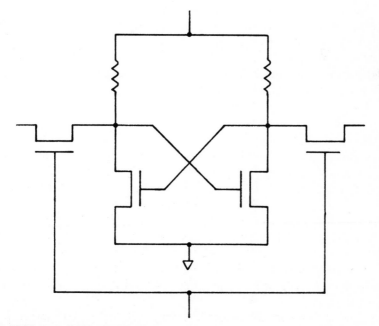

Fig. 8-2. MOS static RAM cell schematic.

in a 4-by-4 memory array. There are four address lines, A0-A3. LOW or HIGH voltage levels on the address lines select one of the sixteen cells. LOW (0) or HIGH (1) data may be written into the RAM by selecting a cell, applying a LOW or HIGH on the DATA IN line and applying a pulse on the WRITE ENABLE line. Data stored in the RAM may be read via the DATA OUT line by selecting a cell and applying a LOW voltage on the OUTPUT ENABLE.

Write mode timing is shown in Fig. 8-4. Data is written into the RAM cell on the rising edge of the WRITE ENABLE. The t_{DW} is the DATA IN setup time and t_{DH} is the DATA IN hold time. Read mode timing is shown in Fig. 8-5. The t_{AA} is called the *address access time* and is the key performance specification in the selection of SRAM and other memories. Manufacturers offer many *speed* versions of their memories. The speed variable is the address access time. A 45 nS RAM, for example, is a RAM with an address access time of 45 nS.

The RAM shown in Fig. 8-3 is an extremely small RAM. Actually, there are no commercially available RAMs that are this small. The smallest static RAM is 16 by 4, which is a 64-bit RAM consisting of sixteen 4-bit *words*. The 16 by 4-bit RAM has four DATA IN lines and four DATA OUT lines. Larger RAMs with 4- or 8-bit words combine the DATA IN and DATA OUT lines into one set of input/output lines with a 3-state output enable line (typically HIGH when writing data into the RAM and LOW when reading data out of the RAM). Figure 8-6 shows the logic symbol of a 2048 (2K) by 8 static RAM with shared input/output lines. Internally, the memory array is 128 bits by 128 bits, or 16,384, or 16K bits. Data is written or read 8 bits at a time. (Note that 1K equals 1024, not 1000, in the world of digital ICs and computers.)

Static RAMs are listed in Tables 8-1 through 8-14 for RAM sizes 16 by 4 through 64K by 1 as follows:

Table	RAM size
8-1	16 × 4
8-2	128 × 8
8-3	256 × 1
8-4	256 × 4
8-5	256 × 9
8-6	1K × 1
8-7	1K × 4
8-8	2K × 8
8-9	4K × 1
8-10	4K × 4
8-11	8K × 8
8-12	16K × 1
8-13	16K × 4
8-14	64K × 1

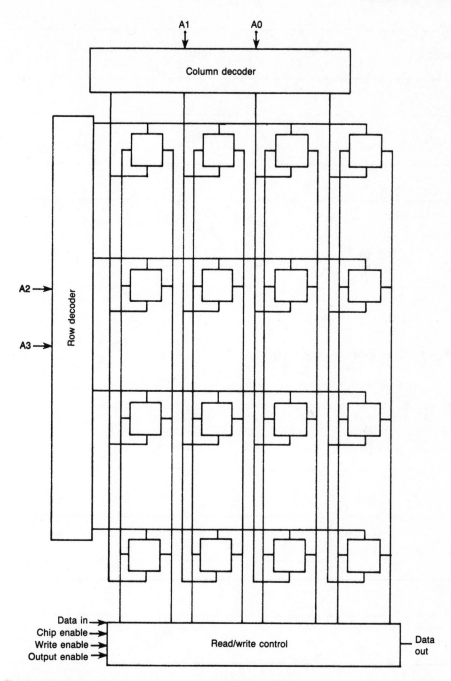

Fig. 8-3. Simplified block diagram of a 16-bit by 1-bit static RAM.

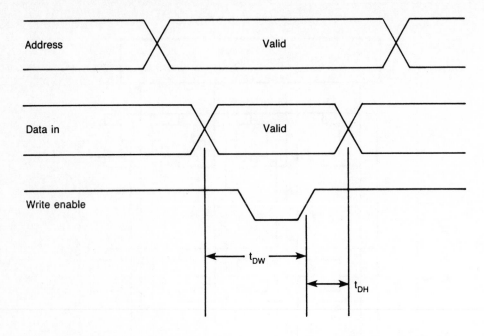

Fig. 8-4. Static RAM write mode timing.

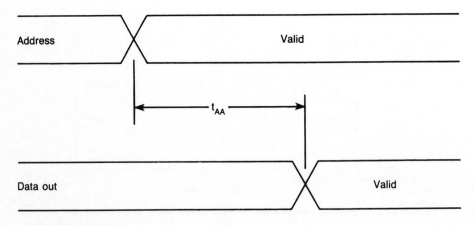

Fig. 8-5. Timing waveforms showing static RAM address access time.

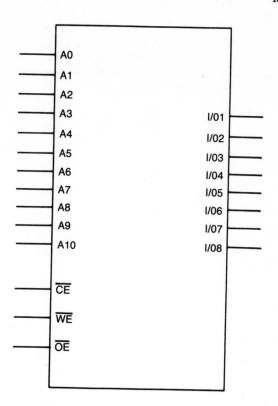

Fig. 8-6. Logic symbol for a 2K × 8 static RAM.

Table 8-1. 16 × 4 Static RAMs.

TYPE	TEMP	TECH	OUTPUT	MAX ACCESS TIME (nS)	MAX SUPPLY CURRENT (mA)	PINS	PRICE ($)
27LS02	C	TTL	OC	55	35	16	3.80
27LS02	M	TTL	OC	65	38	16	10.65
27S02	C	TTL	OC	25	100	16	4.10
27S02	M	TTL	OC	30	105	16	11.50
27S02	C	TTL	OC	35	100	16	2.35
27S02	M	TTL	OC	50	105	16	8.75
27LS03	C	TTL	3S	55	35	16	3.80
27LS03	M	TTL	3S	65	38	16	10.65

TYPE	TEMP	TECH	OUTPUT	MAX ACCESS TIME (nS)	MAX SUPPLY CURRENT (mA)	PINS	PRICE ($)
27S03	C	TTL	3S	25	100	16	4.10
27S03	M	TTL	3S	30	105	16	11.50
27S03	C	TTL	3S	35	100	16	2.35
27S03	M	TTL	3S	50	105	16	8.75
27LS06	C	TTL	OC	55	35	16	4.75
27LS06	M	TTL	OC	65	38	16	13.15
27S06	C	TTL	OC	25	100	16	6.35
27S06	M	TTL	OC	30	105	16	15.50
27S06	C	TTL	OC	35	100	16	4.75
27S06	M	TTL	OC	50	105	16	10.15
27LS07	C	TTL	3S	55	35	16	4.75
27LS07	M	TTL	3S	65	38	16	13.15
27S07	C	TTL	3S	25	100	16	6.35
27S07	M	TTL	3S	30	105	16	15.50
27S07	C	TTL	3S	35	100	16	4.75
27S07	M	TTL	3S	50	105	16	10.15
7489	C	TTL	OC	60	105	16	1.96
75S06	M	TTL	OC	50	100	16	8.70
75S07	M	TTL	3S	50	100	16	8.70
85S06	C	TTL	OC	35	100	16	2.60
85S07	C	TTL	3S	25	100	16	3.60
85S07	C	TTL	3S	35	100	16	2.60
54F189	M	TTL	3S	32	55	16	12.87
54LS189	M	TTL	3S	90	60	16	4.50
54S189	M	TTL	3S	30	100	16	8.70
54S189	M	TTL	3S	50	110	16	4.20
54F219	M	TTL	3S	32	55	16	20.59
54LS219	M	TTL	3S	90	60	16	4.50
54LS289	M	TTL	OC	90	60	16	4.50

TYPE	TEMP	TECH	OUTPUT	MAX ACCESS TIME (nS)	MAX SUPPLY CURRENT (mA)	PINS	PRICE ($)
54S289	M	TTL	OC	35	110	16	4.20
54LS319	M	TTL	OC	90	60	16	4.50
74F189	C	TTL	3S	27	55	16	4.29
74LS189	C	TTL	3S	80	60	16	3.60
74S189	C	TTL	3S	25	100	16	3.25
74S189	C	TTL	3S	35	110	16	2.15
74F219	C	TTL	3S	27	55	16	4.29
74LS219	C	TTL	3S	80	60	16	3.60
74LS289	C	TTL	OC	80	60	16	3.60
74S289	C	TTL	OC	35	110	16	2.15
74LS319	C	TTL	OC	80	60	16	3.60

Table 8-2. 128 × 8 Static RAMs.

TYPE	TEMP	TECH	OUTPUT	MAX ACCESS TIME (nS)	MAX SUPPLY CURRENT (mA)	PINS	PRICE ($)
6810	C	MOS	3S	450	80	24	1.75
6810	I	MOS	3S	450	80	24	2.90
68A10	C	MOS	3S	360	100	24	2.20
68A10	I	MOS	3S	360	100	24	3.20
68B10	C	MOS	3S	250	100	24	2.85

Table 8-3. 256 × 1 Static RAMs.

TYPE	TEMP	TECH	OUTPUT	MAX ACCESS TIME (nS)	MAX SUPPLY CURRENT (mA)	PINS	PRICE ($)
27LS00	C	TTL	3S	35	115	16	7.15

TYPE	TEMP	TECH	OUTPUT	MAX ACCESS TIME (nS)	MAX SUPPLY CURRENT (mA)	PINS	PRICE ($)
27LS00	C	TTL	3S	45	70	16	4.20
27LS00	M	TTL	3S	45	115	16	16.85
27LS00	M	TTL	3S	55	70	16	11.25
27LS01	C	TTL	OC	35	115	16	7.15
27LS01	C	TTL	OC	45	70	16	4.20
27LS01	M	TTL	OC	45	115	16	16.85
27LS01	M	TTL	OC	55	70	16	11.25
74S201	C	TTL	3S	65	140	16	4.32
74S301	C	TTL	OC	65	140	16	4.32

Table 8-4. 256 × 4 Static RAMs.

TYPE	TEMP	TECH	OUTPUT	MAX ACCESS TIME (nS)	MAX SUPPLY CURRENT (mA)	PINS	PRICE ($)
2101	C	MOS	3S	250	70	22	3.93
2101	C	MOS	3S	300	70	22	3.79
2101	C	MOS	3S	400	70	22	3.65
2101	C	MOS	3S	500	70	22	3.50
2101	C	MOS	3S	1000	70	22	3.50
2111	C	MOS	3S	250	70	18	4.65
2111	C	MOS	3S	300	70	18	4.50
2111	C	MOS	3S	400	70	18	4.36
2111	C	MOS	3S	500	70	18	4.22
2111	C	MOS	3S	1000	70	18	4.22
2112	C	MOS	3S	250	70	16	5.01
2112	C	MOS	3S	300	70	16	4.86
2112	C	MOS	3S	400	70	16	4.72
2112	C	MOS	3S	1000	70	16	4.58
6551	I	CMOS	3S	220	4	22	9.09

TYPE	TEMP	TECH	OUTPUT	MAX ACCESS TIME (nS)	MAX SUPPLY CURRENT (mA)	PINS	PRICE ($)
6551	M	CMOS	3S	220	4	22	14.58
6551	I	CMOS	3S	300	4	22	6.86
6551	M	CMOS	3S	300	4	22	11.23
6561	I	CMOS	3S	220	4	18	9.09
6561	M	CMOS	3S	220	4	18	14.58
6561	I	CMOS	3S	300	4	18	6.86
6561	M	CMOS	3S	300	4	18	11.23
9101	C	MOS	3S	250	60	22	3.93
9101	C	MOS	3S	300	60	22	3.79
9101	M	MOS	3S	300	65	22	30.39
9101	C	MOS	3S	400	55	22	3.65
9101	M	MOS	3S	400	60	22	19.88
9101	C	MOS	3S	500	55	22	3.50
9101	M	MOS	3S	500	60	22	13.80
91L01	C	MOS	3S	300	36	22	3.93
91L01	M	MOS	3S	300	40	22	34.75
91L01	C	MOS	3S	400	33	22	3.79
91L01	M	MOS	3S	400	37	22	21.09
91L01	C	MOS	3S	500	33	22	3.65
91L01	M	MOS	3S	500	37	22	16.37
9111	C	MOS	3S	250	60	18	4.65
9111	C	MOS	3S	300	60	18	4.50
9111	M	MOS	3S	300	65	18	30.39
9111	C	MOS	3S	400	55	18	4.36
9111	M	MOS	3S	400	60	18	18.45
9111	C	MOS	3S	500	55	18	4.22
9111	M	MOS	3S	500	60	18	13.80
91L11	C	MOS	3S	300	36	18	4.80
91L11	M	MOS	3S	300	40	18	34.75

TYPE	TEMP	TECH	OUTPUT	MAX ACCESS TIME (nS)	MAX SUPPLY CURRENT (mA)	PINS	PRICE ($)
91L11	C	MOS	3S	400	33	18	4.65
91L11	M	MOS	3S	400	37	18	21.09
91L11	C	MOS	3S	500	33	18	4.50
91L11	M	MOS	3S	500	37	18	16.37
9112	C	MOS	3S	250	60	16	5.01
9112	C	MOS	3S	300	60	16	4.86
9112	M	MOS	3S	300	65	16	30.39
9112	C	MOS	3S	400	55	16	4.72
9112	M	MOS	3S	400	60	16	18.45
9112	C	MOS	3S	500	55	16	4.58
9112	M	MOS	3S	500	60	16	13.80
91L12	C	MOS	3S	300	36	16	5.15
91L12	M	MOS	3S	300	40	16	34.75
91L12	C	MOS	3S	400	33	16	5.00
91L12	M	MOS	3S	400	37	16	21.09
91L12	C	MOS	3S	500	33	16	4.90
91L12	M	MOS	3S	500	37	16	16.37
9122	C	MOS	3S	25	120	22	15.02
9122	C	MOS	3S	35	120	22	8.45
9122	M	MOS	3S	35	135	22	39.80
91L22	C	MOS	3S	35	80	22	14.30
91L22	C	MOS	3S	45	80	22	7.25
91L22	M	MOS	3S	45	90	22	39.80
93412	C	TTL	OC	35	155	22	7.25
93412	C	TTL	OC	45	155	22	5.75
93412	M	TTL	OC	45	170	22	22.60
93412	M	TTL	OC	60	170	22	19.70
93L412	C	TTL	OC	45	80	22	7.25

TYPE	TEMP	TECH	OUTPUT	MAX ACCESS TIME (nS)	MAX SUPPLY CURRENT (mA)	PINS	PRICE ($)
93L412	M	TTL	OC	55	90	22	22.60
93L412	C	TTL	OC	60	80	22	5.75
93L412	M	TTL	OC	75	90	22	19.70
93422	C	TTL	3S	35	155	22	4.72
93422	C	TTL	3S	45	155	22	4.29
93422	M	TTL	3S	45	170	22	19.31
93422	M	TTL	3S	60	170	22	16.45
93L422	C	TTL	3S	45	80	22	6.44
93L422	M	TTL	3S	55	90	22	17.88
93L422	C	TTL	3S	60	80	22	5.01
93L422	M	TTL	3S	75	90	22	15.02

Table 8-5. 256 × 9 Static RAMs.

TYPE	TEMP	TECH	OUTPUT	MAX ACCESS TIME (nS)	MAX SUPPLY CURRENT (mA)	PINS	PRICE ($)
93479	C	TTL	3S	35	185	22	24.31
93479	C	TTL	3S	45	185	22	20.74
93479	M	TTL	3S	45	200	22	30.75
93479	M	TTL	3S	60	200	22	27.89

Table 8-6. 1K × 1 Static RAMs.

TYPE	TEMP	TECH	OUTPUT	MAX ACCESS TIME (nS)	MAX SUPPLY CURRENT (mA)	PINS	PRICE ($)
2115	C	MOS	3S	30	125	16	5.25
2115	C	MOS	3S	35	125	16	4.40

TYPE	TEMP	TECH	OUTPUT	MAX ACCESS TIME (nS)	MAX SUPPLY CURRENT (mA)	PINS	PRICE ($)
2115	C	MOS	3S	45	125	16	2.80
2115	C	MOS	3S	70	125	16	2.50
2115L	C	MOS	3S	45	75	16	3.00
2115L	C	MOS	3S	70	75	16	3.30
2125	C	MOS	OC	20	150	16	8.30
2125	C	MOS	OC	25	125	16	7.30
2125	C	MOS	OC	35	125	16	4.20
2125	C	MOS	OC	45	125	16	3.30
2125	C	MOS	OC	70	125	16	3.05
2125L	C	MOS	OC	45	75	16	3.35
2125L	C	MOS	OC	70	75	16	3.25
6508	I	CMOS	3S	180	4	16	7.94
6508	M	CMOS	3S	180	4	16	12.76
6508	I	CMOS	3S	250	4	16	5.91
6508	M	CMOS	3S	250	4	16	9.85
6508	C	CMOS	3S	310	4	16	4.94
6518	I	CMOS	3S	180	4	18	7.94
6518	M	CMOS	3S	180	4	18	12.81
6518	I	CMOS	3S	250	4	18	5.91
6518	M	CMOS	3S	250	4	18	9.85
6518	C	CMOS	3S	310	4	18	4.28
93415	C	TTL	OC	20	155	16	13.25
93415	C	TTL	OC	25	125	16	5.29
93415	C	TTL	OC	30	155	16	4.00
93415	M	TTL	OC	30	170	16	29.00
93415	M	TTL	OC	40	170	16	13.59
93415	C	TTL	OC	45	155	16	4.25
93415	M	TTL	OC	60	170	16	10.72
93L415	C	TTL	OC	35	65	16	5.29

TYPE	TEMP	TECH	OUTPUT	MAX ACCESS TIME (nS)	MAX SUPPLY CURRENT (mA)	PINS	PRICE ($)
93L415	M	TTL	OC	40	135	16	16.45
93L415	C	TTL	OC	45	80	16	3.93
93L415	M	TTL	OC	50	75	16	15.02
93L415	M	TTL	OC	55	90	16	18.25
93L415	C	TTL	OC	60	80	16	4.10
93L415	M	TTL	OC	70	90	16	15.02
93425	C	TTL	3S	20	155	16	13.25
93425	C	TTL	3S	25	125	16	5.29
93425	C	TTL	3S	30	155	16	4.00
93425	M	TTL	3S	30	170	16	29.00
93425	M	TTL	3S	40	170	16	13.59
93425	C	TTL	3S	45	155	16	4.25
93425	M	TTL	3S	60	170	16	10.30
93L425	C	TTL	3S	35	65	16	5.29
93L425	M	TTL	3S	40	135	16	16.45
93L425	C	TTL	3S	45	80	16	3.93
93L425	M	TTL	3S	50	75	16	15.02
93L425	M	TTL	3S	55	90	16	18.25
93L425	C	TTL	3S	60	80	16	5.01
93L425	M	TTL	3S	70	90	16	15.37

Table 8-7. 1K × 4 Static RAMs.

TYPE	TEMP	TECH	OUTPUT	MAX ACCESS TIME (nS)	MAX SUPPLY CURRENT (mA)	PINS	PRICE ($)
2114	C	MOS	3S	150	100	18	2.45
2114	C	MOS	3S	200	100	18	1.37
2114	C	MOS	3S	200	70	18	2.80

TYPE	TEMP	TECH	OUTPUT	MAX ACCESS TIME (nS)	MAX SUPPLY CURRENT (mA)	PINS	PRICE ($)
2114	M	MOS	3S	200	70	18	9.85
2114	C	MOS	3S	250	100	18	1.33
2114	M	MOS	3S	250	70	18	9.50
2114	C	MOS	3S	300	100	18	1.33
2114	C	MOS	3S	450	100	18	1.33
2114L	C	MOS	3S	100	40	18	3.05
2114L	C	MOS	3S	120	40	18	2.95
2114L	C	MOS	3S	150	40	18	2.75
2114L	C	MOS	3S	150	70	18	2.55
2114L	M	MOS	3S	150	50	18	15.35
2114L	C	MOS	3S	200	40	18	2.75
2114L	C	MOS	3S	200	70	18	2.25
2114L	M	MOS	3S	200	50	18	13.50
2114L	C	MOS	3S	250	70	18	2.15
2114L	C	MOS	3S	300	70	18	2.10
2114L	C	MOS	3S	450	70	18	2.00
2148	C	MOS	3S	35	180	18	7.51
2148	C	MOS	3S	45	180	18	4.85
2148	M	MOS	3S	45	180	18	47.00
2148	C	MOS	3S	55	180	18	4.25
2148	M	MOS	3S	55	180	18	38.42
2148	C	MOS	3S	70	180	18	3.35
2148	M	MOS	3S	70	180	18	26.85
21L48	C	MOS	3S	45	125	18	6.44
21L48/2148L	C	MOS	3S	55	125	18	4.65
21L48/2148L	C	MOS	3S	70	125	18	4.15
2149	C	MOS	3S	35	180	18	7.51
2149	C	MOS	3S	45	180	18	5.25
2149	M	MOS	3S	45	180	18	47.00

TYPE	TEMP	TECH	OUTPUT	MAX ACCESS TIME (nS)	MAX SUPPLY CURRENT (mA)	PINS	PRICE ($)
2149	C	MOS	3S	55	150	18	4.65
2149	C	MOS	3S	55	180	18	4.65
2149	M	MOS	3S	55	180	18	38.42
2149	C	MOS	3S	70	180	18	3.35
2149	M	MOS	3S	70	180	18	26.85
21L49	C	MOS	3S	45	125	18	6.44
21L49	C	MOS	3S	55	125	18	4.86
21L49/2149L	C	MOS	3S	70	125	18	4.25
6514	I	CMOS	3S	120	7	18	10.40
6514	M	CMOS	3S	120	7	18	21.14
6514	I	CMOS	3S	220	7	18	7.59
6514	M	CMOS	3S	220	7	18	15.43
6514	I	CMOS	3S	320	7	18	6.02
6514	M	CMOS	3S	320	7	18	11.87
9114	C	MOS	3S	200	70	18	5.15
9114	M	MOS	3S	200	80	18	12.70
9114	C	MOS	3S	300	70	18	1.95
9114	M	MOS	3S	300	80	18	8.70
9114	C	MOS	3S	450	70	18	1.90
9114	M	MOS	3S	450	80	18	7.95
91L14	C	MOS	3S	200	50	18	2.75
91L14	C	MOS	3S	300	50	18	2.54
91L14	M	MOS	3S	300	60	18	9.80
91L14	C	MOS	3S	450	50	18	2.47
91L14	M	MOS	3S	450	60	18	8.70
9124	C	MOS	3S	300	70	18	3.58
9124	M	MOS	3S	300	80	18	15.95
9124	C	MOS	3S	450	70	18	3.43
9124	M	MOS	3S	450	80	18	14.50

TYPE	TEMP	TECH	OUTPUT	MAX ACCESS TIME (nS)	MAX SUPPLY CURRENT (mA)	PINS	PRICE ($)
91L24	C	MOS	3S	300	50	18	3.93
91L24	M	MOS	3S	300	60	18	17.30
91L24	C	MOS	3S	450	50	18	3.79
91L24	M	MOS	3S	450	60	18	15.73
9150–20	C	MOS	3S	20	180	24	22.95
9150–25	C	MOS	3S	25	180	24	19.50
9150–25	M	MOS	3S	25	180	24	65.00
9150–35	C	MOS	3S	35	180	24	17.45
9150–35	M	MOS	3S	35	180	24	55.00
9150–45	C	MOS	3S	45	180	24	15.90
9150–45	M	MOS	3S	45	180	24	50.00
91L50–25	C	MOS	3S	25	130	24	22.45
91L50–35	C	MOS	3S	35	130	24	20.00
91L50–45	C	MOS	3S	45	130	24	18.25
9151–40	C	MOS	3S	40	180	24	12.50
9151–50	C	MOS	3S	50	180	24	10.50
9151–50	M	MOS	3S	50	180	24	50.00
9151–60	C	MOS	3S	60	180	24	9.35
9151–60	M	MOS	3S	60	180	24	45.00

Table 8-8. 2K × 8 Static RAMs.

TYPE	TEMP	TECH	OUTPUT	MAX ACCESS TIME (nS)	MAX SUPPLY CURRENT (mA)	PINS	PRICE ($)
2016	C	MOS	3S	45	120	24	5.56
2016	C	MOS	3S	55	120	24	4.88
2016	C	MOS	3S	70	120	24	4.19
6116	C	CMOS	3S	25	80	24	11.04

TYPE	TEMP	TECH	OUTPUT	MAX ACCESS TIME (nS)	MAX SUPPLY CURRENT (mA)	PINS	PRICE ($)
6116	C	CMOS	3S	30	80	24	9.20
6116	C	CMOS	3S	35	80	24	7.50
6116	M	CMOS	3S	35	90	24	94.80
6116	C	CMOS	3S	45	80	24	5.20
6116	M	CMOS	3S	45	90	24	79.60
6116	C	CMOS	3S	55	80	24	3.60
6116	M	CMOS	3S	55	90	24	63.70
6116	C	CMOS	3S	70	80	24	3.20
6116	M	CMOS	3S	70	90	24	53.50
6116	C	CMOS	3S	90	80	24	2.80
6116	M	CMOS	3S	90	90	24	46.20
6116	M	CMOS	3S	120	90	24	40.15
6116	M	CMOS	3S	150	90	24	37.00
6116L	C	CMOS	3S	25	75	24	13.80
6116L	C	CMOS	3S	30	75	24	11.50
6116L	C	CMOS	3S	35	75	24	9.50
6116L	M	CMOS	3S	35	85	24	105.00
6116L	C	CMOS	3S	45	75	24	6.50
6116L	M	CMOS	3S	45	85	24	87.56
6116L	C	CMOS	3S	55	75	24	4.50
6116L	M	CMOS	3S	55	85	24	70.07
6116L	C	CMOS	3S	70	75	24	4.00
6116L	M	CMOS	3S	70	85	24	58.36
6116L	C	CMOS	3S	90	75	24	3.50
6116L	M	CMOS	3S	90	85	24	50.82
6116L	M	CMOS	3S	120	85	24	44.17
6116L	M	CMOS	3S	150	85	24	40.00
6516	I	CMOS	3S	120	10	24	27.60
6516	M	CMOS	3S	120	10	24	94.58

TYPE	TEMP	TECH	OUTPUT	MAX ACCESS TIME (nS)	MAX SUPPLY CURRENT (mA)	PINS	PRICE ($)
6516	I	CMOS	3S	200	10	24	21.23
6516	M	CMOS	3S	200	10	24	70.06
9128	C	MOS	3S	70	140	24	9.57
9128	M	MOS	3S	90	180	24	84.85
9128	C	MOS	3S	100	120	24	4.71
9128	M	MOS	3S	120	150	24	61.65
9128	C	MOS	3S	150	100	24	4.35
9128	M	MOS	3S	150	150	24	43.50
9128	C	MOS	3S	200	140	24	3.98
9128	M	MOS	3S	200	150	24	36.25
65162	I	CMOS	3S	70	70	24	21.52
65162	M	CMOS	3S	70	70	24	75.33
65162	I	CMOS	3S	90	70	24	13.55
65162	I	CMOS	3S	90	70	24	15.94
65162	M	CMOS	3S	90	70	24	55.80
65162	M	CMOS	3S	90	70	24	39.06

Table 8-9. 4K × 1 Static RAMs.

TYPE	TEMP	TECH	OUTPUT	MAX ACCESS TIME (nS)	MAX SUPPLY CURRENT (mA)	PINS	PRICE ($)
21L41	C	MOS	3S	120	55	18	5.29
21L41	C	MOS	3S	150	40	18	4.15
21L41	C	MOS	3S	200	40	18	3.86
21L41	C	MOS	3S	250	40	18	3.50
2147	C	MOS	3S	35	180	18	4.25
2147	C	MOS	3S	45	180	18	4.00
2147	M	MOS	3S	45	180	18	28.75

TYPE	TEMP	TECH	OUTPUT	MAX ACCESS TIME (nS)	MAX SUPPLY CURRENT (mA)	PINS	PRICE ($)
2147	C	MOS	3S	55	180	18	3.50
2147	M	MOS	3S	55	180	18	20.15
2147	C	MOS	3S	70	160	18	3.00
2147	M	MOS	3S	70	180	18	13.78
2147L	C	MOS	3S	45	125	18	5.65
2147L	C	MOS	3S	55	125	18	3.70
2147L	C	MOS	3S	70	125	18	4.29
6147	C	MOS	3S	55	35	18	2.80
6147	C	MOS	3S	70	35	18	2.59
61L47	C	MOS	3S	55	35	18	2.94
61L47	C	MOS	3S	70	35	18	2.73
6504	I	CMOS	3S	120	7	18	10.40
6504	M	CMOS	3S	120	7	18	18.88
6504	I	CMOS	3S	220	7	18	6.02
6504	M	CMOS	3S	220	7	18	10.61
9044	C	MOS	3S	200	70	18	5.72
9044	C	MOS	3S	250	70	18	5.43
9044	M	MOS	3S	250	80	18	29.32
9044	C	MOS	3S	300	70	18	5.15
9044	M	MOS	3S	300	80	18	28.24
9044	C	MOS	3S	450	70	18	4.86
9044	M	MOS	3S	450	80	18	27.55
90L44	C	MOS	3S	250	50	18	6.79
90L44	C	MOS	3S	300	50	18	6.51
90L44	C	MOS	3S	450	50	18	6.22
9244	C	MOS	3S	200	70	18	5.72
9244	C	MOS	3S	250	70	18	5.43
9244	M	MOS	3S	250	80	18	29.32
9244	C	MOS	3S	300	70	18	5.15

TYPE	TEMP	TECH	OUTPUT	MAX ACCESS TIME (nS)	MAX SUPPLY CURRENT (mA)	PINS	PRICE ($)
9244	M	MOS	3S	300	80	18	28.24
9244	C	MOS	3S	450	70	18	4.86
9244	M	MOS	3S	450	80	18	27.17
92L44	C	MOS	3S	250	50	18	6.79
92L44	C	MOS	3S	300	50	18	6.51
92L44	M	MOS	3S	300	60	18	40.00
92L44	C	MOS	3S	450	50	18	6.22
92L44	M	MOS	3S	450	60	18	38.40

Table 8-10. 4K × 4 Static RAMs.

TYPE	TEMP	TECH	OUTPUT	MAX ACCESS TIME (nS)	MAX SUPPLY CURRENT (mA)	PINS	PRICE ($)
51C68	C	CMOS	3S	30	90	20	16.88
51C68	C	CMOS	3S	35	90	20	13.85
51C68	M	CMOS	3S	35	100	20	67.14
51C68	M	CMOS	3S	45	100	20	53.70
51C68	M	CMOS	3S	55	100	20	47.67
51C68	M	CMOS	3S	70	100	20	38.15
51C68L	C	CMOS	3S	35	65	20	16.88
51C69	C	CMOS	3S	30	90	20	16.88
51C69	C	CMOS	3S	35	90	20	13.85
51C69L	C	CMOS	3S	35	65	20	16.88
6168	C	CMOS	3S	20	90	20	17.37
6168	C	CMOS	3S	25	90	20	12.87
6168	M	CMOS	3S	25	100	20	117.76
6168	C	CMOS	3S	35	90	20	7.11
6168	M	CMOS	3S	35	100	20	65.06

TYPE	TEMP	TECH	OUTPUT	MAX ACCESS TIME (nS)	MAX SUPPLY CURRENT (mA)	PINS	PRICE ($)
6168	C	CMOS	3S	45	90	20	5.67
6168	M	CMOS	3S	45	100	20	51.88
6168	C	CMOS	3S	55	90	20	4.82
6168	M	CMOS	3S	55	100	20	44.06
6168	M	CMOS	3S	70	100	20	36.71
6168	M	CMOS	3S	85	100	20	30.60
6168	M	CMOS	3S	100	100	20	25.50
6168L	C	CMOS	3S	20	70	20	19.30
6168L	C	CMOS	3S	25	70	20	14.30
6168L	M	CMOS	3S	25	80	20	130.85
6168L	C	CMOS	3S	35	70	20	7.90
6168L	M	CMOS	3S	35	80	20	72.29
6168L	C	CMOS	3S	45	70	20	6.30
6168L	M	CMOS	3S	45	80	20	94.50
6168L	C	CMOS	3S	55	70	20	5.35
6168L	M	CMOS	3S	55	80	20	48.95
6168L	M	CMOS	3S	70	80	20	40.79
6168L	M	CMOS	3S	85	80	20	33.99
6168L	M	CMOS	3S	100	80	20	28.33
99C58-20	C	CMOS	3S	20	180	24	24.75
99C58-25	C	CMOS	3S	25	180	24	19.95
99C58-35	C	CMOS	3S	35	180	24	17.25
99C58-45	C	CMOS	3S	45	180	24	16.00
99C59-20	C	CMOS	3S	20	180	24	24.75
99C59-25	C	CMOS	3S	25	180	24	19.95
99C59-35	C	CMOS	3S	35	180	24	17.25
99C59-45	C	CMOS	3S	45	180	24	16.00
99C68-35	C	CMOS	3S	35	100	20	8.00
99C68-45	C	CMOS	3S	45	100	20	5.35

TYPE	TEMP	TECH	OUTPUT	MAX ACCESS TIME (nS)	MAX SUPPLY CURRENT (mA)	PINS	PRICE ($)
99C68–55	C	CMOS	3S	55	100	20	4.75
99C68–55	M	CMOS	3S	55	120	20	60.00
99C68–70	C	CMOS	3S	70	100	20	4.00
99C68–70	M	CMOS	3S	70	120	20	51.20
99CL68–45	C	CMOS	3S	45	100	20	14.96
99CL68–55	C	CMOS	3S	55	100	20	10.56
99CL68–55	M	CMOS	3S	55	120	20	62.00
99CL68–70	C	CMOS	3S	70	100	20	9.68
99CL68–70	M	CMOS	3S	70	120	20	53.20
71681L	C	CMOS	3S	20	70	24	22.25
71681L	C	CMOS	3S	25	70	24	16.45
71681L	M	CMOS	3S	25	80	24	148.05
71681L	C	CMOS	3S	35	70	24	9.10
71681L	M	CMOS	3S	35	80	24	81.90
71681L	C	CMOS	3S	45	70	24	7.25
71681L	M	CMOS	3S	45	80	24	65.25
71681L	C	CMOS	3S	55	70	24	6.15
71681L	M	CMOS	3S	55	80	24	55.35
71681L	M	CMOS	3S	70	80	24	46.13
71681L	M	CMOS	3S	85	80	24	38.44
71681L	M	CMOS	3S	100	80	24	32.03
71681S	C	CMOS	3S	20	90	24	20.03
71681S	C	CMOS	3S	25	90	24	14.81
71681S	M	CMOS	3S	25	100	24	133.25
71681S	C	CMOS	3S	35	90	24	8.19
71681S	M	CMOS	3S	35	100	24	73.71
71681S	C	CMOS	3S	45	90	24	6.53
71681S	M	CMOS	3S	45	100	24	58.73
71681S	C	CMOS	3S	55	90	24	5.54

TYPE	TEMP	TECH	OUTPUT	MAX ACCESS TIME (nS)	MAX SUPPLY CURRENT (mA)	PINS	PRICE ($)
71681S	M	CMOS	3S	55	100	24	49.82
71681S	M	CMOS	3S	70	100	24	41.51
71681S	M	CMOS	3S	85	100	24	34.59
71681S	M	CMOS	3S	100	100	24	28.83
71682L	C	CMOS	3S	20	70	24	22.25
71682L	C	CMOS	3S	25	70	24	16.45
71682L	M	CMOS	3S	25	80	24	148.05
71682L	C	CMOS	3S	35	70	24	9.10
71682L	M	CMOS	3S	35	80	24	81.90
71682L	C	CMOS	3S	45	70	24	7.25
71682L	M	CMOS	3S	45	80	24	65.25
71682L	C	CMOS	3S	55	70	24	6.15
71682L	M	CMOS	3S	55	80	24	55.35
71682L	M	CMOS	3S	70	80	24	46.13
71682L	M	CMOS	3S	85	80	24	38.44
71682L	M	CMOS	3S	100	80	24	32.03
71682S	C	CMOS	3S	20	90	24	20.03
71682S	C	CMOS	3S	25	90	24	14.81
71682S	M	CMOS	3S	25	100	24	133.25
71682S	C	CMOS	3S	35	90	24	8.19
71682S	M	CMOS	3S	35	100	24	73.71
71682S	C	CMOS	3S	45	90	24	6.53
71682S	M	CMOS	3S	45	100	24	58.73
71682S	C	CMOS	3S	55	90	24	5.54
71682S	M	CMOS	3S	55	100	24	49.82
71682S	M	CMOS	3S	70	100	24	41.51
71682S	M	CMOS	3S	85	100	24	34.59
71682S	M	CMOS	3S	100	100	24	28.83

Table 8-11. 8K × 8 Static RAMs.

TYPE	TEMP	TECH	OUTPUT	MAX ACCESS TIME (nS)	MAX SUPPLY CURRENT (mA)	PINS	PRICE ($)
7164L	C	CMOS	3S	30	80	28	37.20
7164L	C	CMOS	3S	35	80	28	26.40
7164L	M	CMOS	3S	35	90	28	268.00
7164L	C	CMOS	3S	45	80	28	19.20
7164L	M	CMOS	3S	45	90	28	223.00
7164L	C	CMOS	3S	55	80	28	17.40
7164L	M	CMOS	3S	55	90	28	186.00
7164L	C	CMOS	3S	70	80	28	15.00
7164L	M	CMOS	3S	70	90	28	155.00
7164L	M	CMOS	3S	85	90	28	129.00
7164L	M	CMOS	3S	100	90	28	108.00
7164L	M	CMOS	3S	120	90	28	108.00
7164L	M	CMOS	3S	150	90	28	108.00
7164L	M	CMOS	3S	200	90	28	108.00
7164S	C	CMOS	3S	30	90	28	30.50
7164S	C	CMOS	3S	35	90	28	21.50
7164S	M	CMOS	3S	35	100	28	246.00
7164S	C	CMOS	3S	45	90	28	15.50
7164S	M	CMOS	3S	45	100	28	205.00
7164S	C	CMOS	3S	55	90	28	14.00
7164S	M	CMOS	3S	55	100	28	171.00
7164S	C	CMOS	3S	70	90	28	12.00
7164S	M	CMOS	3S	70	100	28	142.00
7164S	M	CMOS	3S	85	100	28	118.00
7164S	M	CMOS	3S	100	100	28	99.00
7164S	M	CMOS	3S	120	100	28	99.00
7164S	M	CMOS	3S	150	100	28	99.00
7164S	M	CMOS	3S	200	100	28	99.00

TYPE	TEMP	TECH	OUTPUT	MAX ACCESS TIME (nS)	MAX SUPPLY CURRENT (mA)	PINS	PRICE ($)
7165L	C	CMOS	3S	30	80	28	44.60
7165L	C	CMOS	3S	35	80	28	31.70
7165L	M	CMOS	3S	35	90	28	310.00
7165L	C	CMOS	3S	45	80	28	23.00
7165L	M	CMOS	3S	45	90	28	258.00
7165L	C	CMOS	3S	55	80	28	20.90
7165L	M	CMOS	3S	55	90	28	215.00
7165L	C	CMOS	3S	70	80	28	18.00
7165L	M	CMOS	3S	70	90	28	179.00
7165L	M	CMOS	3S	85	90	28	122.00
7165S	C	CMOS	3S	30	90	28	36.60
7165S	C	CMOS	3S	35	90	28	25.80
7165S	M	CMOS	3S	35	100	28	282.00
7165S	C	CMOS	3S	45	90	28	18.60
7165S	M	CMOS	3S	45	100	28	235.00
7165S	C	CMOS	3S	55	90	28	16.80
7165S	M	CMOS	3S	55	100	28	196.00
7165S	C	CMOS	3S	70	90	28	14.40
7165S	M	CMOS	3S	70	100	28	163.00
7165S	M	CMOS	3S	85	100	28	135.00
99C88-10	C	CMOS	3S	100	60	28	14.25
99C88-10	M	CMOS	3S	100	60	28	215.00
99C88-12	M	CMOS	3S	120	60	28	175.00
99C88-15	M	CMOS	3S	150	60	28	145.00
99C88-20	M	CMOS	3S	200	60	28	130.00
99C88-20	M	CMOS	3S	200	60	28	130.00
99C88-70	C	CMOS	3S	70	60	28	55.00
99C88-70	M	CMOS	3S	70	60	28	245.00
99CL88-10	C	CMOS	3S	100	40	28	17.00

TYPE	TEMP	TECH	OUTPUT	MAX ACCESS TIME (nS)	MAX SUPPLY CURRENT (mA)	PINS	PRICE ($)
99CL88-70	C	CMOS	3S	70	40	28	66.00
99CS88-70	M	CMOS	3S	70	60	28	245.00

Table 8-12. 16K × 1 Static RAMs.

TYPE	TEMP	TECH	OUTPUT	MAX ACCESS TIME (nS)	MAX SUPPLY CURRENT (mA)	PINS	PRICE ($)
2167	C	MOS	3S	35	120	20	14.40
2167	C	MOS	3S	45	120	20	6.93
2167	M	MOS	3S	45	160	20	104.00
2167	C	MOS	3S	55	120	20	5.53
2167	M	MOS	3S	55	160	20	72.00
2167	C	MOS	3S	70	120	20	4.90
2167	M	MOS	3S	70	160	20	56.00
51C66	C	CMOS	3S	25	80	20	17.00
51C66	C	CMOS	3S	30	80	20	15.25
51C66	C	CMOS	3S	35	80	20	12.50
51C66L	C	CMOS	3S	35	60	20	15.25
51C67	C	CMOS	3S	30	80	20	15.25
51C67	C	CMOS	3S	35	80	20	12.50
51C67	M	CMOS	3S	35	100	20	67.14
51C67	M	CMOS	3S	45	100	20	53.70
51C67	M	CMOS	3S	55	100	20	47.67
51C67L	C	CMOS	3S	35	60	20	15.25
6167	C	CMOS	3S	15	90	20	33.30
6167	C	CMOS	3S	20	90	20	17.37
6167	M	CMOS	3S	20	90	20	156.33
6167	C	CMOS	3S	25	90	20	12.87

TYPE	TEMP	TECH	OUTPUT	MAX ACCESS TIME (nS)	MAX SUPPLY CURRENT (mA)	PINS	PRICE ($)
6167	M	CMOS	3S	25	90	20	115.83
6167	C	CMOS	3S	35	90	20	7.11
6167	M	CMOS	3S	35	90	20	63.99
6167	C	CMOS	3S	45	90	20	5.67
6167	M	CMOS	3S	45	90	20	51.03
6167	C	CMOS	3S	55	90	20	4.82
6167	M	CMOS	3S	55	90	20	43.34
6167	M	CMOS	3S	70	90	20	36.11
6167	M	CMOS	3S	85	90	20	30.09
6167	M	CMOS	3S	100	90	20	25.08
6167L	C	CMOS	3S	15	55	20	37.00
6167L	C	CMOS	3S	20	55	20	19.30
6167L	M	CMOS	3S	20	60	20	173.70
6167L	C	CMOS	3S	25	55	20	14.30
6167L	M	CMOS	3S	25	60	20	128.70
6167L	C	CMOS	3S	35	55	20	7.90
6167L	M	CMOS	3S	35	60	20	71.10
6167L	C	CMOS	3S	45	55	20	6.30
6167L	M	CMOS	3S	45	60	20	56.70
6167L	C	CMOS	3S	55	55	20	5.35
6167L	M	CMOS	3S	55	60	20	48.15
6167L	M	CMOS	3S	70	60	20	40.13
6167L	M	CMOS	3S	85	60	20	33.44
6167L	M	CMOS	3S	100	60	20	27.86
65262	I	CMOS	3S	70	50	20	21.52
65262	M	CMOS	3S	70	50	20	75.33
65262	I	CMOS	3S	85	50	20	13.55
65262	I	CMOS	3S	85	50	20	15.94
65262	M	CMOS	3S	85	50	20	55.80

Table 8-13. 16K × 4 Static RAMs.

TYPE	TEMP	TECH	OUTPUT	MAX ACCESS TIME (nS)	MAX SUPPLY CURRENT (mA)	PINS	PRICE ($)
7188L	C	CMOS	3S	25	70	22	49.50
7188L	M	CMOS	3S	25	85	22	297.00
7188L	C	CMOS	3S	30	70	22	44.00
7188L	M	CMOS	3S	30	85	22	264.00
7188L	C	CMOS	3S	35	70	22	38.50
7188L	M	CMOS	3S	35	85	22	231.00
7188L	C	CMOS	3S	45	70	22	27.50
7188L	M	CMOS	3S	45	85	22	177.69
7188L	C	CMOS	3S	55	70	22	19.80
7188L	M	CMOS	3S	55	85	22	142.15
7188L	C	CMOS	3S	70	70	22	13.20
7188L	M	CMOS	3S	70	85	22	118.46
7188L	M	CMOS	3S	85	85	22	103.01
7188S	C	CMOS	3S	25	90	22	45.00
7188S	M	CMOS	3S	25	105	22	270.00
7188S	C	CMOS	3S	30	90	22	40.00
7188S	M	CMOS	3S	30	105	22	240.00
7188S	C	CMOS	3S	35	90	22	35.00
7188S	M	CMOS	3S	35	105	22	210.00
7188S	C	CMOS	3S	45	90	22	25.00
7188S	M	CMOS	3S	45	105	22	161.54
7188S	C	CMOS	3S	55	90	22	18.00
7188S	M	CMOS	3S	55	105	22	129.23
7188S	C	CMOS	3S	70	90	22	12.00
7188S	M	CMOS	3S	70	105	22	107.69
7188S	M	CMOS	3S	85	105	22	93.65
7198L	C	CMOS	3S	25	85	24	49.50
7198L	C	CMOS	3S	30	85	24	44.00

TYPE	TEMP	TECH	OUTPUT	MAX ACCESS TIME (nS)	MAX SUPPLY CURRENT (mA)	PINS	PRICE ($)
7198L	M	CMOS	3S	30	95	24	259.88
7198L	C	CMOS	3S	35	85	24	38.50
7198L	M	CMOS	3S	35	95	24	231.00
7198L	C	CMOS	3S	45	85	24	27.50
7198L	M	CMOS	3S	45	95	24	177.69
7198L	C	CMOS	3S	55	85	24	19.80
7198L	M	CMOS	3S	55	95	24	142.15
7198L	C	CMOS	3S	70	85	24	13.20
7198L	M	CMOS	3S	70	95	24	118.46
7198L	M	CMOS	3S	85	95	24	103.01
7198S	C	CMOS	3S	25	100	24	45.00
7198S	C	CMOS	3S	30	100	24	40.00
7198S	M	CMOS	3S	30	110	24	240.00
7198S	C	CMOS	3S	35	100	24	35.00
7198S	M	CMOS	3S	35	110	24	210.00
7198S	C	CMOS	3S	45	100	24	25.00
7198S	M	CMOS	3S	45	110	24	161.54
7198S	C	CMOS	3S	55	100	24	18.00
7198S	M	CMOS	3S	55	110	24	129.23
7198S	C	CMOS	3S	70	100	24	12.00
7198S	M	CMOS	3S	70	110	24	107.69
7198S	M	CMOS	3S	85	110	24	93.65
71981L	C	CMOS	3S	25	85	28	56.93
71981L	C	CMOS	3S	30	85	28	50.60
71981L	M	CMOS	3S	30	95	28	433.13
71981L	C	CMOS	3S	35	85	28	44.28
71981L	M	CMOS	3S	35	95	28	385.00
71981L	C	CMOS	3S	45	85	28	31.63
71981L	M	CMOS	3S	45	95	28	296.15

TYPE	TEMP	TECH	OUTPUT	MAX ACCESS TIME (nS)	MAX SUPPLY CURRENT (mA)	PINS	PRICE ($)
71981L	C	CMOS	3S	55	85	28	22.77
71981L	M	CMOS	3S	55	95	28	236.92
71981L	C	CMOS	3S	70	85	28	15.18
71981L	M	CMOS	3S	70	95	28	197.44
71981L	M	CMOS	3S	85	95	28	171.68
71981S	C	CMOS	3S	25	100	28	51.75
71981S	C	CMOS	3S	30	100	28	46.00
71981S	M	CMOS	3S	30	110	28	393.75
71981S	C	CMOS	3S	35	100	28	40.25
71981S	M	CMOS	3S	35	110	28	350.00
71981S	C	CMOS	3S	45	100	28	28.75
71981S	M	CMOS	3S	45	110	28	269.23
71981S	C	CMOS	3S	55	100	28	20.70
71981S	M	CMOS	3S	55	110	28	215.38
71981S	C	CMOS	3S	70	100	28	13.80
71981S	M	CMOS	3S	70	110	28	179.49
71981S	M	CMOS	3S	85	110	28	156.08
71982L	C	CMOS	3S	25	85	28	56.93
71982L	C	CMOS	3S	30	85	28	50.60
71982L	M	CMOS	3S	30	95	28	433.13
71982L	C	CMOS	3S	35	85	28	44.28
71982L	M	CMOS	3S	35	95	28	385.00
71982L	C	CMOS	3S	45	85	28	31.63
71982L	M	CMOS	3S	45	95	28	296.15
71982L	C	CMOS	3S	55	85	28	22.77
71982L	M	CMOS	3S	55	95	28	236.92
71982L	C	CMOS	3S	70	85	28	15.18
71982L	M	CMOS	3S	70	95	28	197.44
71982L	M	CMOS	3S	85	95	28	171.68

TYPE	TEMP	TECH	OUTPUT	MAX ACCESS TIME (nS)	MAX SUPPLY CURRENT (mA)	PINS	PRICE ($)
71982S	C	CMOS	3S	25	100	28	51.75
71982S	C	CMOS	3S	30	100	28	46.00
71982S	M	CMOS	3S	30	110	28	393.75
71982S	C	CMOS	3S	35	100	28	40.25
71982S	M	CMOS	3S	35	110	28	350.00
71982S	C	CMOS	3S	45	100	28	28.75
71982S	M	CMOS	3S	45	110	28	269.23
71982S	C	CMOS	3S	55	100	28	20.70
71982S	M	CMOS	3S	55	110	28	215.38
71982S	C	CMOS	3S	70	100	28	13.80
71982S	M	CMOS	3S	70	110	28	179.49
71982S	M	CMOS	3S	85	110	28	156.08

Table 8-14. 64K × 1 Static RAMs.

TYPE	TEMP	TECH	OUTPUT	MAX ACCESS TIME (nS)	MAX SUPPLY CURRENT (mA)	PINS	PRICE ($)
7187L	C	CMOS	3S	25	70	22	49.50
7187L	M	CMOS	3S	25	85	22	297.00
7187L	C	CMOS	3S	30	70	22	44.00
7187L	M	CMOS	3S	30	85	22	264.00
7187L	C	CMOS	3S	35	70	22	38.50
7187L	M	CMOS	3S	35	85	22	231.00
7187L	C	CMOS	3S	45	70	22	27.50
7187L	M	CMOS	3S	45	85	22	177.69
7187L	C	CMOS	3S	55	70	22	19.80
7187L	M	CMOS	3S	55	85	22	142.15
7187L	C	CMOS	3S	70	70	22	13.20

TYPE	TEMP	TECH	OUTPUT	MAX ACCESS TIME (nS)	MAX SUPPLY CURRENT (mA)	PINS	PRICE ($)
7187L	M	CMOS	3S	70	85	22	118.46
7187L	M	CMOS	3S	85	85	22	103.01
7187S	C	CMOS	3S	25	90	22	45.00
7187S	M	CMOS	3S	25	105	22	270.00
7187S	C	CMOS	3S	30	90	22	40.00
7187S	M	CMOS	3S	30	105	22	240.00
7187S	C	CMOS	3S	35	90	22	35.00
7187S	M	CMOS	3S	35	105	22	210.00
7187S	C	CMOS	3S	45	90	22	25.00
7187S	M	CMOS	3S	45	105	22	161.54
7187S	C	CMOS	3S	55	90	22	18.00
7187S	M	CMOS	3S	55	105	22	129.23
7187S	C	CMOS	3S	70	90	22	12.00
7187S	M	CMOS	3S	70	105	22	107.69
7187S	M	CMOS	3S	85	105	22	93.65
99C641-25	C	CMOS	3S	25	130	22	55.80
99C641-35	C	CMOS	3S	35	110	22	36.25
99C641-45	C	CMOS	3S	45	90	22	28.30
99C641-55	C	CMOS	3S	55	90	22	24.40
99C641-70	C	CMOS	3S	70	90	22	21.80

The largest SRAM available from *domestic* suppliers is 16K by 4 and 64K by 1. The Japanese are now supplying 32K × 8 SRAMs.

8.2 DRAMs

Figure 8-7 shows the schematic for a dynamic RAM cell. When the capacitor is charged, the cell holds a value of 1; when discharged, a value of 0. The advantage of this type of RAM cell is its small physical size. This means higher density memories, or more bits per package.

The disadvantage of this type of memory cell is that the charge will eventually

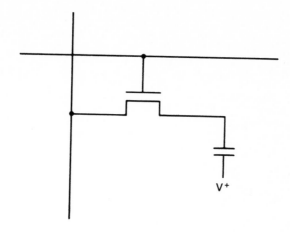

Fig. 8-7. Dynamic RAM cell schematic.

be reduced to zero due to leakage currents. To prevent this, each cell in the array must be periodically read, the voltage compared to a reference value, and then the charge restored to the capacitor if the data is supposed to be a 1. In order to maintain the data in the memory cell, the charge must be restored approximately every 2 milliseconds. This process is called *memory refresh*.

For each column of memory cells in the DRAM there is a circuit that performs the refresh function each time a cell is read. Therefore, to refresh the entire memory it is necessary to address each row at least once every 2 mS.

Another feature of dynamic RAMs is that row and column address lines are multiplexed. With this technique, it is possible to squeeze a 256K by 1 dynamic RAM in a 16-pin package. Figure 8-8 shows the logic symbol for a 256K by 1 DRAM. Notice the nine address lines, A0-A8; the row address select line, RAS; and the column address select line, CAS.

Figure 8-9 shows read mode timing for a DRAM. Row and column address are presented sequentially on the address lines. The row address is latched internally when the RAS line goes LOW. The column address is latched internally when the CAS line goes LOW. Some time later (less than 200 ns for slow DRAMs), the D_{OUT} goes to the state corresponding to the selected cell. The t_{RAC} is the row address access time; t_{CAC} is the column access time. The governing access time is the row access time, and it is this specification that manufacturers use to differentiate the various speed versions of the DRAMs they offer.

Tables 8-15 through 8-19 lists DRAMs available from domestic suppliers:

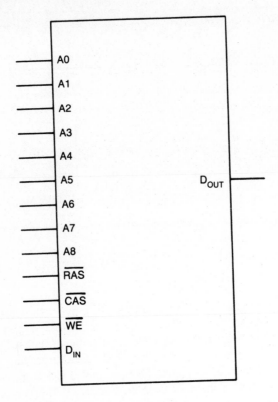

Fig. 8-8. Logic symbol for a 256K × 1 dynamic RAM.

Table	RAM size
8-15	16K × 1
8-16	16K × 4
8-17	64K × 1
8-18	64K × 4
8-19	256K × 1

Since this market is dominated by the Japanese suppliers, the reader can probably do better by checking mail order prices in such publications as *Byte* and *Computer Shopper.*

8.3 PROMS

Programmable Read Only Memories are also random access memories (like SRAMs and DRAMs) but they are never called RAMs. Figure 8-10 shows the

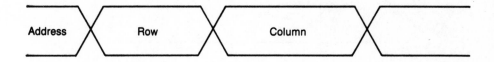

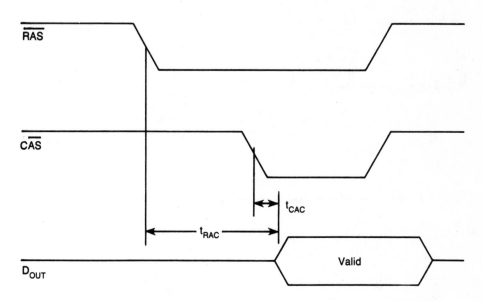

Fig. 8-9. Dynamic RAM access times.

Table 8-15. 16K × 1 Dynamic RAMs.

TYPE	TEMP	TECH	OUTPUT	MAX ACCESS TIME (nS)	MAX SUPPLY CURRENT (mA)	PINS	PRICE ($)
4517	C	MOS	3S	100	31	16	1.75
4517	C	MOS	3S	120	28	16	1.54
4517	C	MOS	3S	150	25	16	1.47
4517	C	MOS	3S	200	23	16	1.40

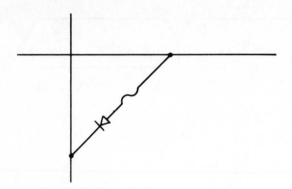

Fig. 8-10. Bipolar PROM cell schematic.

Table 8-16. 16K × 4 Dynamic RAMs.

TYPE	TEMP	TECH	OUTPUT	MAX ACCESS TIME (nS)	MAX SUPPLY CURRENT (mA)	PINS	PRICE ($)
4416	C	MOS	3S	120	54	18	3.20
4416	C	MOS	3S	150	48	18	2.56
4416	M	MOS	3S	150	48	18	34.50
4416	C	MOS	3S	200	42	18	2.56
4416	M	MOS	3S	200	42	18	30.36

Table 8-17. 64K × 1 Dynamic RAMs.

TYPE	TEMP	TECH	OUTPUT	MAX ACCESS TIME (nS)	MAX SUPPLY CURRENT (mA)	PINS	PRICE ($)
4164	C	MOS	3S	120	48	16	2.32
4164	M	MOS	3S	120	48	16	26.81
4164	C	MOS	3S	150	45	16	2.00
4164	M	MOS	3S	150	45	16	21.45
4164	C	MOS	3S	200	37	16	2.00
4164	M	MOS	3S	200	37	16	19.31

Table 8-18. 64K × 4 Dynamic RAMs.

TYPE	TEMP	TECH	OUTPUT	MAX ACCESS TIME (nS)	MAX SUPPLY CURRENT (mA)	PINS	PRICE ($)
4464	C	MOS	3S	120	80	18	5.60
4464	C	MOS	3S	150	70	18	4.80
4464	C	MOS	3S	200	60	18	4.80

Table 8-19. 256K × 1 Dynamic RAMs.

TYPE	TEMP	TECH	OUTPUT	MAX ACCESS TIME (nS)	MAX SUPPLY CURRENT (mA)	PINS	PRICE ($)
4256	C	MOS	3S	120	78	16	5.60
4256	C	MOS	3S	150	68	16	4.80
4256	M	MOS	3S	150	75	16	107.25
4256	C	MOS	3S	200	58	16	4.80
4256	M	MOS	3S	200	60	16	92.95
4257	C	MOS	3S	120	78	16	5.60
4257	C	MOS	3S	150	68	16	4.80
4257	C	MOS	3S	200	58	16	4.80

schematic for the bipolar PROM cell. The PROM cell shown consists of a diode and a fusible link made of platinum silicide or titanium-tungsten.

PROM cells are initially set to the LOW or 0 state (not fused) and may be programmed the HIGH or 1 state by applying a high voltage (10.5 V or 21 V or other voltage depending on manufacturer) to the outputs when the desired address is selected. Although PROM manufacturers supply detailed electrical information and programming procedures, most PROMs are programmed by using a PROM programmer, a piece of electronic equipment (either stand-alone or usable with a personal computer) that allows the user to easily program the PROM cells manually or by computer. The required voltages and timing are built into the PROM programmer. The user only needs to look up the particular part type he wants to program and then enter the appropriate code into the PROM programmer.

Tables 8-20 through 8-31 list PROMs ranging in size from 32 by 8 to 8K by 8 as follows:

Table	PROM size
8-20	32 × 8
8-21	256 × 4
8-22	256 × 8
8-23	512 × 4
8-24	512 × 8
8-25	1K × 4
8-26	1K × 8
8-27	2K × 4
8-28	2K × 8
8-29	4K × 4
8-30	4K × 8
8-31	8K × 8

Table 8-20. 32 × 8 PROMs.

TYPE	TEMP	TECH	OUTPUT	MAX ACCESS TIME (nS)	MAX SUPPLY CURRENT (mA)	PINS	PRICE ($)
27LS18	C	TTL	OC	55	80	16	5.35
27LS18	M	TTL	OC	70	80	16	18.15
27S18	C	TTL	OC	40	115	16	1.45
27S18	M	TTL	OC	50	115	16	3.25
27S18A	C	TTL	OC	25	115	16	1.45
27S18A	M	TTL	OC	35	115	16	3.80
27S18SA	C	TTL	OC	15	115	16	2.75
27S18SA	M	TTL	OC	20	115	16	6.50
27LS19	C	TTL	3S	55	80	16	5.35
27LS19	M	TTL	3S	70	80	16	18.15
27S19	C	TTL	3S	40	115	16	1.45
27S19	M	TTL	3S	50	115	16	3.25
27S19A	C	TTL	3S	25	115	16	1.45

TYPE	TEMP	TECH	OUTPUT	MAX ACCESS TIME (nS)	MAX SUPPLY CURRENT (mA)	PINS	PRICE ($)
27S19A	M	TTL	3S	35	115	16	3.80
27S19SA	C	TTL	3S	15	115	16	2.75
27S19SA	M	TTL	3S	20	115	16	6.50
82S23	C	TTL	OC	50	96	16	1.00
82S23	M	TTL	OC	65	110	16	2.86
82S23A	C	TTL	OC	25	96	16	1.45
82S23A	M	TTL	OC	35	110	16	3.56
18S030	C	TTL	3S	40	110	16	1.65
18S030	M	TTL	3S	50	110	16	3.15
18SA030	C	TTL	OC	40	110	16	1.65
38S030-25	C	TTL	3S	25	125	16	1.17
38SA030-25	C	TTL	OC	25	125	16	1.17
53S080	M	TTL	OC	35	125	16	3.34
53S081	M	TTL	3S	35	125	16	3.34
54S188	M	TTL	OC	45	110	16	2.60
54S288	M	TTL	3S	45	110	16	2.60
63S080	C	TTL	OC	25	125	16	1.50
63S081	C	TTL	3S	25	125	16	1.50
63S081A	C	TTL	3S	15	125	16	2.25
74S188	C	TTL	OC	35	110	16	1.45
74S288	C	TTL	3S	35	110	16	1.45
82S123	C	TTL	3S	50	96	16	1.07
82S123	M	TTL	3S	65	110	16	2.87
82S123A	C	TTL	3S	25	96	16	1.45
82S123A	M	TTL	3S	35	110	16	3.47

Table 8-21. 256 × 4 PROMs.

TYPE	TEMP	TECH	OUTPUT	MAX ACCESS TIME (nS)	MAX SUPPLY CURRENT (mA)	PINS	PRICE ($)
24S10	C	TTL	3S	55	100	16	2.17
24S10	M	TTL	3S	75	100	16	3.58
24SA10	C	TTL	OC	65	100	16	2.17
27S20	C	TTL	OC	45	130	16	1.70
27S20	M	TTL	OC	60	130	16	4.00
27S20A	C	TTL	OC	30	130	16	1.70
27S20A	M	TTL	OC	40	130	16	4.40
27S21	C	TTL	3S	45	130	16	1.70
27S21	M	TTL	3S	60	130	16	4.00
27S21A	C	TTL	3S	30	130	16	1.70
27S21A	M	TTL	3S	40	130	16	4.40
34L10–25	C	TTL	3S	25	50	16	1.70
34L10–35	C	TTL	3S	35	50	16	1.32
34S10–18	C	TTL	3S	18	95	16	5.05
34S10–25	C	TTL	3S	25	95	16	1.32
34SA10–25	C	TTL	OC	25	95	16	1.32
53S140	M	TTL	OC	55	130	16	3.42
53S141	M	TTL	3S	55	130	16	3.42
53S141A	M	TTL	3S	40	130	16	4.34
54S287	M	TTL	3S	60	130	16	2.85
54S387	M	TTL	OC	60	130	16	2.85
63S140	C	TTL	OC	45	130	16	1.59
63S141	C	TTL	3S	45	130	16	1.59
63S141A	C	TTL	3S	30	130	16	2.00
74S287	C	TTL	3S	50	130	16	1.50
74S387	C	TTL	OC	50	130	16	1.50
82S126	C	TTL	OC	50	120	16	1.30

TYPE	TEMP	TECH	OUTPUT	MAX ACCESS TIME (nS)	MAX SUPPLY CURRENT (mA)	PINS	PRICE ($)
82S126	M	TTL	OC	70	125	16	3.87
82S126A	C	TTL	OC	30	120	16	1.30
82S126A	M	TTL	OC	35	125	16	4.28
82S129	C	TTL	3S	50	120	16	1.30
82S129	M	TTL	3S	70	125	16	3.87
82S129A	C	TTL	3S	27	120	16	1.30
82S129A	M	TTL	3S	35	125	16	4.28

Table 8-22. 256 × 8 PROMs.

TYPE	TEMP	TECH	OUTPUT	MAX ACCESS TIME (nS)	MAX SUPPLY CURRENT (mA)	PINS	PRICE ($)
28L22	C	TTL	3S	70	100	20	3.91
28L22	M	TTL	3S	75	100	20	5.72
28LA22	C	TTL	OC	75	100	20	3.91
53S280	M	TTL	OC	50	140	20	5.18
53S281	M	TTL	3S	50	140	20	5.18
53S281A	M	TTL	3S	40	140	20	5.36
54LS471	M	TTL	3S	70	100	20	6.40
63S280	C	TTL	OC	45	140	20	3.34
63S281	C	TTL	3S	45	140	20	3.34
63S281A	C	TTL	3S	28	140	20	3.67
74LS471	C	TTL	3S	60	100	20	3.25
82LS135	C	TTL	3S	100	100	20	3.36
82S135	C	TTL	3S	45	150	20	3.43

Table 8-23. 512 × 4 PROMs.

TYPE	TEMP	TECH	OUTPUT	MAX ACCESS TIME (nS)	MAX SUPPLY CURRENT (mA)	PINS	PRICE ($)
27S12	C	TTL	OC	50	130	16	2.90
27S12	M	TTL	OC	60	130	16	6.90
27S12A	C	TTL	OC	30	130	16	3.35
27S12A	M	TTL	OC	40	130	16	7.15
27S13	C	TTL	3S	50	130	16	2.90
27S13	M	TTL	3S	60	130	16	6.90
27S13A	C	TTL	3S	30	130	16	3.35
27S13A	M	TTL	3S	40	130	16	7.15
53S240	M	TTL	OC	55	130	16	4.68
53S241	M	TTL	3S	55	130	16	4.68
53S241A	M	TTL	3S	45	130	16	5.61
54S570	M	TTL	OC	65	130	16	4.85
54S570A	M	TTL	OC	60	130	16	5.80
54S571	M	TTL	3S	65	130	16	4.85
54S571A	M	TTL	3S	60	130	16	5.80
54S571B	M	TTL	3S	50	130	16	6.95
63S240	C	TTL	OC	45	130	16	2.76
63S241	C	TTL	3S	45	130	16	2.76
63S241A	C	TTL	3S	35	130	16	3.09
74S570	C	TTL	OC	55	130	16	2.55
74S570A	C	TTL	OC	45	130	16	3.35
74S571	C	TTL	3S	55	130	16	2.55
74S571A	C	TTL	3S	45	130	16	3.35
82S130	C	TTL	OC	50	140	16	2.46
82S130	M	TTL	OC	70	140	16	5.66
82S130A	C	TTL	OC	33	140	16	2.91
82S130A	M	TTL	OC	35	140	16	10.27

TYPE	TEMP	TECH	OUTPUT	MAX ACCESS TIME (nS)	MAX SUPPLY CURRENT (mA)	PINS	PRICE ($)
82S131	C	TTL	3S	50	140	16	2.46
82S131	M	TTL	3S	70	140	16	5.66
82S131A	C	TTL	3S	30	140	16	2.91
82S131A	M	TTL	3S	35	140	16	10.27

Table 8-24. 512 × 8 PROMs.

TYPE	TEMP	TECH	OUTPUT	MAX ACCESS TIME (nS)	MAX SUPPLY CURRENT (mA)	PINS	PRICE ($)
27S15	C	TTL	3S	60	175	24	8.00
27S15	M	TTL	3S	90	185	24	19.90
27S28	C	TTL	OC	55	160	20	4.35
27S28	M	TTL	OC	70	160	20	9.40
27S28A	C	TTL	OC	40	160	20	6.00
27S28A	M	TTL	OC	50	160	20	10.90
27S29	C	TTL	3S	55	160	20	4.35
27S29	M	TTL	3S	70	160	20	9.40
27S29A	C	TTL	3S	40	160	20	6.00
27S29A	M	TTL	3S	50	160	20	10.90
27S30	C	TTL	OC	55	175	24	4.80
27S30	M	TTL	OC	70	175	24	9.85
27S30A	C	TTL	OC	40	175	24	7.15
27S30A	M	TTL	OC	50	175	24	12.20
27S31	C	TTL	3S	55	175	24	4.80
27S31	M	TTL	3S	70	175	24	9.85
27S31A	C	TTL	3S	40	175	24	7.15
27S31A	M	TTL	3S	50	175	24	12.20
28L42	C	TTL	3S	95	85	20	5.58

TYPE	TEMP	TECH	OUTPUT	MAX ACCESS TIME (nS)	MAX SUPPLY CURRENT (mA)	PINS	PRICE ($)
28L42	M	TTL	3S	110	85	20	10.73
28S42	C	TTL	3S	60	135	20	5.33
28S42	M	TTL	3S	70	135	20	8.58
28SA42	C	TTL	OC	65	135	20	5.33
28L46	C	TTL	3S	95	85	24	5.86
28S46	C	TTL	3S	60	135	24	5.33
28SA46	C	TTL	OC	65	135	24	5.25
6641	I	CMOS	3S	250	15	24	15.52
6641	M	CMOS	3S	250	15	24	27.94
53S480	M	TTL	OC	50	155	20	9.02
53S481	M	TTL	3S	50	155	20	9.02
53S481A	M	TTL	3S	40	155	20	10.82
54S472	M	TTL	3S	75	155	20	7.10
54S472A	M	TTL	3S	60	155	20	8.50
54S472B	M	TTL	3S	50	155	20	10.15
54S473	M	TTL	OC	75	155	20	7.10
54S473A	M	TTL	OC	60	155	20	8.50
54S474	M	TTL	3S	75	170	24	8.10
54S474A	M	TTL	3S	60	170	24	9.85
54S474B	M	TTL	3S	50	170	24	11.80
54S475	M	TTL	OC	75	170	24	8.10
54S475A	M	TTL	OC	60	170	24	9.85
63S480	C	TTL	OC	45	155	20	4.18
63S481	C	TTL	3S	45	155	20	4.18
63S481A	C	TTL	3S	30	155	20	4.51
74S472	C	TTL	3S	60	155	20	4.35
74S472A	C	TTL	3S	45	155	20	4.35
74S472B	C	TTL	3S	35	155	20	6.25
74S473	C	TTL	OC	60	155	20	4.35

TYPE	TEMP	TECH	OUTPUT	MAX ACCESS TIME (nS)	MAX SUPPLY CURRENT (mA)	PINS	PRICE ($)
74S473A	C	TTL	OC	45	155	20	4.35
74S474	C	TTL	3S	65	170	24	4.80
74S474A	C	TTL	3S	45	170	24	4.80
74S474B	C	TTL	3S	35	170	24	6.95
74S475	C	TTL	OC	65	170	24	4.80
74S475A	C	TTL	OC	45	170	24	4.80
82S115	C	TTL	3S	60	175	24	7.35
82S115	M	TTL	3S	90	185	24	16.61
82S147	C	TTL	3S	60	155	20	2.50
82S147	M	TTL	3S	75	165	20	7.86
82S147A	C	TTL	3S	45	155	20	2.85

Table 8-25. 1K × 4 PROMs.

TYPE	TEMP	TECH	OUTPUT	MAX ACCESS TIME (nS)	MAX SUPPLY CURRENT (mA)	PINS	PRICE ($)
24S41	C	TTL	3S	60	140	18	4.90
24SA41	C	TTL	OC	60	140	18	4.90
27S32	C	TTL	OC	55	140	18	3.80
27S32	M	TTL	OC	70	145	18	9.25
27S32A	C	TTL	OC	35	140	18	5.40
27S32A	M	TTL	OC	45	145	18	12.70
27S33	C	TTL	3S	55	140	18	3.80
27S33	M	TTL	3S	70	145	18	9.25
27S33A	C	TTL	3S	35	140	18	5.40
27S33A	M	TTL	3S	45	145	18	12.70
53S440	M	TTL	OC	55	140	18	7.26
53S441	M	TTL	3S	55	140	18	7.26

TYPE	TEMP	TECH	OUTPUT	MAX ACCESS TIME (nS)	MAX SUPPLY CURRENT (mA)	PINS	PRICE ($)
53S441A	M	TTL	3S	50	140	18	8.27
54S572	M	TTL	OC	75	140	18	8.35
54S572A	M	TTL	OC	60	140	18	10.00
54S573	M	TTL	3S	75	140	18	8.35
54S573A	M	TTL	3S	60	140	18	10.00
54S573B	M	TTL	3S	50	140	18	12.00
63S440	C	TTL	OC	45	140	18	3.51
63S441	C	TTL	3S	45	140	18	3.51
63S441A	C	TTL	3S	35	140	18	3.84
54S572	C	TTL	OC	60	140	18	4.55
54S572A	C	TTL	OC	45	140	18	4.55
54S573	C	TTL	3S	60	140	18	4.55
54S573A	C	TTL	3S	45	140	18	4.55
54S573B	C	TTL	3S	35	140	18	6.60
82S137	C	TTL	3S	60	140	18	2.45
82S137	M	TTL	3S	80	150	18	7.93
82S137A	C	TTL	3S	45	140	18	2.65
82S137A	M	TTL	3S	55	150	18	12.33
82S137B	C	TTL	3S	35	140	18	3.73

Table 8-26. 1K × 8 PROMs.

TYPE	TEMP	TECH	OUTPUT	MAX ACCESS TIME (nS)	MAX SUPPLY CURRENT (mA)	PINS	PRICE ($)
27S35	C	TTL	3S	40	185	24	13.25
27S35	M	TTL	3S	45	185	24	36.50
27S35A	C	TTL	3S	35	185	24	18.00
27S35A	M	TTL	3S	40	185	24	48.00

TYPE	TEMP	TECH	OUTPUT	MAX ACCESS TIME (nS)	MAX SUPPLY CURRENT (mA)	PINS	PRICE ($)
27S37	C	TTL	3S	40	185	24	13.25
27S37	M	TTL	3S	45	185	24	36.50
27S37A	C	TTL	3S	35	185	24	18.00
27S37A	M	TTL	3S	40	185	24	48.00
28L86A	C	TTL	3S	110	80	24	9.66
28L86A	M	TTL	3S	200	95	24	20.74
28S86A	C	TTL	3S	65	165	24	9.52
27S180	C	TTL	OC	60	185	24	7.60
27S180	M	TTL	OC	80	185	24	16.50
27S180A	C	TTL	OC	35	185	24	9.60
27S180A	M	TTL	OC	50	185	24	18.85
27PS181	C	TTL	3S	65	185	24	11.45
27PS181	M	TTL	3S	75	185	24	25.25
27S181	C	TTL	3S	60	185	24	7.60
27S181	M	TTL	3S	80	185	24	16.50
27S181A	C	TTL	3S	35	185	24	9.60
27S181A	M	TTL	3S	50	185	24	18.85
27S280	C	TTL	OC	60	185	24	7.60
27S280	M	TTL	OC	80	185	24	25.00
27S280A	C	TTL	OC	35	185	24	9.60
27S280A	M	TTL	OC	50	185	24	33.00
27S281	C	TTL	3S	60	185	24	7.60
27S281	M	TTL	3S	80	185	24	25.00
27S281A	C	TTL	3S	35	185	24	9.60
27S281A	M	TTL	3S	50	185	24	33.00
77S180	M	TTL	OC	75	170	24	14.15
77LS181	M	TTL	3S	120	100	24	21.60
77S181	M	TTL	3S	75	170	24	14.15
77S181A	M	TTL	3S	75	170	24	16.95

TYPE	TEMP	TECH	OUTPUT	MAX ACCESS TIME (nS)	MAX SUPPLY CURRENT (mA)	PINS	PRICE ($)
77S280	M	TTL	OC	75	170	24	17.70
77S281	M	TTL	3S	75	170	24	17.70
77S281A	M	TTL	3S	75	170	24	21.25
82S141	M	TTL	3S	90	165	24	8.26
82S181	C	TTL	3S	70	175	24	4.65
82S181	M	TTL	3S	90	185	24	8.33
82S181A	C	TTL	3S	55	175	24	5.30
82S181A	M	TTL	3S	55	185	24	11.33
82S181C	C	TTL	3S	35	175	24	6.27
82S183	C	TTL	3S	60	175	24	16.90
87S180	C	TTL	OC	55	170	24	7.95
87LS181	C	TTL	3S	100	100	24	12.95
87S181	C	TTL	3S	55	170	24	7.95
87S181A	C	TTL	3S	45	170	24	9.55
87S280	C	TTL	OC	55	170	24	7.95
87S281	C	TTL	3S	55	170	24	7.95
87S281A	C	TTL	3S	45	170	24	9.55
93Z451	C	TTL	3S	40	135	24	5.36
93Z451	M	TTL	3S	55	135	24	8.58
93Z451A	C	TTL	3S	35	135	24	6.01
93Z451A	M	TTL	3S	45	135	24	11.44
82S2708	M	TTL	3S	90	185	24	42.30

Table 8-27. 2K × 4 PROMs.

TYPE	TEMP	TECH	OUTPUT	MAX ACCESS TIME (nS)	MAX SUPPLY CURRENT (mA)	PINS	PRICE ($)
24S81	C	TTL	3S	70	175	18	9.59
24SA81	C	TTL	OC	70	175	18	9.59

TYPE	TEMP	TECH	OUTPUT	MAX ACCESS TIME (nS)	MAX SUPPLY CURRENT (mA)	PINS	PRICE ($)
27S184	C	TTL	OC	50	150	18	8.35
27S184	M	TTL	OC	55	150	18	13.80
27S184A	C	TTL	OC	35	150	18	10.50
27S184A	M	TTL	OC	45	150	18	21.75
27LS185	C	TTL	3S	60	125	18	12.00
27LS185	M	TTL	3S	65	125	18	33.75
27PS185	C	TTL	3S	50	150	18	12.00
27PS185	M	TTL	3S	55	150	18	33.75
27S185	C	TTL	3S	50	150	18	8.35
27S185	M	TTL	3S	55	150	18	13.80
27S185A	C	TTL	3S	35	150	18	10.50
27S185A	M	TTL	3S	45	150	18	21.75
53S841	M	TTL	3S	55	150	18	11.02
53S841A	M	TTL	3S	50	150	18	11.62
63S841	C	TTL	3S	50	150	18	5.43
63S841A	C	TTL	3S	35	150	18	5.85
77S184	M	TTL	OC	70	140	18	15.10
77S185	M	TTL	3S	70	140	18	15.10
77S185A	M	TTL	3S	60	140	18	12.10
77S185B	M	TTL	3S	50	140	18	21.75
82S185	C	TTL	3S	100	120	18	5.00
82S185	M	TTL	3S	115	130	18	13.50
82S185A	C	TTL	3S	50	155	18	5.37
82S185A	M	TTL	3S	55	160	18	20.75
82S185B	C	TTL	3S	45	155	18	5.75
87S184	C	TTL	OC	55	140	18	8.60
87S185	C	TTL	3S	55	140	18	8.60
87S185A	C	TTL	3S	45	140	18	10.35
87S185B	C	TTL	3S	35	140	18	12.40

Table 8-28. 2K × 8 PROMs.

TYPE	TEMP	TECH	OUTPUT	MAX ACCESS TIME (nS)	MAX SUPPLY CURRENT (mA)	PINS	PRICE ($)
27S45	C	TTL	3S	45	185	24	22.00
27S45	M	TTL	3S	50	185	24	83.00
27S45A	C	TTL	3S	40	185	24	27.00
27S45A	M	TTL	3S	45	185	24	105.75
27S47	C	TTL	3S	45	185	24	22.00
27S47	M	TTL	3S	50	185	24	83.00
27S47A	C	TTL	3S	40	185	24	27.00
27S47A	M	TTL	3S	45	185	24	105.75
6616	I	CMOS	3S	140	15	24	22.00
6616	M	CMOS	3S	140	15	24	66.00
27S190	C	TTL	OC	50	185	24	14.25
27S190	M	TTL	OC	65	185	24	26.10
27S190A	C	TTL	OC	35	185	24	17.35
27S190A	M	TTL	OC	50	185	24	34.80
27PS191	C	TTL	3S	65	185	24	23.60
27PS191	M	TTL	3S	75	185	24	68.25
27S191	C	TTL	3S	50	185	24	14.25
27S191	M	TTL	3S	65	185	24	26.10
27S191A	C	TTL	3S	35	185	24	17.35
27S191A	M	TTL	3S	50	185	24	34.80
27S290	C	TTL	OC	50	185	24	14.25
27S290	M	TTL	OC	65	185	24	26.10
27S290A	C	TTL	OC	35	185	24	17.35
27S290A	M	TTL	OC	50	185	24	34.80
27PS291	C	TTL	3S	65	185	24	28.30
27PS291	M	TTL	3S	75	185	24	82.00
27S291	C	TTL	3S	50	185	24	14.25
27S291	M	TTL	3S	65	185	24	26.10

TYPE	TEMP	TECH	OUTPUT	MAX ACCESS TIME (nS)	MAX SUPPLY CURRENT (mA)	PINS	PRICE ($)
27S291A	C	TTL	3S	35	185	24	18.50
27S291A	M	TTL	3S	50	185	24	34.80
28L166	C	TTL	3S	125	110	24	12.44
28S166	C	TTL	3S	75	175	24	11.37
38L165-35	C	TTL	3S	35	100	24	18.15
38L165-45	C	TTL	3S	45	100	24	10.11
38S165-25	C	TTL	3S	25	160	24	29.86
38S165-35	C	TTL	3S	35	160	24	10.66
77S190	M	TTL	OC	70	175	24	23.40
77S190A	M	TTL	OC	60	175	24	29.35
77S191	M	TTL	3S	70	175	24	23.40
77S191A	M	TTL	3S	60	175	24	29.35
77S191B	M	TTL	3S	50	175	24	35.20
77S290	M	TTL	OC	70	175	24	34.65
77S290A	M	TTL	OC	60	175	24	41.60
77S291	M	TTL	3S	70	175	24	34.65
77S291B	M	TTL	3S	50	175	24	49.90
82S191	C	TTL	3S	80	175	24	7.15
82S191	M	TTL	3S	100	185	24	11.33
82S191A	C	TTL	3S	55	175	24	8.21
82S191A	M	TTL	3S	55	185	24	14.57
82S191C	C	TTL	3S	35	175	24	10.71
87S190	C	TTL	OC	55	175	24	11.95
87S190A	C	TTL	OC	45	175	24	14.35
87S191	C	TTL	3S	55	175	24	11.95
87S191A	C	TTL	3S	45	175	24	14.35
87S191B	C	TTL	3S	35	175	24	17.25
87S290	C	TTL	OC	55	175	24	11.95
87S290A	C	TTL	OC	45	175	24	14.35

TYPE	TEMP	TECH	OUTPUT	MAX ACCESS TIME (nS)	MAX SUPPLY CURRENT (mA)	PINS	PRICE ($)
87S291	C	TTL	3S	55	175	24	11.95
87S291A	C	TTL	3S	45	175	24	14.35
87S291B	C	TTL	3S	35	175	24	17.25
93Z511	C	TTL	3S	45	175	24	10.01
93Z511	M	TTL	3S	55	175	24	12.87
53S1681	M	TTL	3S	60	175	24	20.54
53S1681A	M	TTL	3S	45	175	24	22.63
63S1681	C	TTL	3S	50	175	24	6.68
63S1681A	C	TTL	3S	35	175	24	8.35

Table 8-29. 4K × 4 PROMs.

TYPE	TEMP	TECH	OUTPUT	MAX ACCESS TIME (nS)	MAX SUPPLY CURRENT (mA)	PINS	PRICE ($)
27PS41	C	TTL	3S	50	165	20	27.20
27PS41	M	TTL	3S	65	170	20	77.25
27S41	C	TTL	3S	50	165	20	15.50
27S41	M	TTL	3S	65	170	20	34.00
27S41A	C	TTL	3S	35	165	20	18.50
27S41A	M	TTL	3S	50	170	20	41.75
77S195A	M	TTL	3S	60	170	20	22.75
77S195B	M	TTL	3S	50	170	20	27.90
82HS195	C	TTL	3S	45	145	20	12.15
82HS195A	C	TTL	3S	35	145	20	14.00
82HS195A	M	TTL	3S	35	155	20	38.33
82HS195B	C	TTL	3S	25	145	20	21.00
87S195A	C	TTL	3S	45	170	20	17.40
87S195B	C	TTL	3S	35	170	20	21.75

TYPE	TEMP	TECH	OUTPUT	MAX ACCESS TIME (nS)	MAX SUPPLY CURRENT (mA)	PINS	PRICE ($)
53S1641	M	TTL	3S	65	175	20	24.88
53S1641A	M	TTL	3S	50	175	20	26.64
63S1641	C	TTL	3S	50	175	20	14.20
63S1641A	C	TTL	3S	35	175	20	16.70

Table 8-30. 4K × 8 PROMs.

TYPE	TEMP	TECH	OUTPUT	MAX ACCESS TIME (nS)	MAX SUPPLY CURRENT (mA)	PINS	PRICE ($)
27S43	C	TTL	3S	55	185	24	26.10
27S43	M	TTL	3S	65	185	24	46.40
27S43A	C	TTL	3S	40	185	24	33.35
27S43A	M	TTL	3S	55	185	24	51.00
77S321	M	TTL	3S	65	185	24	60.30
77S421	M	TTL	3S	65	185	24	60.30
82HS321	C	TTL	3S	45	175	24	15.00
82HS321A	C	TTL	3S	35	175	24	17.00
82HS321A	M	TTL	3S	45	185	24	41.42
82HS321B	C	TTL	3S	30	175	24	20.70
87S321	C	TTL	3S	55	185	24	17.14
87S421	C	TTL	3S	55	185	24	21.43
53S3281	M	TTL	3S	60	190	24	41.08
53S3281A	M	TTL	3S	50	190	24	45.26
63S3281	C	TTL	3S	50	190	24	17.54
63S3281A	C	TTL	3S	40	190	24	19.62

Table 8-31. 8K × 8 PROMs.

TYPE	TEMP	TECH	OUTPUT	MAX ACCESS TIME (nS)	MAX SUPPLY CURRENT (mA)	PINS	PRICE ($)
27S49	C	TTL	3S	55	190	24	53.65
27S49	M	TTL	3S	65	190	24	162.50
27S49A	C	TTL	3S	40	190	24	71.00
27S49A	M	TTL	3S	55	190	24	210.25
82HS641	C	TTL	3S	55	175	24	32.85
82HS641A	C	TTL	3S	45	175	24	37.00
82HS641A	M	TTL	3S	55	185	24	156.00
82HS641B	C	TTL	3S	35	175	24	41.50
93Z565	C	TTL	3S	55	180	24	32.89
93Z565	M	TTL	3S	65	180	24	114.40
93Z565A	C	TTL	3S	45	180	24	38.61
93Z565A	M	TTL	3S	55	180	24	121.55

8.4 Registered PROMs

A registered PROM is simply a PROM with an output register. Address access time is a combination of two times: (1) the address setup time between a valid address and the rising edge of the clock; and (2) the delay time between the rising edge of the clock and valid data appearing at the output (as a result of being stored in the output register). See Fig. 8-11.

Tables 8-32 to 8-37 list registered PROMs as follows:

Table	PROM size
8-32	512 × 8
8-33	1K × 4
8-34	1K × 8
8-35	2K × 4
8-36	2K × 8
8-37	4K × 4

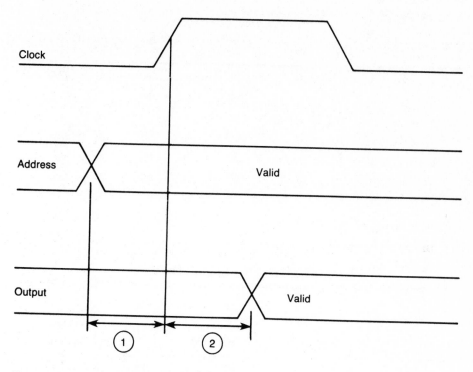

Fig. 8-11. Registered PROM address access time.

Table 8-32. 512 × 8 Registered PROMs.

TYPE	TEMP	TECH	OUTPUT	MAX SETUP TIME (nS)	MAX DELAY TIME (nS)	MAX SUPPLY CURRENT (mA)	PINS	PRICE ($)
27S25	C	TTL	3S	50	27	185	24	8.50
27S25	M	TTL	3S	55	30	185	24	23.00
27S25A	C	TTL	3S	30	20	185	24	11.75
27S25A	M	TTL	3S	35	25	185	24	29.00
27S27	C	TTL	3S	55	27	185	22	12.35
27S27	M	TTL	3S	65	30	185	22	30.45
53RA481	M	TTL	3S	45	25	180	24	18.04

TYPE	TEMP	TECH	OUTPUT	MAX ACCESS TIME (nS)	MAX SUPPLY CURRENT (mA)	PINS	PRICE ($)
53RA481A	M	TTL	3S	35	20	180	24	21.64
63RA481	C	TTL	3S	35	20	180	24	7.52
63RA481A	C	TTL	3S	30	15	180	24	9.44
77SR476	M	TTL	3S	55	30	185	24	15.00
87SR474	C	TTL	3S	50	27	185	24	6.80
87SR474B	C	TTL	3S	35	20	185	24	9.00
87SR476	C	TTL	3S	50	27	185	24	6.80
87SR476B	C	TTL	3S	35	20	185	24	9.00

Table 8-33. 1K × 4 Registered PROMs.

TYPE	TEMP	TECH	OUTPUT	MAX SETUP TIME (nS)	MAX DELAY TIME (nS)	MAX SUPPLY CURRENT (mA)	PINS	PRICE ($)
27S65	C	TTL	3S	30	15	185	24	11.75
27S65	M	TTL	3S	35	20	185	24	38.00
27S65A	C	TTL	3S	23	10	185	24	17.50
27S65A	M	TTL	3S	27	13	185	24	49.00
53DA441	M	TTL	3S	45	25	180	24	22.55
53DA442	M	TTL	3S	45	25	180	24	22.55
63DA441	C	TTL	3S	35	18	180	24	10.02
63DA442	C	TTL	3S	35	18	180	24	10.02

Table 8-34. 1K × 8 Registered PROMs.

TYPE	TEMP	TECH	OUTPUT	MAX SETUP TIME (nS)	MAX DELAY TIME (nS)	MAX SUPPLY CURRENT (mA)	PINS	PRICE ($)
53RS881	M	TTL	3S	45	25	180	24	23.38
53RS881A	M	TTL	3S	40	20	180	24	29.23

TYPE	TEMP	TECH	OUTPUT	MAX ACCESS TIME (nS)	MAX SUPPLY CURRENT (mA)	PINS	PRICE ($)
63RS881	C	TTL	3S	35	20	180	24	10.35
63RS881A	C	TTL	3S	30	15	180	24	12.94
77SR181	M	TTL	3S	50	30	175	24	35.35
82HS187	C	TTL	3S	35	20	175	24	9.80
82HS187A	C	TTL	3S	30	15	175	24	12.65
82HS187A	M	TTL	3S	40	25	185	24	36.50
82HS189	C	TTL	3S	35	20	175	24	9.80
82HS189A	C	TTL	3S	30	15	175	24	12.65
82HS189A	M	TTL	3S	40	25	185	24	36.50
87SR181	C	TTL	3S	40	20	175	24	9.90

Table 8-35. 2K × 4 Registered PROMs.

TYPE	TEMP	TECH	OUTPUT	MAX SETUP TIME (nS)	MAX DELAY TIME (nS)	MAX SUPPLY CURRENT (mA)	PINS	PRICE ($)
27S75	C	TTL	3S	30	15	185	24	14.25
27S75	M	TTL	3S	35	20	185	24	60.00
27S75A	C	TTL	3S	25	12	185	24	25.50
27S75A	M	TTL	3S	30	17	185	24	77.00
53DA841	M	TTL	3S	45	25	185	24	38.33
63DA841	C	TTL	3S	40	20	185	24	16.28

Table 8-36. 2K × 8 Registered PROMs.

TYPE	TEMP	TECH	OUTPUT	MAX SETUP TIME (nS)	MAX DELAY TIME (nS)	MAX SUPPLY CURRENT (mA)	PINS	PRICE ($)
53RA1681	M	TTL	3S	45	25	185	24	33.65
53RA1681A	M	TTL	3S	40	20	185	24	38.33

TYPE	TEMP	TECH	OUTPUT	MAX ACCESS TIME (nS)	MAX SUPPLY CURRENT (mA)	PINS	PRICE ($)
53RS1681	M	TTL	3S	45	25	185	24	33.65
53RS1681A	M	TTL	3S	40	20	185	24	38.33
63RA1681	C	TTL	3S	40	20	185	24	14.20
63RA1681A	C	TTL	3S	35	15	185	24	16.28
63RS1681	C	TTL	3S	40	20	185	24	14.20
63RS1681A	C	TTL	3S	35	15	185	24	16.28

Table 8-37. 4K × 4 Registered PROMs.

TYPE	TEMP	TECH	OUTPUT	MAX SETUP TIME (nS)	MAX DELAY TIME (nS)	MAX SUPPLY CURRENT (mA)	PINS	PRICE ($)
27S85	C	TTL	3S	35	15	185	24	17.00
27S85	M	TTL	3S	40	20	185	24	96.00
27S85A	C	TTL	3S	27	12	185	24	34.00
27S85A	M	TTL	3S	30	17	185	24	120.00
53D1641	M	TTL	3S	45	25	190	24	45.09
53DA1643	M	TTL	2S	45	25	190	24	45.09
63D1641	C	TTL	3S	40	20	190	24	20.04
63DA1643	C	TTL	2S	40	20	190	24	20.04

8.5 Erasable PROMs (EPROMs)

Erasable PROMs are reprogrammable. The EPROM is packaged in ceramic dual-in-line package (DIP) that has a quartz window that allows the EPROM to be erased using ultraviolet light. Figure 8-12 shows the schematic for the EPROM cell. The cell consists of one MOS transistor with two gates: (1) a floating gate shown by the three dashes; and (2) a control gate.

When the cell is programmed by a high voltage (V_{PP}), high energy electrons penetrate the gate oxide and are held on the floating gate. This causes a shift in the MOS transistor threshold voltage to a value higher than a reference voltage that is applied to the control gate. If the threshold voltage is above the reference voltage, no current will flow in the transistor. This state is logic O.

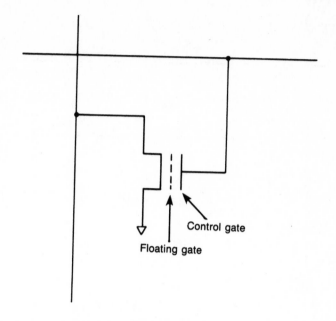

Fig. 8-12. MOS ultraviolet erasable PROM cell schematic.

Table 8-38. 2K × 8 Erasable PROMs.

TYPE	TEMP	TECH	OUTPUT	MAX ACCESS TIME (nS)	MAX SUPPLY CURRENT (mA)	VCC TOL (%)	VPP (V)	PINS	PRICE ($)
2716	M	MOS	3S	450	115	10	25.0	24	12.15
27C16	C	CMOS	3S	350	5	5	25.0	24	8.40
27C16	C	CMOS	3S	450	5	5	25.0	24	7.25
27C16	I	CMOS	3S	450	5	5	25.0	24	10.15

Table 8-39. 4K × 8 Erasable PROMs.

TYPE	TEMP	TECH	OUTPUT	MAX ACCESS TIME (nS)	MAX SUPPLY CURRENT (mA)	VCC TOL (%)	VPP (V)	PINS	PRICE ($)
2732	C	MOS	3S	150	125	5	21.0	24	6.32
2732	C	MOS	3S	150	100	10	21.0	24	17.55

TYPE	TEMP	TECH	OUTPUT	MAX ACCESS TIME (nS)	MAX SUPPLY CURRENT (mA)	VCC TOL (%)	VPP (V)	PINS	PRICE ($)
2732	C	MOS	3S	200	125	5	21.0	24	4.46
2732	C	MOS	3S	200	100	10	21.0	24	4.90
2732	C	MOS	3S	250	125	5	21.0	24	4.05
2732	C	MOS	3S	250	100	10	21.0	24	4.25
2732	M	MOS	3S	250	115	10	21.0	24	18.90
2732	C	MOS	3S	300	125	5	21.0	24	3.65
2732	C	MOS	3S	300	100	10	21.0	24	4.01
2732	C	MOS	3S	350	125	5	21.0	24	5.14
2732	C	MOS	3S	450	125	5	21.0	24	3.44
2732	C	MOS	3S	450	100	10	21.0	24	5.00
2732	M	MOS	3S	450	115	10	21.0	24	13.50
27C32	C	CMOS	3S	350	5	5	25.0	24	11.00
27C32	C	CMOS	3S	450	5	5	25.0	24	10.15
27C32	I	CMOS	3S	450	5	5	25.0	24	12.30

Table 8-40. 8K × 8 Erasable PROMs.

TYPE	TEMP	TECH	OUTPUT	MAX ACCESS TIME (nS)	MAX SUPPLY CURRENT (mA)	VCC TOL (%)	VPP (V)	PINS	PRICE ($)
2764	C	MOS	3S	150	100	10	12.5	28	6.75
2764	C	MOS	3S	170	150	5	12.5	28	5.40
2764	C	MOS	3S	180	75	5	12.5	28	8.90
2764	C	MOS	3S	200	150	5	12.5	28	4.90
2764	C	MOS	3S	200	75	10	12.5	28	5.35
2764	M	MOS	3S	200	100	10	12.5	28	47.25
2764	C	MOS	3S	250	150	5	12.5	28	4.40
2764	C	MOS	3S	250	75	10	12.5	28	4.68
2764	M	MOS	3S	250	100	10	12.5	28	40.00
2764	C	MOS	3S	300	75	5	12.5	28	4.01

TYPE	TEMP	TECH	OUTPUT	MAX ACCESS TIME (nS)	MAX SUPPLY CURRENT (mA)	VCC TOL (%)	VPP (V)	PINS	PRICE ($)
2764	C	MOS	3S	300	75	10	12.5	28	4.41
2764	M	MOS	3S	350	100	10	12.5	28	34.00
2764	C	MOS	3S	450	150	5	12.5	28	4.05
2764	C	MOS	3S	450	75	10	12.5	28	4.90
2764	M	MOS	3S	450	100	10	12.5	28	33.75
27C64	C	CMOS	3S	150	10	5	12.5	28	7.50
27C64	C	CMOS	3S	150	10	10	12.5	28	6.00
27C64	I	CMOS	3S	150	10	10	12.5	28	7.30
27C64	C	CMOS	3S	200	10	5	12.5	28	6.40
27C64	C	CMOS	3S	200	10	10	12.5	28	4.95
27C64	I	CMOS	3S	200	10	10	12.5	28	6.35
27C64	M	CMOS	3S	200	10	10	12.5	28	14.00
27C64	C	CMOS	3S	250	10	5	12.5	28	5.40
27C64	C	CMOS	3S	250	10	10	12.5	28	5.90
27C64	M	CMOS	3S	250	10	10	12.5	28	10.75
27C64	C	CMOS	3S	300	10	5	12.5	28	5.40
27C64	C	CMOS	3S	300	10	10	12.5	28	5.90
27C64	M	CMOS	3S	350	10	10	12.5	28	56.50
87C64	C	CMOS	3S	150	10	5	12.5	28	7.50
87C64	C	CMOS	3S	150	10	10	12.5	28	8.30
87C64	C	CMOS	3S	200	10	5	12.5	28	6.40
87C64	C	CMOS	3S	200	10	10	12.5	28	7.10
87C64	C	CMOS	3S	250	10	10	12.5	28	5.40
87C64	C	CMOS	3S	250	10	10	12.5	28	5.90
87C64	C	CMOS	3S	300	10	10	12.5	28	5.90
87C64	C	CMOS	3S	300	10	5	12.5	28	5.40
68764	C	MOS	3S	450	85	5	25.0	24	11.20
68766	C	MOS	3S	350	85	5	25.0	24	12.60
68766	C	MOS	3S	450	85	5	25.0	24	11.20

Table 8-41. 16K × 8 Erasable PROMs.

TYPE	TEMP	TECH	OUTPUT	MAX ACCESS TIME (nS)	MAX SUPPLY CURRENT (mA)	VCC TOL (%)	VPP (V)	PINS	PRICE ($)
27128	M	MOS	3S	110	140	10	12.5	28	523.85
27128	C	MOS	3S	150	100	5	21.0	28	24.30
27128	C	MOS	3S	150	100	10	21.0	28	27.00
27128	C	MOS	3S	200	100	5	21.0	28	19.60
27128	M	MOS	3S	200	100	10	21.0	28	81.00
27128	C	MOS	3S	250	100	5	21.0	28	5.70
27128	C	MOS	3S	250	100	10	21.0	28	6.60
27128	M	MOS	3S	250	100	10	21.0	28	60.75
27128	C	MOS	3S	300	100	10	21.0	28	6.60
27128	C	MOS	3S	300	100	5	21.0	28	5.70
27128	C	MOS	3S	450	100	5	21.0	28	5.70
27128	C	MOS	3S	450	100	10	21.0	28	6.60
27128	M	MOS	3S	450	100	10	21.0	28	47.25
27128A	C	MOS	3S	150	100	5	12.5	28	6.50
27128A	C	MOS	3S	150	100	10	12.5	28	7.15
27128A	M	MOS	3S	150	140	10	12.5	28	351.00
27128A	C	MOS	3S	200	100	10	12.5	28	7.90
27128A	C	MOS	3S	200	100	5	12.5	28	5.40
27128A	M	MOS	3S	200	140	10	12.5	28	81.00
27128A	C	MOS	3S	250	100	5	12.5	28	4.73
27128A	C	MOS	3S	250	100	10	12.5	28	5.20
27128A	M	MOS	3S	250	100	10	12.5	28	60.75
27128A	C	MOS	3S	300	100	10	12.5	28	4.68
27128A	C	MOS	3S	300	100	5	12.5	28	4.27
27128A	M	MOS	3S	300	140	10	12.5	28	52.50
27128A	C	MOS	3S	450	100	10	12.5	28	4.45
27128A	C	MOS	3S	450	100	5	12.5	28	4.27
27128A	M	MOS	3S	450	100	10	12.5	28	47.25

TYPE	TEMP	TECH	OUTPUT	MAX ACCESS TIME (nS)	MAX SUPPLY CURRENT (mA)	VCC TOL (%)	VPP (V)	PINS	PRICE ($)
27C128	C	CMOS	3S	150	40	10	12.5	28	11.70
27C128	C	CMOS	3S	150	40	5	12.5	28	9.75
27C128	C	CMOS	3S	200	40	5	12.5	28	8.45
27C128	C	CMOS	3S	200	40	10	12.5	28	9.72
27C128	C	CMOS	3S	250	40	5	12.5	28	5.85
27C128	C	CMOS	3S	250	40	10	12.5	28	6.44
27C128	C	CMOS	3S	300	40	5	12.5	28	5.53
27C128	C	CMOS	3S	300	40	10	12.5	28	6.08
27C128	C	CMOS	3S	450	40	5	12.5	28	5.20
27C128	C	CMOS	3S	450	40	10	12.5	28	5.72

Table 8-42. 32K × 8 Erasable PROMs.

TYPE	TEMP	TECH	OUTPUT	MAX ACCESS TIME (nS)	MAX SUPPLY CURRENT (mA)	VCC TOL (%)	VPP (V)	PINS	PRICE ($)
27256	C	MOS	3S	170	125	5	12.5	28	9.50
27256	M	MOS	3S	170	140	10	12.5	28	264.00
27256	C	MOS	3S	200	125	5	12.5	28	7.80
27256	C	MOS	3S	200	125	10	12.5	28	8.54
27256	M	MOS	3S	200	125	10	12.5	28	135.00
27256	C	MOS	3S	250	100	10	12.5	28	7.43
27256	C	MOS	3S	250	100	5	12.5	28	7.10
27256	M	MOS	3S	250	125	10	12.5	28	114.75
27256	C	MOS	3S	300	100	10	12.5	28	6.75
27256	C	MOS	3S	300	100	5	12.5	28	6.45
27256	M	MOS	3S	350	125	10	12.5	28	108.00
27256	C	MOS	3S	450	100	10	12.5	28	6.75
27256	C	MOS	3S	450	100	5	12.5	28	6.45

TYPE	TEMP	TECH	OUTPUT	MAX ACCESS TIME (nS)	MAX SUPPLY CURRENT (mA)	VCC TOL (%)	VPP (V)	PINS	PRICE ($)
27256	M	MOS	3S	450	100	10	12.5	28	94.50
27256L	C	MOS	3S	170	100	5	12.5	28	21.40
27256L	C	MOS	3S	200	100	5	12.5	28	16.70
27256L	C	MOS	3S	200	100	10	12.5	28	18.30
27C256	C	CMOS	3S	170	40	5	12.5	28	17.50
27C256	C	CMOS	3S	170	40	10	12.5	28	21.00
27C256	C	CMOS	3S	200	40	10	12.5	28	14.09
27C256	C	CMOS	3S	200	40	5	12.5	28	10.00
27C256	M	CMOS	3S	200	10	10	12.5	28	150.00
27C256	C	CMOS	3S	250	40	10	12.5	28	9.86
27C256	C	CMOS	3S	250	40	5	12.5	28	8.96
27C256	I	CMOS	3S	250	10	10	12.5	28	13.50
27C256	M	CMOS	3S	250	10	10	12.5	28	24.00
27C256	C	CMOS	3S	300	40	10	12.5	28	9.24
27C256	C	CMOS	3S	300	40	5	12.5	28	8.40
27C256	M	CMOS	3S	350	10	10	12.5	28	20.00
27C256	C	CMOS	3S	450	40	5	12.5	28	8.12
27C256	C	CMOS	3S	450	40	10	12.5	28	8.93

Table 8-43. 64K × 8 Erasable PROMs.

TYPE	TEMP	TECH	OUTPUT	MAX ACCESS TIME (nS)	MAX SUPPLY CURRENT (mA)	VCC TOL (%)	VPP (V)	PINS	PRICE ($)
27512	C	MOS	3S	200	125	10	12.5	28	22.00
27512	C	MOS	3S	200	125	5	12.5	28	20.00
27512	C	MOS	3S	250	125	5	12.5	28	15.70
27512	C	MOS	3S	250	125	10	12.5	28	17.30
27512	M	MOS	3S	250	150	10	12.5	28	309.00

TYPE	TEMP	TECH	OUTPUT	MAX ACCESS TIME (nS)	MAX SUPPLY CURRENT (mA)	VCC TOL (%)	VPP (V)	PINS	PRICE ($)
27512	C	MOS	3S	300	125	5	12.5	28	14.30
27512	C	MOS	3S	300	125	10	12.5	28	15.70
27512	M	MOS	3S	350	150	10	12.5	28	206.00
27512	M	MOS	3S	450	120	10	12.5	28	243.00

If the reference voltage is applied to the control gate, and current flows, then the cell is in the logic 1 state.

Tables 8-38 through 8-43 list address access times, power supply tolerances (for which the access times are guaranteed), and programming voltages (V_{PP}) for erasable PROMs:

Table	PROM size
8-38	2K × 8
8-39	4K × 8
8-40	8K × 8
8-41	16K × 8
8-42	32K × 8
8-43	64K × 8

Suppliers for all memory ICs listed in this chapter may be found in the Memory Index in Appendix C.

Chapter 9

Microprocessors

Microprocessors are used in general purpose computers (such as personal computers made by IBM, Compaq, and Apple), which may run a variety of programs, and special purpose computers (or microcontrollers, such as a traffic light controller), which are designed to run only one specific application program. The microprocessor is the *central processing unit*, or CPU, in a personal computer. The microprocessor inside the personal computer I am using to write this book is the Intel 8088 microprocessor.

The purpose of this chapter is to present functional descriptions and selection guides for 8-bit, 16-bit, 32-bit, and bit-slice microprocessors.

9.1 THE BASIC MICROPROCESSOR SYSTEM

The basic microprocessor system, or *microcomputer*, is shown in Fig. 9-1. The microcomputer has three basic elements: the *microprocessor, memory,* and *input/output* (I/O) ports.

The microprocessor executes programs stored in memory and transfers data to and from the outside world via the I/O ports. An input port may be a simple 8-bit buffer; an output port may be as simple as an 8-bit flip-flop register.

In a personal computer the I/O function is implemented using specific peripheral devices: the *DMA controller* IC to transfer data from the floppy or hard disk to the memory; the *CRT controller* IC to transfer data to the monitor; the *asynchronous communications adapter* IC to communicate with external serial I/O devices (a modem, for example); and a *peripheral interface adapter*

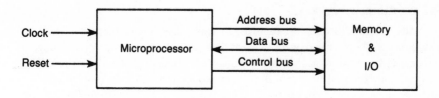

Fig. 9-1. Block diagram of the basic microprocessor system.

IC to communicate with external parallel I/O devices (a printer, for example). (DMA stands for *direct memory access* and CRT stands for *cathode-ray tube*.)

Microcomputer memory consists of two types of memory: RAM and ROM. ROM (read-only memory) holds fixed programs and data. RAM (random access memory) is used to store variables and temporary programs. This computer has 64K bytes of ROM and 640K bytes of RAM. The ROM tells the microprocessor what to do when first powered-up and also holds fixed routines that are used by the operating system (a program that allows the operator to run other programs) after it is transferred from the disk into RAM. (Note that in the microprocessor world, 1K bytes equals 1024 bytes, not 1000 bytes.)

9.1.1 Program Languages

The memory holds both instructions and data in the form of 1s and 0s. This form is called *machine language* and is the only language that microprocessors understand. *Assembly language* is a symbolic form of machine language. Abbreviations, or *mnemonics*, are used in the place of 1s and 0s. JZ, or *jump on zero*, is an 8088 assembly language instruction that is used for the machine language binary code 01110100.

Assembly language (and machine language) is specific to each microprocessor. 8088 assembly language is not the same as 68000 assembly language (although all assembly languages are similar). The assembly language programmer must understand the internal architecture of the microprocessor, memory allocation (the *memory map*), and the operation of I/O devices connected to the microprocessor. On the other hand, *high-level languages* such as BASIC, C, or PASCAL, are independent of the microprocessor. Both assembly language programs and high-level language programs must be translated into machine language before they can be executed. Translation programs are called *compilers*.

Microprocessor manufacturers provide hardware and software user manuals and sell software development equipment required for program development and in-circuit emulation of their microprocessors.

9.1.2   Clock and Reset

After the microcomputer receives a reset pulse (either on power-up or at any time that the user may want to reset the system), the microprocessor begins executing the program at memory location 0 (or some other fixed location). The program is executed at a speed determined by the clock frequency and the number of clock cycles per instruction. The number of clock cycles per instruction for the 8088 varies from two for a register-to-register move instruction to over 100 for a register multiply instruction.

9.1.3   The Address Bus

The microprocessor sends out addresses of memory locations on the address bus. The address is in the form of a binary number—a HIGH voltage level equals 1; a LOW voltage level equals 0. Each memory location holds 8 bits, or one *byte*, of data. The address bus width in bits, or number of lines in the bus, determines the maximum number of bytes of memory that the microprocessor may address according to the following equation:

$$A = 2^n$$

A equals the maximum addressable memory and *n* equals the address bus width. thus a microprocessor with a 16-bit address bus can address 2^{16}, or 65536, bytes of memory. The Intel 8088 has a 20-bit address bus and can address over 1 million bytes of memory.

The address bus is also used to address I/O. Microprocessors are typically designed to be able to distinguish between memory addresses and I/O addresses. However, it is possible to use some memory addresses for I/O devices, in which case the I/O devices are said to be *memory-mapped*.

A 16-bit address bus is labeled A0-A15. A0 is the least significant bit, or LSB, and A15 is the most significant bit, or MSB. The place values for A0-A15 are as follows:

Bit	Place Value	Bit	Place Value
A0	1	A8	256
A1	2	A9	512
A2	4	A10	1024
A3	8	A11	2048
A4	16	A12	4096
A5	32	A13	8192
A6	64	A14	16384
A7	128	A15	32768

In binary form a 16-bit address is presented with the MSB on the left and the LSB on the right:

Address		MSB A15	A14	A13	A12	A11	A10	A9	A8	A7	A6	A5	A4	A3	A2	A1	LSB A0
0	=	0	0	0	0	0	0	0	0	0	0	0	0	0	0	0	0
65535	=	1	1	1	1	1	1	1	1	1	1	1	1	1	1	1	1

In this chapter, 16-bit addresses are expressed in *hexadecimal* form. There is one hexadecimal number for every four bits in a binary number: 0-9 for binary numbers 0000-1001 and A-F for binary numbers 1010-1111 (10-15 decimal). For example, the binary address 0111 1101 0000 0101 (spaces used for clarity only) is 7D05 hexadecimal.

9.1.4   The Data Bus

The data bus is *bidirectional*. That is, data can be transferred from the microprocessor to the memory and I/O devices or from the memory and I/O to the microprocessor. However, data cannot be transferred in both directions at the same time.

Inside the microprocessor is an internal data bus, which may or may not be the same width as the external data bus, the bus that connects to the memory and I/O. The 8088, for example, has an external 8-bit data bus and an internal 16-bit data bus. When performing a 16-bit memory read or write operation, the 8088 must read, or write, two consecutive 8-bit numbers.

A microprocessor is classified by the width of its data bus. An 8-bit microprocessor has an 8-bit data bus; a 16-bit microprocessor has a 16-bit data bus. In the case where the internal and external data busses are not the same width, the microprocessor may be classified by its external data bus, its internal data bus, or both. The 8088 is sometimes classified as an 8-bit microprocessor (see the Intel data sheet), sometimes as a 16-bit microprocessor (see advertisements for 8088-based computers), or occasionally as an 8/16-bit microprocessor (*EDN* magazine in their annual microcomputer issue). In the tables in this chapter, I classify microprocessors by their internal data bus. Therefore the 8088 is listed in the table for 16-bit microprocessors.

The internal data bus width determines the maximum size of the numbers that may be processed by the microprocessor according to the following equation:

$$D = 2^n - 1$$

D equals the largest number and n equals the width of the internal data bus. Thus a microprocessor with an internal 8-bit data bus can process any number up to 255. A microprocessor with an internal 16-bit data bus can process a number up to 65535. By *process* I mean that the microprocessor can perform a single operation on a number no larger than that determined by its internal bus width. Larger numbers, however, may be processed by multiple operations.

An 8-bit data bus is labeled D0-D7. D0 is the least significant bit (LSB) and D7 is the most significant bit (MSB). In binary form 8-bit data is presented with the MSB on the left and the LSB on the right:

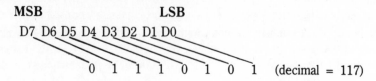

MSB   LSB

D7 D6 D5 D4 D3 D2 D1 D0

0 1 1 1 0 1 0 1   (decimal = 117)

A 16-bit data bus is labeled D0-D15. D0 is the LSB and D15 is the MSB. The place values for D0-D15 are the same as A0-A15 presented above.

9.1.5 The Control Bus

The control bus consists of all remaining signal lines. The number, names and functions of these lines are not standardized. The most common lines (by various names) are:

R/W   read/write control.
M/IO   memory-I/O to distinguish between memory and I/O during read or write.
HOLD   allows a device such as a DMA controller to take over the address and data busses.
HLDA   hold acknowledge from the CPU tells the DMA controller that it may take over the busses.
INTR   interrupt; tells the CPU that an external device needs to be read or *serviced*.
INTA   interrupt acknowledge; the CPU tells the external device that it received the interrupt request.
READY   input to the CPU that allows the use of slow memories or I/O devices.

HOLD and HLDA. For a CPU to transfer data from an I/O device (like a disk drive) to memory, it is necessary for every data byte to be moved into the CPU first and then to a particular memory location. For a large block of data, this can be extremely time consuming. A direct memory access (DMA) controller is designed to do this more efficiently than the microprocessor. However, to do so, it is necessary for the DMA controller to take over the address and data busses. This is accomplished through the HOLD and HLDA lines.

INTR and INTA. Typically, when an I/O device interrupts the CPU, that same device will place an 8-bit number on the data bus, thereby telling the CPU what service routine to execute. Also, interrupts may have assigned priorities. External interrupts can be "masked" by the programmer. That is, the programmer can tell the CPU to ignore interrupt requests that are below a certain priority level. Because of this, microprocessors sometimes provide for a "nonmaskable" interrupt request that the CPU cannot be programmed to ignore.

READY. For slow memories and I/O the CPU can be forced to idle for one or more so-called "wait states." The CPU samples the READY input at a certain time in the bus cycle (usually two or four clock periods in length). If the READY is HIGH then the CPU inserts wait states (one per clock period) until the READY goes LOW.

9.2 INSIDE THE MICROPROCESSOR

Figure 9-2 shows a block diagram of a generalized microprocessor. This drawing does not represent any specific commercially available microprocessor. The purpose of the drawing is to show the functions that are common to most microprocessors, namely:

- ☐ The arithmetic logic unit (ALU)
- ☐ The status register
- ☐ The general registers
- ☐ The stack pointer
- ☐ The program counter
- ☐ The control unit

The multiplexers and demultiplexers are secondary functions that facilitate the movement of data between blocks and to the outside world. Not shown are the clock and reset lines and lines between the control unit and the other blocks—lines that are used to control the modes and timing of the other blocks.

9.2.1 The Arithmetic Logic Unit

The *arithmetic logic unit*, or ALU, is the heart of the microprocessor and performs arithmetic and logic operations on either one or two *operands*. In Fig. 9-3, these operands are called operand A and operand B. Two outputs are generated each time an operation is performed: one is the *result* of the operation and the other is the *status*, or *condition code*.

The *function select* in Fig. 9-3 represents one or more control lines from

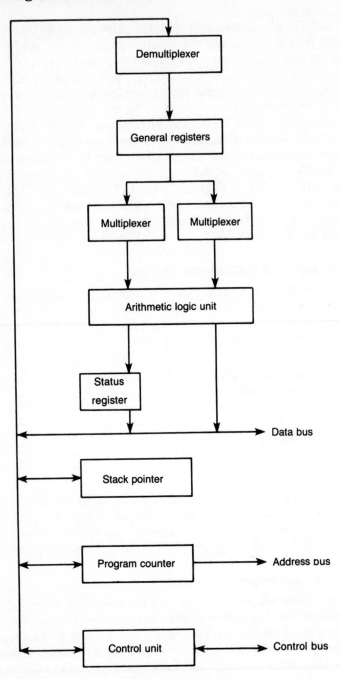

Fig. 9-2. Block diagram of a generalized microprocessor.

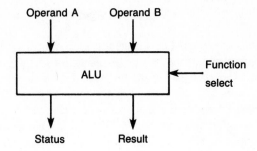

Fig. 9-3. Inputs and outputs of the ALU.

the control unit that determine which of the following typical operations the ALU is to perform:

☐ A plus B.
☐ A minus B.
☐ B minus A.
☐ A OR B.
☐ A AND B.
☐ A exclusive-OR B.
☐ Set result to all zeros.
☐ Set result to all ones.

Plus and minus are arithmetic operations (addition and subtraction); OR, AND, and exclusive-OR are logic operations. *Set result to ones* and *set result to zero* are neither arithmetic nor logic operations (they do not involve input operands at all), but are used when it is desirable to write all zeros or all ones to a particular memory location.

9.2.2 The Status Register

The status output from an ALU operation is stored in the status register. The status gives us additional information about the result of the ALU operation. The status word is a group of bits. The state (0 or 1) of each bit location in the status word corresponds to the occurrence or nonoccurrence of a particular condition. One or more status bits is updated at the end of each operation.

The four most common conditions that are monitored are called carry, overflow, zero, and negative. When two numbers are added a carry may occur. If a carry does occur, the *carry* bit is set to 1, otherwise it is reset to 0. The *overflow* bit is set when the result of the operation is too large or too small to be correctly represented in 2s complement form (see Chapter 7). The *zero* bit will be set if the result is zero, and the *negative* bit will be set if the result is less than zero.

The condition code is used as a basis for decision-making during program operation. The programmer may want the machine executing the program to branch, or jump, to another part of the program depending on the state of one or more of the status bits. He may want the machine to perform one task if the previous result is zero and a different task if the result is negative. The BASIC language programmer uses the IF-THEN-ELSE combination statements to jump to another location in his program. The assembly language programmer uses a *jump on zero* or other conditional branching instruction to cause the computer to go to another memory location (other than the next one in sequence) based on the condition code contained in the status register.

9.2.3   The General Registers

A set of general purpose registers is usually included in the microprocessor to improve processor speed. It takes the processor less time to read or write to an internal register than it does to read or write to an external memory location.

Programming is also simplified. Early microprocessors had only one register for ALU operations. It was called the accumulator. To perform an ALU operation, the programmer had to first copy data from an external memory location into the accumulator. Next, for example, he added the contents of the accumulator to the contents of a memory location and then stored the result back into the accumulator. Before the programmer could perform another ALU operation he had to store the contents of the accumulator in an external memory location. Thus it took at least four assembly language instructions to perform a simple addition. If, however, the microprocessor has a number of general purpose internal registers, then many ALU operations may be performed and it may not be necessary to ever store the results in external memory.

In Fig. 9-2 the multiplexers select which register will be the *source* for each ALU operand in an ALU operation; or which register will be passed through the ALU in a memory write operation. The demultiplexer selects which register will be the *destination* for the result of an ALU operation or a memory read operation.

9.2.4   The Stack Pointer

The stack pointer is a register that contains a special memory address. The programmer may designate a block of memory addresses to be used for temporary storage of variables. This block of memory is called the *stack* and data is moved from a general register to the stack by a *push* instruction and moved from the stack to a general register by a *pop* instruction.

Microprocessors use a stack because it is faster than moving data to and from memory using a *move* instruction. Once the stack pointer register is loaded with the value of the first memory location in the stack, it is not necessary to specify the memory address to which or from which data is being moved. The *move* instruction (when moving data to and from memory) requires that the microprocessor always fetch the memory address from the memory via the data bus (the memory address stored as data in memory) first before it can send out the memory address on the address bus for a memory read or write.

After the stack pointer is initialized to some address, it is incremented by 1 (if storing 8-bit data; by 2 if storing 16-bit data) when data is pushed onto the stack, and decremented by 1 when data is popped off the stack.

9.2.5 The Program Counter

The program counter contains the memory address of the next instruction to be executed. Normally all instructions are executed sequentially. After an instruction has been read into memory, the program counter is automatically incremented by one. Most programs, however, involve jumping, or branching, to some other location in memory. In these cases, the program counter is first loaded with the new location and then incremented thereafter or until another jump instruction is encountered.

When the microprocessor is instructed to begin a subroutine, the contents (plus one) of the program counter is saved either in another internal register or an external memory location. The address of the first instruction in the subroutine is then loaded into the program counter and incremented until a *return* instruction is encountered. Then the old program counter value is loaded into the program counter and the program continues, executing each instruction sequentially until encountering either a jump instruction or a subroutine call.

9.2.6 The Control Unit

The control unit is the most complex of all the microprocessor functions. It is shown as a simple block in Fig. 9-2. Not shown is the fact that the control unit is connected to every other block.

The control unit causes the addresses to be sent out on the address bus to the memory. The control unit sends out a read command to the memory and reads the instruction (or data) that comes back on the data bus. The control unit then decodes the instruction and sends out appropriate signals to the ALU, the multiplexers, the demultiplexer, general registers, and the program counter. If the instruction was to store data in memory, the control unit sends out the address and the data and a write command to the memory.

9.3 MICROPROCESSOR OPERATIONS

Microprocessors perform five basic types of operations: data transfer, arithmetic, logic, shift/rotate, and control transfer.

9.3.1 Data Transfer Operations

The *move* instruction is probably the most used instruction in the entire instruction set of any microprocessor. This instruction is used to transfer data from one location (the source) to another location (the destination). These locations may be anywhere in the microcomputer system. Thus, I may move data from the memory to a register, from a register to memory, from one register to another register, or from one memory location to another memory location.

By the word *move* I really mean that the data is copied. After I move data from a memory location to a register, for example, the original data is still in the memory—it has not been lost, nor is the memory location empty. However, any data in the register (to which I moved data) has been overwritten and is lost (unless previously moved elsewhere, of course).

Load and *store* instructions are variations on the basic move instruction. Generally, I *load* a register with data, where the data to be loaded is located in the memory location immediately following the memory location that contains the load instruction. Thus, in a load instruction, only the destination needs to be specified because the source is implied. Similarly, I store a result in a register or memory location.

9.3.2 Arithmetic Operations

Microprocessors perform four basic arithmetic operations: add, subtract, multiply and divide. As mentioned above, addition and subtraction are ALU functions and are performed in a few clock cycles. Multiplication and division, however, are performed using built-in ROM routines (called *microcode*) in the microprocessor control unit. The execution of a multiply or divide instruction may take 50 to over 100 clock cycles. Earlier 8-bit microprocessors do not have a multiply or divide instruction, in which case the programmer must write his own multiply or divide subroutine using add and subtract and shift instructions.

9.3.3 Logic Operations

Microprocessors perform four basic logic operations: NOT (inversion), AND, OR, and XOR (exclusive-OR). Logic operations are performed on a bit-for-bit basis on either bytes or words (two bytes, 16 bits). For example, 11000101 AND 01110111 equals 01000101; 11000101 OR 01110111 equals 11110111; 11000101 XOR 01110111 equals 10110010; NOT 11000101 equals 00111010.

9.3.4 Shift and Rotate Operations

Microprocessors perform two basic shift operations: shift left and shift right. Rotate operations are specialized shift operations.

In a shift left operation, all bits in a register or memory location are shifted one position to the left. The left-most bit (the MSB) is transferred to the carry in the status register. The right-most bit (the LSB), after the shift, is set to 0. This operation is typically called *arithmetic shift left.*

In a shift right operation, all bits in a register or memory location are shifted right one position. The right-most bit is transferred to the carry in the status register, and the left-most bit, after the shift, is set to 0. This operation is typically called *logic shift right.* An *arithmetic shift right* is the same as the logic shift right except that the left-most bit is left unchanged after the shift instead of set to 0.

In rotate operations, the bits are circulated back into the register. The carry may or may not be included in the loop. For example, in a rotate left including carry, all bits would be shifted to the left one position. The left-most bit would be transferred to the carry while the carry would be transferred to the right-most bit.

9.3.5 Control Transfer Operations

Microprocessors perform three basic control transfer operations: unconditional jump, conditional jump, and jump to subroutine.

In an unconditional jump the microprocessor is instructed to load a new address into the program counter and then begin executing instructions starting at that address.

In a conditional jump, the program counter is loaded with a new instruction address only if and when certain conditions have occurred. The microprocessor reads the appropriate status register bits to see if the condition has occurred. If so, then a jump occurs. Otherwise the next consecutive instruction is executed.

Subroutines are subprograms with one or more instructions in them. When the microprocessor encounters a subroutine call, it saves the program counter value (plus 1) and loads the address of the first instruction in the subroutine and then begins executing the subroutine instructions. The last instruction in a subroutine is a *return* instruction. When the return instruction is encountered, the microprocessor loads the old value of the program counter (plus 1) into the program counter and begins executing the instruction at that address.

9.4 ADDRESSING MODES

Microprocessors perform operations on data and place the results in registers or memory locations. The data to be processed and the address of the result are called *operands.*

The operand itself or the location of the operand within the microcomputer system is determined by what is called the *addressing mode*, which must be specified for each operand in the assembly language instruction.

If the operand is data, then the programmer must specify the data itself or where the data can be found. If the operand is an address, then the programmer must specify either the address directly, or indirectly by specifying the register or memory location where that address is stored.

Although a microprocessor may have a dozen or more addressing modes, there are five basic addressing modes that are common to most microprocessors: immediate, direct, indirect, indexed, and relative. A single instruction with two operands may specify one addressing mode for the first operand and a different addressing mode for the second operand.

In the examples that follow, I will use plain language versions of typical assembly language instructions rather than use the mnemonics of a specific microprocessor assembly language. Also, addressing modes are specified by use of special symbols in assembly language. These symbols are different for different microprocessor manufacturers. No such symbols will be used in these examples. See individual data sheets and users manuals for exact assembly language syntax.

9.4.1   Immediate Addressing

Immediate addressing applies to data operands only. In the instruction, *load into register 1 the number 23*, the number 23 is the data operand. The addressing mode is called *immediate* because the data operand "number 23" is located in the memory location *immediately* following the memory location that holds the machine code corresponding to "load into register 1."

9.4.2   Direct Addressing

Direct addressing applies only to address operands. In the previous instruction, load into register 1 the number 23, register 1 is an address operand. It is specified *directly*, in contrast to indirectly, which I will get to in the next section.

This mode is also called *register direct*, contrasting this mode with memory direct addressing. The instruction, *move the contents of memory location 7E00 to register 1*, is an example where both operands are addresses, and both are specified directly. Note that in this example that a data operand is concealed in the words "the contents of." Thus, it is data that is moved, even though the instruction contains an address operand. In fact, data operands are specified directly only in the immediate addressing mode.

9.4.3 Indirect Addressing

When the indirect addressing mode is specified, then the address of either the data or the address must be looked up. In the instruction, *load the number 23 into the memory location the address of which is stored in register 1*, the microprocessor must read the contents of register 1 to find out the destination address for the number 23.

As another example, *move the contents of register 1 to the memory location the address of which is stored in register 2*, the first operand ("the contents of register 1") is specified using the direct addressing mode, and the second operand ("register 2") is specified using the indirect addressing mode. The words "the memory location the contents of which is stored in" specify the indirect addressing mode.

9.4.4 Indexed Addressing

When the indexed addressing mode is specified, the address is formed by adding the contents of a register with a constant. Example: *move the number 23 to the memory location the address of which is the sum of the contents of register 2 and the number 5*. If register 2 contained the address 7D00, then the number 23 would be stored in memory location 7D05.

9.4.5 Relative Addressing

Relative addressing may be specified for jump, or branch, instructions only. *Jump forward 16 memory locations* is an example of relative addressing. In this example, the number 16 is added to the address in the program counter. This new address (the program counter plus 16) is loaded into the program counter and is the address of the next instruction to be executed. The new program counter address is *relative* to the old program counter address.

Relative addressing is not the only way to specify a jump or branch address. The microprocessor could be programmed to jump to the address stored in register 1 (indirect) or jump to address 7E0A (direct), for example.

9.5 8-BIT MICROPROCESSORS

Table 9-1 lists 8-bit microprocessors. The most popular 8-bit microprocessors are the 6502 (and other 6500 family microprocessors), the 6800 (and other 6800 family microprocessors), the 8085 (and its precursor the 8080) and the Z80 (part number Z8400 in the table).

9.5.1 The 6500 Family

The 6502 function symbol and signal names are shown in Fig. 9-4. The 6502

Table 9-1. 8-Bit Microprocessors.

TYPE	TEMP	TECH	DATA BUS (BITS)	ADDRESS BUS (BITS)	CLOCK (MHz)	PINS	MAX POWER (mW)	PRICE ($)
6500/1E	C	NMOS	8	12	1.0	64	1200.00	10.98
6500/1EA	C	NMOS	8	12	2.0	64	1200.00	12.07
6501	C	NMOS	8	16	1.0	64	1100.00	11.69
6501A	C	NMOS	8	16	2.0	64	1100.00	12.86
6502	C	NMOS	8	16	1.0	40	700.00	4.80
6502	I	NMOS	8	16	1.0	40	700.00	5.50
6502A	C	NMOS	8	16	2.0	40	700.00	5.30
6502A	I	NMOS	8	16	2.0	40	700.00	6.10
6503	C	NMOS	8	12	1.0	28	700.00	5.30
6503	I	NMOS	8	12	1.0	28	700.00	6.10
6503A	C	NMOS	8	12	2.0	28	700.00	5.85
6503A	I	NMOS	8	12	2.0	28	700.00	6.65
6504	C	NMOS	8	13	1.0	28	700.00	5.30
6504	I	NMOS	8	13	1.0	28	700.00	6.10
6504A	C	NMOS	8	13	2.0	28	700.00	5.85
6504A	I	NMOS	8	13	2.0	28	700.00	6.65
6505	C	NMOS	8	12	1.0	28	700.00	5.30
6505	I	NMOS	8	12	1.0	28	700.00	6.10
6505A	C	NMOS	8	12	2.0	28	700.00	5.85
6505A	I	NMOS	8	12	2.0	28	700.00	6.65
6506	C	NMOS	8	12	1.0	28	700.00	5.30
6506	I	NMOS	8	12	1.0	28	700.00	6.10
6506A	C	NMOS	8	12	2.0	28	700.00	5.85
6506A	I	NMOS	8	12	2.0	28	700.00	6.65
6507	C	NMOS	8	13	1.0	28	700.00	4.00
6507	I	NMOS	8	13	1.0	28	700.00	4.60
6507A	C	NMOS	8	13	2.0	28	700.00	4.40
6507A	I	NMOS	8	13	2.0	28	700.00	5.05

TYPE	TEMP	TECH	DATA BUS (BITS)	ADDRESS BUS (BITS)	CLOCK (MHz)	PINS	MAX POWER (mW)	PRICE ($)
6511	C	NMOS	8	16	1.0	64	1100.00	11.69
6511A	C	NMOS	8	16	2.0	64	1100.00	12.86
6512	C	NMOS	8	16	1.0	40	700.00	6.30
6512	I	NMOS	8	16	1.0	40	700.00	7.25
6512A	C	NMOS	8	16	2.0	40	700.00	7.00
6512A	I	NMOS	8	16	2.0	40	700.00	8.10
6518	C	NMOS	8	14	1.0	40	1000.00	8.78
6518A	C	NMOS	8	14	2.0	40	1000.00	9.67
65C02P1	C	CMOS	8	16	1.0	40	21.00	4.95
65C02P1	I	CMOS	8	16	1.0	40	21.00	5.05
65C02P2	C	CMOS	8	16	2.0	40	42.00	5.45
65C02P2	I	CMOS	8	16	2.0	40	42.00	5.80
65C02P3	C	CMOS	8	16	3.0	40	63.00	6.80
65C02P3	I	CMOS	8	16	3.0	40	63.00	7.85
65C02P4	C	CMOS	8	16	4.0	40	84.00	8.25
65C02P4	I	CMOS	8	16	4.0	40	84.00	9.50
65C102P1	C	CMOS	8	16	1.0	40	36.75	4.95
65C102P1	I	CMOS	8	16	1.0	40	36.75	5.05
65C102P2	C	CMOS	8	16	2.0	40	73.50	5.45
65C102P2	I	CMOS	8	16	2.0	40	73.50	5.80
65C102P3	C	CMOS	8	16	3.0	40	110.25	6.80
65C102P3	I	CMOS	8	16	3.0	40	110.25	7.85
65C102P4	C	CMOS	8	16	4.0	40	147.00	8.25
65C102P4	I	CMOS	8	16	4.0	40	147.00	9.50
65C112P1	C	CMOS	8	16	1.0	40	21.00	4.95
65C112P1	I	CMOS	8	16	1.0	40	21.00	5.05
65C112P2	C	CMOS	8	16	2.0	40	42.00	5.45
65C112P2	I	CMOS	8	16	2.0	40	42.00	5.80
65C112P3	C	CMOS	8	16	3.0	40	63.00	6.80

TYPE	TEMP	TECH	DATA BUS (BITS)	ADDRESS BUS (BITS)	CLOCK (MHz)	PINS	MAX POWER (mW)	PRICE ($)
65C112P3	I	CMOS	8	16	3.0	40	63.00	7.85
6800	C	NMOS	8	16	1.0	40	1000.00	2.85
6800C	I	NMOS	8	16	1.0	40	1000.00	5.95
6802	C	NMOS	8	16	1.0	40	1000.00	2.65
6802C	I	NMOS	8	16	1.0	40	1000.00	7.02
6809	C	NMOS	8	16	1.0	40	1000.00	3.75
6809E	C	NMOS	8	16	1.0	40	1000.00	5.40
68A00	C	NMOS	8	16	1.5	40	1000.00	4.45
68A00C	I	NMOS	8	16	1.5	40	1000.00	6.90
68A02	C	NMOS	8	16	1.5	40	1000.00	5.10
68A09	C	NMOS	8	16	1.5	40	1000.00	7.00
68A09E	C	NMOS	8	16	1.5	40	1000.00	7.00
68B00	C	NMOS	8	16	2.0	40	1000.00	4.75
68B02	C	NMOS	8	16	2.0	40	1000.00	5.80
68B09	C	NMOS	8	16	2.0	40	1000.00	8.55
68B09E	C	NMOS	8	16	2.0	40	1000.00	7.85
8031AH	C	NMOS	8	16	12.0	40	840.00	4.15
8031AH	I	NMOS	8	16	12.0	40	880.00	8.00
8031AH	M	NMOS	8	16	12.0	40	880.00	107.00
8032AH	C	NMOS	8	16	12.0	40	962.50	7.60
8035AHL	C	NMOS	8	12	11.0	40	357.50	4.00
8035AHL	M	NMOS	8	12	11.0	40	577.50	33.00
8039AHL	C	NMOS	8	12	11.0	40	385.00	4.30
8040AHL	C	NMOS	8	12	11.0	40	440.00	10.10
8080A	C	NMOS	8	16	2.0	40	1307.25	5.87
8080A	I	NMOS	8	16	2.0	40	1611.50	23.65
8080A	M	NMOS	8	16	2.0	40	1611.50	35.70
8080A-1	C	NMOS	8	16	3.0	40	1307.25	7.87
8080A-2	C	NMOS	8	16	6.0	40	1307.25	6.70
8080A-2	I	NMOS	8	16	6.0	40	1611.50	31.85

TYPE	TEMP	TECH	DATA BUS (BITS)	ADDRESS BUS (BITS)	CLOCK (MHz)	PINS	MAX POWER (mW)	PRICE ($)
8080A-2	M	NMOS	8	16	6.0	40	1611.50	45.46
8085A	C	NMOS	8	16	3.0	40	892.50	3.35
8085A	I	NMOS	8	16	3.0	40	1100.00	18.40
8085A	M	NMOS	8	16	3.0	40	1100.00	41.80
8085A-2	C	NMOS	8	16	5.0	40	892.50	4.00
8085A-2	M	NMOS	8	16	5.0	40	1100.00	48.30
8085AH	C	NMOS	8	16	3.0	40	742.50	3.55
8085AH	I	NMOS	8	16	3.0	40	1100.00	17.27
8085AH	M	NMOS	8	16	3.0	40	1100.00	42.85
8085AH-1	C	NMOS	8	16	6.0	40	1100.00	12.65
8085AH-2	C	NMOS	8	16	5.0	40	742.50	4.30
80C31BH	C	CMOS	8	16	12.0	40	120.00	10.80
80C31BH	M	CMOS	8	16	12.0	40	120.00	171.90
80C31BH-1	C	CMOS	8	16	16.0	40	150.00	13.50
80C31BH-2	C	CMOS	8	16	12.0	40	120.00	12.40
8344AH	C	NMOS	8	16	12.0	40	1100.00	22.20
8744AH	C	NMOS	8	16	12.0	40	1100.00	112.15
8744H	M	NMOS	8	16	12.0	40	1650.00	470.00
8748H	C	NMOS	8	12	11.0	40	495.00	12.30
8748H	M	NMOS	8	12	11.0	40	770.00	129.95
8749H	C	NMOS	8	12	11.0	40	605.00	14.85
8751H	C	NMOS	8	16	12.0	40	1375.00	52.00
8751H-88	M	NMOS	8	16	8.0	40	1512.50	268.90
Z8400A	C	NMOS	8	16	4.0	40	1050.00	1.71
Z8400A	I	NMOS	8	16	4.0	40	1050.00	3.57
Z8400A	M	NMOS	8	16	4.0	40	1050.00	74.29
Z8400B	C	NMOS	8	16	6.0	40	1050.00	1.86
Z8400B	I	NMOS	8	16	6.0	40	1050.00	4.71
Z8400H	C	NMOS	8	16	8.0	40	1050.00	3.21

TYPE	TEMP	TECH	DATA BUS (BITS)	ADDRESS BUS (BITS)	CLOCK (MHz)	PINS	MAX POWER (mW)	PRICE ($)
Z84C00-4	C	CMOS	8	16	4.0	40	137.50	2.07
Z84C00-4	I	CMOS	8	16	4.0	40	137.50	2.50
Z84C00-6	C	CMOS	8	16	6.0	40	206.25	3.36
Z84C00-6	I	CMOS	8	16	6.0	40	206.25	5.00
Z84C00-8	C	CMOS	8	16	8.0	40	275.00	5.14

was originally made by Commodore Business Machines, which no longer sells the 6502 on the open market. The 6502 is second sourced by Rockwell International. The 6502 is the microprocessor in the VIC-20 home computer, the Commodore 64 home computer, and the Apple *II*e computer.

The 6502 has an 8-bit accumulator (A), two 8-bit index registers (X and Y), a 16-bit program counter (PC), an 8-bit stack pointer (SP) and an 8-bit status register (P). The 6502 has 56 instructions and 13 addressing modes. The 65C02 is the CMOS version of the 6502.

6500 and 65C02 family peripherals are listed in Tables 9-2 and 9-3. Package, power, price, temperature grade, clock speed options, and supplier information for these and other 6500 family ICs is given in Appendix D.

9.5.2   The 6800 Family

The 6800 microprocessor function symbol and signal names are shown in Fig. 9-5. The 6800 has two 8-bit accumulators (ACCA and ACCB), a 16-bit index register (IX), a 16-bit program counter (PC), a 16-bit stack pointer (SP), and an 8-bit status register. The 6800 has 72 instructions and 7 addressing modes. The 6800 has DMA capability (TSC and BA lines).

6800 peripherals are listed in Table 9-4. Package, power, price, temperature grade, clock speed options, and supplier information for these and other 6800 family ICs is given in Appendix E.

The 6802 is a 6800 with an on-chip clock generator and 128 bytes of RAM.

The 6809 has two 8-bit accumulators (A, B) that can be concatenated to form a 16-bit accumulator (D); two 16-bit index registers (X, Y), two 16-bit stack pointers (U, S), a 16-bit program counter (PC), an 8-bit direct page register (DP) and an 8-bit status register.

The 6809 is compatible with 6800 peripherals and is upward source code compatible with the 6800. *Source code compatible* means that if you have 6800 assembly language programs you may recompile them down to machine code,

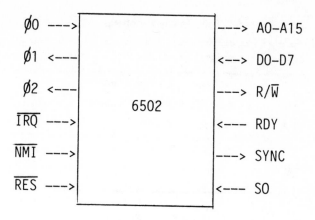

SYMBOL	TYPE	SIGNAL NAME
⌀0	I	CLOCK INPUT
⌀1, ⌀2	O	CLOCK OUTPUTS
A0–A15	O	ADDRESS BUS
D0–D7	I/O	DATA BUS
R/$\overline{W}$	O	READ/WRITE
$\overline{IRQ}$	I	INTERRUPT REQUEST
$\overline{NMI}$	I	NON-MASKABLE INTERRUPT
$\overline{RES}$	I	RESET
RDY	I	READY
SYNC	O	SYNC
SO	I	SET OVERFLOW FLAG

Fig. 9-4. 6502 function symbol and signal names.

Table 9-2. 6500 Family Peripherals.

TYPE	DESCRIPTION
6520	Peripheral Interface Adapter
6522	Versatile Interface Adapter
6532	RAM-I/O-Timer
6545	CRT Controller
6551	Asynchronous Communications Controller

Table 9-3. 65C00 Family Peripherals.

TYPE	DESCRIPTION
65C21	Peripheral Interface Adapter
65C22	Versatile Interface Adapter
65C24	Peripheral Interface Adapter/Timer
65C51	Asynchronous Communications Controller
65C52	Dual Asynchronous Communications Controller

or *object code*, and the recompiled machine code will run on a 6809 machine. The 6809 machine code, however, will not run on a 6800 machine.

The 6809 has 59 instructions and 10 addressing modes. The 6809 has an 8-bit by 8-bit multiply instruction and performs 16-bit arithmetic. The 6809 is not a 16-bit microprocessor. It has an 8-bit internal data bus and an 8-bit ALU. The 6809 is used in the Radio Shack Color Computer.

9.5.3   The 8085

The 8085 microprocessor function symbol and signal names are shown in Fig. 9-6. The 8085 has an on-chip clock generator, serial input and output lines, a multiplexed address/data bus (AD0-AD7 only), 5 interrupt inputs, and DMA capability.

The 8085 has six 8-bit registers (B, C, D, E, H, and L) which may be used as three 16-bit registers (BC, DE, HL); an 8-bit accumulator (A); a 16-bit program counter (PC); a 16-bit stack pointer (SP); and an 8-bit status register (Flags or F).

The 8085 is software compatible with the 8080. The 8085 may be considered a single supply version of the 8080 (which required +12 V, +5 V, and

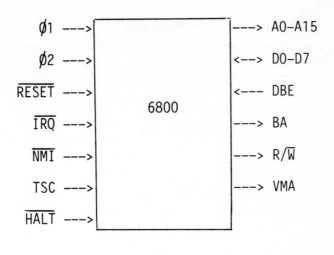

SYMBOL	TYPE	SIGNAL NAME
Ø1,Ø2	I	CLOCK INPUTS
A0–A15	O	ADDRESS BUS
D0–D7	I/O	DATA BUS
DBE	I	DATA BUS ENABLE
BA	O	BUS AVAILABLE
R/W̄	O	READ/WRITE
RESET	I	RESET
ĪRQ	I	INTERRUPT REQUEST
NMI	I	NON-MASKABLE INTERRUPT
TSC	I	THREE STATE CONTROL
VMA	O	VALID MEMORY ADDRESS
HALT	I	HALT

Fig. 9-5. 6800 function symbol and signal names.

Table 9-4. 6800 Peripherals.

TYPE	DESCRIPTION
6810	128 x 8 Static RAM
6821	Peripheral Interface Adapter
6840	Programmable Timer
6844	DMA Controller
6845	CRT Controller
6847	Video Display Generator
6850	Asynchronous Communications Interface Adapter
6852	Synchronous Serial Data Adapter
6854	Advanced Data-Link Controller
6859	Data Security Device
6875	Clock Generator
6880	Quad 3-State Bus Transceiver Inverting
6885	Hex 3-State Buffers Non-Inverting
6886	Hex 3-State Buffers Inverting
6887	Hex 3-State Buffers Non-Inverting
6888	Hex 3-State Buffers Inverting
6889	Quad 3-State Bus Transceiver Non-Inverting

– 5 V) integrated with the 8224 clock generator, and the 8228 system controller.

The 8088 and 8085 peripherals are listed in Table 9-5. Package, power, price, temperature grade, clock speed options, and supplier information for these and other 8000 series ICs is given in Appendix F.

9.5.4   The Z80

The Z80 microprocessor function symbol and signal names are shown in Fig. 9-7. (The Z80 CPU part number is Z8400.) The Z80 has 158 instructions and is upward software compatible with the 8080. The Z80 can perform bit, byte, and word operations. Bit operations include bit set, reset, and test. The Z80 features DMA or multiprocessor capability and an on-chip dynamic memory refresh counter.

The Z80 has duplicate sets of the 8080/8085 8-bit registers: accumulator (A), status or flags register (F), and general purpose registers B, C, D, E, H,

Table 9-5. 8080, 8085 Peripherals.

TYPE	DESCRIPTION
8155	256 x 8 Static RAM with I/O Ports and Timer
8185	1024 x 8 Static RAM for the 8085
8224	Clock Generator for the 8080
8228	Bus Controller for the 8080
8238	Bus Controller for the 8080
8237	Programmable DMA Controller
8257	Programmable DMA Controller
8259	Programmable Interrupt Controller
8755	2K x 8 Erasable PROM with I/O

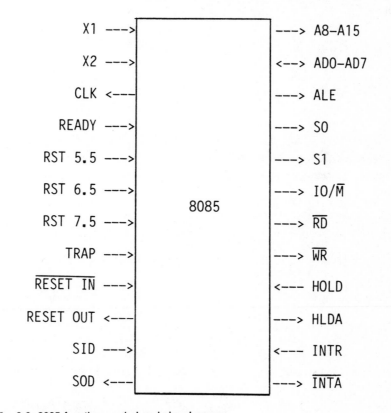

Fig. 9-6. 8085 function symbol and signal names.

SYMBOL	TYPE	SIGNAL NAME
A8–A15	O	ADDRESS BUS
AD0–AD7	I/O	MULTIPLEXED ADDRESS/DATA BUS
ALE	O	ADDRESS LATCH ENABLE
S0, S1, IO/$\overline{\text{M}}$	O	MACHINE CYCLE STATUS
$\overline{\text{RD}}$	O	READ CONTROL
$\overline{\text{WR}}$	O	WRITE CONTROL
READY	O	READY
HOLD	I	HOLD
HLDA	O	HOLD ACKNOWLEDGE
INTR	I	INTERRUPT REQUEST
$\overline{\text{INTA}}$	O	INTERRUPT ACKNOWLEDGE
RST 5.5, RST 6.5, RST 7.5	I	RESTART INTERRUPTS
TRAP	I	TRAP
$\overline{\text{RESET IN}}$	I	RESET IN
RESET OUT	O	RESET OUT
X1, X2	I	CRYSTAL OR RC CLOCK CONNECTIONS
CLK	O	CLOCK OUT
SID	I	SERIAL INPUT DATA LINE
SOD	O	SERIAL OUTPUT DATA LINE

Fig. 9-6. Cont.

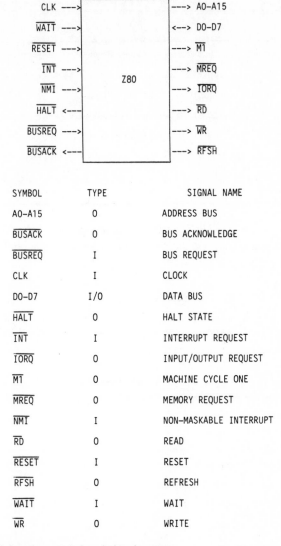

Fig. 9-7. Z80 function symbol and signal names.

and L. There are two accumulators (A and A′), two flags registers (F and F′), etc. Transfer of data between these two sets of registers is accomplished with *exchange* instructions. In addition there are two 16-bit index registers (IX and IY), a 16-bit stack pointer (SP), a 16-bit program counter (PC), an 8-bit interrupt vector register (I), and an 8-bit memory refresh register (R).

Table 9-6. Z80 Peripherals.

TYPE	DESCRIPTION
Z8410	Z80 DMA Direct Memory Access Controller
Z8420	Z80 PIO Parallel Input/Output Controller
Z8430	Z80 CTC Counter/Timer Circuit
Z8440	Z80 SIO/0 Serial Input/Output Controller
Z8441	Z80 SIO/1 Serial Input/Output Controller
Z8442	Z80 SIO/2 Serial Input/Output Controller
Z8470	Z80 DART Dual Asynchronous Receiver/Transmitter

Z80 peripherals are listed in Table 9-6. Package, power, price, temperature grade, clock speed options, and supplier information for these and other Z80 family ICs is given in Appendix G.

9.6   16-BIT MICROPROCESSORS

Table 9-7 lists 16-bit microprocessors. The most popular 16-bit microprocessors are the 68000, the 8086, the 8088, the 80286, the Z8001, and the Z8002.

Table 9-7. 16-Bit Microprocessors.

TYPE	TEMP	TECH	DATA BUS (BITS)	ADDRESS BUS (BITS)	CLOCK (MHz)	PINS	MAX POWER (mW)	PRICE ($)
68000P10	C	NMOS	16	23	10.0	64	1500.00	12.50
68000P12	C	NMOS	16	23	12.5	64	1500.00	25.00
68000P8	C	NMOS	16	23	8.0	64	1500.00	10.00
68008P10	C	NMOS	8	20	10.0	48	1500.00	18.31
68008P8	C	NMOS	8	20	8.0	48	1500.00	10.67
68010P10	C	NMOS	16	24	10.0	64	1500.00	29.20
68010P12	C	NMOS	16	24	12.5	64	1500.00	83.40
68010P8	C	NMOS	16	24	8.0	64	1500.00	20.85
68HC000L10	C	CMOS	16	24	10.0	64	160.00	39.00
68HC000L12	C	CMOS	16	24	12.5	64	190.00	51.00

TYPE	TEMP	TECH	DATA BUS (BITS)	ADDRESS BUS (BITS)	CLOCK (MHz)	PINS	MAX POWER (mW)	PRICE ($)
68HC000L8	C	CMOS	16	24	8.0	64	130.00	30.00
80186	C	NMOS	16	20	8.0	68	3025.00	21.35
80186-10	C	NMOS	16	20	10.0	68	3025.00	26.80
80186-6	C	NMOS	16	20	6.0	68	3025.00	15.95
80186-6	M	NMOS	16	20	6.0	68	3150.00	265.00
80186-8	M	NMOS	16	20	8.0	68	3150.00	310.00
80188	C	NMOS	8	20	8.0	68	3025.00	21.25
80188-10	C	NMOS	8	20	10.0	68	3025.00	35.00
80188-6	C	NMOS	8	20	6.0	68	3025.00	18.95
80286-10	C	NMOS	16	24	10.0	68	3150.00	93.00
80286-6	C	NMOS	16	24	6.0	68	3150.00	50.00
80286-6	M	NMOS	16	24	6.0	68	3300.00	665.00
80286-8	C	NMOS	16	24	8.0	68	3150.00	78.60
80286-8	M	NMOS	16	24	8.0	68	3300.00	784.00
8086	C	NMOS	16	20	5.0	40	1870.00	9.65
8086	I	NMOS	16	20	5.0	40	1870.00	27.99
8086	M	NMOS	16	20	5.0	40	1870.00	175.00
8086-1	C	NMOS	16	20	10.0	40	1890.00	23.35
8086-2	C	NMOS	16	20	8.0	40	1837.50	11.45
8086-2	I	NMOS	16	20	8.0	40	2178.75	29.35
8086-2	M	NMOS	16	20	8.0	40	2178.75	211.00
8088	C	NMOS	8	20	5.0	40	1870.00	6.90
8088	I	NMOS	8	20	5.0	40	1870.00	22.50
8088	M	NMOS	8	20	5.0	40	1870.00	126.67
8088-1	C	NMOS	8	20	10.0	40	1925.00	13.50
8088-2	C	NMOS	8	20	8.0	40	1925.00	9.30
8088-2	I	NMOS	8	20	8.0	40	1925.00	28.00
8094	C	NMOS	16	16	12.0	48	1188.00	32.05
8095	C	NMOS	16	16	12.0	48	1188.00	36.55
8096	C	NMOS	16	16	12.0	68	1188.00	24.75

TYPE	TEMP	TECH	DATA BUS (BITS)	ADDRESS BUS (BITS)	CLOCK (MHz)	PINS	MAX POWER (mW)	PRICE ($)
8097	C	NMOS	16	16	12.0	68	1188.00	29.30
8097	M	NMOS	16	16	12.0	68	1160.50	400.20
80C86	C	CMOS	16	20	5.0	40	275.00	20.00
80C86	I	CMOS	16	20	5.0	40	275.00	26.01
80C86	M	CMOS	16	20	5.0	40	275.00	194.00
80C86-2	C	CMOS	16	20	8.0	40	440.00	43.11
80C86-2	I	CMOS	16	20	8.0	40	440.00	56.03
80C86-2	M	CMOS	16	20	8.0	40	420.00	239.00
80C88	C	CMOS	8	20	5.0	40	275.00	12.20
80C88	I	CMOS	8	20	5.0	40	275.00	19.08
80C88	M	CMOS	8	20	5.0	40	275.00	143.00
Z8001	C	NMOS	16	16	4.0	48	1575.00	12.00
Z8001	M	NMOS	16	16	4.0	48	2200.00	96.74
Z8001A	C	NMOS	16	16	6.0	48	1575.00	13.10
Z8001A	I	NMOS	16	16	6.0	48	2100.00	57.04
Z8001A	M	NMOS	16	16	6.0	48	2200.00	120.26
Z8001A-8	C	NMOS	16	16	8.0	48	1575.00	17.50
Z8001B	C	NMOS	16	16	10.0	48	2100.00	18.57
Z8001B	M	NMOS	16	16	10.0	48	2200.00	519.00
Z8002	C	NMOS	16	23	4.0	40	1575.00	8.80
Z8002	M	NMOS	16	23	4.0	40	2200.00	68.33
Z8002A	C	NMOS	16	23	6.0	40	1575.00	9.35
Z8002A	I	NMOS	16	23	6.0	40	2100.00	29.29
Z8002A	M	NMOS	16	23	6.0	40	2200.00	133.79
Z8002A-8	C	NMOS	16	23	8.0	40	1575.00	14.40
Z8002B	C	NMOS	16	23	10.0	40	2100.00	14.14
Z8002B	M	NMOS	16	23	10.0	40	2200.00	498.00

9.6.1 The 68000

The 68000 microprocessor function symbol and signal names are shown in Fig. 9-8. The 68000 has a 24-bit address bus (A1-A23 in conjunction with the upper and lower byte data strobes, UDS and LDS); eight 32-bit data registers (D0-D7); eight 32-bit address registers (A0-A7); a 32-bit user stack pointer (USP); a 32-bit program counter (PC); and an 8-bit status register (CCR).

The 68000 can address 16 megabytes of memory, has 56 instructions, and 14 addressing modes. The 68000 can perform bit, BCD, byte, word (16-bit), and long word (32-bit) operations. Interfacing to 6800 peripherals is facilitated by use of the E, VMA, and VPA lines.

The 68008 is an 8-bit data bus version of the 68000.

The 68010 is a 68000 with virtual memory capability. In a virtual memory system, the virtual (or logical) memory may be much larger than the physical memory. When a program addresses memory locations outside the physical address space, the processor can trap to a routine that will transfer a block of data out of the physical memory (the RAM) to another storage area (a hard disk, for example) and bring into the physical memory (from the disk) that program or data that was outside of the physical memory space. After the swap is made, program execution resumes.

The 68000, 68008, and 68010 peripherals are listed in Table 9-8. Package, power, price, temperature grade, clock speed options, and supplier information for these and other 68000 family ICs is given in Appendix E.

9.6.2 The 8086 and 8088

The 8086 has a 20-bit address bus (the first sixteen bits are multiplexed with the data bus) and can address 1 megabyte of memory; has fourteen 16-bit registers (includes program counter and status register); has 24 addressing modes; performs bit, byte, word, and block operations; and performs 8 and 16-bit signed and unsigned arithmetic in binary and decimal including multiply and divide.

The 8086 has four segment registers: code (CS), stack (SS), data (DS), and extra (E). These registers are used to keep track of four different areas in memory: program code, the stack area, the data area, and an extra area (a second data area). Each segment register holds the first address (the *base address*) of a 64K memory segment.

The 8086 forms the 20-bit physical address by automatically left-shifting the segment address by four bits (forming a 20-bit number with the lower four bits equal to zero) and adding it to one of the 16-bit registers. When fetching an instruction, for example, the 8086 adds the left-shifted contents of the code segment register to the program counter (called the instruction pointer, or IP register) and sends out a 20-bit address on the address bus. This is called *segmented addressing* as opposed to *linear addressing*. (The 68000

Table 9-8. 68000, 68008, 68010 Peripherals.

TYPE	DESCRIPTION
68230	Parallel Interface/Timer
68450	DMA Controller
68451	Memory Management Unit
68452	Bus Arbitration Module
68652	Multi-Protocol Communications Controller
68661	Enhanced Programmable Communications Interface
68681	Dual Asynchronous Receiver/Transmitter
68901	Multi-Function Peripheral

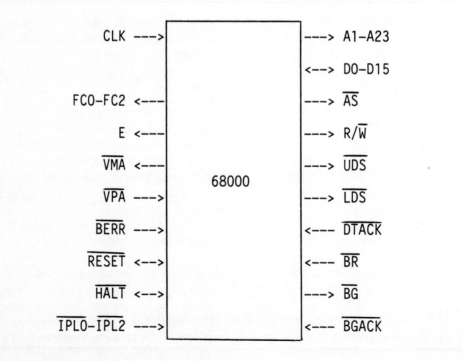

Fig. 9-8. 68000 function symbol and signal names.

SYMBOL	TYPE	SIGNAL NAME
A1–A23	O	ADDRESS BUS
D0–D15	I/O	DATA BUS
$\overline{AS}$	O	ADDRESS STROBE
R/$\overline{W}$	O	READ/WRITE
$\overline{UDS}$, $\overline{LDS}$	O	UPPER AND LOWER DATA STROBES
$\overline{DTACK}$	I	DATA TRANSFER ACKNOWLEDGE
$\overline{BR}$	I	BUS REQUEST
$\overline{BG}$	O	BUS GRANT
$\overline{BGACK}$	I	BUS GRANT ACKNOWLEDGE
$\overline{IPL0}$–$\overline{IPL2}$	I	INTERRUPT PRIORITY LEVEL
$\overline{BERR}$	I	BUS ERROR
$\overline{RESET}$	I/O	RESET
$\overline{HALT}$	I/O	HALT
E	O	ENABLE
$\overline{VPA}$	I	VALID PERIPHERAL ADDRESS
$\overline{VMA}$	O	VALID MEMORY ADDRESS
FC0–FC2	O	FUNCTION CODE OUTPUT
CLK	I	CLOCK

Fig. 9-8. Continued.

microprocessor uses linear addressing since it has 32-bit address registers.)

The 8086 was designed for both small systems (dedicated microcontrollers) and large systems (computers). To accommodate both small and large systems, some of the pins on the 8086 are configurable. When the MN/MX pin is tied HIGH, the 8086 is in the *minimum* mode (for small systems). When the MN/MX pin is tied LOW, the 8086 is in the maximum mode (for large systems). Figure 9-9 shows the 8086 function symbol and signal names in the minimum mode; Fig. 9-10, in the maximum mode. The main difference is that in the maximum mode, the 8086 requires an external 8288 bus controller chip to generate the memory and I/O read and write signals, address latch enable (ALE), data enable (DEN), and data transmit/receive (DT/R).

The 8088 is an 8-bit data bus version of the 8086. Figure 9-11 shows the 8088 function symbol and signal names in the minimum mode; Fig. 9-12, in the maximum mode.

The 80186 and 80188 are high integration versions of the 8086 and 8088. The 80186/80188 has an on-chip clock generator; dual channel DMA controller; three 16-bit timer/counters; a programmable interrupt controller; programmable memory and I/O chip selects; and a programmable wait-state generator.

The 8086, 8088, 80186, 80188 peripherals are listed in Table 9-9. Package,

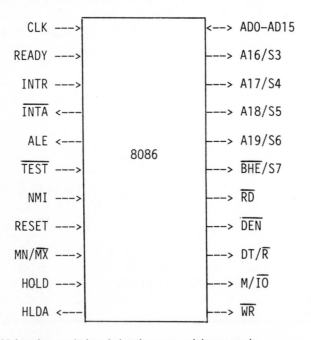

Fig. 9-9. 8086 function symbol and signal names, minimum mode.

SYMBOL	TYPE	SIGNAL NAME
AD0–AD15	I/O	ADDRESS/DATA BUS
A16/S3, A17/S4, A18/S5, A19/S6	O	ADDRESS/STATUS
$\overline{BHE}$/S7	O	BUS HIGH ENABLE/STATUS
$\overline{RD}$	O	READ
$\overline{DEN}$	O	DATA ENABLE
DT/$\overline{R}$	O	DATA TRANSMIT/RECEIVE
M/$\overline{IO}$	O	MEMORY/IO
$\overline{WR}$	O	WRITE
CLK	I	CLOCK
READY	I	READY
INTR	I	INTERRUPT REQUEST
INTA	O	INTERRUPT ACKNOWLEDGE
ALE	O	ADDRESS LATCH ENABLE
$\overline{TEST}$	I	TEST
NMI	I	NON-MASKABLE INTERRUPT
RESET	I	RESET
MN/$\overline{MX}$	I	MINIMUM/MAXIMUM
HOLD	I	HOLD
HLDA	O	HOLD ACKNOWLEDGE

Fig. 9-9. Continued.

power, price, temperature grade, clock speed options, and supplier information for these and other 8000 family ICs is given in Appendix F.

9.6.3   The 80286

The 80286 microprocessor function symbol and signal names are shown in Fig. 9-13. The 80286 is a high-performance 16-bit microprocessor intended for use in multitasking applications. The 80286 is upward software compatible with the 8086 and has two modes: the Real Address Mode (the 8086 mode) and Protected Virtual Address Mode. In the Real Address Mode, the 80286 acts like a high-performance 8086 with 1 megabyte of address space. In the Protected Mode, the 80286 can address 16 megabytes of physical memory and 1 gigabyte of virtual memory per task. The 80286 is the CPU in the IBM AT® personal computer (and compatibles) and is used in the Real Address Mode only (PC-DOS® or MS-DOS® operating systems).

The 80286 has on-chip memory management to provide memory protection

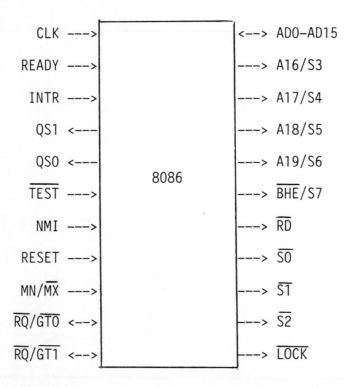

Fig. 9-10. 8086 function symbol and signal names, maximum mode.

SYMBOL	TYPE	SIGNAL NAME
AD0–AD15	I/O	ADDRESS/DATA BUS
A16/S3, A17/S4, A18/S5, A19/S6	O	ADDRESS/STATUS
$\overline{BHE}$/S7	O	BUS HIGH ENABLE/STATUS
$\overline{RD}$	O	READ
$\overline{S0}$–$\overline{S2}$	O	STATUS
$\overline{LOCK}$	O	LOCK
CLK	I	CLOCK
READY	I	READY
INTR	I	INTERRUPT REQUEST
QS0,QS1	O	QUEUE STATUS
$\overline{TEST}$	I	TEST
NMI	I	NON–MASKABLE INTERRUPT
RESET	I	RESET
MN/MX	I	MINIMUM/MAXIMUM
$\overline{RQ/GT0}$, $\overline{RQ/GT1}$	I/O	REQUEST/GRANT

Fig. 9-10. Continued.

for virtual memory systems and to provide task isolation for multitasking operating systems.

The 80286 peripherals are listed in Table 9-10. Package, power, price, temperature grade, clock speed options, and supplier information for these and other 8000 family ICs is given in Appendix F.

9.6.4 The Z8000 Family

The Z8000 Family includes two 16-bit microprocessors: the Z8001 and the Z8002. The Z8001 microprocessor function symbol and signal names are shown in Fig. 9-14.

The Z8001 has 16 general purpose 16-bit registers and can address 8 megabytes of memory using segmented addressing (a 16-bit multiplexed address/data bus, AD0-AD15, and a 7-bit segment bus, SN0-SN6). The Z8001 can perform bit, byte, word, and long word (32-bit), and byte string and byte word operations.

The Z8002 is the nonsegmented version of the Z8001. It has the same function symbol and signal names as the Z8001 except it does not have the segment bus (SN0-SN6) and the segment trap input line (SEGT).

Z8000 peripherals are listed in Table 9-11. Package, power, price, temperature grade, clock speed options, and supplier information for these and other Z8000 family ICs is given in Appendix G.

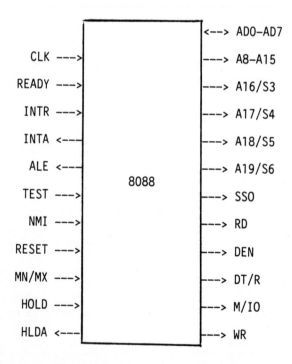

Fig. 9-11. 8088 function symbol and signal names, minimum mode.

SYMBOL	TYPE	SIGNAL NAME
AD0–AD7	I/O	ADDRESS/DATA BUS
A8–A15	O	ADDRESS BUS
A16/S3, A17/S4, A18/S5, A19/S6	O	ADDRESS/STATUS
SSO	O	STATUS LINE
RD	O	READ
DEN	O	DATA ENABLE
DT/R	O	DATA TRANSMIT/RECEIVE
M/IO	O	MEMORY/IO
WR	O	WRITE
CLK	I	CLOCK
READY	I	READY
INTR	I	INTERRUPT REQUEST
INTA	O	INTERRUPT ACKNOWLEDGE
ALE	O	ADDRESS LATCH ENABLE
TEST	I	TEST
NMI	I	NON–MASKABLE INTERRUPT
RESET	I	RESET
MN/MX	I	MINIMUM/MAXIMUM
HOLD	I	HOLD
HLDA	O	HOLD ACKNOWLEDGE

Fig. 9-11. Continued.

Table 9-9. 8086, 8088, 80186, 80188 Peripherals.

TYPE	DESCRIPTION
8087	Numeric Data Coprocessor
8282	Octal Latch
8283	Octal Latch
8284	Clock Generator for the 8086, 8088
8286	Octal Bus Transceiver
8287	Octal Bus Transceiver
8288	Bus Controller for the 8086, 8088
82188	Bus Controller for the 8086, 8088, 80186, 80188
8289	Bus Arbiter

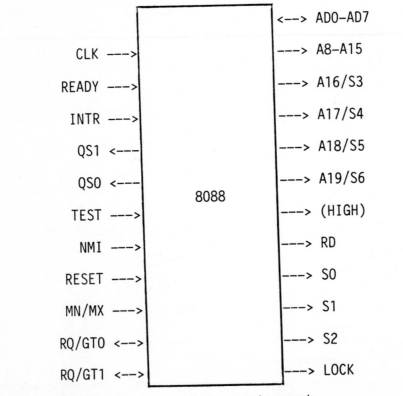

Fig. 9-12. 8088 function symbol and signal names, maximum mode.

SYMBOL	TYPE	SIGNAL NAME
AD0–AD7	I/O	ADDRESS/DATA BUS
A8–A15	O	ADDRESS BUS
A16/S3, A17/S4, A18/S5, A19/S6	O	ADDRESS/STATUS
RD	O	READ
S0–S2	O	STATUS
LOCK	O	LOCK
CLK	I	CLOCK
READY	I	READY
INTR	I	INTERRUPT REQUEST
QS0,QS1	O	QUEUE STATUS
TEST	I	TEST
NMI	I	NON–MASKABLE INTERRUPT
RESET	I	RESET
MN/MX	I	MINIMUM/MAXIMUM
RQ/GT0, RQ/GT1	I/O	REQUEST/GRANT

Fig. 9-12. Continued.

9.7 32-BIT MICROPROCESSORS

Table 9-12 lists various versions of three 32-bit microprocessors: the National Semiconductor 32032, the Motorola 68020, and the Intel 80386.

9.7.1   The 32000 Series

The 32000 Series includes three microprocessors: the 32008, the 32016, and the 32032. The 32008 and 32016 are the 8-bit data bus and 16-bit data bus versions of the 32032. The 32032 function symbol and signal names are shown in Fig. 9-15.

The 32032 has eight 32-bit general registers, six 24-bit dedicated registers (program counter, static base, frame pointer, user stack pointer, interrupt stack pointer, and interrupt base), and two 16-bit dedicated registers (status and module). The static base register points to the global variables of a software

TYPE	DESCRIPTION
80258	DMA Controller
82284	Clock Generator
80287	Numeric Data Coprocessor
82288	Bus Controller
82289	Bus Arbiter

Table 9-10. 80286 Peripherals.

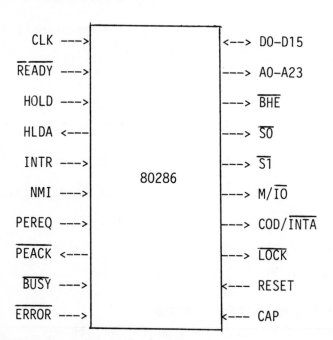

Fig. 9-13. 80286 function symbol and signal names.

SYMBOL	TYPE	SIGNAL NAME
CLK	I	SYSTEM CLOCK
D0–D15	I/O	DATA BUS
A0–A23	O	ADDRESS BUS
$\overline{\text{BHE}}$	O	BUS HIGH ENABLE
$\overline{\text{S0}}, \overline{\text{S1}}$	O	BUS CYCLE STATUS
M/$\overline{\text{IO}}$	O	MEMORY I/O SELECT
COD/$\overline{\text{INTA}}$	O	CODE/INTERRUPT ACKNOWLEDGE
$\overline{\text{LOCK}}$	O	BUS LOCK
$\overline{\text{READY}}$	I	BUS READY
HOLD	I	BUS HOLD REQUEST
HLDA	O	BUS HOLD ACKNOWLEDGE
INTR	I	INTERRUPT REQUEST
NMI	I	NON–MASKABLE INTERRUPT
PEREQ	I	PROCESSOR EXTENSION OPERAND REQUEST
$\overline{\text{PEACK}}$	O	PROCESSOR EXTENSION ACKNOWLEDGE
$\overline{\text{BUSY}}$	I	PROCESSOR EXTENSION BUSY
$\overline{\text{ERROR}}$	I	PROCESSOR EXTENSION ERROR
RESET	I	SYSTEM RESET
CAP	I	SUBSTRATE FILTER CAPACITOR

Fig. 9-13. Continued.

Table 9-11. Z8000 Peripherals.

TYPE	DESCRIPTION
Z8010	Z8000 MMU Memory Management Unit
Z8016	Z8000 DTC Direct Memory Access Transfer Controller
Z8030	Z8000 SCC Serial Communications Controller
Z8031	Z8000 ASCC Asynchronous Serial Communications Controller
Z8036	Z8000 CIO Counter/Timer and Parallel I/O Unit
Z8038	Z8000 FIO FIFO Input/Output Interface Unit
Z8060	Z8000 FIFO Buffer Unit and FIO Expander

module. The frame pointer register is used by a procedure to access parameters and local variables on the stack. The module register holds the address of the module descriptor table (a 16-byte table in memory which contains four 32-bit

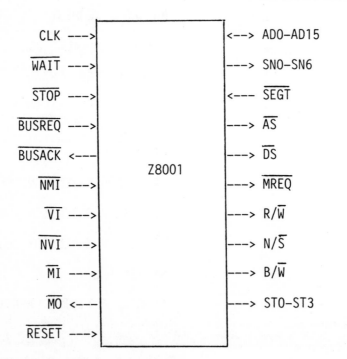

Fig. 9-14. Z8001 function symbol and signal names.

SYMBOL	TYPE	SIGNAL NAME
AD0–AD15	I/O	ADDRESS/DATA BUS
$\overline{AS}$	O	ADDRESS STROBE
$\overline{BUSACK}$	O	BUS ACKNOWLEDGE
$B/\overline{W}$	O	BYTE/WORD
CLK	I	SYSTEM CLOCK
$\overline{DS}$	O	DATA STROBE
$\overline{MREQ}$	O	MEMORY REQUEST
$\overline{MI}$	I	MULTI–MICRO IN
$\overline{MO}$	O	MULTI–MICRO OUT
$\overline{NMI}$	I	NON–MASKABLE INPUT
$N/\overline{S}$	O	NORMAL/SYSTEM MODE
$\overline{NVI}$	I	NON–VECTORED INTERRUPT
$\overline{RESET}$	I	RESET
$R/\overline{W}$	O	READ/WRITE
$\overline{SEGT}$	I	SEGMENT TRAP
SN0–SN6	O	SEGMENT NUMBER
ST0–ST3	O	STATUS
$\overline{STOP}$	I	STOP
$\overline{VI}$	I	VECTORED INTERRUPT
$\overline{WAIT}$	I	WAIT

Fig. 9-14. Continued.

Table 9-12. 32-Bit Microprocessors.

TYPE	TEMP	TECH	DATA BUS (BITS)	ADDRESS BUS (BITS)	CLOCK (MHz)	PINS	MAX POWER (mW)	PRICE ($)
32008–10	C	NMOS	8	24	10.0	48	1575.00	41.45
32008–6	C	NMOS	8	24	6.0	48	1575.00	12.50
32008–8	C	NMOS	8	24	8.0	48	1575.00	31.10
32016–10	C	NMOS	16	24	10.0	48	1575.00	70.00
32016–6	C	NMOS	16	24	6.0	48	1575.00	14.95
32016–8	C	NMOS	16	24	8.0	48	1575.00	40.70
32032–10	C	NMOS	32	24	10.0	68	1575.00	178.60
32032–6	C	NMOS	32	24	6.0	68	1575.00	30.95
32032–8	C	NMOS	32	24	8.0	68	1575.00	98.55
68020RC12	C	NMOS	32	32	12.5	114	2000.00	173.75
68020RC16	C	NMOS	32	32	16.7	114	2000.00	311.25
68020RC20	C	NMOS	32	32	20.0	114	2000.00	579.00
80386–16	C	CMOS	32	32	16.0	132	2100.00	299.00

pointers) of the currently executing software module.

The 32032 has a 24-bit multiplexed address/data bus and can address 16 megabytes of memory. the 32201 Timing Control unit is used to generate the clock inputs for the 32032. Also, the 32201 may be used to decode the status lines (ST0-ST3) to generate system read, write and other control signals. The 32201 and other 32000 series peripherals are listed in Table 9-13. Additional information is given in Appendix H.

9.7.2 The 68020

The 68020 microprocessor function symbol and signal names are shown in Fig. 9-16. The 68020 is a 32-bit version of the 68000 and is object code (machine language) compatible with the 68000.

The 68020 has a 4 gigabyte linear, or direct, memory address range and supports virtual memory systems; has eight 32-bit general purpose data registers; has eight 32-bit general purpose address registers; a 32-bit program counter, a 16-bit status register, a 32-bit vector base register (points to table in memory that holds start addresses, called vectors, of special subroutines), and two 32-bit cache registers.

The cache registers are used for controlling the on-chip instruction cache. The cache is an on-chip memory that holds the last 256 bytes of instruction code.

The 68020 peripherals are listed in Table 9-14. Additional information is given in Appendix E.

9.7.3 The 80386

The 80386 microprocessor function symbol and signal names are shown in Fig. 9-17. The # symbol is used in the Intel data sheet at the end of a signal name and indicates that the active state occurs when the signal is a LOW voltage. This symbol is the same as the bar symbol over the signal name.

The 80386 is a high-performance 32-bit microprocessor intended for use in multitasking applications. The 80386 is upward software compatible with all 8086 family processors (8086, 8088, 80186, 80188, and 80286) and, like the 16-bit 80286, has two modes: the Real Address Mode (the 8086 mode) and Protected Virtual Address Mode. In the Real Address Mode, the 80386 acts like a high-performance 8086 with 1 megabyte of address space. In the Protected Mode, the 80386 can address 4 gigabytes of physical memory and 64 terabytes (2^{46}) of virtual memory per task. The 80386 is the CPU in the Compaq Deskpro 386®, IBM PS/2® Model 80®, and other "386-AT" type personal computers.

The 80386 has on-chip memory management to provide memory protection for virtual memory systems; to provide task isolation for multitasking operating systems; and to provide physical address calculation. The 80386 uses segmented addressing in the Real Mode and either segmented or paging in the Protected Mode. Real Mode segments are 64K bytes. Protected Mode segments are variable length. Paging operates in conjunction with segmentation and is a means of managing large segments. In paging mode, the 80386 translates the segmented address to a physical address by using a directory table and a page table. The page table holds the 32-bit base address of a 4K page in memory. The base address plus the 13-bit offset (bits 0-12 of the segmented address) is the physical address.

80386 peripherals are listed in Table 9-15. Additional information is given in Appendix F.

9.8 BIT-SLICE MICROPROCESSORS

If none of the previous described processors meets your system requirements, then you may want to consider making your own processor using what is called *bit-slice*.

TYPE	DESCRIPTION
32081	Floating-Point Unit
32082	Memory Management Unit
32201	Timing Control Unit
32202	Interrupt Control Unit

Table 9-13. 32000 Peripherals.

The 2901 is a 4-bit bit-slice processor. It is designed to be cascaded to be any length: 8 (two 4-bit slices), 16 (four 4-bit slices), and so forth. Hence, the name *bit-slice*.

Figure 9-18 shows a block diagram of a simple bit-slice microprocessor system. Not shown is the clock input line that goes to the bit-slice microprocessor block and the microsequencer block.

The heart of the system is the bit-slice microprocessor. Inside the bit-slice processor is an ALU and a register set. The microinstruction bus input tells

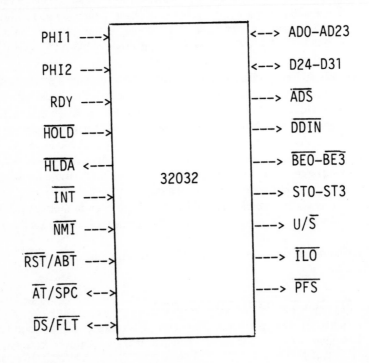

Fig. 9-15. 32032 function symbol and signal names.

SYMBOL	TYPE	SIGNAL NAME
AD0–AD23	I/O	ADDRESS/DATA BUS
D24–D31	O	DATA BUS
PHI1, PHI2	I	CLOCKS
RDY	I	READY
$\overline{\text{HOLD}}$	I	HOLD REQUEST
$\overline{\text{HLDA}}$	O	HOLD ACKNOWLEDGE
$\overline{\text{INT}}$	I	INTERRUPT
$\overline{\text{NMI}}$	I	NON-MASKABLE INTERRUPT
$\overline{\text{RST}}/\overline{\text{ABT}}$	I	RESET/ABORT
$\overline{\text{ADS}}$	O	ADDRESS STROBE
$\overline{\text{DDIN}}$	O	DATA DIRECTION IN
$\overline{\text{BE0}}–\overline{\text{BE3}}$	O	BYTE ENABLE
ST0–ST3	O	STATUS
U/$\overline{\text{S}}$	O	USER/SUPERVISOR
$\overline{\text{ILO}}$	O	INTERLOCKED OPERATION
$\overline{\text{PFS}}$	O	PROGRAM FLOW STATUS
$\overline{\text{AT}}/\overline{\text{SPC}}$	I/O	ADDRESS TRANSLATION/ SLAVE PROCESSOR CONTROL
$\overline{\text{DS}}/\overline{\text{FLT}}$	I/O	DATA STROBE/FLT

Fig. 9-15. Continued.

TYPE	DESCRIPTION
68851	32-Bit Paged Memory Management Unit
68881	Floating-Point Coprocessor
68882	Enhanced Floating-Point Processor

Table 9-14. 68020 Peripherals.

TYPE	DESCRIPTION
82384	Clock Generator
80387	Numeric Data Coprocessor

Table 9-15. 80386 Peripherals.

the ALU which operation to perform and the location of the operands (either inside the bit-slice processor register set or from external data memory). For each operation there is a result and a status.

The microinstruction comes from the microcode memory, which is driven

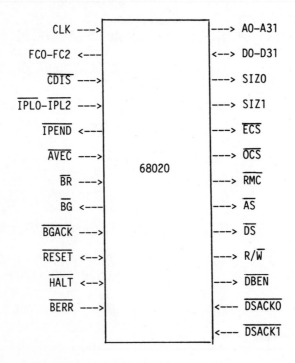

Fig. 9-16. 68020 function symbol and signal names.

SYMBOL	TYPE	SIGNAL NAME
A0–A31	O	ADDRESS BUS
D0–D31	I/O	DATA BUS
FC0–FC2	O	FUNCTION CODES
SIZ0,SIZ1	O	SIZE
$\overline{RMC}$	O	READ–MODIFY–WRITE CYCLE
$\overline{ECS}$	O	EXTERNAL CYCLE START
$\overline{OCS}$	O	OPERAND CYCLE START
$\overline{AS}$	O	ASSRESS STROBE
$\overline{DS}$	O	DATA STROBE
R/$\overline{W}$	O	READ/WRITE
$\overline{DBEN}$	O	DATA BUFFER ENABLE
$\overline{DSACK0}$, DSACK1	I	DATA TRANSFER AND SIZE ACKNOWLEDGE
$\overline{CDIS}$	I	CACHE DISABLE
$\overline{IPL0}$–$\overline{IPL2}$	I	INTERRUPT PRIORITY LEVEL
$\overline{AVEC}$	I	AUTOVECTOR
$\overline{IPEND}$	O	INTERRUPT PENDING
$\overline{BR}$	I	BUS REQUEST
$\overline{BG}$	O	BUS GRANT
$\overline{BGACK}$	I	BUS GRANT ACKNOWLEDGE
$\overline{RESET}$	I/O	RESET
$\overline{HALT}$	I/O	HALT
$\overline{BERR}$	I	BUS ERROR
CLK	I	CLOCK

Fig. 9-16. Continued.

by the microsequencer. The microcode memory holds the program. The microinstruction bus width is as many bits wide as required to control all functional blocks in the system. In many systems the microinstruction is over 100 bits wide.

The microsequencer includes a program counter, a small memory stack, usually a counter/timer (for loop counting), and a multiplexer to select the source for the next address it will send out to the microcode memory. The microsequencer normally begins at address zero and increments its internal program counter by 1 until it encounters a microinstruction that causes it to jump to some other address (either included in the microinstruction itself or previously stored in the microsequencer's internal stack).

The condition code mux multiplexes the status bits from the ALU. The selected status bit to be sent to the microsequencer is determined by the microinstruction being executed.

The advantage of the bit-slice system is that it can be optimized for any computational task. For example, multiplication is typically very slow (several microseconds at best) on standard microprocessors. In a bit-slice system, you can add a hardware multiplier that can do a 16-by-16 multiply in less than 100 nanoseconds, 20 to 50 times better than most microprocessors.

Table 9-16 lists bit-slice microprocessors.

The 2901 includes a 16-by-4-bit two-port RAM (two locations may be read

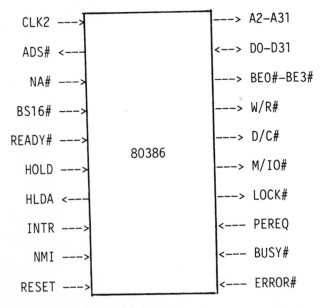

Fig. 9-17. 80386 function symbol and signal names.

SYMBOL	TYPE	SIGNAL NAME
CLK2	I	CLOCK
A2–A31	O	ADDRESS BUS
D0–D31	I/O	DATA BUS
BE0–BE3	O	BYTE ENABLES
W/R#	O	WRITE–READ INDICATION
D/C#	O	DATA–CONTROL INDICATION
M/IO#	O	MEMORY–I/O INDICATION
LOCK#	O	BUS LOCK INDICATION
PEREQ	I	COPROCESSOR REQUEST
BUSY#	I	COPROCESSOR BUSY
ERROR#	I	COPROCESSOR ERROR
ADS#	O	ADDRESS STATUS
NA#	I	NEXT ADDRESS REQUEST
BS16#	I	BUS SIZE 16
READY#	I	READY (TRANSFER ACKNOWLEDGE)
HOLD	I	BUS HOLD REQUEST
HLDA	O	BUS HOLD ACKNOWLEDGE
INTR	I	MASKABLE INTERRUPT REQUEST
NMI	I	NON–MASKABLE INTERRUPT REQUEST
RESET	I	RESET

Fig. 9-17. Continued.

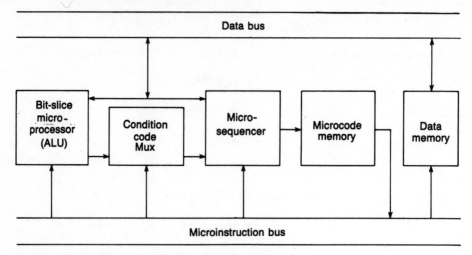

Fig. 9-18. Block diagram of a bit-slice microprocessor system.

Table 9-16. Bit-Slice Microprocessors.

TYPE	TEMP	TECH	BITS	MAX CLOCK (MHz)	PINS	MAX POWER (mW)	PRICE ($)
2901C	C	BIPOLAR	4	32.0	40	1391.25	6.65
2901C	M	BIPOLAR	4	31.0	40	1540.00	33.50
2903A	C	BIPOLAR	4	16.7	48	1837.50	20.50
2903A	M	BIPOLAR	4	16.7	48	2172.50	52.50
29116	C	BIPOLAR	16	20.0	52	3858.75	95.00
29116	M	BIPOLAR	16	13.3	52	4097.50	560.00
29203	C	BIPOLAR	4	16.7	48	1837.50	20.50
29203	M	BIPOLAR	4	16.7	48	2172.50	65.60
29501	C	BIPOLAR	8	33.0	64	2100.00	47.00
29501	M	BIPOLAR	8	33.0	64	2300.00	192.50
IDT39C01C	C	CMOS	4	32.0	40	157.50	6.25
IDT39C01C	M	CMOS	4	31.0	40	192.50	25.00
IDT39C01D	C	CMOS	4	43.0	40	183.75	8.25
IDT39C01D	M	CMOS	4	37.0	40	220.00	39.90
IDT39C01E	C	CMOS	4	50.0	40	210.00	10.75

TYPE	TEMP	TECH	BITS	MAX CLOCK (MHz)	PINS	MAX POWER (mW)	PRICE ($)
IDT39C01E	M	CMOS	4	46.0	40	247.50	51.85
IDT39C03A	C	CMOS	4	16.7	48	262.50	18.25
IDT39C03A	M	CMOS	4	16.7	48	330.00	39.50
IDT49C402	C	CMOS	16	20.8	68	656.25	27.90
IDT49C402	M	CMOS	16	20.0	68	825.00	102.00
IDT49C402A	C	CMOS	16	32.3	68	656.25	44.00
IDT49C402A	M	CMOS	16	27.8	68	825.00	144.00

or written at the same time), an 8-function ALU, and shifting circuitry. The 2903 is similar to the 2901 and has an addition data input path. The 29203 has three bidirectional input ports (2903 has two). Table 9-17 lists peripherals for the 2901, 2903, and 29203 processors. Additional information is in Appendix I, the 2900 Family Index.

Table 9-17. 2901, 2903, 29203 Peripherals.

TYPE	DESCRIPTION
2902	Look-Ahead Carry Generator
2904	Status and Shift Control Unit
2909	4-Bit Microprogram Sequencer
2910	12-Bit Microprogram Sequencer
2911	4-Bit Microprogram Sequencer
2914	Vectored Interrupt Control Unit
2917	Bus Transceiver
2918	Pipeline Register
2920	Octal Register
2922	Condition Code Mux
2925	System Clock Generator
2940	DMA Controller
2952	Bidirectional I/O Port

TYPE	DESCRIPTION
IDT39C02	Look-Ahead Carry Generator
IDT39C09	4-Bit Microprogram Sequencer
IDT39C10	12-Bit Microprogram Sequencer
IDT39C11	4-Bit Microprogram Sequencer
IDT49C410	16-Bit Microprogram Sequencer

Table 9-18. IDT39C01, IDT39C03, IDT49C402 Peripherals.

TYPE	DESCRIPTION
29112	8-Bit Slice Microprogram Sequencer
29118	8-Bit I/O Support

Table 9-19. 29116 Peripherals.

Table 9-20. 29501 Peripherals.

TYPE	DESCRIPTION
29510	16 x 16 Multiplier Accumulator
29516	16 x 16 Multiplier
29517	16 x 16 Multiplier
29520	Multilevel Pipeline Register
29521	Multilevel Pipeline Register
29526	Sine Generator (Most Significant Byte)
29527	Sine Generator (Least Significant Byte)
29528	Cosine Generator (Most Significant Byte)
29529	Cosine Generator (Least Significant Byte)
29540	Programmable FFT Address Sequencer

The IDT39C01 and IDT39C03 are CMOS versions of the 2901 and 2903. These processors are made by Integrated Devices Technology. The IDT49C402 is functionally equivalent to four 2901s and one 2902. Table 9-18 lists peripherals for the IDT CMOS processors.

The 29116 is a 16-bit slice and includes 32 registers and a 16-bit barrel shifter that can shift or rotate a word up to 15 positions in a single instruction cycle. Table 9-19 lists 29116 peripherals.

The 29501 is an 8-bit slice and includes three bidirectional ports and six pipelined registers. *Pipelined* means that the output of the first register is connected to the second, and so forth. In the case of the 29501 there is a mux between each register. The mux selects the previous register, the ALU output, or one of the two ALU input operands. 29501 peripherals are listed in Table 9-20.

Appendices

Appendix A
54/74 Index

PART NUMBER	DESCRIPTION	PINS	POWER (mW)	PRICE ($)	SUPPLIERS
5400	Quad 2-Input NAND Gates	14	121.00	1.00	F,N,TI
5401	Quad 2-Input NAND Gates with Open-Collector Outputs	14	121.00	1.00	N,TI
5402	Quad 2-Input NOR Gates	14	148.50	1.00	F,N,TI
5403	Quad 2-Input NAND Gates with Open-Collector Outputs	14	121.00	0.97	N,TI
5404	Hex Inverters	14	181.50	1.03	F,N,TI
5405	Hex Inverters with Open-Collector Outputs	14	181.50	1.06	N,TI
5406	Hex Inverting Buffers/Drivers with High-Voltage Open-Collector Outputs	14	280.50	1.79	N,TI
5407	Hex Buffers/Drivers with High-Voltage Open-Collector Outputs	14	225.50	1.79	N,TI
5408	Quad 2-Input AND Gates	14	181.50	1.06	F,N,TI
5409	Quad 2-Input AND Gates with Open-Collector Outputs	14	181.50	1.06	F,TI
5410	Triple 3-Input NAND Gates	14	90.75	1.00	F,N,TI
5412	Triple 3-Input NAND Gates with Open-Collector Outputs	14	90.75	1.36	N,TI
5413	Dual 4-Input Schmitt Trigger NAND Gates	14	176.00	1.73	N,TI
5414	Hex Schmitt Trigger Inverters	14	330.00	2.57	F,N,TI
5416	Hex Inverting Buffers/Drivers with High-Voltage Open-Collector Outputs	14	280.50	1.79	N,TI
5417	Hex Buffers/Drivers with High-Voltage Open-Collector Outputs	14	165.00	1.79	N,TI
5420	Dual 4-Input NAND Gates	14	60.50	1.02	F,N,TI
5423	Dual 4-Input NOR Gates with Strobe	16	104.50	1.00	TI
5425	Dual 4-Input NOR Gates with Strobe	14	104.50	1.00	F,TI
5426	Quad 2-Input NAND Buffers with High-Voltage Open-Collector Outputs	14	121.00	1.00	TI
5427	Triple 3-Input NOR Gates	14	143.00	1.00	TI

PART NUMBER	DESCRIPTION	PINS	POWER (mW)	PRICE ($)	SUPPLIERS
5428	Quad 2-Input NOR Buffers	14	313.50	1.82	TI
5430	8-Input NAND Gate	14	33.00	1.00	F,N,TI
5432	Quad 2-Input OR Gates	14	209.00	1.06	F,N,TI
5433	Quad 2-Input NOR Buffers with Open-Collector Outputs	14	313.50	1.82	TI
5437	Quad 2-Input NAND Buffers	14	297.00	1.06	F,N,TI
5438	Quad 2-Input Nand Buffers with Open-Collector Outputs	14	297.00	1.06	N,TI
5440	Dual 4-Input NAND Buffers	14	148.50	1.00	F,TI
5441	BCD to Decimal Decoder/Driver (NIXIE Driver)	16	198.00	7.10	N
5442	BCD to Decimal Decoder	16	308.00	1.99	F,TI
5445	BCD to Decimal Decoder/Driver	16	385.00	3.26	N,TI
5446	BCD to 7-Segment Decoder/Driver with Open-Collector Outputs	16	566.50	3.69	TI
5447	BCD to 7-Segment Decoder/Driver with Open-Collector Outputs	16	566.50	3.69	N,TI
5448	BCD to 7-Segment Decoder/Driver with Internal Pull-Up Resistor Outputs	16	495.00	2.75	TI
5450	Dual Expandable 2-Wide 2-Input AND-OR-INVERT Gates	14	77.00	1.00	TI
5451	Dual 2-Wide 2-Input AND-OR-INVERT Gates	14	77.00	1.00	F,TI
5453	Expandable 4-Wide AND-OR-INVERT Gate	14	52.25	1.00	TI
5454	4-Wide 2-Input AND-OR-INVERT Gate	14	52.25	1.00	TI
5470	AND-Gated Positive-Edge-Triggered J-K Flip-Flop with Preset and Clear	14	143.00	1.27	TI
5473	Dual Negative-Edge-Triggered J-K Flip-Flops with Clear	14	110.00	1.19	F,N,TI
5474	Dual Positive-Edge-Triggered D-Type Flip-Flops with Preset and Clear	14	82.50	1.19	F,N,TI
5475	4-Bit Bistable Latch	16	291.50	1.60	F,N,TI

PART NUMBER	DESCRIPTION	PINS	POWER (mW)	PRICE ($)	SUPPLIERS
5476	Dual Negative-Edge-Triggered J-K Flip-Flops with Preset and Clear	16	110.00	1.19	F,N,TI
5483	4-Bit Binary Full Adder with Fast Carry	16	605.00	1.99	F,TI
5485	4-Bit Magnitude Comparator	16	484.00	1.64	F,N,TI
5486	Quad 2-Input Exclusive-OR Gate	14	275.00	1.19	F,TI
5490	Decade Counter	14	231.00	1.72	F,N,TI
5492	Divide by 12 Counter	14	214.50	1.72	TI
5493	4-Bit Binary Counter	14	214.50	1.56	N,TI
5495	4-Bit Parallel-Access Shift Register	14	346.50	2.02	F,N,TI
5496	5-Bit Shift Register	16	434.50	1.99	TI
5497	Synchronous 6-Bit Binary Rate Multiplier	16	660.00	3.29	F,TI
54100	8-Bit Bistable Latch	24	583.00	6.08	TI
54107	Dual Master-Slave J-K Flip-Flops with Clear	14	110.00	1.27	N,TI
54109	Dual Positive-Edge-Triggered J-K Flip-Flops with Preset and Clear	16	82.50	1.22	N,TI
54111	Dual Master-Slave J-K Flip-Flip with Data Lockout	16	112.75	1.73	TI
54116	Dual 4-Bit Latches with Clear	24	550.00	4.12	TI
54120	Dual Pulse Synchronizers/Drivers	16	495.00	3.26	TI
54121	Monostable Multivibrator with Schmitt-Trigger Input	14	220.00	1.06	F,N,TI
54122	Retriggerable Monostable Multivibrator with Clear	14	198.00	1.29	F,TI
54123	Dual Retriggerable Monostable Multivibrators with Clear	16	363.00	1.99	F,TI
54125	Quad Buffers with 3-State Outputs	14	297.00	1.00	F,N,TI
54126	Quad Buffers with 3-State Outputs	14	341.00	1.00	TI
54128	Quad 2-Input NOR Line Drivers	14	313.50	5.12	TI

PART NUMBER	DESCRIPTION	PINS	POWER (mW)	PRICE ($)	SUPPLIERS
54132	Quad 2-Input Schmitt-Trigger NAND Gates	14	220.00	1.99	N,TI
54136	Quad 2-Input Exclusive-OR Gates with Open-Collector Outputs	14	275.00	1.63	TI
54145	BCD to Decimal Decoder/Driver	16	341.00	3.30	N
54148	8-Line Decimal to 3-Line Octal Priority Encoder	16	330.00	1.99	N,TI
54150	1 of 16 Line Data Selector/Multiplexer	24	374.00	5.86	F,N,TI
54151	1 of 8 Line Data Selector/Multiplexer	16	264.00	1.90	F,N,TI
54153	Dual 4 to 1 Line Data Selectors/Multiplexers	16	236.50	1.90	F,N,TI
54154	4 to 16 Line Decoder/Demultiplexer	24	308.00	5.93	F,TI
54155	Dual 2 to 4 Line Decoders/Demultiplexers	16	220.00	2.49	N,TI
54156	Dual 2 to 4 Line Decoders/Demultiplexers with Open-Collector Outputs	16	220.00	2.49	TI
54157	Quad 2 to 1 Line Data Selectors/Multiplexers	16	264.00	1.90	F,N,TI
54161	Synchronous 4-Bit Binary Counter with Asynchronous Clear	16	555.50	2.12	F,N,TI
54162	Synchronous 4-Bit Decade Counter with Synchronous Clear	16	555.50	2.32	TI
54163	Synchronous 4-Bit Binary Counter with Synchronous Clear	16	555.50	2.12	N,TI
54164	8-Bit Serial In/Parallel Out Shift Register with Asynchronous Clear	14	297.00	2.10	F,TI
54165	8-Bit Parallel In/Serial Out Shift Register with Complementary Outputs	16	346.50	2.45	F,TI
54166	8-Bit Parallel or Serial In/Serial Out Shift Register	16	698.50	2.06	N,TI
54167	Synchronous Decade Rate Multiplier	16	544.50	6.35	TI
54170	4 by 4 Register File with Open-Collector Outputs	16	825.00	3.69	F,TI

PART NUMBER	DESCRIPTION	PINS	POWER (mW)	PRICE ($)	SUPPLIERS
54173	4-Bit D-Type Register with 3-State Outputs	16	396.00	3.05	F,N,TI
54174	Hex D-Type Flip-Flops with Clear	16	357.50	2.09	F,N,TI
54175	Quad D-Type Flip-Flops with Clear	16	247.50	2.12	F,N,TI
54176	Presettable Decade (Bi-Quinary) Counter	14	264.00	2.66	TI
54178	4-Bit Parallel-Access Shift Register	14	412.50	6.79	TI
54179	4-Bit Parallel-Access Shift Register	16	412.50	6.79	TI
54180	9-Bit Parity Generator/Checker	14	308.00	2.63	N,TI
54181	Arithmetic Logic Unit/Function Generator	24	825.00	6.08	N,TI
54182	Look-Ahead Carry Generator	16	396.00	3.26	TI
54184	BCD to Binary Converter	16	544.50	4.75	N,TI
54185	Binary to BCD Converter	16	544.50	4.75	TI
54190	Synchronous Up/Down Decade Counter with Mode Control	16	577.50	2.75	TI
54191	Synchronous 4-Bit Up/Down Binary Counter with Mode Control	16	577.50	2.55	F,N,TI
54192	Synchronous Up/Down Decade Counter with Dual Clock	16	561.00	2.75	TI
54193	Synchronous 4-Bit Up/Down Binary Counter with Dual Clock	16	561.00	2.63	N,TI
54194	4-Bit Bidirectional Universal Shift Register	16	346.50	3.30	N
54195	4-Bit Parallel-Access Shift Register	16	346.50	2.32	TI
54197	Presettable Binary Counter	14	324.50	2.75	TI
54198	8-Bit Bidirectional Universal Shift Register	24	698.50	6.08	TI
54199	8-Bit Bidirectional Universal Shift Register	24	698.50	6.08	TI
54221	Dual Monostable Multivibrators with Schmitt-Trigger Input	16	440.00	3.36	TI

PART NUMBER	DESCRIPTION	PINS	POWER (mW)	PRICE ($)	SUPPLIERS
54251	3-State 1 of 8 Line Data Selector/Multiplexer	16	341.00	2.95	TI
54265	Quad Complementary-Output Elements	16	187.00	3.26	TI
54279	Quad S-R Latches	16	165.00	1.66	F,TI
54283	4-Bit Binary Full Adder with Fast Carry	16	605.00	3.60	F,TI
54284	4-Bit by 4-Bit Parallel Binary Multiplier	16	715.00	7.15	N,TI
54285	4-Bit by 4-Bit Parallel Binary Multiplier	16	715.00	7.15	N,TI
54290	Decade Counter	14	231.00	3.26	TI
54293	4-Bit Binary Counter	14	214.50	3.26	TI
54298	Quad 2 to 1 Line Data Selectors/Multiplexers with Storage	16	357.50	2.55	F,TI
54365	Hex 3-State Buffers/Bus Drivers	16	467.50	1.66	N,TI
54366	Hex 3-State Inverting Buffers/Bus Drivers	16	423.50	1.66	TI
54367	Hex 3-State Buffers/Bus Drivers	16	467.50	1.66	N,TI
54368	Hex 3-State Inverting Buffers/Bus Drivers	16	423.50	1.66	N,TI
54376	Quad J-K Flip-Flops	16	407.00	5.49	TI
54390	Dual Decade (Bi-Quinary) Counters	16	379.50	4.98	TI
54393	Dual 4-Bit Binary Counters	14	352.00	4.98	TI

PART NUMBER	DESCRIPTION	PINS	POWER (mW)	PRICE ($)	SUPPLIERS
54AC00	Quad 2-Input NAND Gates	14	0.55	2.65	F
54AC74	Dual Positive-Edge-Triggered D-Type Flip-Flops with Preset and Clear	14	0.55	3.72	F
54AC109	Dual Positive-Edge-Triggered J-K Flip-Flops with Preset and Clear	16	0.55	3.86	F
54AC153	Dual 4 to 1 Line Data Selectors/Multiplexers	16	0.55	3.93	F
54AC240	Octal 3-State Inverting Buffers/Line Drivers/Line Receivers	20	0.55	11.44	F
54AC241	Octal 3-State Buffers/Line Drivers/Line Receivers	20	0.55	11.44	F
54AC244	Octal 3-State Buffers/Line Drivers/Line Receivers	20	0.55	11.44	F
54AC253	Dual 3-State 1 of 4 Line Data Selectors/Multiplexers	16	0.55	4.86	F

PART NUMBER	DESCRIPTION	PINS	POWER (mW)	PRICE ($)	SUPPLIERS
54ACT240	Octal 3-State Inverting Buffers/Line Drivers/Line Receivers	20	0.88	11.44	F
54ACT241	Octal 3-State Buffers/Line Drivers/Line Receivers	20	0.88	11.44	F
54ACT244	Octal 3-State Buffers/Line Drivers/Line Receivers	20	0.88	11.44	F

PART NUMBER	DESCRIPTION	PINS	POWER (mW)	PRICE ($)	SUPPLIERS
54ALS00	Quad 2-Input NAND Gates	14	16.50	0.84	M,TI
54ALS01	Quad 2-Input NAND Gates with Open-Collector Outputs	14	16.50	0.84	TI
54ALS02	Quad 2-Input NOR Gates	14	22.00	0.84	TI
54ALS03	Quad 2-Input NAND Gates with Open-Collector Outputs	14	16.50	0.84	TI
54ALS04	Hex Inverters	14	23.10	0.84	M,TI
54ALS05	Hex Inverters with Open-Collector Outputs	14	23.10	0.84	TI
54ALS08	Quad 2-Input AND Gates	14	22.00	0.84	M,TI
54ALS09	Quad 2-Input AND Gates with Open-Collector Outputs	14	22.00	0.84	TI
54ALS10	Triple 3-Input NAND Gates	14	12.10	0.84	TI
54ALS11	Triple 3-Input AND Gates	14	16.50	0.84	TI
54ALS12	Triple 3-Input NAND Gates with Open-Collector Outputs	14	12.10	0.84	TI
54ALS15	Triple 3-Input AND Gates with Open-Collector Outputs	14	16.50	0.84	TI
54ALS20	Dual 4-Input NAND Gates	14	8.25	0.84	TI
54ALS21	Dual 4-Input AND Gates	14	11.00	0.84	TI
54ALS22	Dual 4-Input NAND Gates with Open-Collector Outputs	14	8.25	0.84	TI
54ALS27	Triple 3-Input NOR Gates	14	22.00	0.84	TI
54ALS28	Quad 2-Input NOR Buffers	14	49.50	0.90	TI
54ALS30	8-Input NAND Gate	14	4.95	0.84	TI
54ALS32	Quad 2-Input OR Gates	14	26.95	0.84	M,TI
54ALS33	Quad 2-Input NOR Buffers with Open-Collector Outputs	14	49.50	0.90	TI
54ALS37	Quad 2-Input NAND Buffers	14	42.90	0.90	TI

PART NUMBER	DESCRIPTION	PINS	POWER (mW)	PRICE ($)	SUPPLIERS
54ALS38	Quad 2-Input Nand Buffers with Open-Collector Outputs	14	42.90	0.90	TI
54ALS74	Dual Positive-Edge-Triggered D-Type Flip-Flops with Preset and Clear	14	22.00	1.06	TI
54ALS109	Dual Positive-Edge-Triggered J-K Flip-Flops with Preset and Clear	16	22.00	1.06	TI
54ALS112	Dual Negative-Edge-Triggered J-K Flip-Flops with Preset and Clear	16	24.75	1.06	TI
54ALS113	Dual Negative-Edge-Triggered J-K Flip-Flops with Preset	14	24.75	1.06	TI
54ALS114	Dual J-K Flip-Flops with Preset, Common Clear, and Common Clock	14	24.75	1.06	TI
54ALS133	13-Input NAND Gate	16	4.40	0.90	TI
54ALS138	3 to 8 Line Decoder/Demultiplexer	16	55.00	1.84	M,TI
54ALS151	1 of 8 Line Data Selector/Multiplexer	16	66.00	1.46	TI
54ALS153	Dual 4 to 1 Line Data Selectors/Multiplexers	16	77.00	1.46	TI
54ALS161	Synchronous 4-Bit Binary Counter with Asynchronous Clear	16	115.50	2.19	M,TI
54ALS163	Synchronous 4-Bit Binary Counter with Synchronous Clear	16	88.00	3.15	M
54ALS169	Synchronous 4-Bit Up/Down Binary Counter	16	137.50	1.96	TI
54ALS174	Hex D-Type Flip-Flops with Clear	16	104.50	1.80	TI
54ALS175	Quad D-Type Flip-Flops with Clear	16	77.00	1.80	TI
54ALS193	Synchronous 4-Bit Up/Down Binary Counter with Dual Clock	16	121.00	2.25	TI
54ALS240	Octal 3-State Inverting Buffers/Line Drivers/Line Receivers	20	137.50	3.22	TI
54ALS241	Octal 3-State Buffers/Line Drivers/Line Receivers	20	176.00	3.22	TI
54ALS242	Quad 3-State Inverting Bus Transceivers	14	148.50	3.65	TI
54ALS243	Quad 3-State Bus Transceivers	14	203.50	3.65	TI

PART NUMBER	DESCRIPTION	PINS	POWER (mW)	PRICE ($)	SUPPLIERS
54ALS244	Octal 3-State Buffers/Line Drivers/Line Receivers	20	148.50	3.22	TI
54ALS245	Octal 3-State Bus Transceivers	20	346.50	4.20	TI
54ALS251	3-State 1 of 8 Line Data Selector/Multiplexer	16	77.00	1.69	TI
54ALS253	Dual 3-State 1 of 4 Line Data Selectors/Multiplexers	16	77.00	1.69	TI
54ALS257	Quad 3-State 2 to 1 Line Data Selectors/Multiplexers	16	77.00	1.69	TI
54ALS258	Quad 3-State 2 to 1 Line Inverting Data Selectors/Multiplexers	16	71.50	1.69	TI
54ALS273	Octal D-Type Flip-Flop with Clear	20	159.50	3.22	TI
54ALS299	8-Bit Universal Shift/Storage Register with 3-State Outputs	20	220.00	8.12	TI
54ALS352	Dual 1 of 4 Line Inverting Data Selectors/Multiplexers	16	55.00	1.69	TI
54ALS353	Dual 3-State 1 of 4 Line Data Selectors/Multiplexers	16	71.50	1.69	TI
54ALS373	Octal 3-State Transparent D-Type Latches	20	148.50	3.22	TI
54ALS374	Octal 3-State Positive-Edge-Triggered D-Type Flip-Flops	20	170.50	3.36	TI
54ALS520	8-Bit Identity Comparator	20	104.50	8.69	TI
54ALS563	Octal 3-State Inverting Transparent D-Type Latches	20	148.50	3.36	TI
54ALS569	Synchronous 4-Bit Binary Up/Down Binary Counter with 3-State Outputs	20	176.00	3.65	TI
54ALS573	Octal 3-State Transparent D-Type Latches	20	148.50	3.36	M,TI
54ALS574	Octal 3-State Positive-Edge-Triggered D-Type Flip-Flops	20	148.50	3.36	M,TI
54ALS576	Octal 3-State Inverting Positive-Edge-Triggered D-Type Flip-Flops	20	148.50	3.36	TI

PART NUMBER	DESCRIPTION	PINS	POWER (mW)	PRICE ($)	SUPPLIERS
54ALS580	Octal 3-State Inverting D-Type Latches	20	148.50	3.36	TI
54ALS632	3-State 32-Bit Error Detection and Correction Circuit	52	1375.00	197.06	TI
54ALS640	Octal 3-State Inverting Bus Transceivers	20	264.00	4.20	TI
54ALS645	Octal 3-State Bus Transceivers	20	346.50	4.20	TI
54ALS804	Hex 2-Input NAND Line Drivers	20	66.00	2.80	TI
54ALS805	Hex 2-Input NOR Line Drivers	20	77.00	2.80	TI
54ALS808	Hex 2-Input AND Line Drivers	20	88.00	2.80	TI
54ALS832	Hex 2-Input OR Line Drivers	20	88.00	2.80	TI
54ALS873	Dual 3-State 4-Bit Transparent D-Type Latches	24	170.50	4.35	TI
54ALS874	Dual 3-State 4-Bit Positive-Edge-Triggered D-Type Flip-Flops	24	170.50	4.35	TI
54ALS1010	Triple 3-Input NAND Buffers	14	31.90	0.90	TI
54ALS1034	Hex Non-Inverting Buffers	14	77.00	0.90	TI
54ALS1244	Octal 3-State Bus Driver/Receivers	20	137.50	2.92	TI
54ALS1245	Octal 3-State Bus Transceivers	20	220.00	3.15	TI

PART NUMBER	DESCRIPTION	PINS	POWER (mW)	PRICE ($)	SUPPLIERS
54AS74	Dual Positive-Edge-Triggered D-Type Flip-Flops with Preset and Clear	14	88.00	1.73	TI
54AS240	Octal 3-State Inverting Buffers/Line Drivers/Line Receivers	20	412.50	5.41	TI
54AS241	Octal 3-State Buffers/Line Drivers/Line Receivers	20	495.00	5.41	TI
54AS373	Octal 3-State Transparent D-Type Latches	20	550.00	5.95	TI
54AS374	Octal 3-State Positive-Edge-Triggered D-Type Flip-Flops	20	704.00	5.95	TI
54AS804	Hex 2-Input NAND Line Drivers	20	148.50	7.11	TI
54AS832	Hex 2-Input OR Line Drivers	20	198.00	7.11	TI
54AS869	Synchronous 8-Bit Up/Down Counter	24	990.00	14.41	TI

PART NUMBER	DESCRIPTION	PINS	POWER (mW)	PRICE ($)	SUPPLIERS
54C00	Quad 2-Input NAND Gates	14	0.23	2.14	N
54C02	Quad 2-Input NOR Gates	14	0.23	2.14	N
54C04	Hex Inverters	14	0.23	1.30	N
54C08	Quad 2-Input AND Gates	14	0.23	2.14	N
54C10	Triple 3-Input NAND Gates	14	0.23	2.14	N
54C14	Hex Schmitt Trigger Inverters	14	0.23	3.98	N
54C30	8-Input NAND Gate	14	0.23	2.14	N
54C32	Quad 2-Input OR Gates	14	0.23	2.14	N
54C42	BCD to Decimal Decoder	16	4.50	4.05	N
54C48	BCD to 7-Segment Decoder/Driver with Internal Pull-Up Resistor Outputs	16	4.50	5.50	N
54C74	Dual Positive-Edge-Triggered D-Type Flip-Flops with Preset and Clear	14	0.90	2.85	N
54C76	Dual Negative-Edge-Triggered J-K Flip-Flops with Preset and Clear	16	0.90	2.85	N
54C83	4-Bit Binary Full Adder with Fast Carry	16	4.50	4.17	N
54C85	4-Bit Magnitude Comparator	16	4.50	4.17	N
54C86	Quad 2-Input Exclusive-OR Gate	14	0.23	1.30	N
54C89	64-Bit Read/Write Memory	16	4.50	19.38	N
54C90	Decade Counter	14	4.50	5.30	N
54C107	Dual Master-Slave J-K Flip-Flops with Clear	14	0.90	2.85	N
54C151	1 of 8 Line Data Selector/Multiplexer	16	4.50	8.24	N
54C154	4 to 16 Line Decoder/Demultiplexer	24	4.50	11.34	N
54C157	Quad 2 to 1 Line Data Selectors/Multiplexers	16	0.90	7.60	N
54C160	Synchronous 4-Bit Decade Counter with Asynchronous Clear	16	4.50	3.20	N

PART NUMBER	DESCRIPTION	PINS	POWER (mW)	PRICE ($)	SUPPLIERS
54C161	Synchronous 4-Bit Binary Counter with Asynchronous Clear	16	4.50	3.20	N
54C162	Synchronous 4-Bit Decade Counter with Synchronous Clear	16	4.50	3.20	N
54C163	Synchronous 4-Bit Binary Counter with Synchronous Clear	16	4.50	3.20	N
54C164	8-Bit Serial In/Parallel Out Shift Register with Asynchronous Clear	14	4.50	4.30	N
54C165	8-Bit Parallel In/Serial Out Shift Register with Complementary Outputs	16	4.50	4.30	N
54C173	4-Bit D-Type Register with 3-State Outputs	16	4.50	2.85	N
54C174	Hex D-Type Flip-Flops with Clear	16	4.50	3.00	N
54C175	Quad D-Type Flip-Flops with Clear	16	4.50	3.00	N
54C192	Synchronous Up/Down Decade Counter with Dual Clock	16	4.50	3.20	N
54C193	Synchronous 4-Bit Up/Down Binary Counter with Dual Clock	16	4.50	3.20	N
54C195	4-Bit Parallel-Access Shift Register	16	4.50	3.00	N
54C200	256-Bit Random-Access Memory with 3-State Outputs	16	9.00	19.15	N
54C221	Dual Monostable Multivibrators with Schmitt-Trigger Input	16	4.50	5.24	N
54C244	Octal 3-State Buffers/Line Drivers/Line Receivers	20	4.50	7.14	N
54C373	Octal 3-State Transparent D-Type Latches	20	4.50	7.71	N
54C374	Octal 3-State Positive-Edge-Triggered D-Type Flip-Flops	20	4.50	7.71	N
54C901	Hex Inverting TTL Buffers	14	0.23	2.85	N
54C902	Hex Non-Inverting TTL Buffers	14	0.23	2.85	N
54C905	12-Bit Successive Approximation Register	24	4.50	17.72	N
54C906	Hex Open Drain N-Channel Buffers	14	0.23	2.85	N

PART NUMBER	DESCRIPTION	PINS	POWER (mW)	PRICE ($)	SUPPLIERS
54C907	Hex Open Drain P-Channel Buffers	14	0.23	2.85	N
54C909	Quad Comparator	14	30.00	4.61	N
54C914	Hex Schmitt Trigger with Extended Input Voltage	14	4.50	5.67	N
54C922	16-Key Keyboard Encoder	18	39.00	10.10	N
54C923	20-Key Keyboard Encoder	18	39.00	12.02	N
54C932	Phase Comparator	8	27.00	2.00	N
54C941	Octal 3-State Buffers/Line Receivers/Line Drivers	20	4.50	4.42	N

PART NUMBER	DESCRIPTION	PINS	POWER (mW)	PRICE ($)	SUPPLIERS
54F00	Quad 2-Input NAND Gates	14	56.10	1.16	F,M
54F02	Quad 2-Input NOR Gates	14	71.50	1.16	F,M
54F04	Hex Inverters	14	84.15	1.16	F,M
54F08	Quad 2-Input AND Gates	14	70.95	1.16	F,M
54F10	Triple 3-Input NAND Gates	14	42.35	1.16	F,M
54F11	Triple 3-Input AND Gates	14	53.35	1.16	F,M
54F20	Dual 4-Input NAND Gates	14	28.05	1.16	F,M
54F32	Quad 2-Input OR Gates	14	85.25	1.16	F,M
54F64	4-Wide AND-OR-INVERT Gate	14	25.85	1.16	F,M
54F74	Dual Positive-Edge-Triggered D-Type Flip-Flops with Preset and Clear	14	88.00	1.44	F,M
54F86	Quad 2-Input Exclusive-OR Gate	14	154.00	1.68	F,M
54F109	Dual Positive-Edge-Triggered J-K Flip-Flops with Preset and Clear	16	93.50	1.68	F,M
54F138	3 to 8 Line Decoder/Demultiplexer	16	110.00	2.02	F,M
54F139	Dual 2 to 4 Line Decoders/Demultiplexers	16	110.00	2.02	F,M
54F151	1 of 8 Line Data Selector/Multiplexer	16	115.50	2.02	F,M
54F153	Dual 4 to 1 Line Data Selectors/Multiplexers	16	110.00	2.02	F,M
54F157	Quad 2 to 1 Line Data Selectors/Multiplexers	16	126.50	2.02	F,M
54F158	Quad 2 to 1 Line Inverting Data Selectors/Multiplexers	16	82.50	2.02	F,M
54F160	Synchronous 4-Bit Decade Counter with Asynchronous Clear	16	302.50	6.01	F
54F161	Synchronous 4-Bit Binary Counter with Asynchronous Clear	16	302.50	6.01	F
54F162	Synchronous 4-Bit Decade Counter with Synchronous Clear	16	302.50	6.01	F

PART NUMBER	DESCRIPTION	PINS	POWER (mW)	PRICE ($)	SUPPLIERS
54F163	Synchronous 4-Bit Binary Counter with Synchronous Clear	16	302.50	6.01	F
54F164	8-Bit Serial In/Parallel Out Shift Register with Asynchronous Clear	14	302.50	6.01	F
54F174	Hex D-Type Flip-Flops with Clear	16	247.50	3.22	F,M
54F175	Quad D-Type Flip-Flops with Clear	16	187.00	3.22	F,M
54F181	Arithmetic Logic Unit/Function Generator	24	357.50	14.43	F
54F182	Look-Ahead Carry Generator	16	189.00	4.64	M
54F189	64-Bit Random-Access Memory with 3-State Outputs	16	302.50	12.87	F
54F190	Synchronous Up/Down Decade Counter with Mode Control	16	302.50	8.44	F
54F191	Synchronous 4-Bit Up/Down Binary Counter with Mode Control	16	302.50	8.44	F
54F192	Synchronous Up/Down Decade Counter with Dual Clock	16	302.50	10.87	F
54F193	Synchronous 4-Bit Up/Down Binary Counter with Dual Clock	16	302.50	10.87	F
54F194	4-Bit Bidirectional Universal Shift Register	16	198.00	7.29	F
54F219	64-Bit Random-Access Memory with 3-State Outputs	16	302.50	20.59	F
54F240	Octal 3-State Inverting Buffers/Line Drivers/Line Receivers	20	412.50	4.74	F,M
54F241	Octal 3-State Buffers/Line Drivers/Line Receivers	20	495.00	4.74	F,M
54F243	Quad 3-State Bus Transceivers	14	495.00	4.46	F,M
54F244	Octal 3-State Buffers/Line Drivers/Line Receivers	20	495.00	4.74	F,M
54F245	Octal 3-State Bus Transceivers	20	660.00	12.87	F
54F251	3-State 1 of 8 Line Data Selector/Multiplexer	16	132.00	2.02	F,M

PART NUMBER	DESCRIPTION	PINS	POWER (mW)	PRICE ($)	SUPPLIERS
54F253	Dual 3-State 1 of 4 Line Data Selectors/Multiplexers	16	126.50	2.02	F,M
54F257	Quad 3-State 2 to 1 Line Data Selectors/Multiplexers	16	126.50	2.02	F,M
54F258	Quad 3-State 2 to 1 Line Inverting Data Selectors/Multiplexers	16	126.50	2.02	F,M
54F280	9-Bit Parity Generator/Checker	14	209.00	2.02	F,M
54F283	4-Bit Binary Full Adder with Fast Carry	16	302.50	5.72	F
54F322	8-Bit Shift Register with Sign Extend	20	495.00	19.73	F
54F352	Dual 1 of 4 Line Inverting Data Selectors/Multiplexers	16	110.00	2.02	F,M
54F353	Dual 3-State 1 of 4 Line Data Selectors/Multiplexers	16	126.50	2.02	F,M
54F373	Octal 3-State Transparent D-Type Latches	20	302.50	5.04	F,M
54F374	Octal 3-State Positive-Edge-Triggered D-Type Flip-Flops	20	473.00	5.04	F,M
54F378	Hex D-Type Flip-Flops with Enable	16	247.50	3.94	F,M
54F379	Quad D-Type Flip-Flops with Enable	16	220.00	3.94	F,M
54F385	Quad Serial Adder/Subtractor	20	522.50	22.31	F
54F398	Quad 2-Input Multiplexers with Storage	20	209.00	14.09	F
54F399	Quad 2-Input Multiplexers with Storage	16	187.00	6.01	F
54F412	Multimode Octal Latch	24	330.00	14.80	F
54F521	8-Bit Identity Comparator	20	176.00	5.38	F,M
54F533	Octal 3-State Inverting Transparent D-Type Latches	20	335.50	5.38	F,M
54F534	Octal 3-State Inverting Positive-Edge-Triggered D-Type Flip-Flops	20	473.00	5.38	F,M
54F544	Octal Registered Transceiver	24	715.00	23.17	F
54F545	Octal Transceiver	20	660.00	14.80	F

PART NUMBER	DESCRIPTION	PINS	POWER (mW)	PRICE ($)	SUPPLIERS
54F547	3 to 8 Line Decoder/Demultiplexer with Address Latches	20	137.50	14.30	F
54F548	3 to 8 Line Decoder/Demultiplexer with Acknowledge	20	115.50	21.09	F
54F563	Octal 3-State Inverting Transparent D-Type Latches	20	302.50	14.09	F
54F573	Octal 3-State Transparent D-Type Latches	20	302.50	14.09	F
54F583	4-Bit BCD Adder	16	330.00	16.52	F
54F676	16-Bit Serial/Parallel In, Serial Out Shift Register	24	396.00	24.02	F

PART NUMBER	DESCRIPTION	PINS	POWER (mW)	PRICE ($)	SUPPLIERS
54HC00	Quad 2-Input NAND Gates	14	0.24	0.57	M,N,RCA,TI
54HC02	Quad 2-Input NOR Gates	14	0.24	0.57	M,N,RCA,TI
54HC03	Quad 2-Input NAND Gates with Open-Collector Outputs	14	0.24	0.66	M,N,RCA,TI
54HC04	Hex Inverters	14	0.24	0.57	M,N,RCA,TI
54HC05	Hex Inverters with Open-Collector Outputs	14	0.24	1.00	TI
54HC08	Quad 2-Input AND Gates	14	0.24	0.57	M,N,RCA,TI
54HC09	Quad 2-Input AND Gates with Open-Collector Outputs	14	0.24	0.79	TI
54HC10	Triple 3-Input NAND Gates	14	0.24	0.57	M,N,RCA,TI
54HC11	Triple 3-Input AND Gates	14	0.24	0.57	M,N,RCA,TI
54HC14	Hex Schmitt Trigger Inverters	14	0.24	1.52	M,N,RCA,TI
54HC20	Dual 4-Input NAND Gates	14	0.24	0.57	M,N,RCA,TI
54HC21	Dual 4-Input AND Gates	14	0.24	0.66	RCA,TI
54HC27	Triple 3-Input NOR Gates	14	0.24	0.57	M,N,RCA,TI
54HC30	8-Input NAND Gate	14	0.24	0.57	M,N,RCA,TI
54HC32	Quad 2-Input OR Gates	14	0.24	0.57	M,N,RCA,TI
54HC36	Quad 2-Input NOR Gates	14	0.24	0.79	TI
54HC42	BCD to Decimal Decoder	16	0.96	1.24	M,N,RCA,TI
54HC51	Dual 2-Wide 2-Input AND-OR-INVERT Gates	14	0.24	0.79	M,N,TI
54HC58	Dual AND-OR Gates	14	0.24	0.91	M,N
54HC73	Dual Negative-Edge-Triggered J-K Flip-Flops with Clear	14	0.48	0.94	M,N,RCA
54HC74	Dual Positive-Edge-Triggered D-Type Flip-Flops with Preset and Clear	14	0.48	0.82	M,N,RCA,TI
54HC75	4-Bit Bistable Latch	16	0.48	0.94	M,N,RCA
54HC76	Dual Negative-Edge-Triggered J-K Flip-Flops with Preset and Clear	16	0.48	1.29	M,N

PART NUMBER	DESCRIPTION	PINS	POWER (mW)	PRICE ($)	SUPPLIERS
54HC85	4-Bit Magnitude Comparator	16	0.96	1.90	M,N,RCA
54HC86	Quad 2-Input Exclusive-OR Gate	14	0.24	0.74	M,N,RCA,TI
54HC107	Dual Master-Slave J-K Flip-Flops with Clear	14	0.48	0.82	M,N,RCA,TI
54HC109	Dual Positive-Edge-Triggered J-K Flip-Flops with Preset and Clear	16	0.48	0.82	M,N,RCA,TI
54HC112	Dual Negative-Edge-Triggered J-K Flip-Flops with Preset and Clear	16	0.48	0.94	M,N,RCA,TI
54HC113	Dual Negative-Edge-Triggered J-K Flip-Flops with Preset	14	0.48	1.00	M,N,TI
54HC114	Dual J-K Flip-Flops with Preset, Common Clear, and Common Clock	14	0.48	1.00	TI
54HC123	Dual Retriggerable Monostable Multivibrators with Clear	16	0.96	2.18	N,RCA
54HC125	Quad Buffers with 3-State Outputs	14	0.96	0.79	M,N,RCA,TI
54HC126	Quad Buffers with 3-State Outputs	14	0.96	0.79	M,N,RCA,TI
54HC132	Quad 2-Input Schmitt-Trigger NAND Gates	14	0.24	1.52	M,N,RCA
54HC133	13-Input NAND Gate	16	0.24	0.79	M,N,TI
54HC137	3 to 8 Line Decoder/Demultiplexer with Address Latches	16	0.96	1.49	M,N,RCA,TI
54HC138	3 to 8 Line Decoder/Demultiplexer	16	0.96	1.04	M,N,RCA,TI
54HC139	Dual 2 to 4 Line Decoders/Demultiplexers	16	0.96	1.04	M,N,RCA,TI
54HC147	10-Line Decimal to 4-Line BCD Priority Encoder	16	0.96	1.90	N,RCA
54HC151	1 of 8 Line Data Selector/Multiplexer	16	0.96	0.96	M,N,RCA,TI
54HC152	1 of 8 Line Data Selector/Multiplexer	14	0.96	1.77	TI
54HC153	Dual 4 to 1 Line Data Selectors/Multiplexers	16	0.96	1.11	M,N,RCA,TI
54HC154	4 to 16 Line Decoder/Demultiplexer	24	0.96	4.70	M,N,RCA
54HC157	Quad 2 to 1 Line Data Selectors/Multiplexers	16	0.96	1.11	M,N,RCA,TI

PART NUMBER	DESCRIPTION	PINS	POWER (mW)	PRICE ($)	SUPPLIERS
54HC158	Quad 2 to 1 Line Inverting Data Selectors/Multiplexers	16	0.96	0.96	M,N,RCA,TI
54HC160	Synchronous 4-Bit Decade Counter with Asynchronous Clear	16	0.96	1.39	M,N,RCA,TI
54HC161	Synchronous 4-Bit Binary Counter with Asynchronous Clear	16	0.96	1.39	M,N,RCA,TI
54HC162	Synchronous 4-Bit Decade Counter with Synchronous Clear	16	0.96	1.60	M,N,RCA
54HC163	Synchronous 4-Bit Binary Counter with Synchronous Clear	16	0.96	1.60	M,N,RCA
54HC164	8-Bit Serial In/Parallel Out Shift Register with Asynchronous Clear	14	0.96	1.39	M,N,RCA,TI
54HC165	8-Bit Parallel In/Serial Out Shift Register with Complementary Outputs	16	0.96	2.10	M,N,RCA,TI
54HC166	8-Bit Parallel or Serial In/Serial Out Shift Register	16	0.96	2.43	RCA
54HC173	4-Bit D-Type Register with 3-State Outputs	16	0.96	1.44	M,N,RCA
54HC174	Hex D-Type Flip-Flops with Clear	16	0.96	1.29	M,N,RCA,TI
54HC175	Quad D-Type Flip-Flops with Clear	16	0.48	1.07	M,N,RCA,TI
54HC180	9-Bit Parity Generator/Checker	14	0.96	2.96	TI
54HC181	Arithmetic Logic Unit/Function Generator	24	0.96	3.22	N,RCA
54HC182	Look-Ahead Carry Generator	16	0.96	1.45	N,RCA
54HC190	Synchronous Up/Down Decade Counter with Mode Control	16	0.96	1.46	RCA,TI
54HC191	Synchronous 4-Bit Up/Down Binary Counter with Mode Control	16	0.96	1.68	RCA,TI
54HC192	Synchronous Up/Down Decade Counter with Dual Clock	16	0.96	1.68	N,RCA,TI
54HC193	Synchronous 4-Bit Up/Down Binary Counter with Dual Clock	16	0.96	1.68	N,RCA,TI
54HC194	4-Bit Bidirectional Universal Shift Register	16	0.96	1.34	M,N,RCA

PART NUMBER	DESCRIPTION	PINS	POWER (mW)	PRICE ($)	SUPPLIERS
54HC195	4-Bit Parallel-Access Shift Register	16	0.96	1.34	M,N,RCA
54HC221	Dual Monostable Multivibrators with Schmitt-Trigger Input	16	0.96	2.18	N,RCA
54HC237	3 to 8 Line Decoder/Demultiplexer with Address Latches	16	0.96	1.49	M,N,RCA,TI
54HC238	3 to 8 Line Decoder/Demultiplexer	16	0.96	1.04	RCA,TI
54HC240	Octal 3-State Inverting Buffers/Line Drivers/Line Receivers	20	0.96	3.00	M,N,RCA,TI
54HC241	Octal 3-State Buffers/Line Drivers/Line Receivers	20	0.96	3.00	M,N,RCA,TI
54HC242	Quad 3-State Inverting Bus Transceivers	14	0.96	2.10	M,N,RCA,TI
54HC243	Quad 3-State Bus Transceivers	14	0.96	2.10	M,N,RCA,TI
54HC244	Octal 3-State Buffers/Line Drivers/Line Receivers	20	0.96	3.00	M,N,RCA,TI
54HC245	Octal 3-State Bus Transceivers	20	0.96	3.58	M,N,RCA,TI
54HC251	3-State 1 of 8 Line Data Selector/Multiplexer	16	0.96	0.96	M,N,RCA,TI
54HC253	Dual 3-State 1 of 4 Line Data Selectors/Multiplexers	16	0.96	0.96	M,N,RCA,TI
54HC257	Quad 3-State 2 to 1 Line Data Selectors/Multiplexers	16	0.96	0.96	M,N,RCA,TI
54HC258	Quad 3-State 2 to 1 Line Inverting Data Selectors/Multiplexers	16	0.96	0.96	RCA,TI
54HC259	8-Bit Addressable Latch	16	0.96	2.26	M,N,RCA
54HC266	Quad 2-Input Exclusive-NOR Gates with Open-Collector Outputs	14	0.24	1.02	M,N,TI
54HC273	Octal D-Type Flip-Flop with Clear	20	0.96	2.25	M,RCA,TI
54HC280	9-Bit Parity Generator/Checker	14	0.96	3.03	M,N,RCA,TI
54HC283	4-Bit Binary Full Adder with Fast Carry	16	0.96	1.49	N,RCA
54HC298	Quad 2 to 1 Line Data Selectors/Multiplexers with Storage	16	0.96	2.15	N,TI

PART NUMBER	DESCRIPTION	PINS	POWER (mW)	PRICE ($)	SUPPLIERS
54HC299	8-Bit Universal Shift/Storage Register with 3-State Outputs	20	0.96	5.02	M,N,RCA
54HC352	Dual 1 of 4 Line Inverting Data Selectors/Multiplexers	16	0.96	1.74	TI
54HC353	Dual 3-State 1 of 4 Line Data Selectors/Multiplexers	16	0.96	1.74	TI
54HC354	3-State 8 to 1 Line Data Selector/Multiplexer/Register	20	0.96	4.62	M,N,RCA
54HC356	3-State 8 to 1 Line Data Selector/Multiplexer/Register	20	0.96	4.62	M,N,RCA
54HC365	Hex 3-State Buffers/Bus Drivers	16	0.96	1.07	M,N,RCA,TI
54HC366	Hex 3-State Inverting Buffers/Bus Drivers	16	0.96	1.07	M,N,RCA,TI
54HC367	Hex 3-State Buffers/Bus Drivers	16	0.96	1.07	M,N,RCA,TI
54HC368	Hex 3-State Inverting Buffers/Bus Drivers	16	0.96	1.07	M,N,RCA,TI
54HC373	Octal 3-State Transparent D-Type Latches	20	0.96	3.09	M,N,RCA,TI
54HC374	Octal 3-State Positive-Edge-Triggered D-Type Flip-Flops	20	0.96	3.09	M,N,RCA,TI
54HC377	OCTAL D-TYPE FLIP-FLOPS	20	0.96	3.02	RCA,TI
54HC378	Hex D-Type Flip-Flops with Enable	16	0.96	1.64	TI
54HC379	Quad D-Type Flip-Flops with Enable	16	0.48	1.64	TI
54HC386	Quad 2-Input Exclusive-OR Gates	14	0.24	1.02	TI
54HC390	Dual Decade (Bi-Quinary) Counters	16	0.96	1.73	M,N,RCA,TI
54HC393	Dual 4-Bit Binary Counters	14	0.96	1.73	M,N,RCA
54HC423	Dual Retriggerable Monostable Multivibrators	16	0.96	2.18	N,RCA
54HC490	Dual Decade Counters	16	0.96	3.58	TI
54HC533	Octal 3-State Inverting Transparent D-Type Latches	20	0.96	3.56	M,N,RCA

PART NUMBER	DESCRIPTION	PINS	POWER (mW)	PRICE ($)	SUPPLIERS
54HC534	Octal 3-State Inverting Positive-Edge-Triggered D-Type Flip-Flops	20	0.96	3.56	M,N,RCA
54HC540	Octal 3-State Inverting Buffer	20	0.96	3.18	M,RCA
54HC541	Octal 3-State Buffer	20	0.96	3.18	M,RCA
54HC563	Octal 3-State Inverting Transparent D-Type Latches	20	0.96	3.73	M,N,RCA,TI
54HC564	OCTAL D-TYPE FLIP-FLOPS	20	0.96	3.88	M,N,RCA
54HC573	Octal 3-State Transparent D-Type Latches	20	0.96	3.88	M,N,RCA
54HC574	Octal 3-State Positive-Edge-Triggered D-Type Flip-Flops	20	0.96	3.88	M,RCA
54HC589	8-Bit Shift Register with Input Latches and 3-State Serial Output	16	0.96	3.50	M
54HC595	8-BIT Shift Register with Output Latches	16	0.96	2.95	M
54HC597	8-Bit Shift Register with Input Latches	16	0.96	3.50	M
54HC620	Octal 3-State Inverting Bus Transceivers	20	0.96	4.76	TI
54HC623	Octal 3-State Bust Transceivers	20	0.96	4.76	TI
54HC640	Octal 3-State Inverting Bus Transceivers	20	0.96	3.12	M,N,RCA,TI
54HC643	Octal 3-State True/Inverting Bus Transceivers	20	0.96	3.12	M,N,RCA,TI
54HC645	Octal 3-State Bus Transceivers	20	0.96	4.40	TI
54HC646	Octal 3-State Bus Transceivers	24	0.96	6.98	M,N,RCA
54HC648	Octal 3-State Inverting Bus Transceivers	24	0.96	6.98	M,N,RCA
54HC670	4x4 Register File with 3-State Outputs	16	0.96	3.63	RCA
54HC688	8-Bit Identity Comparator	20	0.96	2.11	M,N,RCA
54HC4002	Dual 4-Input NOR Gates	14	0.24	0.66	M,N,RCA,TI
54HC4015	Dual 4-Bit Serial In/Parallel Out Shift Register	16	0.96	1.96	RCA
54HC4016	Quad Analog Switch	14	3.84	1.27	N,RCA

PART NUMBER	DESCRIPTION	PINS	POWER (mW)	PRICE ($)	SUPPLIERS
54HC4017	Decate Counter/Divider with 10 Decoded Outputs	16	0.96	1.73	M,N,RCA
54HC4020	14-Stage Binary Counter	16	0.96	1.73	M,N,RCA
54HC4024	7-Stage Binary Counter	14	0.96	1.70	M,RCA
54HC4040	12-Stage Binary Counter	16	0.96	1.73	M,N,RCA
54HC4046	Phase Lock Loop	16	0.96	2.56	N,RCA
54HC4049	Hex Inverting Logic Level Down Converter	16	0.24	1.34	M,N,RCA
54HC4050	Hex Logic Level Down Converter	16	0.24	1.34	M,N,RCA
54HC4051	8-Channel Analog Multiplexer	16	1.92	2.54	M,RCA
54HC4052	Dual 4-Channel Analog Multiplexer	16	1.92	2.54	M,RCA
54HC4053	Triple 2-Channel Analog Multiplexer	16	1.92	2.54	M,RCA
54HC4060	14-Stage Binary Counter	16	0.96	1.50	M,N,RCA,TI
54HC4066	Quad Analog Switch	14	3.84	1.27	N,RCA
54HC4075	Triple 3-Input OR Gates	14	0.24	0.57	M,N,RCA,TI
54HC4078	8-Input OR/NOR Gate	14	0.24	0.68	M,N,TI
54HC4316	Quad Analog Switch with Level Translator	16	1.92	1.27	N,RCA
54HC4351	8-Channel Analog Multiplexer with Address Latch	18	1.92	4.35	M
54HC4352	Dual 4-Channel Analog Multiplexer with Address Latch	18	1.92	1.82	M,RCA
54HC4353	Triple 2-Channel Analog Multiplexer with Address Latch	18	1.92	4.67	M
54HC4511	BCD to 7-Segment Latch/Decoder/Display Driver	16	0.96	2.33	RCA
54HC4514	4 to 16 Line Decoder with Address Latch	24	0.96	4.39	M,N,RCA
54HC4515	4 to 16 Line Inverting Decoder with Address Latch	24	0.96	4.39	RCA
54HC4518	Dual BCD Counter	16	0.96	2.44	RCA
54HC4520	Dual 4-Bit Binary Counter	16	0.96	2.44	RCA

PART NUMBER	DESCRIPTION	PINS	POWER (mW)	PRICE ($)	SUPPLIERS
54HC4538	Dual Retriggerable Monostable Multivibrator	16	2.40	2.89	M,N,RCA
54HC4543	BCD to 7-Segment Latch/Decoder/Driver for Liquid Crystal Displays	16	0.96	4.26	RCA
54HC4724	8-Bit Addressable Latch	16	0.96	4.46	TI
54HC7266	Quad 2-Input Exclusive-NOR Gates	14	0.24	0.83	RCA
54HC40102	8-Bit Synchronous BCD Down Counter	16	0.96	3.05	RCA
54HC40103	8-Bit Binary Down Counter	16	0.96	3.05	RCA
54HC40104	4-Bit Bidirectional Universal Shift Register with 3-State Outputs	16	0.96	3.12	RCA

PART NUMBER	DESCRIPTION	PINS	POWER (mW)	PRICE ($)	SUPPLIERS
54HCT00	Quad 2-Input NAND Gates	14	0.22	0.64	N,RCA
54HCT02	Quad 2-Input NOR Gates	14	0.22	0.64	RCA
54HCT04	Hex Inverters	14	0.22	0.64	N,RCA
54HCT05	Hex Inverters with Open-Collector Outputs	14	0.22	1.05	N
54HCT08	Quad 2-Input AND Gates	14	0.22	0.64	RCA
54HCT10	Triple 3-Input NAND Gates	14	0.22	0.64	RCA
54HCT11	Triple 3-Input AND Gates	14	0.22	0.64	RCA
54HCT20	Dual 4-Input NAND Gates	14	0.22	0.64	RCA
54HCT27	Triple 3-Input NOR Gates	14	0.22	0.64	RCA
54HCT30	8-Input NAND Gate	14	0.22	0.64	RCA
54HCT32	Quad 2-Input OR Gates	14	0.22	0.64	RCA
54HCT34	Hex Non-Inverters	14	0.22	1.05	N
54HCT42	BCD to Decimal Decoder	16	0.88	1.09	RCA
54HCT74	Dual Positive-Edge-Triggered D-Type Flip-Flops with Preset and Clear	14	0.44	0.69	RCA
54HCT75	4-Bit Bistable Latch	16	0.44	0.69	RCA
54HCT86	Quad 2-Input Exclusive-OR Gate	14	0.22	0.69	RCA
54HCT107	Dual Master-Slave J-K Flip-Flops with Clear	14	0.44	0.69	RCA
54HCT109	Dual Positive-Edge-Triggered J-K Flip-Flops with Preset and Clear	16	0.44	0.69	RCA
54HCT112	Dual Negative-Edge-Triggered J-K Flip-Flops with Preset and Clear	16	0.44	0.69	RCA
54HCT132	Quad 2-Input Schmitt-Trigger NAND Gates	14	0.22	1.39	RCA
54HCT137	3 to 8 Line Decoder/Demultiplexer with Address Latches	16	0.88	1.24	RCA,TI
54HCT138	3 to 8 Line Decoder/Demultiplexer	16	0.88	0.97	RCA,TI

PART NUMBER	DESCRIPTION	PINS	POWER (mW)	PRICE ($)	SUPPLIERS
54HCT139	Dual 2 to 4 Line Decoders/Demultiplexers	16	0.44	1.12	RCA
54HCT151	1 of 8 Line Data Selector/Multiplexer	16	0.88	1.01	RCA
54HCT154	4 to 16 Line Decoder/Demultiplexer	24	0.88	4.21	RCA
54HCT157	Quad 2 to 1 Line Data Selectors/Multiplexers	16	0.88	1.01	RCA
54HCT158	Quad 2 to 1 Line Inverting Data Selectors/Multiplexers	16	0.88	1.01	RCA
54HCT160	Synchronous 4-Bit Decade Counter with Asynchronous Clear	16	0.22	1.37	RCA
54HCT161	Synchronous 4-Bit Binary Counter with Asynchronous Clear	16	0.22	1.37	RCA
54HCT162	Synchronous 4-Bit Decade Counter with Synchronous Clear	16	0.22	1.37	RCA
54HCT163	Synchronous 4-Bit Binary Counter with Synchronous Clear	16	0.22	1.37	RCA
54HCT164	8-Bit Serial In/Parallel Out Shift Register with Asynchronous Clear	14	0.44	1.32	RCA
54HCT165	8-Bit Parallel In/Serial Out Shift Register with Complementary Outputs	16	0.88	2.01	RCA
54HCT166	8-Bit Parallel or Serial In/Serial Out Shift Register	16	0.44	2.01	RCA
54HCT173	4-Bit D-Type Register with 3-State Outputs	16	0.88	1.30	RCA
54HCT174	Hex D-Type Flip-Flops with Clear	16	0.88	1.15	RCA
54HCT175	Quad D-Type Flip-Flops with Clear	16	0.88	1.15	RCA
54HCT190	Synchronous Up/Down Decade Counter with Mode Control	16	0.88	1.68	RCA
54HCT191	Synchronous 4-Bit Up/Down Binary Counter with Mode Control	16	0.88	1.68	RCA
54HCT192	Synchronous Up/Down Decade Counter with Dual Clock	16	0.88	1.47	RCA
54HCT193	Synchronous 4-Bit Up/Down Binary Counter with Dual Clock	16	0.88	1.47	RCA

PART NUMBER	DESCRIPTION	PINS	POWER (mW)	PRICE ($)	SUPPLIERS
54HCT194	4-Bit Bidirectional Universal Shift Register	16	0.88	1.07	RCA
54HCT195	4-Bit Parallel-Access Shift Register	16	0.88	1.07	RCA
54HCT221	Dual Monostable Multivibrators with Schmitt-Trigger Input	16	0.88	1.96	RCA
54HCT237	3 to 8 Line Decoder/Demultiplexer with Address Latches	16	0.88	1.24	RCA,TI
54HCT238	3 to 8 Line Decoder/Demultiplexer	16	0.88	0.97	RCA,TI
54HCT240	Octal 3-State Inverting Buffers/Line Drivers/Line Receivers	20	0.88	2.39	M,N,RCA
54HCT241	Octal 3-State Buffers/Line Drivers/Line Receivers	20	0.88	2.39	M,N,RCA
54HCT242	Quad 3-State Inverting Bus Transceivers	14	0.88	2.18	RCA
54HCT243	Quad 3-State Bus Transceivers	14	0.88	2.18	RCA
54HCT244	Octal 3-State Buffers/Line Drivers/Line Receivers	20	0.88	2.07	M,RCA,TI
54HCT245	Octal 3-State Bus Transceivers	20	0.88	3.18	M,N,RCA
54HCT251	3-State 1 of 8 Line Data Selector/Multiplexer	16	0.88	1.01	RCA
54HCT253	Dual 3-State 1 of 4 Line Data Selectors/Multiplexers	16	0.88	1.01	RCA
54HCT257	Quad 3-State 2 to 1 Line Data Selectors/Multiplexers	16	0.88	1.01	RCA
54HCT273	Octal D-Type Flip-Flop with Clear	20	0.88	2.06	RCA
54HCT280	9-Bit Parity Generator/Checker	14	0.88	2.31	RCA
54HCT299	8-Bit Universal Shift/Storage Register with 3-State Outputs	20	0.88	4.13	RCA
54HCT354	3-State 8 to 1 Line Data Selector/Multiplexer/Register	20	0.88	3.71	RCA
54HCT356	3-State 8 to 1 Line Data Selector/Multiplexer/Register	20	0.88	3.71	RCA

PART NUMBER	DESCRIPTION	PINS	POWER (mW)	PRICE ($)	SUPPLIERS
54HCT365	Hex 3-State Buffers/Bus Drivers	16	0.88	0.89	RCA
54HCT366	Hex 3-State Inverting Buffers/Bus Drivers	16	0.88	0.89	RCA
54HCT367	Hex 3-State Buffers/Bus Drivers	16	0.88	0.89	RCA
54HCT368	Hex 3-State Inverting Buffers/Bus Drivers	16	0.88	0.89	RCA
54HCT373	Octal 3-State Transparent D-Type Latches	20	0.88	2.48	M,N,RCA
54HCT374	Octal 3-State Positive-Edge-Triggered D-Type Flip-Flops	20	0.88	2.48	M,N,RCA
54HCT377	OCTAL D-TYPE FLIP-FLOPS	20	0.88	2.39	RCA
54HCT393	Dual 4-Bit Binary Counters	14	0.88	1.49	RCA
54HCT533	Octal 3-State Inverting Transparent D-Type Latches	20	0.88	2.48	M,RCA
54HCT534	Octal 3-State Inverting Positive-Edge-Triggered D-Type Flip-Flops	20	0.88	2.48	M,RCA
54HCT540	Octal 3-State Inverting Buffer	20	0.88	2.23	M,RCA
54HCT541	Octal 3-State Buffer	20	0.88	2.23	M,RCA
54HCT563	Octal 3-State Inverting Transparent D-Type Latches	20	0.88	3.30	RCA
54HCT564	OCTAL D-TYPE FLIP-FLOPS	20	0.88	3.30	RCA
54HCT573	Octal 3-State Transparent D-Type Latches	20	0.88	3.30	RCA
54HCT574	Octal 3-State Positive-Edge-Triggered D-Type Flip-Flops	20	0.88	3.30	RCA
54HCT640	Octal 3-State Inverting Bus Transceivers	20	0.88	3.27	M,N,RCA
54HCT643	Octal 3-State True/Inverting Bus Transceivers	20	0.88	3.27	M,N,RCA
54HCT646	Octal 3-State Bus Transceivers	24	0.88	6.27	RCA
54HCT648	Octal 3-State Inverting Bus Transceivers	24	0.88	6.27	RCA
54HCT670	4x4 Register File with 3-State Outputs	16	0.88	3.30	RCA

PART NUMBER	DESCRIPTION	PINS	POWER (mW)	PRICE ($)	SUPPLIERS
54HCT688	8-Bit Identity Comparator	20	0.88	1.90	N,RCA
54HCT4015	Dual 4-Bit Serial In/Parallel Out Shift Register	16	0.88	1.75	RCA
54HCT4017	Decate Counter/Divider with 10 Decoded Outputs	16	0.88	1.57	RCA
54HCT4020	14-Stage Binary Counter	16	0.88	1.57	RCA
54HCT4024	7-Stage Binary Counter	14	0.88	1.47	RCA
54HCT4040	12-Stage Binary Counter	16	0.88	1.57	RCA
54HCT4051	8-Channel Analog Multiplexer	16	3.20	2.29	RCA
54HCT4052	Dual 4-Channel Analog Multiplexer	16	3.20	2.29	RCA
54HCT4053	Triple 2-Channel Analog Multiplexer	16	3.20	2.29	RCA
54HCT4060	14-Stage Binary Counter	16	0.88	1.57	RCA
54HCT4514	4 to 16 Line Decoder with Address Latch	24	0.88	3.96	RCA
54HCT4515	4 to 16 Line Inverting Decoder with Address Latch	24	0.88	3.96	RCA
54HCT4518	Dual BCD Counter	16	0.88	2.19	RCA
54HCT4520	Dual 4-Bit Binary Counter	16	0.88	2.19	RCA
54HCT4538	Dual Retriggerable Monostable Multivibrator	16	0.88	2.48	RCA
54HCT40102	8-Bit Synchronous BCD Down Counter	16	0.88	2.76	RCA
54HCT40103	8-Bit Binary Down Counter	16	0.88	2.76	RCA
54HCT40104	4-Bit Bidirectional Universal Shift Register with 3-State Outputs	16	0.88	2.79	RCA

PART NUMBER	DESCRIPTION	PINS	POWER (mW)	PRICE ($)	SUPPLIERS
54L00	Quad 2-Input NAND Gates	14	11.22	8.30	N
54L02	Quad 2-Input NOR Gates	14	14.30	8.30	N
54L10	Triple 3-Input NAND Gates	14	8.42	5.23	N
54L73	Dual Negative-Edge-Triggered J-K Flip-Flops with Clear	14	15.84	7.83	N
54L74	Dual Positive-Edge-Triggered D-Type Flip-Flops with Preset and Clear	14	16.50	7.83	N
54L93	4-Bit Binary Counter	14	30.25	14.60	N
54L95	4-Bit Parallel-Access Shift Register	14	44.00	14.60	N
54L98	4-Bit Data Selector/Storage Register	16	44.00	17.57	N

PART NUMBER	DESCRIPTION	PINS	POWER (mW)	PRICE ($)	SUPPLIERS
54LS00	Quad 2-Input NAND Gates	14	24.20	0.56	F,M,N,TI
54LS01	Quad 2-Input NAND Gates with Open-Collector Outputs	14	24.20	0.56	M,TI
54LS02	Quad 2-Input NOR Gates	14	29.70	0.56	F,M,N,TI
54LS03	Quad 2-Input NAND Gates with Open-Collector Outputs	14	24.20	0.56	F,M,N,TI
54LS04	Hex Inverters	14	36.30	0.56	F,M,N,TI
54LS05	Hex Inverters with Open-Collector Outputs	14	36.30	0.56	F,M,N,TI
54LS08	Quad 2-Input AND Gates	14	48.40	0.56	F,M,N,TI
54LS09	Quad 2-Input AND Gates with Open-Collector Outputs	14	48.40	0.56	F,M,N,TI
54LS10	Triple 3-Input NAND Gates	14	18.15	0.56	F,M,N,TI
54LS11	Triple 3-Input AND Gates	14	36.30	0.56	F,M,N,TI
54LS12	Triple 3-Input NAND Gates with Open-Collector Outputs	14	18.15	0.56	M,N,TI
54LS13	Dual 4-Input Schmitt Trigger NAND Gates	14	38.50	0.60	F,M,TI
54LS14	Hex Schmitt Trigger Inverters	14	115.50	0.98	F,M,TI
54LS15	Triple 3-Input AND Gates with Open-Collector Outputs	14	36.30	0.56	F,M,TI
54LS20	Dual 4-Input NAND Gates	14	12.10	0.56	F,M,N,TI
54LS21	Dual 4-Input AND Gates	14	24.20	0.56	F,M,N,TI
54LS22	Dual 4-Input NAND Gates with Open-Collector Outputs	14	12.10	0.56	F,M,TI
54LS26	Quad 2-Input NAND Buffers with High-Voltage Open-Collector Outputs	14	24.20	0.56	F,M,TI
54LS27	Triple 3-Input NOR Gates	14	37.40	0.56	F,M,N,TI
54LS28	Quad 2-Input NOR Buffers	14	75.90	0.56	F,M,TI
54LS30	8-Input NAND Gate	14	6.05	0.56	F,M,N,TI

PART NUMBER	DESCRIPTION	PINS	POWER (mW)	PRICE ($)	SUPPLIERS
54LS32	Quad 2-Input OR Gates	14	53.90	0.56	F,M,N,TI
54LS33	Quad 2-Input NOR Buffers with Open-Collector Outputs	14	75.90	0.57	F,M,TI
54LS37	Quad 2-Input NAND Buffers	14	66.00	0.57	F,M,TI
54LS38	Quad 2-Input Nand Buffers with Open-Collector Outputs	14	66.00	0.57	F,M,N,TI
54LS40	Dual 4-Input NAND Buffers	14	33.00	0.56	F,M,TI
54LS42	BCD to Decimal Decoder	16	71.50	0.94	F,M,N,TI
54LS47	BCD to 7-Segment Decoder/Driver with Open-Collector Outputs	16	71.50	1.49	F,TI
54LS48	BCD to 7-Segment Decoder/Driver with Internal Pull-Up Resistor Outputs	16	209.00	1.49	F,TI
54LS49	BCD to 7-Segment Decoder/Driver with Open-Collector Outputs	16	82.50	1.49	F,TI
54LS51	Dual 2-Wide 2-Input AND-OR-INVERT Gates	14	15.40	0.56	F,M,TI
54LS54	4-Wide 2-Input AND-OR-INVERT Gate	14	11.00	0.56	F,M,TI
54LS55	2-Wide 4-Input AND-OR-INVERT Gate	14	7.15	0.64	F,M
54LS63	Hex Current-Sensing Gates	14	88.00	1.92	TI
54LS73	Dual Negative-Edge-Triggered J-K Flip-Flops with Clear	14	33.00	0.60	M,N,TI
54LS74	Dual Positive-Edge-Triggered D-Type Flip-Flops with Preset and Clear	14	44.00	0.60	F,M,N,TI
54LS75	4-Bit Bistable Latch	16	66.00	0.86	M,N,TI
54LS76	Dual Negative-Edge-Triggered J-K Flip-Flops with Preset and Clear	16	33.00	0.60	M,TI
54LS77	4-Bit Bistable Latch	14	71.50	1.10	M
54LS78	Dual J-K Flip-Flops with Preset, Common Clear, and Common Clock	14	33.00	0.60	M,TI
54LS83	4-Bit Binary Full Adder with Fast Carry	16	214.50	1.28	F,M,TI
54LS85	4-Bit Magnitude Comparator	16	110.00	1.34	F,M,N,TI

PART NUMBER	DESCRIPTION	PINS	POWER (mW)	PRICE ($)	SUPPLIERS
54LS86	Quad 2-Input Exclusive-OR Gate	14	55.00	0.60	M,N,TI
54LS90	Decade Counter	14	82.50	0.96	M,TI
54LS91	8-Bit Shift Register	14	110.00	1.76	TI
54LS92	Divide by 12 Counter	14	82.50	0.96	M,TI
54LS93	4-Bit Binary Counter	14	82.50	0.96	M,TI
54LS95	4-Bit Parallel-Access Shift Register	14	115.50	1.20	F,M,TI
54LS96	5-Bit Shift Register	16	110.00	1.20	TI
54LS107	Dual Master-Slave J-K Flip-Flops with Clear	14	33.00	0.60	M,N,TI
54LS109	Dual Positive-Edge-Triggered J-K Flip-Flops with Preset and Clear	16	44.00	0.60	F,M,N,TI
54LS112	Dual Negative-Edge-Triggered J-K Flip-Flops with Preset and Clear	16	33.00	0.90	F,M,N
54LS113	Dual Negative-Edge-Triggered J-K Flip-Flops with Preset	14	33.00	0.90	F,M
54LS114	Dual J-K Flip-Flops with Preset, Common Clear, and Common Clock	14	33.00	0.90	F,M
54LS122	Retriggerable Monostable Multivibrator with Clear	14	110.00	0.89	M,TI
54LS123	Dual Retriggerable Monostable Multivibrators with Clear	16	110.00	1.50	M,TI
54LS125	Quad Buffers with 3-State Outputs	14	121.00	0.56	F,M,N,TI
54LS126	Quad Buffers with 3-State Outputs	14	121.00	0.56	F,M,TI
54LS132	Quad 2-Input Schmitt-Trigger NAND Gates	14	77.00	1.04	M,N,TI
54LS133	13-Input NAND Gate	16	6.05	0.78	F,M
54LS136	Quad 2-Input Exclusive-OR Gates with Open-Collector Outputs	14	55.00	0.60	F,TI
54LS137	3 to 8 Line Decoder/Demultiplexer with Address Latches	16	99.00	1.63	TI
54LS138	3 to 8 Line Decoder/Demultiplexer	16	55.00	0.94	F,M,N,TI

PART NUMBER	DESCRIPTION	PINS	POWER (mW)	PRICE ($)	SUPPLIERS
54LS139	Dual 2 to 4 Line Decoders/Demultiplexers	16	60.50	0.94	F,M,N,TI
54LS145	BCD to Decimal Decoder/Driver	16	71.50	0.94	TI
54LS147	10-Line Decimal to 4-Line BCD Priority Encoder	16	110.00	2.69	TI
54LS148	8-Line Decimal to 3-Line Octal Priority Encoder	16	110.00	1.80	M,TI
54LS151	1 of 8 Line Data Selector/Multiplexer	16	55.00	0.94	F,M,N,TI
54LS153	Dual 4 to 1 Line Data Selectors/Multiplexers	16	55.00	0.94	F,M,N,TI
54LS155	Dual 2 to 4 Line Decoders/Demultiplexers	16	55.00	1.20	F,M,N,TI
54LS156	Dual 2 to 4 Line Decoders/Demultiplexers with Open-Collector Outputs	16	55.00	1.20	F,M,N,TI
54LS157	Quad 2 to 1 Line Data Selectors/Multiplexers	16	88.00	0.94	F,M,N,TI
54LS158	Quad 2 to 1 Line Inverting Data Selectors/Multiplexers	16	60.50	0.94	F,M,N,TI
54LS160	Synchronous 4-Bit Decade Counter with Asynchronous Clear	16	176.00	1.20	F,M,TI
54LS161	Synchronous 4-Bit Binary Counter with Asynchronous Clear	16	176.00	1.20	F,M,N,TI
54LS162	Synchronous 4-Bit Decade Counter with Synchronous Clear	16	176.00	1.20	F,M,TI
54LS163	Synchronous 4-Bit Binary Counter with Synchronous Clear	16	176.00	1.20	F,M,N,TI
54LS164	8-Bit Serial In/Parallel Out Shift Register with Asynchronous Clear	14	148.50	1.22	F,M,N,TI
54LS165	8-Bit Parallel In/Serial Out Shift Register with Complementary Outputs	16	165.00	1.64	F,M,TI
54LS166	8-Bit Parallel or Serial In/Serial Out Shift Register	16	176.00	1.74	M,TI
54LS168	Synchronous 4-Bit Up/Down Decade Counter	16	187.00	2.68	F,M
54LS169	Synchronous 4-Bit Up/Down Binary Counter	16	247.50	1.79	F,M,N,TI

PART NUMBER	DESCRIPTION	PINS	POWER (mW)	PRICE ($)	SUPPLIERS
54LS170	4 by 4 Register File with Open-Collector Outputs	16	220.00	2.44	F,M,TI
54LS173	4-Bit D-Type Register with 3-State Outputs	16	132.00	1.20	F,M,TI
54LS174	Hex D-Type Flip-Flops with Clear	16	143.00	1.06	F,M,N,TI
54LS175	Quad D-Type Flip-Flops with Clear	16	99.00	1.06	F,M,N,TI
54LS181	Arithmetic Logic Unit/Function Generator	24	203.50	2.95	F,M,TI
54LS182	Look-Ahead Carry Generator	16	88.00	1.90	M
54LS183	Dual Carry-Save Full Adders	14	93.50	4.45	TI
54LS189	64-Bit Random-Access Memory with 3-State Outputs	16	330.00	4.50	TI
54LS190	Synchronous Up/Down Decade Counter with Mode Control	16	192.50	1.38	M,N,TI
54LS191	Synchronous 4-Bit Up/Down Binary Counter with Mode Control	16	192.50	1.38	M,N,TI
54LS192	Synchronous Up/Down Decade Counter with Dual Clock	16	187.00	1.38	F,M,TI
54LS193	Synchronous 4-Bit Up/Down Binary Counter with Dual Clock	16	187.00	1.46	F,M,N,TI
54LS194	4-Bit Bidirectional Universal Shift Register	16	126.50	1.20	F,M,TI
54LS195	4-Bit Parallel-Access Shift Register	16	115.50	1.20	F,M,TI
54LS196	Presettable Decade (Bi-Quinary) Counter	14	148.50	1.20	M,TI
54LS197	Presettable Binary Counter	14	148.50	1.20	M,TI
54LS219	64-Bit Random-Access Memory with 3-State Outputs	16	330.00	4.50	TI
54LS221	Dual Monostable Multivibrators with Schmitt-Trigger Input	16	148.50	1.54	M,TI
54LS240	Octal 3-State Inverting Buffers/Line Drivers/Line Receivers	20	275.00	2.07	F,M,MM,TI
54LS241	Octal 3-State Buffers/Line Drivers/Line Receivers	20	297.00	2.07	F,M,MM,TI

PART NUMBER	DESCRIPTION	PINS	POWER (mW)	PRICE ($)	SUPPLIERS
54LS242	Quad 3-State Inverting Bus Transceivers	14	275.00	1.89	M,TI
54LS243	Quad 3-State Bus Transceivers	14	297.00	1.89	M,TI
54LS244	Octal 3-State Buffers/Line Drivers/Line Receivers	20	297.00	2.07	F,M,MM,N,TI
54LS245	Octal 3-State Bus Transceivers	20	522.50	2.76	F,M,MM,N,TI
54LS247	BCD to 7 Segment Decoder/Driver with Open-Collector Outputs	16	71.50	1.49	F,TI
54LS248	BCD to 7 Segment Decoder/Driver	16	209.00	1.49	F,TI
54LS249	BCD to 7 Segment Decoder/Driver with Open-Collector Outputs	16	82.50	1.49	F,TI
54LS251	3-State 1 of 8 Line Data Selector/Multiplexer	16	66.00	0.94	F,N,TI
54LS253	Dual 3-State 1 of 4 Line Data Selectors/Multiplexers	16	77.00	0.94	F,M,N,TI
54LS256	Dual 4-Bit Addressable Latch	16	137.50	1.82	F,M
54LS257	Quad 3-State 2 to 1 Line Data Selectors/Multiplexers	16	104.50	0.94	F,M,N,TI
54LS258	Quad 3-State 2 to 1 Line Inverting Data Selectors/Multiplexers	16	88.00	0.94	F,M,N,TI
54LS259	8-Bit Addressable Latch	16	198.00	1.29	F,M,TI
54LS260	Dual 5-Input NOR Gates	14	30.25	0.78	F,M
54LS261	2-Bit by 4-Bit Parallel Binary Multiplexer	16	220.00	2.95	TI
54LS266	Quad 2-Input Exclusive-NOR Gates with Open-Collector Outputs	14	71.50	0.60	F,M,TI
54LS273	Octal D-Type Flip-Flop with Clear	20	148.50	2.07	F,M,MM,TI
54LS279	Quad S-R Latches	16	38.50	0.86	F,M,N,TI
54LS280	9-Bit Parity Generator/Checker	14	148.50	2.00	TI
54LS283	4-Bit Binary Full Adder with Fast Carry	16	187.00	1.20	F,M,N,TI
54LS289	64-BIT RAM 16x4 OC	16	330.00	4.50	TI

PART NUMBER	DESCRIPTION	PINS	POWER (mW)	PRICE ($)	SUPPLIERS
54LS290	Decade Counter	14	82.50	1.32	M,TI
54LS293	4-Bit Binary Counter	14	82.50	1.34	M,TI
54LS295	4-Bit Bidirectional Shift Register with 3-State Outputs	14	181.50	1.20	F,TI
54LS298	Quad 2 to 1 Line Data Selectors/Multiplexers with Storage	16	115.50	1.28	F,M,TI
54LS299	8-Bit Universal Shift/Storage Register with 3-State Outputs	20	291.50	4.22	F,TI
54LS319	64-BIT RAM 16x4 OC	16	330.00	4.50	TI
54LS320	Crystal Controlled Oscillator	16	385.00	4.19	TI
54LS321	Crystal Controlled Oscillator	16	412.50	4.62	TI
54LS322	8-Bit Shift Register with Sign Extend	20	330.00	3.90	F,TI
54LS323	8-Bit Universal Shift/Storage Register with 3-State Outputs	20	291.50	3.90	F,TI
54LS347	BCD to 7-Segment Decoder/Driver	16	71.50	1.29	F,TI
54LS348	8 to 3 Line Priority Encoder with 3-State Outputs	16	137.50	2.16	TI
54LS352	Dual 1 of 4 Line Inverting Data Selectors/Multiplexers	16	55.00	1.63	F,TI
54LS353	Dual 3-State 1 of 4 Line Data Selectors/Multiplexers	16	77.00	1.92	F,TI
54LS356	3-State 8 to 1 Line Data Selector/Multiplexer/Register	20	253.00	4.49	TI
54LS365	Hex 3-State Buffers/Bus Drivers	16	132.00	0.77	F,M,N,TI
54LS366	Hex 3-State Inverting Buffers/Bus Drivers	16	115.50	0.77	F,M,TI
54LS367	Hex 3-State Buffers/Bus Drivers	16	132.00	0.77	F,M,N,TI
54LS368	Hex 3-State Inverting Buffers/Bus Drivers	16	115.50	0.77	F,M,N,TI
54LS373	Octal 3-State Transparent D-Type Latches	20	220.00	2.62	M,MM,N,TI

PART NUMBER	DESCRIPTION	PINS	POWER (mW)	PRICE ($)	SUPPLIERS
54LS374	Octal 3-State Positive-Edge-Triggered D-Type Flip-Flops	20	220.00	2.62	F,M,MM,N,TI
54LS375	4-Bit Bistable Latch	16	66.00	0.86	F,M,TI
54LS377	Octal D-Type Flip-Flops with Enable	20	154.00	2.07	F,M,TI
54LS378	Hex D-Type Flip-Flops with Enable	16	121.00	1.28	F,M,TI
54LS379	Quad D-Type Flip-Flops with Enable	16	82.50	1.28	F,M,TI
54LS380	Multifunction 8-Bit Register	24	990.00	17.95	MM
54LS381	Arithmetic Logic Unit/Function Generator	20	357.50	3.92	TI
54LS382	Arithmetic Logic Unit/Function Generator	20	357.50	3.92	TI
54LS385	Quad Serial Adder/Subtractor	20	412.50	5.78	M,TI
54LS386	Quad 2-Input Exclusive-OR Gates	14	55.00	0.66	M,TI
54LS390	Dual Decade (Bi-Quinary) Counters	16	143.00	1.84	M,TI
54LS393	Dual 4-Bit Binary Counters	14	143.00	1.74	M,TI
54LS395	4-Bit Cascadable Shift Register with 3-State Outputs	16	187.00	1.20	F,TI
54LS396	Octal Storage Register	16	220.00	2.69	TI
54LS398	Quad 2-Input Multiplexers with Storage	20	71.50	3.03	M,TI
54LS399	Quad 2-Input Multiplexers with Storage	16	71.50	1.68	M,TI
54LS442	Quad 3-State Bus Transceivers	20	522.50	6.31	TI
54LS447	BCD to 7-Segment Decoder/Driver	16	71.50	2.17	F
54LS450	16 to 1 Multiplexer	24	550.00	6.43	MM
54LS451	Dual 8 to 1 Multiplexer	24	550.00	6.43	MM
54LS453	Quad 4 to 1 Multiplexer	24	550.00	6.43	MM
54LS460	10-Bit Comparator	24	550.00	6.43	MM
54LS461	8-Bit Counter	24	990.00	17.95	MM
54LS469	8-Bit Up/Down Counter	24	990.00	17.95	MM
54LS471	2048-Bit Programmable Read-Only Memory	20	550.00	6.40	N

PART NUMBER	DESCRIPTION	PINS	POWER (mW)	PRICE ($)	SUPPLIERS
54LS490	Dual Decade Counters	16	143.00	2.10	F,M,TI
54LS491	10-Bit Counter	24	990.00	17.95	MM
54LS498	8-Bit Shift Register	24	990.00	17.95	MM
54LS502	8-Bit Successive Approximation Register	16	357.50	2.63	F
54LS503	8-Bit Successive Approximation Register with Expansion Control	16	357.50	2.43	F
54LS540	Octal 3-State Inverting Buffer	20	286.00	1.93	TI
54LS541	Octal 3-State Buffer	20	302.50	1.93	TI
54LS546	8-Bit Bus Register Transceiver	24	990.00	6.95	MM
54LS549	8-Bit Two-Stage Pipelined Latch	24	880.00	6.95	MM
54LS566	8-Bit Inverting Bus Register Transceiver	24	990.00	6.95	MM
54LS567	8-Bit Inverting Bus Latch Transceiver	24	990.00	6.95	MM
54LS568	Synchronous 4-Bit Decade Up/Down Binary Counter with 3-State Outputs	20	236.50	6.12	M
54LS569	Synchronous 4-Bit Binary Up/Down Binary Counter with 3-State Outputs	20	236.50	6.12	M
54LS590	8-Bit Binary Counter with Output Registers	16	357.50	7.71	TI
54LS592	8-Bit Binary Counter with Input Registers	16	330.00	7.71	TI
54LS595	8-BIT Shift Register with Output Latches	16	357.50	7.71	TI
54LS597	8-Bit Shift Register with Input Latches	16	291.50	7.71	TI
54LS610	Memory Mapper	40	1265.00	91.52	TI
54LS623	Octal 3-State Bust Transceivers	20	522.50	2.77	TI
54LS624	Voltage Controlled Oscillator	14	192.50	3.36	TI
54LS626	Dual Voltage Controlled Oscillators	16	302.50	3.22	TI
54LS628	Voltage Controlled Oscillator	14	192.50	2.36	TI
54LS629	Dual Voltage Controlled Oscillators	16	302.50	3.22	TI

PART NUMBER	DESCRIPTION	PINS	POWER (mW)	PRICE ($)	SUPPLIERS
54LS630	3-State 16-Bit Error Detection and Correction Circuit	28	1265.00	105.11	TI
54LS640	Octal 3-State Inverting Bus Transceivers	20	522.50	2.90	M,TI
54LS641	Octal Bus Transceivers with Open Collector Outputs	20	522.50	2.77	M,TI
54LS642	Octal Inverting Bus Transceivers with Open Collector Outputs	20	522.50	2.77	M,TI
54LS643	Octal 3-State True/Inverting Bus Transceivers	20	522.50	3.22	M
54LS644	Octal True/Inverting Bus Transceivers with Open Collector Outputs	20	522.50	2.77	M,TI
54LS645	Octal 3-State Bus Transceivers	20	522.50	2.77	M,TI
54LS646	Octal 3-State Bus Transceivers/Registers	24	907.50	6.95	MM
54LS647	Octal Bus Transceivers/Registers with Open Collector Outputs	24	825.00	6.95	MM
54LS648	Octal 3-State Inverting Bus Transceivers/Registers	24	907.50	6.95	MM
54LS649	Octal Inverting Bus Transceivers/Registers with Open Collector Outputs	24	825.00	6.95	MM
54LS651	Octal 3-State Inverting Bus Transceivers/Registers	24	907.50	6.95	MM
54LS652	Octal 3-State Bus Transceivers/Registers	24	907.50	6.95	MM
54LS653	Octal Inverting Bus Transceivers/Registers with Open Collector Outputs	24	907.50	6.95	MM
54LS654	Octal Bus Transceivers/Registers with Open Collector Outputs	24	907.50	6.95	MM
54LS668	Synchronous 4-Bit Up/Down Decade Counter	16	187.00	1.60	TI
54LS669	Synchronous 4-Bit Up/Down Binary Counter	16	187.00	1.60	TI
54LS670	4x4 Register File with 3-State Outputs	16	275.00	2.84	F,N,TI
54LS673	16-Bit Shift Register	24	440.00	10.15	TI

PART NUMBER	DESCRIPTION	PINS	POWER (mW)	PRICE ($)	SUPPLIERS
54LS674	16-Bit Shift Register	24	220.00	6.74	TI
54LS681	4-Bit Binary Accumulator	20	825.00	10.94	TI
54LS682	8-Bit Identity Comparator	20	385.00	4.49	TI
54LS683	8-Bit Identity Comparator	20	385.00	4.49	TI
54LS684	8-Bit Identity Comparator	20	357.50	4.49	TI
54LS685	8-Bit Identity Comparator	20	357.50	4.49	TI
54LS688	8-Bit Identity Comparator	20	357.50	4.49	TI
54LS689	8-Bit Identity Comparator	20	357.50	4.49	TI
54LS691	Synchronous Binary Counter with Output Register	20	385.00	4.20	TI
54LS693	Synchronous Decade Counter with Output Register	20	385.00	4.20	TI
54LS696	Synchronous Up/Down Decade Counter with Output Register	20	385.00	4.20	TI
54LS697	Synchronous Up/Down Binary Counter with Output Register	20	385.00	4.20	TI
54LS699	Synchronous Up/Down Binary Counter with Output Register	20	385.00	4.20	TI
54LS793	8-Bit Latch with Readback	20	660.00	6.68	MM
54LS794	8-Bit Register with Readback	20	660.00	6.68	MM
54LS952	Dual Rank 3-State 8-Bit Positive-Edge-Triggered Shift Registers	18	544.50	11.70	N
54LS962	Dual Rank 3-State 8-Bit Positive-Edge-Triggered Shift Registers	18	544.50	11.70	N

PART NUMBER	DESCRIPTION	PINS	POWER (mW)	PRICE ($)	SUPPLIERS
54S00	Quad 2-Input NAND Gates	14	198.00	1.22	N,TI
54S02	Quad 2-Input NOR Gates	14	247.50	1.22	N,TI
54S03	Quad 2-Input NAND Gates with Open-Collector Outputs	14	198.00	1.22	N,TI
54S04	Hex Inverters	14	297.00	1.22	N,TI
54S05	Hex Inverters with Open-Collector Outputs	14	297.00	1.29	N,TI
54S08	Quad 2-Input AND Gates	14	313.50	1.22	N,TI
54S09	Quad 2-Input AND Gates with Open-Collector Outputs	14	313.50	1.22	TI
54S10	Triple 3-Input NAND Gates	14	148.50	1.22	N,TI
54S11	Triple 3-Input AND Gates	14	231.00	1.22	N,TI
54S15	Triple 3-Input AND Gates with Open-Collector Outputs	14	231.00	1.29	TI
54S20	Dual 4-Input NAND Gates	14	99.00	1.22	N,TI
54S22	Dual 4-Input NAND Gates with Open-Collector Outputs	14	99.00	1.29	TI
54S30	8-Input NAND Gate	14	55.00	1.22	TI
54S32	Quad 2-Input OR Gates	14	374.00	1.32	N,TI
54S37	Quad 2-Input NAND Buffers	14	440.00	1.72	TI
54S38	Quad 2-Input Nand Buffers with Open-Collector Outputs	14	440.00	1.72	TI
54S40	Dual 4-Input NAND Buffers	14	242.00	1.22	N,TI
54S51	Dual 2-Wide 2-Input AND-OR-INVERT Gates	14	121.00	1.22	TI
54S64	4-Wide AND-OR-INVERT Gate	14	88.00	1.37	N,TI
54S65	4-Wide AND-OR-INVERT Gate with Open-Collector Output	14	88.00	1.37	TI
54S74	Dual Positive-Edge-Triggered D-Type Flip-Flops with Preset and Clear	14	137.50	1.72	N,TI

PART NUMBER	DESCRIPTION	PINS	POWER (mW)	PRICE ($)	SUPPLIERS
54S85	4-Bit Magnitude Comparator	16	632.50	4.08	TI
54S86	Quad 2-Input Exclusive-OR Gate	14	412.50	1.72	N,TI
54S112	Dual Negative-Edge-Triggered J-K Flip-Flops with Preset and Clear	16	137.50	1.72	N,TI
54S113	Dual Negative-Edge-Triggered J-K Flip-Flops with Preset	14	137.50	1.72	N,TI
54S114	Dual J-K Flip-Flops with Preset, Common Clear, and Common Clock	14	137.50	1.79	TI
54S124	Dual Voltage-Controlled Oscillators with Enable Inputs	16	825.00	4.28	TI
54S132	Quad 2-Input Schmitt-Trigger NAND Gates	14	374.00	3.43	TI
54S133	13-Input NAND Gate	16	55.00	1.36	N,TI
54S134	12-Input NAND Gate with 3-State Output	16	137.50	1.37	TI
54S135	Quad Exclusive-OR/NOR Gates	16	544.50	2.12	TI
54S138	3 to 8 Line Decoder/Demultiplexer	16	495.00	3.12	N,TI
54S139	Dual 2 to 4 Line Decoders/Demultiplexers	16	495.00	3.12	N,TI
54S140	Dual 4-Input NAND 50-Ohm Line Drivers	14	242.00	1.83	N,TI
54S151	1 of 8 Line Data Selector/Multiplexer	16	385.00	3.12	N,TI
54S153	Dual 4 to 1 Line Data Selectors/Multiplexers	16	385.00	3.12	N,TI
54S157	Quad 2 to 1 Line Data Selectors/Multiplexers	16	429.00	3.12	N,TI
54S158	Quad 2 to 1 Line Inverting Data Selectors/Multiplexers	16	445.50	3.12	N,TI
54S162	Synchronous 4-Bit Decade Counter with Synchronous Clear	16	880.00	3.43	TI
54S163	Synchronous 4-Bit Binary Counter with Synchronous Clear	16	880.00	3.36	N,TI
54S168	Synchronous 4-Bit Up/Down Decade Counter	16	880.00	4.68	TI
54S169	Synchronous 4-Bit Up/Down Binary Counter	16	880.00	4.68	TI

PART NUMBER	DESCRIPTION	PINS	POWER (mW)	PRICE ($)	SUPPLIERS
54S174	Hex D-Type Flip-Flops with Clear	16	792.00	3.29	N,TI
54S175	Quad D-Type Flip-Flops with Clear	16	528.00	3.29	N,TI
54S181	Arithmetic Logic Unit/Function Generator	24	1210.00	6.93	N,TI
54S182	Look-Ahead Carry Generator	16	599.50	4.00	N,TI
54S188	256-Bit Programmable Read-Only Memory with Open Collector Outputs	16	605.00	2.60	N
54S189	64-Bit Random-Access Memory with 3-State Outputs	16	605.00	4.20	N
54S194	4-Bit Bidirectional Universal Shift Register	16	742.50	3.15	N,TI
54S195	4-Bit Parallel-Access Shift Register	16	599.50	3.15	N,TI
54S196	Presettable Decade (Bi-Quinary) Counter	14	660.00	3.65	TI
54S197	Presettable Binary Counter	14	660.00	4.08	TI
54S226	4-Bit Parallel Latched Bus Transceivers	16	1017.50	14.80	TI
54S240	Octal 3-State Inverting Buffers/Line Drivers/Line Receivers	20	825.00	4.62	MM,N,TI
54S241	Octal 3-State Buffers/Line Drivers/Line Receivers	20	990.00	4.62	MM,N,TI
54S244	Octal 3-State Buffers/Line Drivers/Line Receivers	20	990.00	4.62	MM,N,TI
54S251	3-State 1 of 8 Line Data Selector/Multiplexer	16	467.50	2.79	N,TI
54S253	Dual 3-State 1 of 4 Line Data Selectors/Multiplexers	16	385.00	3.14	N
54S257	Quad 3-State 2 to 1 Line Data Selectors/Multiplexers	16	544.50	3.15	N,TI
54S258	Quad 3-State 2 to 1 Line Inverting Data Selectors/Multiplexers	16	478.50	3.15	N,TI
54S260	Dual 5-Input NOR Gates	14	247.50	1.22	TI
54S280	9-Bit Parity Generator/Checker	14	577.50	4.36	N,TI
54S281	4-Bit Parallel Binary Accumulator	24	1265.00	18.35	TI

PART NUMBER	DESCRIPTION	PINS	POWER (mW)	PRICE ($)	SUPPLIERS
54S283	4-Bit Binary Full Adder with Fast Carry	16	880.00	4.50	N,TI
54S287	1024-Bit Programmable Read-Only Memory with 3-State Outputs	16	715.00	2.85	N
54S288	256-Bit Programmable Read-Only Memory with 3-State Outputs	16	605.00	2.60	N
54S289	64-Bit Random Access Memory with Open Collector Outputs	16	605.00	4.20	N
54S299	8-Bit Universal Shift/Storage Register with 3-State Outputs	20	1237.50	17.00	TI
54S373	Octal 3-State Transparent D-Type Latches	20	1045.00	5.06	MM,N,TI
54S374	Octal 3-State Positive-Edge-Triggered D-Type Flip-Flops	20	880.00	5.06	MM,N,TI
54S381	Arithmetic Logic Unit/Function Generator	20	880.00	5.58	TI
54S387	1024-Bit Programmable Read-Only Memory with Open Collector Outputs	16	715.00	2.85	N
54S472	4096-Bit Programmable Read-Only Memory with 3-State Outputs	20	852.50	7.10	N
54S473	4096-Bit Programmable Read-Only Memory with Open Collector Outputs	20	852.50	7.10	N
54S474	4096-Bit Programmable Read-Only Memory with 3-State Outputs	24	935.00	8.10	N
54S475	4096-Bit Programmable Read-Only Memory with Open Collector Outputs	24	935.00	8.10	N
54S558	8x8 Multiplier	40	1540.00	81.16	MM
54S570	2048-Bit Programmable Read-Only Memory with Open Collector Outputs	16	715.00	4.85	N
54S571	2048-Bit Programmable Read-Only Memory with 3-State Outputs	16	715.00	4.85	N
54S572	4096-Bit Programmable Read-Only Memory with Open Collector Outputs	18	770.00	8.35	N
54S730	8-Bit Dynamic RAM Driver with 3-State Outputs	20	687.50	7.21	MM

PART NUMBER	DESCRIPTION	PINS	POWER (mW)	PRICE ($)	SUPPLIERS
54S734	8-Bit Dynamic RAM Driver with 3-State Outputs	20	825.00	7.21	MM
54S940	Octal 3-State Inverting Buffers/Line Receivers/Line Drivers	20	797.50	5.00	N
54S941	Octal 3-State Buffers/Line Receivers/Line Drivers	20	797.50	5.00	N

PART NUMBER	DESCRIPTION	PINS	POWER (mW)	PRICE ($)	SUPPLIERS
7400	Quad 2-Input NAND Gates	14	115.50	0.26	F,N,TI
7401	Quad 2-Input NAND Gates with Open-Collector Outputs	14	115.50	0.26	F,N,TI
7402	Quad 2-Input NOR Gates	14	141.75	0.26	F,N,TI
7403	Quad 2-Input NAND Gates with Open-Collector Outputs	14	115.50	0.26	F,N,TI
7404	Hex Inverters	14	173.25	0.26	F,N,TI
7405	Hex Inverters with Open-Collector Outputs	14	173.25	0.26	F,N,TI
7406	Hex Inverting Buffers/Drivers with High-Voltage Open-Collector Outputs	14	267.75	0.29	F,N,TI
7407	Hex Buffers/Drivers with High-Voltage Open-Collector Outputs	14	215.25	0.29	F,N,TI
7408	Quad 2-Input AND Gates	14	173.25	0.26	F,N,TI
7409	Quad 2-Input AND Gates with Open-Collector Outputs	14	173.25	0.26	F,N,TI
7410	Triple 3-Input NAND Gates	14	86.62	0.26	F,N,TI
7411	Triple 3-Input AND Gates	14	126.00	0.26	F
7412	Triple 3-Input NAND Gates with Open-Collector Outputs	14	86.62	0.41	TI
7413	Dual 4-Input Schmitt Trigger NAND Gates	14	168.00	0.42	TI
7414	Hex Schmitt Trigger Inverters	14	315.00	0.29	F,N,TI
7416	Hex Inverting Buffers/Drivers with High-Voltage Open-Collector Outputs	14	267.75	0.29	F,N,TI
7417	Hex Buffers/Drivers with High-Voltage Open-Collector Outputs	14	157.50	0.29	F,N,TI
7420	Dual 4-Input NAND Gates	14	57.75	0.26	F,N,TI
7422	Dual 4-Input NAND Gates with Open-Collector Outputs	14	57.75	0.41	TI
7423	Dual 4-Input NOR Gates with Strobe	16	99.75	0.41	TI
7425	Dual 4-Input NOR Gates with Strobe	14	99.75	0.29	F,TI

PART NUMBER	DESCRIPTION	PINS	POWER (mW)	PRICE ($)	SUPPLIERS
7426	Quad 2-Input NAND Buffers with High-Voltage Open-Collector Outputs	14	115.50	0.30	N,TI
7427	Triple 3-Input NOR Gates	14	136.50	0.29	F,N,TI
7428	Quad 2-Input NOR Buffers	14	299.25	0.42	TI
7430	8-Input NAND Gate	14	31.50	0.26	F,N,TI
7432	Quad 2-Input OR Gates	14	199.50	0.29	F,N,TI
7433	Quad 2-Input NOR Buffers with Open-Collector Outputs	14	299.25	0.42	TI
7437	Quad 2-Input NAND Buffers	14	283.50	0.29	F,N,TI
7438	Quad 2-Input Nand Buffers with Open-Collector Outputs	14	283.50	0.29	F,N,TI
7439	Quad 2-Input NAND Buffers with Open-Collector Outputs	14	283.50	0.66	F,TI
7440	Dual 4-Input NAND Buffers	14	141.75	0.26	F,TI
7441	BCD to Decimal Decoder/Driver (NIXIE Driver)	16	189.00	0.93	N
7442	BCD to Decimal Decoder	16	294.00	0.42	F,N,TI
7445	BCD to Decimal Decoder/Driver	16	367.50	0.73	F,N,TI
7446	BCD to 7-Segment Decoder/Driver with Open-Collector Outputs	16	540.75	0.78	N,TI
7447	BCD to 7-Segment Decoder/Driver with Open-Collector Outputs	16	540.75	0.67	F,N,TI
7448	BCD to 7-Segment Decoder/Driver with Internal Pull-Up Resistor Outputs	16	472.50	1.92	TI
7450	Dual Expandable 2-Wide 2-Input AND-OR-INVERT Gates	14	73.50	0.23	F,TI
7451	Dual 2-Wide 2-Input AND-OR-INVERT Gates	14	73.50	0.26	F,TI
7453	Expandable 4-Wide AND-OR-INVERT Gate	14	49.88	0.72	TI
7454	4-Wide 2-Input AND-OR-INVERT Gate	14	49.88	0.76	TI
7470	AND-Gated Positive-Edge-Triggered J-K Flip-Flop with Preset and Clear	14	136.50	0.43	TI

PART NUMBER	DESCRIPTION	PINS	POWER (mW)	PRICE ($)	SUPPLIERS
7472	AND-Gated Master-Slave J-K Flip-Flop with Preset and Clear	14	105.00	0.86	TI
7473	Dual Negative-Edge-Triggered J-K Flip-Flops with Clear	14	105.00	0.33	F,N,TI
7474	Dual Positive-Edge-Triggered D-Type Flip-Flops with Preset and Clear	14	78.75	0.33	F,N,TI
7475	4-Bit Bistable Latch	16	278.25	0.37	F,N,TI
7476	Dual Negative-Edge-Triggered J-K Flip-Flops with Preset and Clear	16	105.00	0.33	F,N,TI
7482	2-Bit Binary Full Adder	14	304.50	2.88	TI
7483	4-Bit Binary Full Adder with Fast Carry	16	577.50	0.70	TI
7485	4-Bit Magnitude Comparator	16	462.00	0.53	F,N,TI
7486	Quad 2-Input Exclusive-OR Gate	14	262.50	0.33	F,N,TI
7489	64-Bit Read/Write Memory	16	551.25	1.96	N,TI
7490	Decade Counter	14	220.50	0.34	F,N,TI
7492	Divide by 12 Counter	14	204.75	0.43	TI
7493	4-Bit Binary Counter	14	204.75	0.40	F,N,TI
7495	4-Bit Parallel-Access Shift Register	14	330.75	0.40	F,N,TI
7496	5-Bit Shift Register	16	414.75	0.64	TI
7497	Synchronous 6-Bit Binary Rate Multiplier	16	630.00	0.93	F,TI
74100	8-Bit Bistable Latch	24	556.50	3.32	TI
74107	Dual Master-Slave J-K Flip-Flops with Clear	14	105.00	0.39	N,TI
74109	Dual Positive-Edge-Triggered J-K Flip-Flops with Preset and Clear	16	78.75	0.39	N,TI
74111	Dual Master-Slave J-K Flip-Flip with Data Lockout	16	107.62	1.40	TI
74116	Dual 4-Bit Latches with Clear	24	525.00	1.42	TI
74120	Dual Pulse Synchronizers/Drivers	16	472.50	1.50	TI

PART NUMBER	DESCRIPTION	PINS	POWER (mW)	PRICE ($)	SUPPLIERS
74121	Monostable Multivibrator with Schmitt-Trigger Input	14	210.00	0.36	F,N,TI
74122	Retriggerable Monostable Multivibrator with Clear	14	189.00	0.62	TI
74123	Dual Retriggerable Monostable Multivibrators with Clear	16	346.50	0.43	F,N,TI
74125	Quad Buffers with 3-State Outputs	14	283.50	0.44	F,N,TI
74126	Quad Buffers with 3-State Outputs	14	325.50	0.62	TI
74128	Quad 2-Input NOR Line Drivers	14	299.25	0.66	TI
74132	Quad 2-Input Schmitt-Trigger NAND Gates	14	210.00	0.47	F,N,TI
74136	Quad 2-Input Exclusive-OR Gates with Open-Collector Outputs	14	262.50	0.58	TI
74141	BCD to Decimal Decoder/Driver	16	131.25	1.00	N,TI
74143	4-Bit Counter/Latch/7-Segment Decoder/Driver	24	488.25	4.20	TI
74144	4-Bit Counter/Latch/7-Segment Decoder/Driver	24	488.25	8.00	TI
74145	BCD to Decimal Decoder/Driver	16	367.50	0.63	F,N,TI
74147	10-Line Decimal to 4-Line BCD Priority Encoder	16	367.50	1.64	TI
74148	8-Line Decimal to 3-Line Octal Priority Encoder	16	315.00	0.85	N,TI
74150	1 of 16 Line Data Selector/Multiplexer	24	357.00	1.16	F,N,TI
74151	1 of 8 Line Data Selector/Multiplexer	16	252.00	0.39	F,N,TI
74153	Dual 4 to 1 Line Data Selectors/Multiplexers	16	225.75	0.41	F,N,TI
74154	4 to 16 Line Decoder/Demultiplexer	24	294.00	1.12	F,N,TI
74155	Dual 2 to 4 Line Decoders/Demultiplexers	16	210.00	0.41	F,TI
74156	Dual 2 to 4 Line Decoders/Demultiplexers with Open-Collector Outputs	16	210.00	0.70	TI

PART NUMBER	DESCRIPTION	PINS	POWER (mW)	PRICE ($)	SUPPLIERS
74157	Quad 2 to 1 Line Data Selectors/Multiplexers	16	252.00	0.41	F,N,TI
74159	4 to 16 Line Decoder/Demultiplexer with Open-Collector Outputs	24	294.00	1.50	TI
74160	Synchronous 4-Bit Decade Counter with Asynchronous Clear	16	530.25	0.63	TI
74161	Synchronous 4-Bit Binary Counter with Asynchronous Clear	16	530.25	0.54	F,N,TI
74162	Synchronous 4-Bit Decade Counter with Synchronous Clear	16	530.25	1.56	TI
74163	Synchronous 4-Bit Binary Counter with Synchronous Clear	16	530.25	0.54	F,N,TI
74164	8-Bit Serial In/Parallel Out Shift Register with Asynchronous Clear	14	283.50	0.51	F,N,TI
74165	8-Bit Parallel In/Serial Out Shift Register with Complementary Outputs	16	330.75	0.59	F,TI
74166	8-Bit Parallel or Serial In/Serial Out Shift Register	16	666.75	0.70	N,TI
74167	Synchronous Decade Rate Multiplier	16	519.75	3.20	TI
74170	4 by 4 Register File with Open-Collector Outputs	16	787.50	1.07	F,TI
74172	16-Bit Multi-Port Register File with 3-State Outputs	24	892.50	5.00	TI
74173	4-Bit D-Type Register with 3-State Outputs	16	378.00	0.79	F,N,TI
74174	Hex D-Type Flip-Flops with Clear	16	341.25	0.43	F,N,TI
74175	Quad D-Type Flip-Flops with Clear	16	236.25	0.43	F,N,TI
74176	Presettable Decade (Bi-Quinary) Counter	14	252.00	0.96	TI
74177	Presettable Binary Counter	14	252.00	0.96	TI
74178	4-Bit Parallel-Access Shift Register	14	393.75	2.60	TI
74179	4-Bit Parallel-Access Shift Register	16	393.75	2.60	TI
74180	9-Bit Parity Generator/Checker	14	294.00	0.64	F,N,TI

PART NUMBER	DESCRIPTION	PINS	POWER (mW)	PRICE ($)	SUPPLIERS
74181	Arithmetic Logic Unit/Function Generator	24	787.50	1.86	N,TI
74182	Look-Ahead Carry Generator	16	378.00	2.00	TI
74184	BCD to Binary Converter	16	519.75	2.10	N,TI
74185	Binary to BCD Converter	16	519.75	2.10	N,TI
74190	Synchronous Up/Down Decade Counter with Mode Control	16	551.25	0.86	TI
74191	Synchronous 4-Bit Up/Down Binary Counter with Mode Control	16	551.25	0.63	F,N,TI
74192	Synchronous Up/Down Decade Counter with Dual Clock	16	535.50	0.72	TI
74193	Synchronous 4-Bit Up/Down Binary Counter with Dual Clock	16	535.50	0.67	N,TI
74194	4-Bit Bidirectional Universal Shift Register	16	330.75	0.67	N,TI
74195	4-Bit Parallel-Access Shift Register	16	330.75	0.70	TI
74196	Presettable Decade (Bi-Quinary) Counter	14	309.75	0.96	TI
74197	Presettable Binary Counter	14	309.75	0.69	F,TI
74198	8-Bit Bidirectional Universal Shift Register	24	666.75	1.50	TI
74199	8-Bit Bidirectional Universal Shift Register	24	666.75	1.50	TI
74221	Dual Monostable Multivibrators with Schmitt-Trigger Input	16	420.00	0.90	TI
74247	BCD to 7 Segment Decoder/Driver with Open-Collector Outputs	16	540.75	3.00	TI
74251	3-State 1 of 8 Line Data Selector/Multiplexer	16	325.50	1.00	TI
74259	8-Bit Addressable Latch	16	472.50	2.20	TI
74265	Quad Complementary-Output Elements	16	178.50	0.75	TI
74273	Octal D-Type Flip-Flop with Clear	20	493.50	2.20	TI
74276	Quad J-K Flip-Flops	20	425.25	2.50	TI

PART NUMBER	DESCRIPTION	PINS	POWER (mW)	PRICE ($)	SUPPLIERS
74278	4-Bit Cascadable Priority Register	14	420.00	2.78	TI
74279	Quad S-R Latches	16	157.50	0.54	F,TI
74283	4-Bit Binary Full Adder with Fast Carry	16	577.50	0.74	F,TI
74284	4-Bit by 4-Bit Parallel Binary Multiplier	16	682.50	2.06	N,TI
74285	4-Bit by 4-Bit Parallel Binary Multiplier	16	682.50	2.06	N,TI
74290	Decade Counter	14	220.50	2.16	TI
74293	4-Bit Binary Counter	14	204.75	1.08	TI
74298	Quad 2 to 1 Line Data Selectors/Multiplexers with Storage	16	341.25	1.08	TI
74365	Hex 3-State Buffers/Bus Drivers	16	446.25	0.51	N,TI
74366	Hex 3-State Inverting Buffers/Bus Drivers	16	404.25	0.66	TI
74367	Hex 3-State Buffers/Bus Drivers	16	446.25	0.51	N,TI
74368	Hex 3-State Inverting Buffers/Bus Drivers	16	404.25	0.51	N,TI
74376	Quad J-K Flip-Flops	16	388.50	1.40	TI
74390	Dual Decade (Bi-Quinary) Counters	16	362.25	1.38	TI
74393	Dual 4-Bit Binary Counters	14	336.00	1.66	TI
74425	Quad Bus Buffers with 3-State Outputs	14	283.50	1.48	TI

PART NUMBER	DESCRIPTION	PINS	POWER (mW)	PRICE ($)	SUPPLIERS
74AC00	Quad 2-Input NAND Gates	14	0.28	0.33	F
74AC74	Dual Positive-Edge-Triggered D-Type Flip-Flops with Preset and Clear	14	0.28	0.44	F
74AC109	Dual Positive-Edge-Triggered J-K Flip-Flops with Preset and Clear	16	0.28	0.44	F
74AC138	3 to 8 Line Decoder/Demultiplexer	16	0.28	0.69	F
74AC139	Dual 2 to 4 Line Decoders/Demultiplexers	16	0.28	0.69	F
74AC153	Dual 4 to 1 Line Data Selectors/Multiplexers	16	0.28	0.69	F
74AC240	Octal 3-State Inverting Buffers/Line Drivers/Line Receivers	20	0.28	1.27	F
74AC241	Octal 3-State Buffers/Line Drivers/Line Receivers	20	0.28	1.27	F
74AC244	Octal 3-State Buffers/Line Drivers/Line Receivers	20	0.28	1.27	F
74AC253	Dual 3-State 1 of 4 Line Data Selectors/Multiplexers	16	0.28	0.69	F
74AC373	Octal 3-State Transparent D-Type Latches	20	0.28	1.27	F
74AC374	Octal 3-State Positive-Edge-Triggered D-Type Flip-Flops	20	0.28	1.27	F

PART NUMBER	DESCRIPTION	PINS	POWER (mW)	PRICE ($)	SUPPLIERS
74ACT240	Octal 3-State Inverting Buffers/Line Drivers/Line Receivers	20	0.44	1.27	F
74ACT241	Octal 3-State Buffers/Line Drivers/Line Receivers	20	0.44	1.27	F
74ACT244	Octal 3-State Buffers/Line Drivers/Line Receivers	20	0.44	1.27	F

PART NUMBER	DESCRIPTION	PINS	POWER (mW)	PRICE ($)	SUPPLIERS
74ALS00	Quad 2-Input NAND Gates	14	16.50	0.34	N,TI
74ALS01	Quad 2-Input NAND Gates with Open-Collector Outputs	14	16.50	0.34	N,TI
74ALS02	Quad 2-Input NOR Gates	14	22.00	0.34	N,TI
74ALS03	Quad 2-Input NAND Gates with Open-Collector Outputs	14	16.50	0.34	N,TI
74ALS04	Hex Inverters	14	23.10	0.34	N,TI
74ALS05	Hex Inverters with Open-Collector Outputs	14	23.10	0.34	N,TI
74ALS08	Quad 2-Input AND Gates	14	22.00	0.34	N,TI
74ALS09	Quad 2-Input AND Gates with Open-Collector Outputs	14	22.00	0.34	N,TI
74ALS10	Triple 3-Input NAND Gates	14	12.10	0.34	N,TI
74ALS11	Triple 3-Input AND Gates	14	16.50	0.34	N,TI
74ALS12	Triple 3-Input NAND Gates with Open-Collector Outputs	14	12.10	0.34	N,TI
74ALS13	Dual 4-Input Schmitt Trigger NAND Gates	14	22.00	0.70	N
74ALS14	Hex Schmitt Trigger Inverters	14	66.00	0.70	N
74ALS15	Triple 3-Input AND Gates with Open-Collector Outputs	14	16.50	0.34	N,TI
74ALS20	Dual 4-Input NAND Gates	14	8.25	0.34	N,TI
74ALS21	Dual 4-Input AND Gates	14	11.00	0.34	N,TI
74ALS22	Dual 4-Input NAND Gates with Open-Collector Outputs	14	8.25	0.34	N,TI
74ALS27	Triple 3-Input NOR Gates	14	22.00	0.34	N,TI
74ALS28	Quad 2-Input NOR Buffers	14	49.50	0.40	N,TI
74ALS30	8-Input NAND Gate	14	4.95	0.34	N,TI
74ALS32	Quad 2-Input OR Gates	14	26.95	0.34	N,TI
74ALS33	Quad 2-Input NOR Buffers with Open-Collector Outputs	14	49.50	0.40	N,TI

PART NUMBER	DESCRIPTION	PINS	POWER (mW)	PRICE ($)	SUPPLIERS
74ALS35	Hex Non-Inverters with Open-Collector Outputs	14	34.65	0.42	TI
74ALS37	Quad 2-Input NAND Buffers	14	42.90	0.42	N,TI
74ALS38	Quad 2-Input Nand Buffers with Open-Collector Outputs	14	42.90	0.40	N,TI
74ALS40	Dual 4-Input NAND Buffers	14	21.45	0.40	N,TI
74ALS74	Dual Positive-Edge-Triggered D-Type Flip-Flops with Preset and Clear	14	22.00	0.43	N,TI
74ALS86	Quad 2-Input Exclusive-OR Gate	14	32.45	0.45	TI
74ALS109	Dual Positive-Edge-Triggered J-K Flip-Flops with Preset and Clear	16	22.00	0.43	N,TI
74ALS112	Dual Negative-Edge-Triggered J-K Flip-Flops with Preset and Clear	16	24.75	0.45	TI
74ALS113	Dual Negative-Edge-Triggered J-K Flip-Flops with Preset	14	24.75	0.45	TI
74ALS114	Dual J-K Flip-Flops with Preset, Common Clear, and Common Clock	14	24.75	0.45	TI
74ALS131	3 to 8 Line Decoder/Demultiplexer with Address Latches	16	60.50	0.66	N,TI
74ALS132	Quad 2-Input Schmitt-Trigger NAND Gates	14	44.00	0.70	N
74ALS133	13-Input NAND Gate	16	4.40	0.43	N,TI
74ALS136	Quad 2-Input Exclusive-OR Gates with Open-Collector Outputs	14	32.45	0.57	TI
74ALS137	3 to 8 Line Decoder/Demultiplexer with Address Latches	16	60.50	0.62	N,TI
74ALS138	3 to 8 Line Decoder/Demultiplexer	16	55.00	0.62	N,TI
74ALS151	1 of 8 Line Data Selector/Multiplexer	16	66.00	0.62	N,TI
74ALS153	Dual 4 to 1 Line Data Selectors/Multiplexers	16	77.00	0.62	N,TI
74ALS160	Synchronous 4-Bit Decade Counter with Asynchronous Clear	16	115.50	0.78	N,TI

PART NUMBER	DESCRIPTION	PINS	POWER (mW)	PRICE ($)	SUPPLIERS
74ALS161	Synchronous 4-Bit Binary Counter with Asynchronous Clear	16	115.50	0.78	N,TI
74ALS162	Synchronous 4-Bit Decade Counter with Synchronous Clear	16	115.50	0.78	N,TI
74ALS163	Synchronous 4-Bit Binary Counter with Synchronous Clear	16	115.50	0.78	N,TI
74ALS168	Synchronous 4-Bit Up/Down Decade Counter	16	137.50	0.78	N,TI
74ALS169	Synchronous 4-Bit Up/Down Binary Counter	16	137.50	0.78	N,TI
74ALS174	Hex D-Type Flip-Flops with Clear	16	104.50	0.66	N,TI
74ALS175	Quad D-Type Flip-Flops with Clear	16	77.00	0.66	N,TI
74ALS190	Synchronous Up/Down Decade Counter with Mode Control	16	121.00	0.87	TI
74ALS191	Synchronous 4-Bit Up/Down Binary Counter with Mode Control	16	121.00	0.87	TI
74ALS192	Synchronous Up/Down Decade Counter with Dual Clock	16	121.00	0.87	TI
74ALS193	Synchronous 4-Bit Up/Down Binary Counter with Dual Clock	16	121.00	0.87	TI
74ALS240	Octal 3-State Inverting Buffers/Line Drivers/Line Receivers	20	137.50	1.20	N,TI
74ALS241	Octal 3-State Buffers/Line Drivers/Line Receivers	20	165.00	1.20	N,TI
74ALS242	Quad 3-State Inverting Bus Transceivers	14	121.00	1.20	N,TI
74ALS243	Quad 3-State Bus Transceivers	14	176.00	1.20	N,TI
74ALS244	Octal 3-State Buffers/Line Drivers/Line Receivers	20	148.50	1.20	N,TI
74ALS245	Octal 3-State Bus Transceivers	20	319.00	1.28	N,TI
74ALS251	3-State 1 of 8 Line Data Selector/Multiplexer	16	77.00	0.72	N,TI
74ALS253	Dual 3-State 1 of 4 Line Data Selectors/Multiplexers	16	77.00	0.72	N,TI

PART NUMBER	DESCRIPTION	PINS	POWER (mW)	PRICE ($)	SUPPLIERS
74ALS257	Quad 3-State 2 to 1 Line Data Selectors/Multiplexers	16	77.00	0.72	N,TI
74ALS258	Quad 3-State 2 to 1 Line Inverting Data Selectors/Multiplexers	16	71.50	0.72	N,TI
74ALS273	Octal D-Type Flip-Flop with Clear	20	159.50	1.36	N,TI
74ALS280	9-Bit Parity Generator/Checker	14	88.00	1.60	TI
74ALS299	8-Bit Universal Shift/Storage Register with 3-State Outputs	20	220.00	3.12	TI
74ALS323	8-Bit Universal Shift/Storage Register with 3-State Outputs	20	220.00	3.12	TI
74ALS352	Dual 1 of 4 Line Inverting Data Selectors/Multiplexers	16	55.00	0.72	N,TI
74ALS353	Dual 3-State 1 of 4 Line Data Selectors/Multiplexers	16	71.50	0.72	N,TI
74ALS373	Octal 3-State Transparent D-Type Latches	20	148.50	1.28	N,TI
74ALS374	Octal 3-State Positive-Edge-Triggered D-Type Flip-Flops	20	170.50	1.28	N,TI
74ALS465	Octal 3-State Buffers/Bus Drivers	20	181.50	1.28	N,TI
74ALS466	Octal 3-State Inverting Buffers/Bus Drivers	20	148.50	1.28	N,TI
74ALS467	Octal 3-State Buffers/Bus Drivers	20	181.50	1.28	N,TI
74ALS468	Octal 3-State Inverting Buffers/Bus Drivers	20	148.50	1.28	N,TI
74ALS518	8-Bit Identity Comparator	20	93.50	2.32	N,TI
74ALS519	8-Bit Identity Comparator	20	93.50	2.32	N,TI
74ALS520	8-Bit Identity Comparator	20	104.50	2.32	N,TI
74ALS521	8-Bit Identity Comparator	20	104.50	2.32	N,TI
74ALS522	8-Bit Identity Comparator	20	93.50	2.32	N,TI
74ALS533	Octal 3-State Inverting Transparent D-Type Latches	20	154.00	1.44	N,TI

PART NUMBER	DESCRIPTION	PINS	POWER (mW)	PRICE ($)	SUPPLIERS
74ALS534	Octal 3-State Inverting Positive-Edge-Triggered D-Type Flip-Flops	20	170.50	1.44	N,TI
74ALS560	Synchronous 4-Bit Decade Counter with 3-State Outputs	20	198.00	2.18	TI
74ALS561	Synchronous 4-Bit Binary Counter with 3-State Outputs	20	198.00	2.18	TI
74ALS563	Octal 3-State Inverting Transparent D-Type Latches	20	148.50	1.36	N,TI
74ALS564	Octal 3-State Inverting Positive-Edge-Triggered D-Type Flip-Flops	20	148.50	1.44	N,TI
74ALS568	Synchronous 4-Bit Decade Up/Down Binary Counter with 3-State Outputs	20	176.00	2.18	TI
74ALS569	Synchronous 4-Bit Binary Up/Down Binary Counter with 3-State Outputs	20	176.00	2.18	TI
74ALS573	Octal 3-State Transparent D-Type Latches	20	148.50	1.34	N,TI
74ALS574	Octal 3-State Positive-Edge-Triggered D-Type Flip-Flops	20	148.50	1.34	N,TI
74ALS575	Octal 3-State Positive-Edge-Triggered D-Type Flip-Flops	24	148.50	2.02	TI
74ALS576	Octal 3-State Inverting Positive-Edge-Triggered D-Type Flip-Flops	20	148.50	1.44	N,TI
74ALS577	Octal 3-State Inverting Positive-Edge-Triggered D-Type Flip-Flops	24	148.50	2.02	TI
74ALS580	Octal 3-State Inverting D-Type Latches	20	148.50	1.36	N,TI
74ALS616	3-State 16-Bit Error Detection and Correction Circuit	40	935.00	42.53	TI
74ALS620	Octal 3-State Inverting Bus Transceivers	20	258.50	1.60	TI
74ALS621	Octal Bus Transceivers with Open Collector Outputs	20	264.00	1.66	TI
74ALS622	Octal Bus Transceivers with Open Collector Outputs	20	154.00	1.66	TI

PART NUMBER	DESCRIPTION	PINS	POWER (mW)	PRICE ($)	SUPPLIERS
74ALS623	Octal 3-State Bust Transceivers	20	302.50	1.66	TI
74ALS632	3-State 32-Bit Error Detection and Correction Circuit	52	1375.00	85.53	TI
74ALS634	3-State 32-Bit Error Detection and Correction Circuit	48	1375.00	54.43	TI
74ALS638	Octal Inverting Bus Transceivers	20	225.50	1.88	TI
74ALS639	Octal Bus Transceivers	20	297.00	1.88	TI
74ALS640	Octal 3-State Inverting Bus Transceivers	20	236.50	1.60	TI
74ALS641	Octal Bus Transceivers with Open Collector Outputs	20	258.50	1.60	TI
74ALS642	Octal Inverting Bus Transceivers with Open Collector Outputs	20	154.00	1.60	TI
74ALS643	Octal 3-State True/Inverting Bus Transceivers	20	264.00	1.60	TI
74ALS644	Octal True/Inverting Bus Transceivers with Open Collector Outputs	20	220.00	1.60	TI
74ALS645	Octal 3-State Bus Transceivers	20	319.00	1.52	N,TI
74ALS646	Octal 3-State Bus Transceivers/Registers	24	484.00	5.68	TI
74ALS647	Octal Bus Transceivers/Registers with Open Collector Outputs	24	357.50	5.63	TI
74ALS648	Octal 3-State Inverting Bus Transceivers/Registers	24	484.00	5.67	TI
74ALS649	Octal Inverting Bus Transceivers/Registers with Open Collector Outputs	24	385.00	5.68	TI
74ALS651	Octal 3-State Inverting Bus Transceivers/Registers	24	451.00	5.67	TI
74ALS652	Octal 3-State Bus Transceivers/Registers	24	484.00	5.68	TI
74ALS666	8-Bit D-Type Read-Back Latches with 3-State Outputs	24	401.50	5.88	TI
74ALS667	8-Bit Invering D-Type Read-Back Latches with 3-State Outputs	24	434.50	5.88	TI

PART NUMBER	DESCRIPTION	PINS	POWER (mW)	PRICE ($)	SUPPLIERS
74ALS677	16-Bit to 4-Bit Address Comparator with Enable	24	181.50	3.19	TI
74ALS678	16-Bit to 4-Bit Address Comparator with Latch	24	192.50	3.19	TI
74ALS679	12-Bit to 4-Bit Address Comparator with Enable	20	154.00	2.69	TI
74ALS680	12-Bit to 4-Bit Address Comparator with Latch	20	148.50	2.69	TI
74ALS688	8-Bit Identity Comparator	20	104.50	2.69	TI
74ALS689	8-Bit Identity Comparator	20	104.50	2.62	N,TI
74ALS804	Hex 2-Input NAND Line Drivers	20	66.00	1.26	N,TI
74ALS805	Hex 2-Input NOR Line Drivers	20	77.00	1.26	N,TI
74ALS808	Hex 2-Input AND Line Drivers	20	88.00	1.26	N,TI
74ALS810	Quad 2-Input Exclusive-NOR Gates	14	41.25	0.57	TI
74ALS811	Quad 2-Input Exclusive-NOR Gates with Open Collector Outputs	14	41.25	0.57	TI
74ALS832	Hex 2-Input OR Line Drivers	20	88.00	1.26	N,TI
74ALS841	10-Bit Bus Interface D-Type Latches with 3-State Outputs	24	341.00	3.19	TI
74ALS842	10-Bit Inverting Bus Interface D-Type Latches with 3-State Outputs	24	407.00	3.17	TI
74ALS857	Hex 2 to 1 Line Multiplexers with 3-State Outputs	24	198.00	1.95	TI
74ALS873	Dual 3-State 4-Bit Transparent D-Type Latches	24	170.50	1.58	N,TI
74ALS874	Dual 3-State 4-Bit Positive-Edge-Triggered D-Type Flip-Flops	24	170.50	1.58	N,TI
74ALS876	Dual 3-State 4-Bit Inverting Positive-Edge-Triggered D-Type Flip-Flops	24	170.50	1.58	N,TI
74ALS878	Dual 3-State 4-Bit Inverting Transparent D-Type Latches	24	170.50	1.76	TI

PART NUMBER	DESCRIPTION	PINS	POWER (mW)	PRICE ($)	SUPPLIERS
74ALS879	Dual 3-State 4-Bit Inverting Positive-Edge-Triggered D-Type Flip-Flops	24	170.50	1.76	TI
74ALS880	Dual 3-State 4-Bit Inverting Transparent D-Type Latches	24	170.50	1.68	N,TI
74ALS990	8-Bit D-Type Read-Back Latches with 3-State Outputs	20	385.00	3.36	TI
74ALS991	8-Bit Inverting D-Type Read-Back Latches with 3-state Outputs	20	412.50	3.36	TI
74ALS1000	Quad 2-Input NAND Buffers	14	42.90	0.40	N,TI
74ALS1002	Quad 2-Input NOR Buffers	14	49.50	0.40	N,TI
74ALS1003	Quad 2-Input NAND Buffers with Open Collector Outputs	14	42.90	0.40	N,TI
74ALS1004	Hex Inverting Buffers	14	66.00	0.40	N,TI
74ALS1005	Hex Inverting Buffers with Open Collector Outputs	14	66.00	0.40	N,TI
74ALS1008	Quad 2-Input AND Buffers	14	51.15	0.40	N,TI
74ALS1010	Triple 3-Input NAND Buffers	14	31.90	0.40	N,TI
74ALS1011	Triple 3-Input AND Buffers	14	38.50	0.40	N,TI
74ALS1020	Dual 4-Input NAND Buffers	14	21.45	0.40	N,TI
74ALS1032	Quad 2-Input OR Buffers	14	58.30	0.40	N,TI
74ALS1034	Hex Non-Inverting Buffers	14	77.00	0.40	N,TI
74ALS1035	Hex Non-Inverting Buffers with Open-Collector Outputs	14	77.00	0.40	N,TI
74ALS1240	Octal 3-State Inverting Bus Drivers/Receivers	20	71.50	1.33	N,TI
74ALS1241	Octal 3-State Bus Drivers/Receivers	20	93.50	1.36	N
74ALS1242	Quad 3-State Inverting Bus Drivers/Receivers	14	77.00	1.17	N,TI
74ALS1243	Quad 3-State Bus Drivers/Receivers	14	93.50	1.20	N

PART NUMBER	DESCRIPTION	PINS	POWER (mW)	PRICE ($)	SUPPLIERS
74ALS1244	Octal 3-State Bus Driver/Receivers	20	110.00	1.36	N,TI
74ALS1245	Octal 3-State Bus Transceivers	20	198.00	1.60	TI
74ALS1640	Octal 3-State Inverting Bus Transceivers	20	176.00	1.58	TI
74ALS1645	Octal 3-State Bus Transceivers	20	198.00	1.60	TI
74ALS8003	Dual 2-Input NAND Gates	8	8.25	0.44	TI

PART NUMBER	DESCRIPTION	PINS	POWER (mW)	PRICE ($)	SUPPLIERS
74AS00	Quad 2-Input NAND Gates	14	95.70	0.50	N,TI
74AS02	Quad 2-Input NOR Gates	14	110.55	0.50	N,TI
74AS04	Hex Inverters	14	144.65	0.51	N,TI
74AS08	Quad 2-Input AND Gates	14	132.00	0.51	N,TI
74AS10	Triple 3-Input NAND Gates	14	71.50	0.50	N,TI
74AS11	Triple 3-Input AND Gates	14	99.00	0.50	N,TI
74AS20	Dual 4-Input NAND Gates	14	47.85	0.50	N,TI
74AS21	Dual 4-Input AND Gates	14	66.00	0.51	N,TI
74AS27	Triple 3-Input NOR Gates	14	94.05	0.51	N,TI
74AS30	8-Input NAND Gate	14	26.95	0.50	N,TI
74AS32	Quad 2-Input OR Gates	14	146.30	0.50	N,TI
74AS34	Hex Non-Inverters	14	190.30	0.51	N,TI
74AS74	Dual Positive-Edge-Triggered D-Type Flip-Flops with Preset and Clear	14	88.00	0.54	N,TI
74AS95	4-Bit Parallel-Access Shift Register	14	214.50	1.15	TI
74AS109	Dual Positive-Edge-Triggered J-K Flip-Flops with Preset and Clear	16	93.50	0.60	N,TI
74AS151	1 of 8 Line Data Selector/Multiplexer	16	165.00	1.20	TI
74AS153	Dual 4 to 1 Line Data Selectors/Multiplexers	16	181.50	1.20	TI
74AS157	Quad 2 to 1 Line Data Selectors/Multiplexers	16	154.00	1.10	N,TI
74AS158	Quad 2 to 1 Line Inverting Data Selectors/Multiplexers	16	123.75	1.10	N,TI
74AS160	Synchronous 4-Bit Decade Counter with Asynchronous Clear	16	291.50	2.30	N,TI
74AS161	Synchronous 4-Bit Binary Counter with Asynchronous Clear	16	291.50	2.30	N,TI
74AS162	Synchronous 4-Bit Decade Counter with Synchronous Clear	16	291.50	2.30	N,TI

PART NUMBER	DESCRIPTION	PINS	POWER (mW)	PRICE ($)	SUPPLIERS
74AS163	Synchronous 4-Bit Binary Counter with Synchronous Clear	16	291.50	2.30	N,TI
74AS168	Synchronous 4-Bit Up/Down Decade Counter	16	346.50	2.30	N,TI
74AS169	Synchronous 4-Bit Up/Down Binary Counter	16	346.50	2.30	N,TI
74AS174	Hex D-Type Flip-Flops with Clear	16	247.50	1.49	N,TI
74AS175	Quad D-Type Flip-Flops with Clear	16	187.00	1.49	N,TI
74AS181	Arithmetic Logic Unit/Function Generator	24	1100.00	6.75	N,TI
74AS182	Look-Ahead Carry Generator	16	110.00	2.02	N
74AS230	Octal 3-State True and Inverting Bus Drivers/Receivers	20	478.50	2.39	N,TI
74AS231	Octal 3-State Inverting Bus Drivers/Receivers	20	451.00	2.50	N,TI
74AS240	Octal 3-State Inverting Buffers/Line Drivers/Line Receivers	20	412.50	2.39	N,TI
74AS241	Octal 3-State Buffers/Line Drivers/Line Receivers	20	495.00	2.39	N,TI
74AS242	Quad 3-State Inverting Bus Transceivers	14	330.00	2.39	N,TI
74AS243	Quad 3-State Bus Transceivers	14	407.00	2.39	N,TI
74AS244	Octal 3-State Buffers/Line Drivers/Line Receivers	20	495.00	2.39	N,TI
74AS250	1 of 16 Line Data Selector/Multiplexer	24	275.00	2.17	TI
74AS253	Dual 3-State 1 of 4 Line Data Selectors/Multiplexers	16	181.50	1.30	TI
74AS257	Quad 3-State 2 to 1 Line Data Selectors/Multiplexers	16	175.45	1.17	N,TI
74AS258	Quad 3-State 2 to 1 Line Inverting Data Selectors/Multiplexers	16	138.60	1.07	N,TI
74AS280	9-Bit Parity Generator/Checker	14	192.50	1.58	N,TI
74AS286	9-Bit Parity Generator/Checker	14	275.00	1.58	N,TI
74AS298	Quad 2 to 1 Line Data Selectors/Multiplexers with Storage	16	198.00	1.15	TI

PART NUMBER	DESCRIPTION	PINS	POWER (mW)	PRICE ($)	SUPPLIERS
74AS352	Dual 1 of 4 Line Inverting Data Selectors/Multiplexers	16	154.00	1.30	TI
74AS353	Dual 3-State 1 of 4 Line Data Selectors/Multiplexers	16	170.50	1.30	TI
74AS373	Octal 3-State Transparent D-Type Latches	20	550.00	2.63	N,TI
74AS374	Octal 3-State Positive-Edge-Triggered D-Type Flip-Flops	20	704.00	2.63	N,TI
74AS533	Octal 3-State Inverting Transparent D-Type Latches	20	605.00	2.63	N,TI
74AS534	Octal 3-State Inverting Positive-Edge-Triggered D-Type Flip-Flops	20	704.00	2.63	N,TI
74AS573	Octal 3-State Transparent D-Type Latches	20	583.00	2.61	N,TI
74AS574	Octal 3-State Positive-Edge-Triggered D-Type Flip-Flops	20	737.00	2.61	N,TI
74AS575	Octal 3-State Positive-Edge-Triggered D-Type Flip-Flops	24	781.00	3.17	TI
74AS576	Octal 3-State Inverting Positive-Edge-Triggered D-Type Flip-Flops	20	742.50	2.61	N,TI
74AS577	Octal 3-State Inverting Positive-Edge-Triggered D-Type Flip-Flops	24	781.00	3.17	TI
74AS580	Octal 3-State Inverting D-Type Latches	20	632.50	2.61	N,TI
74AS620	Octal 3-State Inverting Bus Transceivers	20	671.00	3.75	TI
74AS621	Octal Bus Transceivers with Open Collector Outputs	20	1039.50	3.75	TI
74AS622	Octal Bus Transceivers with Open Collector Outputs	20	566.50	3.75	TI
74AS623	Octal 3-State Bust Transceivers	20	1039.50	3.75	TI
74AS638	Octal Inverting Bus Transceivers	20	671.00	3.75	TI
74AS639	Octal Bus Transceivers	20	847.00	3.75	TI

PART NUMBER	DESCRIPTION	PINS	POWER (mW)	PRICE ($)	SUPPLIERS
74AS640	Octal 3-State Inverting Bus Transceivers	20	676.50	3.75	TI
74AS641	Octal Bus Transceivers with Open Collector Outputs	20	748.00	3.75	TI
74AS642	Octal Inverting Bus Transceivers with Open Collector Outputs	20	572.00	3.75	TI
74AS643	Octal 3-State True/Inverting Bus Transceivers	20	786.50	3.75	TI
74AS644	Octal True/Inverting Bus Transceivers with Open Collector Outputs	20	682.00	3.75	TI
74AS645	Octal 3-State Bus Transceivers	20	819.50	3.60	N,TI
74AS646	Octal 3-State Bus Transceivers/Registers	24	1160.50	5.10	N,TI
74AS648	Octal 3-State Inverting Bus Transceivers/Registers	24	1072.50	5.10	N,TI
74AS651	Octal 3-State Inverting Bus Transceivers/Registers	24	1072.50	5.10	N,TI
74AS652	Octal 3-State Bus Transceivers/Registers	24	1160.50	5.10	N,TI
74AS756	Octal Inverting Buffers/Line Drivers with Open-Collector Outputs	20	440.00	2.50	TI
74AS757	Octal Buffers/Line Drivers with Open-Collector Outputs	20	522.50	2.50	TI
74AS758	Quad Inverting Bus Transceivers with Open-Collector Outputs	14	330.00	2.25	TI
74AS759	Quad Bus Transceivers with Open-Collector Outputs	14	407.00	2.25	TI
74AS760	Octal Buffers/Line Drivers with Open-Collector Outputs	20	517.00	2.50	TI
74AS762	Octal Buffers/Line Drivers with Open-Collector Outputs	20	478.50	2.50	TI
74AS763	Octal Inverting Buffers/Line Drivers with Open-Collector Outputs	20	451.00	2.50	TI
74AS804	Hex 2-Input NAND Line Drivers	20	148.50	1.75	N,TI
74AS805	Hex 2-Input NOR Line Drivers	20	176.00	1.75	N,TI

PART NUMBER	DESCRIPTION	PINS	POWER (mW)	PRICE ($)	SUPPLIERS
74AS808	Hex 2-Input AND Line Drivers	20	176.00	1.75	N,TI
74AS821	10-Bit Bus Interface D-Type Flip-Flops with 3-State Outputs	24	621.50	3.17	TI
74AS822	10-Bit Inverting Bus Interface D-Type Flip-Flops with 3-State Outputs	24	621.50	3.17	TI
74AS823	9-Bit Bus Interface D-Type Flip-Flops with 3-State Outputs	24	566.50	3.17	TI
74AS824	9-BIT Inverting Bus Interface D-Type Flip-Flops with 3-State Outputs	24	566.50	3.17	TI
74AS825	8-Bit Bus Interface D-Type Flip-Flops with 3-State Outputs	24	522.50	3.17	TI
74AS826	8-Bit Inverting Bus Interface D-Type Flip-Flops with 3-State Outputs	24	522.50	3.17	TI
74AS832	Hex 2-Input OR Line Drivers	20	198.00	1.75	N,TI
74AS841	10-Bit Bus Interface D-Type Latches with 3-State Outputs	24	517.00	3.17	TI
74AS842	10-Bit Inverting Bus Interface D-Type Latches with 3-State Outputs	24	533.50	3.17	TI
74AS843	9-Bit Bus Interface D-Type Latches with 3-State Outputs	24	506.00	3.17	TI
74AS844	9-Bit Inverting Bus Interface D-Type Latches with 3-State Outputs	24	522.50	3.17	TI
74AS845	8-Bit Bus Interface D-Type Latches with 3-State Outputs	24	467.50	3.17	TI
74AS846	8-Bit Inverting Bus Interface D-Type Latches with 3-State Outputs	24	478.50	3.17	TI
74AS850	1 of 16 Data Selector/Multiplexer with 3-State Outputs	28	467.50	4.33	TI
74AS851	1 of 16 Data Selector/Multiplexer with 3-State Outputs	28	473.00	4.33	TI
74AS852	8-Bit Transceiver Port Controller	24	1210.00	5.16	TI
74AS856	8-Bit Transceiver Port Controller	24	1100.00	5.16	TI

PART NUMBER	DESCRIPTION	PINS	POWER (mW)	PRICE ($)	SUPPLIERS
74AS857	Hex 2 to 1 Line Multiplexers with 3-State Outputs	24	962.50	2.75	TI
74AS866	8-Bit Magnitude Comparator	28	1320.00	6.91	TI
74AS867	Synchronous 8-Bit Up/Down Counter with Asynchronous Clear	24	1072.50	5.25	TI
74AS869	Synchronous 8-Bit Up/Down Counter with Synchronous Clear	24	990.00	5.25	TI
74AS870	Dual 16 by 4 Register Files	24	1045.00	6.58	TI
74AS871	Dual 16 by 4 Register Files	28	1045.00	7.50	TI
74AS873	Dual 3-State 4-Bit Transparent D-Type Latches	24	709.50	2.91	N,TI
74AS874	Dual 3-State 4-Bit Positive-Edge-Triggered D-Type Flip-Flops	24	880.00	2.91	N,TI
74AS876	Dual 3-State 4-Bit Inverting Positive-Edge-Triggered D-Type Flip-Flops	24	880.00	2.91	N,TI
74AS877	8-Bit Transceiver Port Controller	24	1210.00	5.16	TI
74AS878	Dual 3-State 4-Bit Inverting Transparent D-Type Latches	24	880.00	3.17	TI
74AS879	Dual 3-State 4-Bit Inverting Positive-Edge-Triggered D-Type Flip-Flops	24	880.00	3.17	TI
74AS880	Dual 3-State 4-Bit Inverting Transparent D-Type Latches	24	753.50	2.91	N,TI
74AS881	Arithmetic Logic Unit/Function Generator	24	1155.00	6.75	N,TI
74AS882	32-Bit Look-Ahead Carry Generator	24	577.50	3.75	TI
74AS885	8-Bit Magnitude Comparator	24	1155.00	6.50	TI
74AS887	8-Bit Processor	68	1533.95	47.00	TI
74AS888	8-Bit Processor Slice	68	1533.95	47.00	TI
74AS890	14-Bit Microsequencer	68	1818.85	60.00	TI
74AS1000	Quad 2-Input NAND Buffers	14	104.50	0.75	N,TI

PART NUMBER	DESCRIPTION	PINS	POWER (mW)	PRICE ($)	SUPPLIERS
74AS1004	Hex Inverting Buffers	14	154.00	0.75	N,TI
74AS1008	Quad 2-Input AND Buffers	14	121.00	0.75	N,TI
74AS1032	Quad 2-Input OR Buffers	14	132.00	0.75	N,TI
74AS1034	Hex Non-Inverting Buffers	14	181.50	0.75	N,TI
74AS1036	Quad 2-Input NOR Buffers	14	126.50	0.75	N,TI

PART NUMBER	DESCRIPTION	PINS	POWER (mW)	PRICE ($)	SUPPLIERS
74C00	Quad 2-Input NAND Gates	14	0.23	0.26	N
74C02	Quad 2-Input NOR Gates	14	0.23	0.26	N
74C04	Hex Inverters	14	0.23	0.33	N
74C08	Quad 2-Input AND Gates	14	0.23	0.26	N
74C10	Triple 3-Input NAND Gates	14	0.23	0.26	N
74C14	Hex Schmitt Trigger Inverters	14	0.23	0.63	N
74C20	Dual 4-Input NAND Gates	14	0.23	0.26	N
74C30	8-Input NAND Gate	14	0.23	0.26	N
74C32	Quad 2-Input OR Gates	14	0.23	0.26	N
74C42	BCD to Decimal Decoder	16	4.50	0.98	N
74C48	BCD to 7-Segment Decoder/Driver with Internal Pull-Up Resistor Outputs	16	4.50	1.47	N
74C73	Dual Negative-Edge-Triggered J-K Flip-Flops with Clear	14	0.90	0.60	N
74C74	Dual Positive-Edge-Triggered D-Type Flip-Flops with Preset and Clear	14	0.90	0.60	N
74C76	Dual Negative-Edge-Triggered J-K Flip-Flops with Preset and Clear	16	0.90	0.60	N
74C83	4-Bit Binary Full Adder with Fast Carry	16	4.50	1.38	N
74C85	4-Bit Magnitude Comparator	16	4.50	1.38	N
74C86	Quad 2-Input Exclusive-OR Gate	14	0.23	0.33	N
74C89	64-Bit Read/Write Memory	16	4.50	5.20	N
74C90	Decade Counter	14	4.50	0.89	N
74C93	4-Bit Binary Counter	14	4.50	0.89	N
74C95	4-Bit Parallel-Access Shift Register	14	4.50	1.11	N
74C107	Dual Master-Slave J-K Flip-Flops with Clear	14	0.90	1.26	N
74C150	1 of 16 Line Data Selector/Multiplexer	24	4.50	3.80	N

PART NUMBER	DESCRIPTION	PINS	POWER (mW)	PRICE ($)	SUPPLIERS
74C151	1 of 8 Line Data Selector/Multiplexer	16	4.50	2.54	N
74C154	4 to 16 Line Decoder/Demultiplexer	24	4.50	3.80	N
74C157	Quad 2 to 1 Line Data Selectors/Multiplexers	16	0.90	2.28	N
74C160	Synchronous 4-Bit Decade Counter with Asynchronous Clear	16	4.50	1.06	N
74C161	Synchronous 4-Bit Binary Counter with Asynchronous Clear	16	4.50	0.99	N
74C162	Synchronous 4-Bit Decade Counter with Synchronous Clear	16	4.50	0.99	N
74C163	Synchronous 4-Bit Binary Counter with Synchronous Clear	16	4.50	0.99	N
74C164	8-Bit Serial In/Parallel Out Shift Register with Asynchronous Clear	14	4.50	1.11	N
74C165	8-Bit Parallel In/Serial Out Shift Register with Complementary Outputs	16	4.50	1.11	N
74C173	4-Bit D-Type Register with 3-State Outputs	16	4.50	1.30	N
74C174	Hex D-Type Flip-Flops with Clear	16	4.50	0.87	N
74C175	Quad D-Type Flip-Flops with Clear	16	4.50	0.96	N
74C192	Synchronous Up/Down Decade Counter with Dual Clock	16	4.50	1.32	N
74C193	Synchronous 4-Bit Up/Down Binary Counter with Dual Clock	16	4.50	1.32	N
74C195	4-Bit Parallel-Access Shift Register	16	4.50	1.16	N
74C200	256-Bit Random-Access Memory with 3-State Outputs	16	9.00	8.05	N
74C221	Dual Monostable Multivibrators with Schmitt-Trigger Input	16	4.50	1.45	N
74C240	Octal 3-State Inverting Buffers/Line Drivers/Line Receivers	20	4.50	1.53	N
74C244	Octal 3-State Buffers/Line Drivers/Line Receivers	20	4.50	1.53	N

PART NUMBER	DESCRIPTION	PINS	POWER (mW)	PRICE ($)	SUPPLIERS
74C373	Octal 3-State Transparent D-Type Latches	20	4.50	1.80	N
74C374	Octal 3-State Positive-Edge-Triggered D-Type Flip-Flops	20	4.50	1.80	N
74C901	Hex Inverting TTL Buffers	14	0.23	0.47	N
74C902	Hex Non-Inverting TTL Buffers	14	0.23	0.47	N
74C903	Hex Inverting PMOS Buffers	14	0.23	0.47	N
74C904	HEx Non-Inverting PMOS Buffers	14	0.23	0.47	N
74C905	12-Bit Successive Approximation Register	24	4.50	7.45	N
74C906	Hex Open Drain N-Channel Buffers	14	0.23	0.47	N
74C907	Hex Open Drain P-Channel Buffers	14	0.23	0.47	N
74C908	Dual CMOS 30 Volt Relay Driver	8	0.23	1.00	N
74C909	Quad Comparator	14	30.00	1.71	N
74C910	256-Bit 3-State Randon Access Memory	18	1.50	8.05	N
74C911	4-Digit LED Display Controller	28	12.50	7.40	N
74C912	6-Digit BCD LED Display Controller	28	10.00	7.40	N
74C914	Hex Schmitt Trigger with Extended Input Voltage	14	4.50	1.46	N
74C915	7-Segment to BCD Controller	18	45.00	1.18	N
74C917	6-Digit HEX LED Display Controller Driver	28	10.00	7.40	N
74C918	Dual CMOS 30 Volt Relay Driver	8	0.23	1.10	N
74C922	16-Key Keyboard Encoder	18	39.00	3.80	N
74C923	20-Key Keyboard Encoder	18	39.00	3.90	N
74C925	4-Digit Counter with Multiplexed 7-Segment Output Driver	16	5.00	5.00	N
74C926	4-Digit Counter with Multiplexed 7-Segment Output Driver	16	5.00	5.00	N
74C927	4-Digit Counter with Multiplexed 7-Segment Output Driver	16	5.00	5.00	N

PART NUMBER	DESCRIPTION	PINS	POWER (mW)	PRICE ($)	SUPPLIERS
74C928	4-Digit Counter with Multiplexed 7-Segment Output Driver	16	5.00	5.00	N
74C932	Phase Comparator	8	27.00	1.50	N
74C941	Octal 3-State Buffers/Line Receivers/Line Drivers	20	4.50	1.53	N
74C945	4 Digit LCD Up/Down Counter/Latch/Driver	40	0.30	7.62	N
74C946	4 1/2-Digit LCD Up Counter/Latch/Driver	40	0.30	7.62	N
74C947	4 Digit LCD Up/Down Counter/Latch/Driver	40	0.30	7.62	N
74C956	4 Digit LED Alphanumeric Display Controller Driver (17-Segment)	40	5.00	9.15	N
74C989	64-Bit 3-State Random Access Memory	16	0.75	5.20	N

PART NUMBER	DESCRIPTION	PINS	POWER (mW)	PRICE ($)	SUPPLIERS
74F00	Quad 2-Input NAND Gates	14	53.55	0.26	F,M
74F02	Quad 2-Input NOR Gates	14	68.25	0.26	F,M
74F04	Hex Inverters	14	80.33	0.26	F,M
74F08	Quad 2-Input AND Gates	14	67.73	0.26	F,M
74F10	Triple 3-Input NAND Gates	14	40.43	0.26	F,M
74F11	Triple 3-Input AND Gates	14	50.92	0.26	F,M
74F20	Dual 4-Input NAND Gates	14	26.77	0.26	F,M
74F32	Quad 2-Input OR Gates	14	81.38	0.26	F,M
74F64	4-Wide AND-OR-INVERT Gate	14	24.68	0.26	F,M
74F74	Dual Positive-Edge-Triggered D-Type Flip-Flops with Preset and Clear	14	84.00	0.36	F,M
74F86	Quad 2-Input Exclusive-OR Gate	14	147.00	0.46	F,M
74F109	Dual Positive-Edge-Triggered J-K Flip-Flops with Preset and Clear	16	89.25	0.46	F,M
74F112	Dual Negative-Edge-Triggered J-K Flip-Flops with Preset and Clear	16	99.75	1.14	F
74F113	Dual Negative-Edge-Triggered J-K Flip-Flops with Preset	14	99.75	1.14	F
74F114	Dual J-K Flip-Flops with Preset, Common Clear, and Common Clock	14	99.75	1.14	F
74F138	3 to 8 Line Decoder/Demultiplexer	16	105.00	0.60	F,M
74F139	Dual 2 to 4 Line Decoders/Demultiplexers	16	105.00	0.60	F,M
74F148	8-Line Decimal to 3-Line Octal Priority Encoder	16	183.75	0.80	F,M
74F151	1 of 8 Line Data Selector/Multiplexer	16	110.25	0.60	F,M
74F153	Dual 4 to 1 Line Data Selectors/Multiplexers	16	105.00	0.60	F,M
74F157	Quad 2 to 1 Line Data Selectors/Multiplexers	16	120.75	0.60	F,M

PART NUMBER	DESCRIPTION	PINS	POWER (mW)	PRICE ($)	SUPPLIERS
74F158	Quad 2 to 1 Line Inverting Data Selectors/Multiplexers	16	78.75	0.60	F,M
74F160	Synchronous 4-Bit Decade Counter with Asynchronous Clear	16	288.75	1.43	F,M
74F161	Synchronous 4-Bit Binary Counter with Asynchronous Clear	16	288.75	1.43	F,M
74F162	Synchronous 4-Bit Decade Counter with Synchronous Clear	16	288.75	1.43	F,M
74F163	Synchronous 4-Bit Binary Counter with Synchronous Clear	16	288.75	1.43	F,M
74F164	8-Bit Serial In/Parallel Out Shift Register with Asynchronous Clear	14	288.75	1.39	F
74F168	Synchronous 4-Bit Up/Down Decade Counter	16	273.00	2.82	F
74F169	Synchronous 4-Bit Up/Down Binary Counter	16	273.00	2.82	F
74F174	Hex D-Type Flip-Flops with Clear	16	236.25	0.86	F,M
74F175	Quad D-Type Flip-Flops with Clear	16	178.50	0.86	F,M
74F181	Arithmetic Logic Unit/Function Generator	24	341.25	2.86	F
74F182	Look-Ahead Carry Generator	16	189.00	1.43	F,M
74F189	64-Bit Random-Access Memory with 3-State Outputs	16	288.75	4.29	F
74F190	Synchronous Up/Down Decade Counter with Mode Control	16	288.75	2.80	F
74F191	Synchronous 4-Bit Up/Down Binary Counter with Mode Control	16	288.75	2.80	F
74F192	Synchronous Up/Down Decade Counter with Dual Clock	16	288.75	3.29	F
74F193	Synchronous 4-Bit Up/Down Binary Counter with Dual Clock	16	288.75	2.72	F
74F194	4-Bit Bidirectional Universal Shift Register	16	189.00	1.39	F
74F219	64-Bit Random-Access Memory with 3-State Outputs	16	288.75	4.29	F

PART NUMBER	DESCRIPTION	PINS	POWER (mW)	PRICE ($)	SUPPLIERS
74F240	Octal 3-State Inverting Buffers/Line Drivers/Line Receivers	20	393.75	1.03	F,M
74F241	Octal 3-State Buffers/Line Drivers/Line Receivers	20	472.50	1.03	F,M
74F243	Quad 3-State Bus Transceivers	14	472.50	1.36	F,M
74F244	Octal 3-State Buffers/Line Drivers/Line Receivers	20	472.50	1.03	F,M
74F245	Octal 3-State Bus Transceivers	20	630.00	2.15	F,M
74F251	3-State 1 of 8 Line Data Selector/Multiplexer	16	126.00	0.58	F,M
74F253	Dual 3-State 1 of 4 Line Data Selectors/Multiplexers	16	120.75	0.58	F,M
74F257	Quad 3-State 2 to 1 Line Data Selectors/Multiplexers	16	120.75	0.58	F,M
74F258	Quad 3-State 2 to 1 Line Inverting Data Selectors/Multiplexers	16	120.75	0.58	F,M
74F280	9-Bit Parity Generator/Checker	14	199.50	0.58	F,M
74F283	4-Bit Binary Full Adder with Fast Carry	16	288.75	1.86	F,M
74F299	8-Bit Universal Shift/Storage Register with 3-State Outputs	20	498.75	4.65	F
74F322	8-Bit Shift Register with Sign Extend	20	472.50	5.25	F
74F323	8-Bit Universal Shift/Storage Register with 3-State Outputs	20	498.75	5.25	F
74F350	4-Bit Shifter with 3-State Outputs	16	220.50	1.72	F
74F352	Dual 1 of 4 Line Inverting Data Selectors/Multiplexers	16	105.00	0.58	F,M
74F353	Dual 3-State 1 of 4 Line Data Selectors/Multiplexers	16	120.75	0.58	F,M
74F373	Octal 3-State Transparent D-Type Latches	20	288.75	1.14	F,M
74F374	Octal 3-State Positive-Edge-Triggered D-Type Flip-Flops	20	451.50	1.14	F,M
74F378	Hex D-Type Flip-Flops with Enable	16	236.25	1.14	F,M

PART NUMBER	DESCRIPTION	PINS	POWER (mW)	PRICE ($)	SUPPLIERS
74F379	Quad D-Type Flip-Flops with Enable	16	210.00	1.14	F
74F381	Arithmetic Logic Unit/Function Generator	20	467.25	3.65	F
74F382	Arithmetic Logic Unit/Function Generator	20	425.25	3.86	F
74F384	8-Bit Serial/Parallel Two's Complement Multiplier	16	472.50	8.87	F
74F385	Quad Serial Adder/Subtractor	20	498.75	7.44	F
74F398	Quad 2-Input Multiplexers with Storage	20	199.50	1.14	F,M
74F399	Quad 2-Input Multiplexers with Storage	16	178.50	1.14	F,M
74F401	Cyclic Redundancy Check Generator/Checker	14	577.50	9.01	F
74F402	Serial Data Polynomial Generator/Checker	16	866.25	10.47	F
74F407	Data Access Register	24	761.25	11.73	F
74F410	16x4 RAM 3S	18	367.50	61.18	F
74F412	Multimode Octal Latch	24	315.00	3.22	F
74F432	Inverting Multimode Octal Latch	24	341.25	3.22	F
74F521	8-Bit Identity Comparator	20	168.00	1.29	F,M
74F524	8-Bit Registered Comparator	20	945.00	8.22	F
74F525	16 Stage Programmable Counter/Divider	28	708.75	7.72	F
74F533	Octal 3-State Inverting Transparent D-Type Latches	20	320.25	1.29	F,M
74F534	Octal 3-State Inverting Positive-Edge-Triggered D-Type Flip-Flops	20	451.50	1.29	F,M
74F537	1 of 10 Decoder	20	346.50	3.72	F,M
74F538	1 of 8 Decoder	20	294.00	3.72	F,M
74F539	Dual 1 of 4 Decoders	20	315.00	3.72	F,M
74F543	Octal Registered Transceiver	24	656.25	4.29	F
74F544	Octal Registered Transceiver	24	682.50	4.29	F

PART NUMBER	DESCRIPTION	PINS	POWER (mW)	PRICE ($)	SUPPLIERS
74F545	Octal Transceiver	20	630.00	4.43	F
74F547	3 to 8 Line Decoder/Demultiplexer with Address Latches	20	131.25	4.65	F
74F548	3 to 8 Line Decoder/Demultiplexer with Acknowledge	20	110.25	3.93	F
74F550	Octal Registered Transceiver	28	997.50	5.59	F
74F551	Octal Registered Transceiver	28	997.50	5.59	F
74F552	Octal Registered Transceiver with Parity and Flags	28	866.25	5.75	F
74F563	Octal 3-State Inverting Transparent D-Type Latches	20	288.75	2.79	F
74F568	Synchronous 4-Bit Decade Up/Down Binary Counter with 3-State Outputs	20	351.75	3.20	F
74F569	Synchronous 4-Bit Binary Up/Down Binary Counter with 3-State Outputs	20	351.75	3.20	F
74F573	Octal 3-State Transparent D-Type Latches	20	288.75	2.79	F
74F582	4-Bit BCD Arithmetic Logic Unit	24	446.25	8.04	F
74F583	4-Bit BCD Adder	16	315.00	5.51	F
74F588	GPIB Compatable Octal Transceiver	20	708.75	4.69	F
74F673	16-Bit Serial In, Serial/Parallel Out Shift Register	24	840.00	9.44	F
74F675	16-Bit Serial In, Serial/Parallel Out Shift Register	24	840.00	8.58	F
74F676	16-Bit Serial/Parallel In, Serial Out Shift Register	24	378.00	11.44	F
74F784	8-Bit Serial/Parallel Multiplier	20	525.00	11.21	F

PART NUMBER	DESCRIPTION	PINS	POWER (mW)	PRICE ($)	SUPPLIERS
74H00	Quad 2-Input NAND Gates	14	210.00	3.29	TI
74H01	Quad 2-Input NAND Gates with Open-Collector Outputs	14	210.00	3.29	TI
74H04	Hex Inverters	14	304.50	3.29	TI
74H05	Hex Inverters with Open-Collector Outputs	14	304.50	3.29	TI
74H10	Triple 3-Input NAND Gates	14	157.50	3.29	TI
74H11	Triple 3-Input AND Gates	14	252.00	3.29	TI
74H15	Triple 3-Input AND Gates with Open-Collector Outputs	14	252.00	3.29	TI
74H20	Dual 4-Input NAND Gates	14	105.00	3.29	TI
74H21	Dual 4-Input AND Gates	14	168.00	3.29	TI
74H22	Dual 4-Input NAND Gates with Open-Collector Outputs	14	105.00	3.29	TI
74H30	8-Input NAND Gate	14	52.50	3.29	TI
74H40	Dual 4-Input NAND Buffers	14	210.00	3.29	TI
74H50	Dual Expandable 2-Wide 2-Input AND-OR-INVERT Gates	14	126.00	3.29	TI
74H51	Dual 2-Wide 2-Input AND-OR-INVERT Gates	14	126.00	3.29	TI
74H52	Expandable 4-Wide AND-OR Gate	14	162.75	3.29	TI
74H53	Expandable 4-Wide AND-OR-INVERT Gate	14	73.50	3.29	TI
74H54	4-Wide 2-Input AND-OR-INVERT Gate	14	73.50	3.29	TI
74H55	2-Wide 4-Input AND-OR-INVERT Gate	14	63.00	3.29	TI
74H60	Dual 4-Input Expanders	14	23.62	3.29	TI
74H61	Triple 3-Input Expanders	14	84.00	3.29	TI
74H62	4-Wide AND-OR Expander	14	47.25	3.29	TI
74H71	AND-OR-Gated Master-Slave J-K Flip-Flip with Preset	14	157.50	3.29	TI

PART NUMBER	DESCRIPTION	PINS	POWER (mW)	PRICE ($)	SUPPLIERS
74H72	AND-Gated Master-Slave J-K Flip-Flop with Preset and Clear	14	131.25	3.29	TI
74H73	Dual Negative-Edge-Triggered J-K Flip-Flops with Clear	14	131.25	3.29	TI
74H74	Dual Positive-Edge-Triggered D-Type Flip-Flops with Preset and Clear	14	131.25	3.29	TI
74H76	Dual Negative-Edge-Triggered J-K Flip-Flops with Preset and Clear	16	131.25	3.29	TI
74H78	Dual J-K Flip-Flops with Preset, Common Clear, and Common Clock	14	131.25	3.85	TI
74H87	4-Bit True/Complement, Zero/One Element	14	467.25	7.48	TI
74H101	AND-OR-Gated Negative-Edge-Triggered J-K Flip-Flop with Preset	14	199.50	3.29	TI
74H102	AND-Gated Negative-Edge-Triggered J-K Flip-Flop with Preset and Clear	14	199.50	3.29	TI
74H103	Dual Negative-Edge-Triggered J-K Flip-Flop with Clear	14	199.50	3.29	TI
74H106	Dual Negative-Edge-Triggered J-K Flip-Flops with Preset and Clear	16	199.50	3.29	TI
74H108	Dual J-K Flip-Flops with Preset, Common Clear, and Common Clock	14	199.50	3.29	TI
74H183	Dual Carry-Save Full Adders	14	393.75	6.67	TI

PART NUMBER	DESCRIPTION	PINS	POWER (mW)	PRICE ($)	SUPPLIERS
74HC00	Quad 2-Input NAND Gates	14	0.12	0.38	M,N,RCA,TI
74HC02	Quad 2-Input NOR Gates	14	0.12	0.38	M,N,RCA,TI
74HC03	Quad 2-Input NAND Gates with Open-Collector Outputs	14	0.12	0.38	M,N,RCA,TI
74HC04	Hex Inverters	14	0.12	0.38	M,N,RCA,TI
74HC05	Hex Inverters with Open-Collector Outputs	14	0.12	0.38	TI
74HC08	Quad 2-Input AND Gates	14	0.12	0.38	M,N,RCA,TI
74HC09	Quad 2-Input AND Gates with Open-Collector Outputs	14	0.12	0.38	TI
74HC10	Triple 3-Input NAND Gates	14	0.12	0.38	M,N,RCA,TI
74HC11	Triple 3-Input AND Gates	14	0.12	0.38	M,N,RCA,TI
74HC14	Hex Schmitt Trigger Inverters	14	0.12	0.58	M,N,RCA,TI
74HC20	Dual 4-Input NAND Gates	14	0.12	0.38	M,N,RCA,TI
74HC21	Dual 4-Input AND Gates	14	0.12	0.38	RCA,TI
74HC27	Triple 3-Input NOR Gates	14	0.12	0.38	M,N,RCA,TI
74HC30	8-Input NAND Gate	14	0.12	0.38	M,N,RCA,TI
74HC32	Quad 2-Input OR Gates	14	0.12	0.38	M,N,RCA,TI
74HC36	Quad 2-Input NOR Gates	14	0.12	0.38	TI
74HC42	BCD to Decimal Decoder	16	0.48	0.50	M,N,RCA,TI
74HC51	Dual 2-Wide 2-Input AND-OR-INVERT Gates	14	0.12	0.38	M,N,TI
74HC58	Dual AND-OR Gates	14	0.24	0.44	M,N
74HC73	Dual Negative-Edge-Triggered J-K Flip-Flops with Clear	14	0.24	0.41	M,N,RCA,TI
74HC74	Dual Positive-Edge-Triggered D-Type Flip-Flops with Preset and Clear	14	0.24	0.41	M,N,RCA,TI
74HC75	4-Bit Bistable Latch	16	0.24	0.41	M,N,RCA,TI
74HC76	Dual Negative-Edge-Triggered J-K Flip-Flops with Preset and Clear	16	0.24	0.63	M,N,TI

PART NUMBER	DESCRIPTION	PINS	POWER (mW)	PRICE ($)	SUPPLIERS
74HC77	4-Bit Bistable Latch	14	0.24	0.63	TI
74HC78	Dual J-K Flip-Flops with Preset, Common Clear, and Common Clock	14	0.24	0.63	TI
74HC85	4-Bit Magnitude Comparator	16	0.48	0.63	M,N,RCA,TI
74HC86	Quad 2-Input Exclusive-OR Gate	14	0.12	0.41	M,N,RCA,TI
74HC107	Dual Master-Slave J-K Flip-Flops with Clear	14	0.24	0.41	M,N,RCA,TI
74HC109	Dual Positive-Edge-Triggered J-K Flip-Flops with Preset and Clear	16	0.24	0.41	M,N,RCA,TI
74HC112	Dual Negative-Edge-Triggered J-K Flip-Flops with Preset and Clear	16	0.24	0.53	M,N,RCA,TI
74HC113	Dual Negative-Edge-Triggered J-K Flip-Flops with Preset	14	0.24	0.53	M,N,TI
74HC114	Dual J-K Flip-Flops with Preset, Common Clear, and Common Clock	14	0.24	0.53	TI
74HC123	Dual Retriggerable Monostable Multivibrators with Clear	16	0.48	0.74	N,RCA
74HC125	Quad Buffers with 3-State Outputs	14	0.48	0.43	M,N,RCA,TI
74HC126	Quad Buffers with 3-State Outputs	14	0.48	0.43	M,N,RCA,TI
74HC132	Quad 2-Input Schmitt-Trigger NAND Gates	14	0.12	0.68	M,N,RCA,TI
74HC133	13-Input NAND Gate	16	0.12	0.42	M,N,TI
74HC137	3 to 8 Line Decoder/Demultiplexer with Address Latches	16	0.48	0.54	M,N,RCA,TI
74HC138	3 to 8 Line Decoder/Demultiplexer	16	0.48	0.54	M,N,RCA,TI
74HC139	Dual 2 to 4 Line Decoders/Demultiplexers	16	0.48	0.54	M,N,RCA,TI
74HC147	10-Line Decimal to 4-Line BCD Priority Encoder	16	0.48	0.90	N,RCA,TI
74HC148	8-Line Decimal to 3-Line Octal Priority Encoder	16	0.48	0.90	TI
74HC151	1 of 8 Line Data Selector/Multiplexer	16	0.48	0.54	M,N,RCA,TI
74HC152	1 of 8 Line Data Selector/Multiplexer	14	0.48	0.75	TI

PART NUMBER	DESCRIPTION	PINS	POWER (mW)	PRICE ($)	SUPPLIERS
74HC153	Dual 4 to 1 Line Data Selectors/Multiplexers	16	0.48	0.54	M,N,RCA,TI
74HC154	4 to 16 Line Decoder/Demultiplexer	24	0.48	1.65	M,N,RCA,TI
74HC157	Quad 2 to 1 Line Data Selectors/Multiplexers	16	0.48	0.54	M,N,RCA,TI
74HC158	Quad 2 to 1 Line Inverting Data Selectors/Multiplexers	16	0.48	0.72	M,N,RCA,TI
74HC160	Synchronous 4-Bit Decade Counter with Asynchronous Clear	16	0.48	0.73	M,N,RCA,TI
74HC161	Synchronous 4-Bit Binary Counter with Asynchronous Clear	16	0.48	0.73	M,N,RCA,TI
74HC162	Synchronous 4-Bit Decade Counter with Synchronous Clear	16	0.48	0.73	M,N,RCA,TI
74HC163	Synchronous 4-Bit Binary Counter with Synchronous Clear	16	0.48	0.73	M,N,RCA,TI
74HC164	8-Bit Serial In/Parallel Out Shift Register with Asynchronous Clear	14	0.48	0.73	M,N,RCA,TI
74HC165	8-Bit Parallel In/Serial Out Shift Register with Complementary Outputs	16	0.48	0.83	M,N,RCA,TI
74HC166	8-Bit Parallel or Serial In/Serial Out Shift Register	16	0.48	1.34	RCA,TI
74HC173	4-Bit D-Type Register with 3-State Outputs	16	0.48	0.63	M,N,RCA,TI
74HC174	Hex D-Type Flip-Flops with Clear	16	0.48	0.58	M,N,RCA,TI
74HC175	Quad D-Type Flip-Flops with Clear	16	0.24	0.63	M,N,RCA,TI
74HC180	9-Bit Parity Generator/Checker	14	0.48	0.90	TI
74HC181	Arithmetic Logic Unit/Function Generator	24	0.48	1.98	N,RCA
74HC182	Look-Ahead Carry Generator	16	0.48	0.66	N,RCA
74HC190	Synchronous Up/Down Decade Counter with Mode Control	16	0.48	0.79	RCA,TI
74HC191	Synchronous 4-Bit Up/Down Binary Counter with Mode Control	16	0.48	0.79	RCA,TI

PART NUMBER	DESCRIPTION	PINS	POWER (mW)	PRICE ($)	SUPPLIERS
74HC192	Synchronous Up/Down Decade Counter with Dual Clock	16	0.48	0.79	N,RCA,TI
74HC193	Synchronous 4-Bit Up/Down Binary Counter with Dual Clock	16	0.48	0.79	N,RCA,TI
74HC194	4-Bit Bidirectional Universal Shift Register	16	0.48	0.58	M,N,RCA,TI
74HC195	4-Bit Parallel-Access Shift Register	16	0.48	0.54	M,N,RCA,TI
74HC221	Dual Monostable Multivibrators with Schmitt-Trigger Input	16	0.48	0.96	N,RCA
74HC237	3 to 8 Line Decoder/Demultiplexer with Address Latches	16	0.48	0.79	M,N,RCA,TI
74HC238	3 to 8 Line Decoder/Demultiplexer	16	0.48	0.63	RCA,TI
74HC239	Dual 2 to 4 Line Decoders/Demultiplexers	16	0.48	0.94	TI
74HC240	Octal 3-State Inverting Buffers/Line Drivers/Line Receivers	20	0.48	0.99	M,N,RCA,TI
74HC241	Octal 3-State Buffers/Line Drivers/Line Receivers	20	0.48	0.99	M,N,RCA,TI
74HC242	Quad 3-State Inverting Bus Transceivers	14	0.48	0.91	M,N,RCA,TI
74HC243	Quad 3-State Bus Transceivers	14	0.48	0.91	M,N,RCA,TI
74HC244	Octal 3-State Buffers/Line Drivers/Line Receivers	20	0.48	1.06	M,N,RCA,TI
74HC245	Octal 3-State Bus Transceivers	20	0.48	1.22	M,N,RCA,TI
74HC251	3-State 1 of 8 Line Data Selector/Multiplexer	16	0.48	0.58	M,N,RCA,TI
74HC253	Dual 3-State 1 of 4 Line Data Selectors/Multiplexers	16	0.48	0.58	M,N,RCA,TI
74HC257	Quad 3-State 2 to 1 Line Data Selectors/Multiplexers	16	0.48	0.54	M,N,RCA,TI
74HC258	Quad 3-State 2 to 1 Line Inverting Data Selectors/Multiplexers	16	0.48	0.54	RCA,TI
74HC259	8-Bit Addressable Latch	16	0.48	1.02	M,N,RCA,TI

PART NUMBER	DESCRIPTION	PINS	POWER (mW)	PRICE ($)	SUPPLIERS
74HC266	Quad 2-Input Exclusive-NOR Gates with Open-Collector Outputs	14	0.12	0.58	M,N,TI
74HC273	Octal D-Type Flip-Flop with Clear	20	0.48	1.14	M,RCA,TI
74HC280	9-Bit Parity Generator/Checker	14	0.48	2.06	M,N,RCA,TI
74HC283	4-Bit Binary Full Adder with Fast Carry	16	0.48	0.68	N,RCA,TI
74HC298	Quad 2 to 1 Line Data Selectors/Multiplexers with Storage	16	0.48	1.09	N,TI
74HC299	8-Bit Universal Shift/Storage Register with 3-State Outputs	20	0.48	2.43	M,N,RCA,TI
74HC352	Dual 1 of 4 Line Inverting Data Selectors/Multiplexers	16	0.48	0.89	TI
74HC353	Dual 3-State 1 of 4 Line Data Selectors/Multiplexers	16	0.48	0.97	TI
74HC354	3-State 8 to 1 Line Data Selector/Multiplexer/Register	20	0.48	0.83	M,N,RCA,TI
74HC356	3-State 8 to 1 Line Data Selector/Multiplexer/Register	20	0.48	0.83	M,N,RCA,TI
74HC365	Hex 3-State Buffers/Bus Drivers	16	0.48	0.58	M,N,RCA,TI
74HC366	Hex 3-State Inverting Buffers/Bus Drivers	16	0.48	0.58	M,N,RCA,TI
74HC367	Hex 3-State Buffers/Bus Drivers	16	0.48	0.58	M,N,RCA,TI
74HC368	Hex 3-State Inverting Buffers/Bus Drivers	16	0.48	0.58	M,N,RCA,TI
74HC373	Octal 3-State Transparent D-Type Latches	20	0.48	1.16	M,N,RCA,TI
74HC374	Octal 3-State Positive-Edge-Triggered D-Type Flip-Flops	20	0.48	0.99	M,N,RCA,TI
74HC375	4-Bit Bistable Latch	16	0.24	0.58	TI
74HC377	Octal D-Type Flip-Flops with Enable	20	0.48	1.06	RCA,TI
74HC378	Hex D-Type Flip-Flops with Enable	16	0.48	1.63	TI
74HC379	Quad D-Type Flip-Flops with Enable	16	0.24	1.68	TI
74HC386	Quad 2-Input Exclusive-OR Gates	14	0.12	0.58	TI

PART NUMBER	DESCRIPTION	PINS	POWER (mW)	PRICE ($)	SUPPLIERS
74HC390	Dual Decade (Bi-Quinary) Counters	16	0.48	0.99	M,N,RCA,TI
74HC393	Dual 4-Bit Binary Counters	14	0.48	0.91	M,N,RCA,TI
74HC423	Dual Retriggerable Monostable Multivibrators	16	0.48	0.63	N,RCA
74HC490	Dual Decade Counters	16	0.48	1.67	TI
74HC533	Octal 3-State Inverting Transparent D-Type Latches	20	0.48	1.16	M,N,RCA,TI
74HC534	Octal 3-State Inverting Positive-Edge-Triggered D-Type Flip-Flops	20	0.48	1.59	M,N,RCA,TI
74HC540	Octal 3-State Inverting Buffer	20	0.48	1.03	M,RCA,TI
74HC541	Octal 3-State Buffer	20	0.48	1.02	M,RCA,TI
74HC563	Octal 3-State Inverting Transparent D-Type Latches	20	0.48	1.40	M,N,RCA,TI
74HC564	Octal 3-State Inverting Positive-Edge-Triggered D-Type Flip-Flops	20	0.48	1.40	M,N,RCA,TI
74HC573	Octal 3-State Transparent D-Type Latches	20	0.48	1.40	M,N,RCA,TI
74HC574	Octal 3-State Positive-Edge-Triggered D-Type Flip-Flops	20	0.48	1.40	M,N,RCA,TI
74HC589	8-Bit Shift Register with Input Latches and 3-State Serial Output	16	0.48	2.33	M
74HC590	8-Bit Binary Counter with Output Registers	16	0.48	2.51	TI
74HC594	8-BIT Shift Register with Output Registers	16	0.48	1.97	TI
74HC595	8-BIT Shift Register with Output Latches	16	0.48	1.97	M
74HC597	8-Bit Shift Register with Input Latches	16	0.48	2.33	M
74HC604	Octal 2-Input Multiplexed Latches with 3-State Outputs	28	0.48	5.01	TI
74HC620	Octal 3-State Inverting Bus Transceivers	20	0.48	1.92	TI
74HC623	Octal 3-State Bust Transceivers	20	0.48	1.92	TI

PART NUMBER	DESCRIPTION	PINS	POWER (mW)	PRICE ($)	SUPPLIERS
74HC640	Octal 3-State Inverting Bus Transceivers	20	0.48	1.40	M,N,RCA,TI
74HC643	Octal 3-State True/Inverting Bus Transceivers	20	0.48	1.40	M,N,RCA,TI
74HC645	Octal 3-State Bus Transceivers	20	0.48	1.92	TI
74HC646	Octal 3-State Bus Transceivers/Registers	24	0.48	4.13	M,N,RCA,TI
74HC648	Octal 3-State Inverting Bus Transceivers/Registers	24	0.48	4.13	M,N,RCA,TI
74HC651	Octal 3-State Inverting Bus Transceivers/Registers	24	0.48	4.24	TI
74HC652	Octal 3-State Bus Transceivers/Registers	24	0.48	3.94	TI
74HC658	Octal Bus Transceivers with Parity	24	0.48	3.34	TI
74HC659	Octal Bus Transceivers with Parity	24	0.48	3.34	TI
74HC664	Octal Bus Transceivers with Parity	24	0.48	3.34	TI
74HC665	Octal Bus Transceivers with Parity	24	0.48	3.34	TI
74HC670	4x4 Register File with 3-State Outputs	16	0.48	1.65	RCA
74HC677	16-Bit to 4-Bit Address Comparator with Enable	24	0.48	1.25	TI
74HC678	16-Bit to 4-Bit Address Comparator with Latch	24	0.48	1.25	TI
74HC679	12-Bit to 4-Bit Address Comparator with Enable	20	0.48	2.66	TI
74HC680	12-Bit to 4-Bit Address Comparator with Latch	20	0.48	2.66	TI
74HC682	8-Bit Identity Comparator	20	0.48	3.21	TI
74HC684	8-Bit Identity Comparator	20	0.48	3.21	TI
74HC688	8-Bit Identity Comparator	20	0.48	1.24	M,N,RCA,TI
74HC804	Hex 2-Input NAND Line Drivers	20	0.48	2.72	TI
74HC805	Hex 2-Input NOR Line Drivers	20	0.48	2.72	TI
74HC808	Hex 2-Input AND Line Drivers	20	0.48	2.00	TI

PART NUMBER	DESCRIPTION	PINS	POWER (mW)	PRICE ($)	SUPPLIERS
74HC832	Hex 2-Input OR Line Drivers	20	0.48	2.00	TI
74HC942	300 Baud Modem (+5,-5 Volt Supply)	20	1.38	7.80	N
74HC943	300 Baud Modem (5 Volt Supply)	20	1.38	8.30	N
74HC4002	Dual 4-Input NOR Gates	14	0.12	0.38	M,N,RCA,TI
74HC4015	Dual 4-Bit Serial In/Parallel Out Shift Register	16	0.48	1.96	RCA
74HC4016	Quad Analog Switch	14	1.92	0.63	N,RCA
74HC4017	Decate Counter/Divider with 10 Decoded Outputs	16	0.48	1.04	M,N,RCA,TI
74HC4020	14-Stage Binary Counter	16	0.48	1.04	M,N,RCA,TI
74HC4024	7-Stage Binary Counter	14	0.48	0.85	M,RCA,TI
74HC4040	12-Stage Binary Counter	16	0.48	1.04	M,N,RCA,TI
74HC4046	Phase Lock Loop	16	0.48	1.82	N,RCA
74HC4049	Hex Inverting Logic Level Down Converter	16	0.12	0.53	M,N,RCA
74HC4050	Hex Logic Level Down Converter	16	0.12	0.53	M,N,RCA
74HC4051	8-Channel Analog Multiplexer	16	1.92	0.89	M,RCA
74HC4052	Dual 4-Channel Analog Multiplexer	16	1.92	0.89	M,RCA
74HC4053	Triple 2-Channel Analog Multiplexer	16	1.92	0.89	M,RCA
74HC4060	14-Stage Binary Counter	16	0.48	0.90	M,N,RCA,TI
74HC4061	14-Stage Binary Counter	16	0.12	1.12	TI
74HC4066	Quad Analog Switch	14	1.92	0.53	M,N,RCA
74HC4075	Triple 3-Input OR Gates	14	0.12	0.38	M,N,RCA,TI
74HC4078	8-Input OR/NOR Gate	14	0.12	0.38	M,N,TI
74HC4316	Quad Analog Switch with Level Translator	16	0.96	0.53	M,N,RCA
74HC4351	8-Channel Analog Multiplexer with Address Latch	18	1.92	2.90	M
74HC4352	Dual 4-Channel Analog Multiplexer with Address Latch	18	1.92	1.06	M,RCA

PART NUMBER	DESCRIPTION	PINS	POWER (mW)	PRICE ($)	SUPPLIERS
74HC4353	Triple 2-Channel Analog Multiplexer with Address Latch	18	1.92	2.90	M
74HC4511	BCD to 7-Segment Latch/Decoder/Display Driver	16	0.48	2.33	RCA
74HC4514	4 to 16 Line Decoder with Address Latch	24	0.48	2.81	M,N,RCA,TI
74HC4515	4 to 16 Line Inverting Decoder with Address Latch	24	0.48	2.82	RCA,TI
74HC4518	Dual BCD Counter	16	0.48	1.68	RCA
74HC4520	Dual 4-Bit Binary Counter	16	0.48	1.07	RCA
74HC4538	Dual Retriggerable Monostable Multivibrator	16	1.50	1.07	M,N,RCA
74HC4543	BCD to 7-Segment Latch/Decoder/Driver for Liquid Crystal Displays	16	0.48	1.14	RCA
74HC4724	8-Bit Addressable Latch	16	0.48	1.80	TI
74HC7001	Quad 2-Input AND Gates with Schmitt-Trigger Inputs	14	0.12	0.68	TI
74HC7002	Quad 2-Input NOR Gates with Schmitt-Trigger Inputs	14	0.12	0.68	TI
74HC7006	6-Section Multifunction Circuit	24	0.12	0.89	TI
74HC7022	Octal Counters/Dividers with Power-Up Clear	16	0.48	1.17	TI
74HC7032	Quad 2-Input OR Gates with Schmitt-Trigger Inputs	14	0.12	0.68	TI
74HC7074	6-Section Multifunction Circuit	24	0.24	0.89	TI
74HC7266	Quad 2-Input Exclusive-NOR Gates	14	0.12	0.48	M,RCA,TI
74HC40102	8-Bit Synchronous BCD Down Counter	16	0.48	1.68	RCA
74HC40103	8-Bit Binary Down Counter	16	0.48	1.68	RCA
74HC40104	4-Bit Bidirectional Universal Shift Register with 3-State Outputs	16	0.48	1.40	RCA

PART NUMBER	DESCRIPTION	PINS	POWER (mW)	PRICE ($)	SUPPLIERS
74HCT00	Quad 2-Input NAND Gates	14	0.11	0.33	N,RCA
74HCT02	Quad 2-Input NOR Gates	14	0.11	0.33	RCA
74HCT04	Hex Inverters	14	0.11	0.33	N,RCA
74HCT05	Hex Inverters with Open-Collector Outputs	14	0.11	0.59	N
74HCT08	Quad 2-Input AND Gates	14	0.11	0.33	RCA
74HCT10	Triple 3-Input NAND Gates	14	0.11	0.33	RCA
74HCT11	Triple 3-Input AND Gates	14	0.11	0.33	RCA
74HCT20	Dual 4-Input NAND Gates	14	0.11	0.33	RCA
74HCT27	Triple 3-Input NOR Gates	14	0.11	0.33	RCA
74HCT30	8-Input NAND Gate	14	0.11	0.33	RCA
74HCT32	Quad 2-Input OR Gates	14	0.11	0.33	RCA
74HCT34	Hex Non-Inverters	14	0.11	0.86	N
74HCT42	BCD to Decimal Decoder	16	0.44	0.50	RCA
74HCT74	Dual Positive-Edge-Triggered D-Type Flip-Flops with Preset and Clear	14	0.22	0.41	RCA
74HCT75	4-Bit Bistable Latch	16	0.22	0.41	RCA
74HCT86	Quad 2-Input Exclusive-OR Gate	14	0.11	0.41	RCA
74HCT107	Dual Master-Slave J-K Flip-Flops with Clear	14	0.22	0.41	RCA
74HCT109	Dual Positive-Edge-Triggered J-K Flip-Flops with Preset and Clear	16	0.22	0.41	RCA
74HCT112	Dual Negative-Edge-Triggered J-K Flip-Flops with Preset and Clear	16	0.22	0.41	RCA
74HCT132	Quad 2-Input Schmitt-Trigger NAND Gates	14	0.11	0.68	RCA
74HCT137	3 to 8 Line Decoder/Demultiplexer with Address Latches	16	0.44	0.54	RCA,TI
74HCT138	3 to 8 Line Decoder/Demultiplexer	16	0.44	0.54	RCA,TI
74HCT139	Dual 2 to 4 Line Decoders/Demultiplexers	16	0.22	0.54	RCA

PART NUMBER	DESCRIPTION	PINS	POWER (mW)	PRICE ($)	SUPPLIERS
74HCT151	1 of 8 Line Data Selector/Multiplexer	16	0.44	0.54	RCA
74HCT154	4 to 16 Line Decoder/Demultiplexer	24	0.44	1.65	RCA
74HCT157	Quad 2 to 1 Line Data Selectors/Multiplexers	16	0.44	0.54	RCA
74HCT158	Quad 2 to 1 Line Inverting Data Selectors/Multiplexers	16	0.44	0.54	RCA
74HCT160	Synchronous 4-Bit Decade Counter with Asynchronous Clear	16	0.11	0.73	RCA
74HCT161	Synchronous 4-Bit Binary Counter with Asynchronous Clear	16	0.11	0.73	RCA
74HCT162	Synchronous 4-Bit Decade Counter with Synchronous Clear	16	0.11	0.73	RCA
74HCT163	Synchronous 4-Bit Binary Counter with Synchronous Clear	16	0.11	0.73	RCA
74HCT164	8-Bit Serial In/Parallel Out Shift Register with Asynchronous Clear	14	0.22	0.73	RCA
74HCT165	8-Bit Parallel In/Serial Out Shift Register with Complementary Outputs	16	0.44	0.83	RCA
74HCT166	8-Bit Parallel or Serial In/Serial Out Shift Register	16	0.22	1.49	RCA
74HCT173	4-Bit D-Type Register with 3-State Outputs	16	0.44	0.63	RCA
74HCT174	Hex D-Type Flip-Flops with Clear	16	0.44	0.64	RCA
74HCT175	Quad D-Type Flip-Flops with Clear	16	0.44	0.64	RCA
74HCT190	Synchronous Up/Down Decade Counter with Mode Control	16	0.44	0.79	RCA
74HCT191	Synchronous 4-Bit Up/Down Binary Counter with Mode Control	16	0.44	0.79	RCA
74HCT192	Synchronous Up/Down Decade Counter with Dual Clock	16	0.44	0.79	RCA
74HCT193	Synchronous 4-Bit Up/Down Binary Counter with Dual Clock	16	0.44	0.79	RCA

PART NUMBER	DESCRIPTION	PINS	POWER (mW)	PRICE ($)	SUPPLIERS
74HCT194	4-Bit Bidirectional Universal Shift Register	16	0.44	0.58	RCA
74HCT195	4-Bit Parallel-Access Shift Register	16	0.44	0.54	RCA
74HCT221	Dual Monostable Multivibrators with Schmitt-Trigger Input	16	0.44	0.96	RCA
74HCT237	3 to 8 Line Decoder/Demultiplexer with Address Latches	16	0.44	0.79	RCA,TI
74HCT238	3 to 8 Line Decoder/Demultiplexer	16	0.44	0.63	RCA,TI
74HCT240	Octal 3-State Inverting Buffers/Line Drivers/Line Receivers	20	0.44	1.06	M,N,RCA,TI
74HCT241	Octal 3-State Buffers/Line Drivers/Line Receivers	20	0.44	0.99	M,N,RCA,TI
74HCT242	Quad 3-State Inverting Bus Transceivers	14	0.44	0.91	RCA,TI
74HCT243	Quad 3-State Bus Transceivers	14	0.44	0.91	RCA,TI
74HCT244	Octal 3-State Buffers/Line Drivers/Line Receivers	20	0.44	1.06	M,N,RCA,TI
74HCT245	Octal 3-State Bus Transceivers	20	0.44	1.22	M,N,RCA,TI
74HCT251	3-State 1 of 8 Line Data Selector/Multiplexer	16	0.44	0.58	RCA
74HCT253	Dual 3-State 1 of 4 Line Data Selectors/Multiplexers	16	0.44	0.58	RCA
74HCT257	Quad 3-State 2 to 1 Line Data Selectors/Multiplexers	16	0.44	0.54	RCA
74HCT273	Octal D-Type Flip-Flop with Clear	20	0.44	1.14	RCA
74HCT280	9-Bit Parity Generator/Checker	14	0.44	2.06	RCA
74HCT299	8-Bit Universal Shift/Storage Register with 3-State Outputs	20	0.44	2.39	RCA
74HCT354	3-State 8 to 1 Line Data Selector/Multiplexer/Register	20	0.44	2.48	RCA
74HCT356	3-State 8 to 1 Line Data Selector/Multiplexer/Register	20	0.44	2.48	RCA
74HCT365	Hex 3-State Buffers/Bus Drivers	16	0.44	0.48	RCA

PART NUMBER	DESCRIPTION	PINS	POWER (mW)	PRICE ($)	SUPPLIERS
74HCT366	Hex 3-State Inverting Buffers/Bus Drivers	16	0.44	0.48	RCA
74HCT367	Hex 3-State Buffers/Bus Drivers	16	0.44	0.48	RCA
74HCT368	Hex 3-State Inverting Buffers/Bus Drivers	16	0.44	0.48	RCA
74HCT373	Octal 3-State Transparent D-Type Latches	20	0.44	1.16	M,N,RCA,TI
74HCT374	Octal 3-State Positive-Edge-Triggered D-Type Flip-Flops	20	0.44	1.16	M,N,RCA,TI
74HCT377	Octal D-Type Flip-Flops with Enable	20	0.44	1.06	RCA
74HCT393	Dual 4-Bit Binary Counters	14	0.44	0.91	RCA
74HCT533	Octal 3-State Inverting Transparent D-Type Latches	20	0.44	1.57	M,RCA,TI
74HCT534	Octal 3-State Inverting Positive-Edge-Triggered D-Type Flip-Flops	20	0.44	1.57	M,RCA,TI
74HCT540	Octal 3-State Inverting Buffer	20	0.44	1.02	M,RCA,TI
74HCT541	Octal 3-State Buffer	20	0.44	1.02	M,RCA,TI
74HCT563	Octal 3-State Inverting Transparent D-Type Latches	20	0.44	1.78	RCA,TI
74HCT564	Octal 3-State Inverting Positive-Edge-Triggered D-Type Flip-Flops	20	0.44	1.78	RCA,TI
74HCT573	Octal 3-State Transparent D-Type Latches	20	0.44	1.78	RCA,TI
74HCT574	Octal 3-State Positive-Edge-Triggered D-Type Flip-Flops	20	0.44	1.78	RCA,TI
74HCT620	Octal 3-State Inverting Bus Transceivers	20	0.44	1.92	TI
74HCT623	Octal 3-State Bust Transceivers	20	0.44	1.92	TI
74HCT640	Octal 3-State Inverting Bus Transceivers	20	0.44	1.63	M,N,RCA,TI
74HCT643	Octal 3-State True/Inverting Bus Transceivers	20	0.44	1.63	M,N,RCA,TI
74HCT645	Octal 3-State Bus Transceivers	20	0.44	1.92	TI

PART NUMBER	DESCRIPTION	PINS	POWER (mW)	PRICE ($)	SUPPLIERS
74HCT646	Octal 3–State Bus Transceivers/Registers	24	0.44	4.19	RCA,TI
74HCT648	Octal 3–State Inverting Bus Transceivers/Registers	24	0.44	4.19	RCA
74HCT651	Octal 3–State Inverting Bus Transceivers/Registers	24	0.44	4.24	TI
74HCT652	Octal 3–State Bus Transceivers/Registers	24	0.44	4.24	TI
74HCT659	Octal Bus Transceivers with Parity	24	0.44	3.34	TI
74HCT665	Octal Bus Transceivers with Parity	24	0.44	3.34	TI
74HCT670	4x4 Register File with 3–State Outputs	16	0.44	1.65	RCA
74HCT688	8–Bit Identity Comparator	20	0.44	1.24	N,RCA
74HCT4015	Dual 4–Bit Serial In/Parallel Out Shift Register	16	0.44	0.97	RCA
74HCT4017	Decate Counter/Divider with 10 Decoded Outputs	16	0.44	1.04	RCA
74HCT4020	14–Stage Binary Counter	16	0.44	1.04	RCA
74HCT4024	7–Stage Binary Counter	14	0.44	0.84	RCA
74HCT4040	12–Stage Binary Counter	16	0.44	1.04	RCA
74HCT4051	8–Channel Analog Multiplexer	16	1.60	1.05	RCA
74HCT4052	Dual 4–Channel Analog Multiplexer	16	1.60	1.01	RCA
74HCT4053	Triple 2–Channel Analog Multiplexer	16	1.60	1.05	RCA
74HCT4060	14–Stage Binary Counter	16	0.44	0.97	RCA
74HCT4514	4 to 16 Line Decoder with Address Latch	24	0.44	2.82	RCA
74HCT4515	4 to 16 Line Inverting Decoder with Address Latch	24	0.44	2.82	RCA
74HCT4518	Dual BCD Counter	16	0.44	1.68	RCA
74HCT4520	Dual 4–Bit Binary Counter	16	0.44	1.07	RCA
74HCT4538	Dual Retriggerable Monostable Multivibrator	16	0.44	1.07	RCA

PART NUMBER	DESCRIPTION	PINS	POWER (mW)	PRICE ($)	SUPPLIERS
74HCT40102	8-Bit Synchronous BCD Down Counter	16	0.44	1.68	RCA
74HCT40103	8-Bit Binary Down Counter	16	0.44	1.68	RCA
74HCT40104	4-Bit Bidirectional Universal Shift Register with 3-State Outputs	16	0.44	1.40	RCA

PART NUMBER	DESCRIPTION	PINS	POWER (mW)	PRICE ($)	SUPPLIERS
74L00	Quad 2-Input NAND Gates	14	10.71	0.83	N
74L02	Quad 2-Input NOR Gates	14	13.65	0.83	N
74L04	Hex Inverters	14	16.07	0.90	N
74L10	Triple 3-Input NAND Gates	14	8.03	0.83	N
74L20	Dual 4-Input NAND Gates	14	5.36	0.83	N
74L72	AND-Gated Master-Slave J-K Flip-Flop with Preset and Clear	14	7.56	1.05	N
74L73	Dual Negative-Edge-Triggered J-K Flip-Flops with Clear	14	15.12	1.35	N
74L74	Dual Positive-Edge-Triggered D-Type Flip-Flops with Preset and Clear	14	15.75	1.35	N
74L93	4-Bit Binary Counter	14	28.88	3.45	N
74L95	4-Bit Parallel-Access Shift Register	14	42.00	3.45	N
74L98	4-Bit Data Selector/Storage Register	16	42.00	3.45	N

PART NUMBER	DESCRIPTION	PINS	POWER (mW)	PRICE ($)	SUPPLIERS
74LS00	Quad 2-Input NAND Gates	14	23.10	0.23	F,M,N,TI
74LS01	Quad 2-Input NAND Gates with Open-Collector Outputs	14	23.10	0.25	M,TI
74LS02	Quad 2-Input NOR Gates	14	28.35	0.23	F,M,N,TI
74LS03	Quad 2-Input NAND Gates with Open-Collector Outputs	14	23.10	0.23	F,M,N,TI
74LS04	Hex Inverters	14	34.65	0.23	F,M,N,TI
74LS05	Hex Inverters with Open-Collector Outputs	14	34.65	0.23	F,M,N,TI
74LS08	Quad 2-Input AND Gates	14	46.20	0.23	F,M,N,TI
74LS09	Quad 2-Input AND Gates with Open-Collector Outputs	14	46.20	0.23	F,M,N,TI
74LS10	Triple 3-Input NAND Gates	14	17.32	0.23	F,M,N,TI
74LS11	Triple 3-Input AND Gates	14	34.65	0.23	F,M,N,TI
74LS12	Triple 3-Input NAND Gates with Open-Collector Outputs	14	17.32	0.23	F,M,N,TI
74LS13	Dual 4-Input Schmitt Trigger NAND Gates	14	36.75	0.23	F,M,TI
74LS14	Hex Schmitt Trigger Inverters	14	110.25	0.26	F,M,N,TI
74LS15	Triple 3-Input AND Gates with Open-Collector Outputs	14	34.65	0.23	F,M,TI
74LS19	Hex Schmitt-Trigger Inverters	14	157.50	0.48	TI
74LS20	Dual 4-Input NAND Gates	14	11.55	0.23	F,M,N,TI
74LS21	Dual 4-Input AND Gates	14	23.10	0.23	F,M,N,TI
74LS22	Dual 4-Input NAND Gates with Open-Collector Outputs	14	11.55	0.25	M,N,TI
74LS24	Quad 2-Input Schmitt-Trigger NAND Gates	14	105.00	1.02	TI
74LS26	Quad 2-Input NAND Buffers with High-Voltage Open-Collector Outputs	14	23.10	0.25	F,M,N,TI
74LS27	Triple 3-Input NOR Gates	14	35.70	0.23	F,M,N,TI

PART NUMBER	DESCRIPTION	PINS	POWER (mW)	PRICE ($)	SUPPLIERS
74LS28	Quad 2-Input NOR Buffers	14	72.45	0.23	F,M,TI
74LS30	8-Input NAND Gate	14	5.78	0.23	F,M,N,TI
74LS31	Delay Elements	16	105.00	0.64	TI
74LS32	Quad 2-Input OR Gates	14	51.45	0.23	F,M,N,TI
74LS33	Quad 2-Input NOR Buffers with Open-Collector Outputs	14	72.45	0.25	F,M,TI
74LS37	Quad 2-Input NAND Buffers	14	63.00	0.23	F,M,N,TI
74LS38	Quad 2-Input Nand Buffers with Open-Collector Outputs	14	63.00	0.23	F,M,N,TI
74LS40	Dual 4-Input NAND Buffers	14	31.50	0.23	F,M,TI
74LS42	BCD to Decimal Decoder	16	68.25	0.36	F,M,N,TI
74LS47	BCD to 7-Segment Decoder/Driver with Open-Collector Outputs	16	68.25	0.50	F,M,TI
74LS48	BCD to 7-Segment Decoder/Driver with Internal Pull-Up Resistor Outputs	16	199.50	0.50	F,M,TI
74LS49	BCD to 7-Segment Decoder/Driver with Open-Collector Outputs	16	78.75	0.80	M,TI
74LS51	Dual 2-Wide 2-Input AND-OR-INVERT Gates	14	14.70	0.23	F,M,N,TI
74LS54	4-Wide 2-Input AND-OR-INVERT Gate	14	10.50	0.23	F,M,TI
74LS55	2-Wide 4-Input AND-OR-INVERT Gate	14	6.83	0.23	F,M,TI
74LS56	50 to 1 Frequency Divider	8	157.50	2.64	TI
74LS57	60 to 1 Frequency Divider	8	157.50	2.64	TI
74LS63	Hex Current-Sensing Gates	14	84.00	3.26	TI
74LS68	Dual 4-Bit Decade Counter	16	283.50	1.58	TI
74LS69	Dual 4-Bit Binary Counter	16	283.50	1.58	TI
74LS73	Dual Negative-Edge-Triggered J-K Flip-Flops with Clear	14	31.50	0.34	M,N,TI
74LS74	Dual Positive-Edge-Triggered D-Type Flip-Flops with Preset and Clear	14	42.00	0.26	F,M,N,TI

PART NUMBER	DESCRIPTION	PINS	POWER (mW)	PRICE ($)	SUPPLIERS
74LS75	4-Bit Bistable Latch	16	63.00	0.36	M,N,TI
74LS76	Dual Negative-Edge-Triggered J-K Flip-Flops with Preset and Clear	16	31.50	0.35	M,TI
74LS77	4-Bit Bistable Latch	14	63.00	0.56	M
74LS78	Dual J-K Flip-Flops with Preset, Common Clear, and Common Clock	14	31.50	0.35	M,TI
74LS83	4-Bit Binary Full Adder with Fast Carry	16	204.75	0.36	F,M,N,TI
74LS85	4-Bit Magnitude Comparator	16	105.00	0.36	F,M,N,TI
74LS86	Quad 2-Input Exclusive-OR Gate	14	52.50	0.26	F,M,N,TI
74LS90	Decade Counter	14	78.75	0.36	F,M,N,TI
74LS91	8-Bit Shift Register	14	105.00	0.46	M,TI
74LS92	Divide by 12 Counter	14	78.75	0.45	M,TI
74LS93	4-Bit Binary Counter	14	78.75	0.36	F,M,N,TI
74LS95	4-Bit Parallel-Access Shift Register	14	110.25	0.36	F,M,TI
74LS96	5-Bit Shift Register	16	105.00	0.64	TI
74LS107	Dual Master-Slave J-K Flip-Flops with Clear	14	31.50	0.32	M,N,TI
74LS109	Dual Positive-Edge-Triggered J-K Flip-Flops with Preset and Clear	16	42.00	0.26	F,M,N,TI
74LS112	Dual Negative-Edge-Triggered J-K Flip-Flops with Preset and Clear	16	31.50	0.32	F,M,N,TI
74LS113	Dual Negative-Edge-Triggered J-K Flip-Flops with Preset	14	31.50	0.33	M,TI
74LS114	Dual J-K Flip-Flops with Preset, Common Clear, and Common Clock	14	31.50	0.33	M,TI
74LS122	Retriggerable Monostable Multivibrator with Clear	14	105.00	0.43	M,N,TI
74LS123	Dual Retriggerable Monostable Multivibrators with Clear	16	105.00	0.58	M,N,TI
74LS125	Quad Buffers with 3-State Outputs	14	115.50	0.26	F,M,N,TI

PART NUMBER	DESCRIPTION	PINS	POWER (mW)	PRICE ($)	SUPPLIERS
74LS126	Quad Buffers with 3-State Outputs	14	115.50	0.26	F,M,N,TI
74LS132	Quad 2-Input Schmitt-Trigger NAND Gates	14	73.50	0.36	F,M,N,TI
74LS133	13-Input NAND Gate	16	5.78	0.26	F,M
74LS136	Quad 2-Input Exclusive-OR Gates with Open-Collector Outputs	14	52.50	0.26	F,M,TI
74LS137	3 to 8 Line Decoder/Demultiplexer with Address Latches	16	94.50	0.33	M,TI
74LS138	3 to 8 Line Decoder/Demultiplexer	16	52.50	0.36	F,M,N,TI
74LS139	Dual 2 to 4 Line Decoders/Demultiplexers	16	57.75	0.36	F,M,N,TI
74LS145	BCD to Decimal Decoder/Driver	16	68.25	0.58	M,TI
74LS147	10-Line Decimal to 4-Line BCD Priority Encoder	16	105.00	1.16	M,TI
74LS148	8-Line Decimal to 3-Line Octal Priority Encoder	16	105.00	0.76	M,TI
74LS151	1 of 8 Line Data Selector/Multiplexer	16	52.50	0.36	F,M,N,TI
74LS153	Dual 4 to 1 Line Data Selectors/Multiplexers	16	52.50	0.36	F,M,N,TI
74LS154	4 to 16 Line Decoder/Demultiplexer	24	73.50	0.93	N
74LS155	Dual 2 to 4 Line Decoders/Demultiplexers	16	52.50	0.39	F,M,N,TI
74LS156	Dual 2 to 4 Line Decoders/Demultiplexers with Open-Collector Outputs	16	52.50	0.39	F,M,N,TI
74LS157	Quad 2 to 1 Line Data Selectors/Multiplexers	16	84.00	0.36	F,M,N,TI
74LS158	Quad 2 to 1 Line Inverting Data Selectors/Multiplexers	16	57.75	0.36	F,M,N,TI
74LS160	Synchronous 4-Bit Decade Counter with Asynchronous Clear	16	168.00	0.39	F,M,TI
74LS161	Synchronous 4-Bit Binary Counter with Asynchronous Clear	16	168.00	0.39	F,M,N,TI
74LS162	Synchronous 4-Bit Decade Counter with Synchronous Clear	16	168.00	0.39	F,M,TI

PART NUMBER	DESCRIPTION	PINS	POWER (mW)	PRICE ($)	SUPPLIERS
74LS163	Synchronous 4-Bit Binary Counter with Synchronous Clear	16	168.00	0.39	F,M,N,TI
74LS164	8-Bit Serial In/Parallel Out Shift Register with Asynchronous Clear	14	141.75	0.39	F,M,N,TI
74LS165	8-Bit Parallel In/Serial Out Shift Register with Complementary Outputs	16	157.50	0.39	F,M,N,TI
74LS166	8-Bit Parallel or Serial In/Serial Out Shift Register	16	168.00	1.32	M,N,TI
74LS168	Synchronous 4-Bit Up/Down Decade Counter	16	178.50	0.74	F,M
74LS169	Synchronous 4-Bit Up/Down Binary Counter	16	236.25	0.74	F,M,N,TI
74LS170	4 by 4 Register File with Open-Collector Outputs	16	210.00	0.74	F,M,TI
74LS173	4-Bit D-Type Register with 3-State Outputs	16	126.00	0.50	F,M,N,TI
74LS174	Hex D-Type Flip-Flops with Clear	16	136.50	0.36	F,M,N,TI
74LS175	Quad D-Type Flip-Flops with Clear	16	94.50	0.36	F,M,N,TI
74LS181	Arithmetic Logic Unit/Function Generator	24	194.25	1.72	F,M,TI
74LS183	Dual Carry-Save Full Adders	14	89.25	2.34	M,TI
74LS189	64-Bit Random-Access Memory with 3-State Outputs	16	315.00	3.60	TI
74LS190	Synchronous Up/Down Decade Counter with Mode Control	16	183.75	0.64	F,M,N,TI
74LS191	Synchronous 4-Bit Up/Down Binary Counter with Mode Control	16	183.75	0.66	F,M,N,TI
74LS192	Synchronous Up/Down Decade Counter with Dual Clock	16	178.50	0.50	F,M,TI
74LS193	Synchronous 4-Bit Up/Down Binary Counter with Dual Clock	16	178.50	0.50	F,M,N,TI
74LS194	4-Bit Bidirectional Universal Shift Register	16	120.75	0.50	F,M,N,TI
74LS195	4-Bit Parallel-Access Shift Register	16	110.25	0.43	F,M,N,TI
74LS196	Presettable Decade (Bi-Quinary) Counter	14	141.75	0.50	F,M,TI

PART NUMBER	DESCRIPTION	PINS	POWER (mW)	PRICE ($)	SUPPLIERS
74LS197	Presettable Binary Counter	14	141.75	0.50	F,M,TI
74LS219	64-Bit Random-Access Memory with 3-State Outputs	16	315.00	3.60	TI
74LS221	Dual Monostable Multivibrators with Schmitt-Trigger Input	16	141.75	0.74	M,N,TI
74LS240	Octal 3-State Inverting Buffers/Line Drivers/Line Receivers	20	262.50	0.60	F,M,N,TI
74LS241	Octal 3-State Buffers/Line Drivers/Line Receivers	20	283.50	0.60	F,M,N,TI
74LS242	Quad 3-State Inverting Bus Transceivers	14	262.50	0.88	M,TI
74LS243	Quad 3-State Bus Transceivers	14	283.50	0.88	M,N,TI
74LS244	Octal 3-State Buffers/Line Drivers/Line Receivers	20	283.50	0.60	F,M,N,TI
74LS245	Octal 3-State Bus Transceivers	20	498.75	0.74	F,M,N,TI
74LS247	BCD to 7 Segment Decoder/Driver with Open-Collector Outputs	16	68.25	0.69	F,M,TI
74LS248	BCD to 7 Segment Decoder/Driver	16	199.50	0.69	F,M,TI
74LS249	BCD to 7 Segment Decoder/Driver with Open-Collector Outputs	16	78.75	0.69	F,M,TI
74LS251	3-State 1 of 8 Line Data Selector/Multiplexer	16	63.00	0.36	F,M,N,TI
74LS253	Dual 3-State 1 of 4 Line Data Selectors/Multiplexers	16	73.50	0.36	F,M,N,TI
74LS256	Dual 4-Bit Addressable Latch	16	131.25	0.69	F,M
74LS257	Quad 3-State 2 to 1 Line Data Selectors/Multiplexers	16	99.75	0.36	F,M,N,TI
74LS258	Quad 3-State 2 to 1 Line Inverting Data Selectors/Multiplexers	16	84.00	0.36	F,M,N,TI
74LS259	8-Bit Addressable Latch	16	189.00	0.69	F,M,N,TI
74LS260	Dual 5-Input NOR Gates	14	28.88	0.26	F,M
74LS261	2-Bit by 4-Bit Parallel Binary Multiplexer	16	210.00	2.98	TI

PART NUMBER	DESCRIPTION	PINS	POWER (mW)	PRICE ($)	SUPPLIERS
74LS266	Quad 2-Input Exclusive-NOR Gates with Open-Collector Outputs	14	68.25	0.26	F,M,TI
74LS273	Octal D-Type Flip-Flop with Clear	20	141.75	0.60	F,M,TI
74LS279	Quad S-R Latches	16	36.75	0.26	F,M,N,TI
74LS280	9-Bit Parity Generator/Checker	14	141.75	0.58	M,TI
74LS283	4-Bit Binary Full Adder with Fast Carry	16	178.50	0.50	F,M,N,TI
74LS289	64-Bit Random Access Memory with Open Collector Outputs	16	315.00	3.60	TI
74LS290	Decade Counter	14	78.75	0.50	F,M,N,TI
74LS292	Programmable Frequency Divider/Digital Timer	16	393.75	11.55	TI
74LS293	4-Bit Binary Counter	14	78.75	0.50	F,M,N,TI
74LS294	Programmable Frequency Divider/Digital Timer	16	262.50	11.55	TI
74LS295	4-Bit Bidirectional Shift Register with 3-State Outputs	14	173.25	0.69	F,M,TI
74LS297	Digital Phase-Locked-Loop Filter	16	630.00	11.55	TI
74LS298	Quad 2 to 1 Line Data Selectors/Multiplexers with Storage	16	110.25	0.69	F,M,TI
74LS299	8-Bit Universal Shift/Storage Register with 3-State Outputs	20	278.25	2.02	F,M,TI
74LS319	64-BIT RAM 16x4 OC	16	315.00	3.60	TI
74LS320	Crystal Controlled Oscillator	16	367.50	4.62	TI
74LS321	Crystal Controlled Oscillator	16	393.75	2.31	TI
74LS322	8-Bit Shift Register with Sign Extend	20	315.00	3.28	F,M,TI
74LS323	8-Bit Universal Shift/Storage Register with 3-State Outputs	20	278.25	3.28	F,M,TI
74LS347	BCD to 7-Segment Decoder/Driver	16	68.25	0.50	F,TI
74LS348	8 to 3 Line Priority Encoder with 3-State Outputs	16	131.25	0.88	M,TI

PART NUMBER	DESCRIPTION	PINS	POWER (mW)	PRICE ($)	SUPPLIERS
74LS352	Dual 1 of 4 Line Inverting Data Selectors/Multiplexers	16	52.50	0.57	F,M,N,TI
74LS353	Dual 3-State 1 of 4 Line Data Selectors/Multiplexers	16	73.50	0.57	F,M,TI
74LS354	3-State 8 to 1 Line Data Selector/Multiplexer/Register	20	241.50	2.48	TI
74LS355	Open-Collector 8 to 1 Line Data Selector/Multiplexer/Register	20	241.50	4.96	TI
74LS356	3-State 8 to 1 Line Data Selector/Multiplexer/Register	20	241.50	2.48	TI
74LS357	Open-Collector 8 to 1 Line Data Selector/Multiplexer/Register	20	241.50	4.96	TI
74LS365	Hex 3-State Buffers/Bus Drivers	16	126.00	0.36	F,M,N,TI
74LS366	Hex 3-State Inverting Buffers/Bus Drivers	16	110.25	0.36	F,M,N,TI
74LS367	Hex 3-State Buffers/Bus Drivers	16	126.00	0.36	F,M,N,TI
74LS368	Hex 3-State Inverting Buffers/Bus Drivers	16	110.25	0.36	F,M,N,TI
74LS373	Octal 3-State Transparent D-Type Latches	20	210.00	0.60	F,M,N,TI
74LS374	Octal 3-State Positive-Edge-Triggered D-Type Flip-Flops	20	210.00	0.60	F,M,N,TI
74LS375	4-Bit Bistable Latch	16	63.00	0.36	F,M,TI
74LS377	Octal D-Type Flip-Flops with Enable	20	147.00	0.60	F,M,TI
74LS378	Hex D-Type Flip-Flops with Enable	16	115.50	0.69	F,M,TI
74LS379	Quad D-Type Flip-Flops with Enable	16	78.75	0.69	F,M,TI
74LS380	Multifunction 8-Bit Register	24	945.00	3.84	MM
74LS381	Arithmetic Logic Unit/Function Generator	20	341.25	2.31	TI
74LS382	Arithmetic Logic Unit/Function Generator	20	341.25	2.31	TI
74LS384	8-Bit Serial/Parallel Two's Complement Multiplier	16	813.75	9.74	TI

PART NUMBER	DESCRIPTION	PINS	POWER (mW)	PRICE ($)	SUPPLIERS
74LS385	Quad Serial Adder/Subtractor	20	393.75	2.98	M,TI
74LS386	Quad 2-Input Exclusive-OR Gates	14	52.50	0.31	F,M,TI
74LS390	Dual Decade (Bi-Quinary) Counters	16	136.50	0.50	F,M,N,TI
74LS393	Dual 4-Bit Binary Counters	14	136.50	0.50	F,M,N,TI
74LS395	4-Bit Cascadable Shift Register with 3-State Outputs	16	178.50	0.69	F,M,TI
74LS396	Octal Storage Register	16	210.00	2.80	TI
74LS398	Quad 2-Input Multiplexers with Storage	20	68.25	1.10	M,TI
74LS399	Quad 2-Input Multiplexers with Storage	16	68.25	0.94	M,TI
74LS422	Retriggerable Monostable Multivibrator	14	57.75	1.02	TI
74LS423	Dual Retriggerable Monostable Multivibrators	16	105.00	0.63	TI
74LS442	Quad 3-State Bus Transceivers	20	498.75	3.71	TI
74LS444	Quad 3-State Bus Transceivers	20	498.75	7.42	TI
74LS447	BCD to 7-Segment Decoder/Driver	16	68.25	0.64	F
74LS449	Quad 3-State Bus Transceivers with Individual Direction Controls	16	420.00	7.42	TI
74LS450	16 to 1 Multiplexer	24	525.00	3.42	MM
74LS453	Quad 4 to 1 Multiplexer	24	525.00	3.42	MM
74LS460	10-Bit Comparator	24	525.00	3.84	MM
74LS461	8-Bit Counter	24	945.00	3.84	MM
74LS465	Octal 3-State Buffers/Bus Drivers	20	194.25	1.15	TI
74LS466	Octal 3-State Inverting Buffers/Bus Drivers	20	147.00	1.15	TI
74LS467	Octal 3-State Buffers/Bus Drivers	20	194.25	2.30	TI
74LS468	Octal 3-State Inverting Buffers/Bus Drivers	20	147.00	2.30	TI
74LS469	8-Bit Up/Down Counter	24	945.00	3.84	MM

PART NUMBER	DESCRIPTION	PINS	POWER (mW)	PRICE ($)	SUPPLIERS
74LS471	2048-Bit Programmable Read-Only Memory	20	52.50	3.25	N
74LS490	Dual Decade Counters	16	136.50	1.64	F,M,TI
74LS491	10-Bit Counter	24	945.00	3.84	MM
74LS502	8-Bit Successive Approximation Register	16	341.25	4.25	F
74LS503	8-Bit Successive Approximation Register with Expansion Control	16	341.25	4.72	F
74LS533	Octal 3-State Inverting Transparent D-Type Latches	20	210.00	0.79	F
74LS534	Octal 3-State Inverting Positive-Edge-Triggered D-Type Flip-Flops	20	236.25	0.79	F
74LS540	Octal 3-State Inverting Buffer	20	273.00	0.79	F,M,TI
74LS541	Octal 3-State Buffer	20	288.75	0.90	M,TI
74LS546	8-Bit Bus Register Transceiver	24	945.00	3.57	MM
74LS547	3 to 8 Line Decoder/Demultiplexer with Address Latches	20	945.00	3.57	MM
74LS548	3 to 8 Line Decoder/Demultiplexer with Acknowledge	20	787.50	3.22	MM
74LS549	8-Bit Two-Stage Pipelined Latch	24	840.00	3.22	MM
74LS563	Octal 3-State Inverting Transparent D-Type Latches	20	210.00	1.57	F
74LS566	8-Bit Inverting Bus Register Transceiver	24	945.00	3.57	MM
74LS567	8-Bit Inverting Bus Latch Transceiver	24	945.00	3.57	MM
74LS568	Synchronous 4-Bit Decade Up/Down Binary Counter with 3-State Outputs	20	225.75	1.60	M
74LS569	Synchronous 4-Bit Binary Up/Down Binary Counter with 3-State Outputs	20	225.75	1.60	M
74LS573	Octal 3-State Transparent D-Type Latches	20	210.00	1.00	F
74LS574	Octal 3-State Positive-Edge-Triggered D-Type Flip-Flops	20	236.25	1.00	F

PART NUMBER	DESCRIPTION	PINS	POWER (mW)	PRICE ($)	SUPPLIERS
74LS590	8-Bit Binary Counter with Output Registers	16	341.25	4.54	TI
74LS591	8-Bit Binary Counter with Output Registers	16	341.25	9.08	TI
74LS592	8-Bit Binary Counter with Input Registers	16	315.00	4.54	TI
74LS593	8-Bit Binary Counter with Input Registers	16	446.25	5.78	TI
74LS594	8-Bit Shift Register with Output Registers	16	341.25	9.08	TI
74LS595	8-Bit Shift Register with Output Latches	16	341.25	4.54	TI
74LS597	8-Bit Shift Register with Input Latches	16	278.25	4.54	TI
74LS598	8-Bit Shift Register with Input Latches	20	446.25	5.78	TI
74LS599	8-Bit Shift Register with Output Latches	16	288.75	4.54	TI
74LS600	Memory Refresh Controller	20	446.25	8.26	TI
74LS601	Memory Refresh Controller	20	446.25	8.26	TI
74LS602	Memory Refresh Controller	20	446.25	8.26	TI
74LS603	Memory Refresh Controller	20	446.25	8.26	TI
74LS604	Octal 2-Input Multiplexed Latches with 3-State Outputs	28	367.50	3.50	M,TI
74LS605	Octal 2-Input Multiplexed Latches with Open-Collector Outputs	28	315.00	3.50	M,TI
74LS606	Octal 2-Input Multiplexed Latches with 3-State Outputs	28	367.50	3.50	M
74LS607	Octal 2-Input Multiplexed Latches with Open-Collector Outputs	28	315.00	3.50	M,TI
74LS608	Memory Cycle Controller	16	341.25	15.68	TI
74LS610	Memory Mapper	40	1207.50	16.66	TI
74LS611	Memroy Mapper	40	1050.00	16.66	TI
74LS612	Memory Mapper	40	1207.50	16.66	TI

PART NUMBER	DESCRIPTION	PINS	POWER (mW)	PRICE ($)	SUPPLIERS
74LS613	Memory Mapper	40	1050.00	16.66	TI
74LS620	Octal 3-State Inverting Bus Transceivers	20	498.75	1.44	M,TI
74LS621	Octal Bus Transceivers with Open Collector Outputs	20	472.50	1.44	M,TI
74LS622	Octal Bus Transceivers with Open Collector Outputs	20	472.50	1.44	M,TI
74LS623	Octal 3-State Bust Transceivers	20	498.75	1.44	M,TI
74LS624	Voltage Controlled Oscillator	14	183.75	1.39	TI
74LS625	Dual Voltage Controlled Oscillators	16	288.75	1.39	TI
74LS626	Dual Voltage Controlled Oscillators	16	288.75	2.78	TI
74LS627	Dual Voltage Controlled Oscillators	14	288.75	3.80	TI
74LS628	Voltage Controlled Oscillator	14	183.75	1.39	TI
74LS629	Dual Voltage Controlled Oscillators	16	288.75	1.90	TI
74LS630	3-State 16-Bit Error Detection and Correction Circuit	28	1207.50	61.88	TI
74LS636	3-State 8-Bit Error Detection and Correction Circuit	20	840.00	32.68	TI
74LS638	Octal Inverting Bus Transceivers	20	498.75	3.26	TI
74LS639	Octal Bus Transceivers	20	498.75	3.26	TI
74LS640	Octal 3-State Inverting Bus Transceivers	20	498.75	1.44	M,TI
74LS641	Octal Bus Transceivers with Open Collector Outputs	20	498.75	1.44	M,TI
74LS642	Octal Inverting Bus Transceivers with Open Collector Outputs	20	498.75	1.44	M,TI
74LS643	Octal 3-State True/Inverting Bus Transceivers	20	498.75	1.44	M,TI
74LS644	Octal True/Inverting Bus Transceivers with Open Collector Outputs	20	498.75	1.44	M,TI
74LS645	Octal 3-State Bus Transceivers	20	498.75	1.02	M,N,TI
74LS646	Octal 3-State Bus Transceivers/Registers	24	866.25	4.31	MM,TI

PART NUMBER	DESCRIPTION	PINS	POWER (mW)	PRICE ($)	SUPPLIERS
74LS647	Octal Bus Transceivers/Registers with Open Collector Outputs	24	787.50	4.31	MM,TI
74LS648	Octal 3-State Inverting Bus Transceivers/Registers	24	945.00	4.31	MM,TI
74LS649	Octal Inverting Bus Transceivers/Registers with Open Collector Outputs	24	787.50	4.31	MM,TI
74LS651	Octal 3-State Inverting Bus Transceivers/Registers	24	866.25	4.31	MM,TI
74LS652	Octal 3-State Bus Transceivers/Registers	24	945.00	4.31	MM,TI
74LS653	Octal Inverting Bus Transceivers/Registers with Open Collector Outputs	24	866.25	4.31	MM
74LS654	Octal Bus Transceivers/Registers with Open Collector Outputs	24	945.00	4.31	MM,TI
74LS668	Synchronous 4-Bit Up/Down Decade Counter	16	178.50	0.74	M,TI
74LS669	Synchronous 4-Bit Up/Down Binary Counter	16	178.50	0.74	M,TI
74LS670	4x4 Register File with 3-State Outputs	16	262.50	0.86	F,M,N,TI
74LS671	4-Bit Universal Shift Register Latch with 3-State Outputs	20	367.50	4.96	TI
74LS672	4-Bit Universal Shift Register Latch with 3-State Outputs	20	367.50	4.96	TI
74LS673	16-Bit Serial In, Serial/Parallel Out Shift Register	24	420.00	3.66	M,TI
74LS674	16-Bit Shift Register	24	210.00	3.66	M,TI
74LS681	4-Bit Binary Accumulator	20	787.50	6.44	TI
74LS682	8-Bit Identity Comparator	20	367.50	1.90	M,TI
74LS683	8-Bit Identity Comparator	20	367.50	1.90	M,TI
74LS684	8-Bit Identity Comparator	20	341.25	1.90	M,TI
74LS685	8-Bit Identity Comparator	20	341.25	1.90	M,TI
74LS686	8-Bit Identity Comparator	24	393.75	2.92	M,TI

PART NUMBER	DESCRIPTION	PINS	POWER (mW)	PRICE ($)	SUPPLIERS
74LS687	8-Bit Identity Comparator	24	393.75	2.92	M,TI
74LS688	8-Bit Identity Comparator	20	341.25	1.90	M,TI
74LS689	8-Bit Identity Comparator	20	341.25	1.90	M,TI
74LS690	Synchronous Decade Counter with Output Register	20	367.50	4.96	TI
74LS691	Synchronous Binary Counter with Output Register	20	367.50	4.96	TI
74LS692	Synchronous Decade Counter with Output Register	20	367.50	4.96	TI
74LS693	Synchronous Binary Counter with Output Register	20	367.50	4.96	TI
74LS696	Synchronous Up/Down Decade Counter with Output Register	20	367.50	4.96	TI
74LS697	Synchronous Up/Down Binary Counter with Output Register	20	367.50	2.48	TI
74LS699	Synchronous Up/Down Binary Counter with Output Register	20	367.50	2.48	TI
74LS716	Programmable Decade Counter	16	168.00	5.24	M
74LS718	Programmable Binary Counter	16	168.00	5.24	M
74LS724	Voltage Controlled Oscillator	8	44.63	2.20	M
74LS748	8 to 3 Line Priority Encoder	16	105.00	0.80	M
74LS783	Synchronous Address Multiplexer	40	1207.50	12.41	M
74LS793	8-Bit Latch with Readback	20	630.00	2.34	MM
74LS794	8-Bit Register with Readback	20	630.00	2.34	MM
74LS795	Octal 3-State Buffers	20	136.50	1.02	M
74LS796	Octal 3-State Inverting Buffers	20	110.25	1.02	M
74LS797	Octal 3-State Buffers	20	135.50	1.02	M
74LS798	Octal 3-State Inverting Buffers	20	110.25	1.02	M
74LS848	3-State 8 to 3 Line Priority Encoder	16	131.25	0.92	M

PART NUMBER	DESCRIPTION	PINS	POWER (mW)	PRICE ($)	SUPPLIERS
74LS952	Dual Rank 3-State 8-Bit Positive-Edge-Triggered Shift Registers	18	519.75	2.87	N
74LS962	Dual Rank 3-State 8-Bit Positive-Edge-Triggered Shift Registers	18	519.75	2.87	N

PART NUMBER	DESCRIPTION	PINS	POWER (mW)	PRICE ($)	SUPPLIERS
74S00	Quad 2-Input NAND Gates	14	189.00	0.29	F,N,TI
74S02	Quad 2-Input NOR Gates	14	236.25	0.29	F,N,TI
74S03	Quad 2-Input NAND Gates with Open-Collector Outputs	14	189.00	0.29	F,N,TI
74S04	Hex Inverters	14	283.50	0.29	F,N,TI
74S05	Hex Inverters with Open-Collector Outputs	14	283.50	0.29	F,N,TI
74S08	Quad 2-Input AND Gates	14	299.25	0.29	F,N,TI
74S09	Quad 2-Input AND Gates with Open-Collector Outputs	14	299.25	0.35	N,TI
74S10	Triple 3-Input NAND Gates	14	141.75	0.29	F,N,TI
74S11	Triple 3-Input AND Gates	14	220.50	0.29	F,N,TI
74S15	Triple 3-Input AND Gates with Open-Collector Outputs	14	220.50	0.41	TI
74S20	Dual 4-Input NAND Gates	14	94.50	0.29	F,N,TI
74S22	Dual 4-Input NAND Gates with Open-Collector Outputs	14	94.50	0.41	TI
74S30	8-Input NAND Gate	14	52.50	0.29	F,N,TI
74S32	Quad 2-Input OR Gates	14	357.00	0.29	F,N,TI
74S37	Quad 2-Input NAND Buffers	14	420.00	0.90	TI
74S38	Quad 2-Input Nand Buffers with Open-Collector Outputs	14	420.00	0.90	TI
74S40	Dual 4-Input NAND Buffers	14	231.00	0.29	F,N,TI
74S51	Dual 2-Wide 2-Input AND-OR-INVERT Gates	14	115.50	0.29	F,N,TI
74S64	4-Wide AND-OR-INVERT Gate	14	84.00	0.29	F,N,TI
74S65	4-Wide AND-OR-INVERT Gate with Open-Collector Output	14	84.00	0.40	TI
74S74	Dual Positive-Edge-Triggered D-Type Flip-Flops with Preset and Clear	14	131.25	0.40	F,N,TI

PART NUMBER	DESCRIPTION	PINS	POWER (mW)	PRICE ($)	SUPPLIERS
74S85	4-Bit Magnitude Comparator	16	603.75	1.80	TI
74S86	Quad 2-Input Exclusive-OR Gate	14	393.75	0.49	F,N,TI
74S109	Dual Positive-Edge-Triggered J-K Flip-Flops with Preset and Clear	16	273.00	1.12	F
74S112	Dual Negative-Edge-Triggered J-K Flip-Flops with Preset and Clear	16	131.25	0.50	F,N,TI
74S113	Dual Negative-Edge-Triggered J-K Flip-Flops with Preset	14	131.25	0.51	N,TI
74S114	Dual J-K Flip-Flops with Preset, Common Clear, and Common Clock	14	131.25	0.66	TI
74S124	Dual Voltage-Controlled Oscillators with Enable Inputs	16	787.50	2.90	TI
74S132	Quad 2-Input Schmitt-Trigger NAND Gates	14	357.00	0.57	F,TI
74S133	13-Input NAND Gate	16	52.50	0.29	F,N,TI
74S134	12-Input NAND Gate with 3-State Output	16	131.25	0.58	TI
74S135	Quad Exclusive-OR/NOR Gates	16	519.75	1.00	TI
74S138	3 to 8 Line Decoder/Demultiplexer	16	472.50	0.60	F,N,TI
74S139	Dual 2 to 4 Line Decoders/Demultiplexers	16	472.50	0.60	F,N,TI
74S140	Dual 4-Input NAND 50-Ohm Line Drivers	14	231.00	0.50	N,TI
74S151	1 of 8 Line Data Selector/Multiplexer	16	367.50	0.60	F,N,TI
74S153	Dual 4 to 1 Line Data Selectors/Multiplexers	16	367.50	0.60	F,N,TI
74S157	Quad 2 to 1 Line Data Selectors/Multiplexers	16	409.50	0.60	F,N,TI
74S158	Quad 2 to 1 Line Inverting Data Selectors/Multiplexers	16	425.25	0.60	F,N,TI
74S161	Synchronous 4-Bit Binary Counter with Asynchronous Clear	16	840.00	2.33	N
74S162	Synchronous 4-Bit Decade Counter with Synchronous Clear	16	840.00	3.00	TI

PART NUMBER	DESCRIPTION	PINS	POWER (mW)	PRICE ($)	SUPPLIERS
74S163	Synchronous 4-Bit Binary Counter with Synchronous Clear	16	840.00	2.33	N,TI
74S168	Synchronous 4-Bit Up/Down Decade Counter	16	840.00	9.00	TI
74S169	Synchronous 4-Bit Up/Down Binary Counter	16	840.00	4.50	TI
74S174	Hex D-Type Flip-Flops with Clear	16	756.00	0.60	F,N,TI
74S175	Quad D-Type Flip-Flops with Clear	16	504.00	0.60	F,N,TI
74S181	Arithmetic Logic Unit/Function Generator	24	1155.00	3.41	N,TI
74S182	Look-Ahead Carry Generator	16	572.25	1.40	N,TI
74S188	256-Bit Programmable Read-Only Memory with Open Collector Outputs	16	577.50	1.45	N
74S189	64-Bit Random-Access Memory with 3-State Outputs	16	577.50	2.15	N,TI
74S194	4-Bit Bidirectional Universal Shift Register	16	708.75	0.79	F,N,TI
74S195	4-Bit Parallel-Access Shift Register	16	572.25	1.47	N,TI
74S196	Presettable Decade (Bi-Quinary) Counter	14	630.00	2.00	TI
74S197	Presettable Binary Counter	14	630.00	2.72	TI
74S201	256-Bit Random-Access Memory with 3-State Outputs	16	735.00	4.32	TI
74S226	4-Bit Parallel Latched Bus Transceivers	16	971.25	6.00	TI
74S240	Octal 3-State Inverting Buffers/Line Drivers/Line Receivers	20	787.50	1.78	N,TI
74S241	Octal 3-State Buffers/Line Drivers/Line Receivers	20	945.00	1.78	N,TI
74S244	Octal 3-State Buffers/Line Drivers/Line Receivers	20	945.00	2.02	N,TI
74S251	3-State 1 of 8 Line Data Selector/Multiplexer	16	446.25	1.01	N,TI
74S253	Dual 3-State 1 of 4 Line Data Selectors/Multiplexers	16	446.25	0.60	F,N,TI

PART NUMBER	DESCRIPTION	PINS	POWER (mW)	PRICE ($)	SUPPLIERS
74S257	Quad 3-State 2 to 1 Line Data Selectors/Multiplexers	16	519.75	0.60	F,N,TI
74S258	Quad 3-State 2 to 1 Line Inverting Data Selectors/Multiplexers	16	456.75	0.60	F,N,TI
74S260	Dual 5-Input NOR Gates	14	236.25	0.70	TI
74S280	9-Bit Parity Generator/Checker	14	551.25	1.47	N,TI
74S283	4-Bit Binary Full Adder with Fast Carry	16	840.00	2.56	N,TI
74S287	1024-Bit Programmable Read-Only Memory with 3-State Outputs	16	682.50	1.50	N
74S288	256-Bit Programmable Read-Only Memory with 3-State Outputs	16	577.50	1.45	N
74S289	64-Bit Random Access Memory with Open Collector Outputs	16	551.25	2.15	N,TI
74S299	8-Bit Universal Shift/Storage Register with 3-State Outputs	20	1181.25	5.43	N,TI
74S301	256-BIT RAM 256x1 OC	16	735.00	4.32	TI
74S373	Octal 3-State Transparent D-Type Latches	20	997.50	2.25	N,TI
74S374	Octal 3-State Positive-Edge-Triggered D-Type Flip-Flops	20	840.00	2.25	N,TI
74S381	Arithmetic Logic Unit/Function Generator	20	840.00	4.88	MM,N,TI
74S387	1024-Bit Programmable Read-Only Memory with Open Collector Outputs	16	682.50	1.50	N
74S408	Dynamic RAM Controller/Driver	40	1496.25	26.07	MM
74S409	Multi-Mode Dynamic RAM Controller/Driver	40	1706.25	29.80	MM
74S412	Multimode Octal Latch	24	682.50	7.00	TI
74S436	Line Driver/Memory Driver Circuit	16	315.00	3.20	TI
74S472	4096-Bit Programmable Read-Only Memory with 3-State Outputs	20	813.75	4.35	N
74S473	4096-Bit Programmable Read-Only Memory with Open Collector Outputs	20	813.75	4.35	N

PART NUMBER	DESCRIPTION	PINS	POWER (mW)	PRICE ($)	SUPPLIERS
74S474	4096-Bit Programmable Read-Only Memory with 3-State Outputs	24	892.50	4.80	N
74S475	4096-Bit Programmable Read-Only Memory with Open Collector Outputs	24	892.50	4.80	N
74S484	BCD to Binary Converter	20	525.00	3.53	TI
74S516	16x16 Multiplier/Divider	24	2362.50	45.09	MM
74S557	8x8 Multiplier	40	1470.00	30.86	MM
74S558	8x8 Multiplier	40	1470.00	30.86	MM
74S570	2048-Bit Programmable Read-Only Memory with Open Collector Outputs	16	682.50	2.55	N
74S571	2048-Bit Programmable Read-Only Memory with 3-State Outputs	16	682.50	2.55	N
74S572	4096-Bit Programmable Read-Only Memory with Open Collector Outputs	18	735.00	4.55	N
74S573	Octal 3-State Transparent D-Type Latches	20	735.00	4.55	N
74S700	8-Bit Dynamic RAM Driver with 3-State Inverting Outputs	20	656.25	3.26	MM
74S730	8-Bit Dynamic RAM Driver with 3-State Inverting Outputs	20	656.25	3.26	MM
74S731	8-Bit Dynamic RAM DRiver with 3-State Outputs	20	787.50	3.26	MM
74S734	8-Bit Dynamic RAM Driver with 3-State Outputs	20	787.50	3.26	MM
74S940	Octal 3-State Inverting Buffers/Line Receivers/Line Drivers	20	787.50	2.17	N
74S941	Octal 3-State Buffers/Line Receivers/Line Drivers	20	945.00	2.17	N

Appendix B

4000 Index

TYPE	TEMP GRADE	DESCRIPTION	PINS	POWER (mW)	PRICE ($)	SUPPLIERS
4000A	C	Dual 3-Input NOR Gates plus Inverter	14	0.07	0.45	N
4000A	M	Dual 3-Input NOR Gates plus Inverter	14	0.02	2.50	RCA
4000B	C	Dual 3-Input NOR Gates plus Inverter	14	0.04	0.28	RCA
4000B	M	Dual 3-Input NOR Gates plus Inverter	14	0.04	0.50	RCA
4000UB	C	Dual 3-Input NOR Gates plus Inverter	14	0.04	0.28	M,RCA
4000UB	M	Dual 3-Input NOR Gates plus Inverter	14	0.04	0.50	M,RCA
4001A	C	Quad 2-Input NOR Gates	14	0.07	0.33	N,RCA
4001A	M	Quad 2-Input NOR Gates	14	0.02	0.78	RCA
4001B	C	Quad 2-Input NOR Gates	14	0.04	0.28	F,M,N,RCA
4001B	M	Quad 2-Input NOR Gates	14	0.04	0.50	F,M,N,RCA
4001UB	C	Quad 2-Input NOR Gates	14	0.04	0.28	M,RCA
4001UB	M	Quad 2-Input NOR Gates	14	0.04	0.50	M,RCA
4002A	C	Dual 4-Input NOR Gates	14	0.07	0.40	N,RCA
4002A	M	Dual 4-Input NOR Gates	14	0.02	0.78	RCA
4002B	C	Dual 4-Input NOR Gates	14	0.04	0.28	F,M,N,RCA
4002B	M	Dual 4-Input NOR Gates	14	0.04	0.50	F,M,N,RCA
4002UB	C	Dual 4-Input NOR Gates	14	0.04	0.28	M,RCA
4002UB	M	Dual 4-Input NOR Gates	14	0.04	0.50	M,RCA
4006A	C	18-Bit Static Shift Register	14	0.75	1.25	N
4006A	M	18-Bit Static Shift Register	14	0.15	5.56	RCA
4006B	C	18-Bit Static Shift Register	14	0.75	0.74	F,M,N,RCA
4006B	M	18-Bit Static Shift Register	14	0.75	1.49	F,M,N,RCA
4007A	C	Dual Complementary Pair plus Inverter	14	0.07	0.33	N,RCA
4007A	M	Dual Complementary Pair plus Inverter	14	0.02	0.78	N,RCA
4007UB	C	Dual Complementary Pair plus Inverter	14	0.04	0.28	F,M,RCA

TYPE	TEMP GRADE	DESCRIPTION	PINS	POWER (mW)	PRICE ($)	SUPPLIERS
4007UB	M	Dual Complementary Pair plus Inverter	14	0.04	0.50	F,M,RCA
4008A	M	4-Bit Full Adder	16	1.50	5.65	RCA
4008B	C	4-Bit Full Adder	16	0.75	0.70	F,M,N,RCA
4008B	M	4-Bit Full Adder	16	0.75	1.24	M,RCA
4009A	C	Hex Inverting Buffers/Converters	16	0.21	0.54	N
4009A	M	Hex Inverting Buffers/Converters	16	0.10	2.08	N
4009UB	C	Hex Inverting Buffers/Converters	16	0.15	0.84	RCA
4009UB	M	Hex Inverting Buffers/Converters	16	0.15	1.19	RCA
4010A	C	Hex Buffers/Converters	16	0.21	0.54	N
4010B	C	Hex Buffers/Converters	16	0.15	0.84	RCA
4010B	M	Hex Buffers/Converters	16	0.15	1.19	RCA
4011A	C	Quad 2-Input NAND Gates	14	0.07	0.33	N,RCA
4011A	M	Quad 2-Input NAND Gates	14	0.02	0.78	RCA
4011B	C	Quad 2-Input NAND Gates	14	0.04	0.28	F,M,N,RCA
4011B	M	Quad 2-Input NAND Gates	14	0.04	0.50	F,M,N,RCA
4011UB	C	Quad 2-Input NAND Gates	14	0.04	0.28	M,RCA
4011UB	M	Quad 2-Input NAND Gates	14	0.04	0.50	M,RCA
4012A	C	Dual 4-Input NAND Gates	14	0.07	0.45	N
4012A	M	Dual 4-Input NAND Gates	14	0.02	2.50	RCA
4012B	C	Dual 4-Input NAND Gates	14	0.04	0.28	F,M,N,RCA
4012B	M	Dual 4-Input NAND Gates	14	0.04	0.50	F,M,N,RCA
4012UB	C	Dual 4-Input NAND Gates	14	0.04	0.28	M,RCA
4012UB	M	Dual 4-Input NAND Gates	14	0.04	0.50	M,RCA
4013A	C	Dual D-Type Flip-Flops	14	0.70	0.71	RCA
4013A	M	Dual D-Type Flip-Flops	14	0.30	1.16	RCA
4013B	C	Dual D-Type Flip-Flops	14	0.15	0.41	F,M,N,RCA

TYPE	TEMP GRADE	DESCRIPTION	PINS	POWER (mW)	PRICE ($)	SUPPLIERS
4013B	M	Dual D—Type Flip—Flops	14	0.15	0.89	F,M,N,RCA
4014A	M	8—Bit Static Shift Register	16	1.50	5.65	RCA
4014B	C	8—Bit Static Shift Register	16	0.75	0.74	F,M,N,RCA
4014B	M	8—Bit Static Shift Register	16	0.75	1.34	F,M,N,RCA
4015A	C	Dual 4—Bit Static Shift Register	16	3.50	1.45	N,RCA
4015A	M	Dual 4—Bit Static Shift Register	16	1.50	2.44	RCA
4015B	C	Dual 4—Bit Static Shift Register	16	0.75	0.74	F,M,N,RCA
4015B	M	Dual 4—Bit Static Shift Register	16	0.75	1.42	F,M,RCA
4016A	C	Quad Analog Switch	14	0.03	0.59	N,RCA
4016A	M	Quad Analog Switch	14	0.05	1.16	RCA
4016B	C	Quad Analog Switch	14	0.04	0.41	F,M,N,RCA
4016B	M	Quad Analog Switch	14	0.04	0.89	F,M,N,RCA
4017A	C	Divide—by—10 Counter/Divider with 10 Decoded Outputs	16	3.50	1.25	RCA
4017A	M	Divide—by—10 Counter/Divider with 10 Decoded Outputs	16	1.50	2.44	RCA
4017B	C	Divide—by—10 Counter/Divider with 10 Decoded Outputs	16	0.75	0.74	F,M,N,RCA
4017B	M	Divide—by—10 Counter/Divider with 10 Decoded Outputs	16	0.75	1.40	F,M,N,RCA
4018A	C	Presettable Divide—by—N Counter	16	3.50	1.12	RCA
4018A	M	Presettable Divide—by—N Counter	16	1.50	2.03	RCA
4018B	C	Presettable Divide—by—N Counter	16	0.75	0.73	M,N,RCA
4018B	M	Presettable Divide—by—N Counter	16	0.75	1.42	M,N,RCA
4019A	C	Quad AND/OR Select Gate	16	3.50	0.71	RCA
4019A	M	Quad AND/OR Select Gate	16	1.50	1.96	RCA
4019B	C	Quad AND/OR Select Gate	16	0.15	0.50	F,N,RCA

TYPE	TEMP GRADE	DESCRIPTION	PINS	POWER (mW)	PRICE ($)	SUPPLIERS
4019B	M	Quad AND/OR Select Gate	16	0.15	0.87	F,N,RCA
4020A	C	14-Bit Ripple-Carry Binary Counter/Divider	16	3.50	1.45	RCA
4020A	M	14-Bit Ripple-Carry Binary Counter/Divider	16	4.50	2.56	RCA
4020B	C	14-Bit Ripple-Carry Binary Counter/Divider	16	0.75	0.74	F,M,N,RCA
4020B	M	14-Bit Ripple-Carry Binary Counter/Divider	16	0.75	1.40	F,M,N,RCA
4021A	C	8-Bit Static Shift Register	16	3.50	1.16	N,RCA
4021A	M	8-Bit Static Shift Register	16	1.50	2.41	RCA
4021B	C	8-Bit Static Shift Register	16	0.75	0.74	F,M,N,RCA
4021B	M	8-Bit Static Shift Register	16	0.75	1.35	F,M,RCA
4022A	M	Divide-by-8 Counter/Divider with 8 Decoded Outputs	16	1.50	4.52	RCA
4022B	C	Divide-by-8 Counter/Divider with 8 Decoded Outputs	16	0.75	0.74	F,M,N,RCA
4022B	M	Divide-by-8 Counter/Divider with 8 Decoded Outputs	16	0.75	1.40	F,M,RCA
4023A	C	Triple 3-Input NAND Gates	14	0.07	0.40	N,RCA
4023A	M	Triple 3-Input NAND Gates	14	0.02	0.78	RCA
4023B	C	Triple 3-Input NAND Gates	14	0.04	0.28	F,M,N,RCA
4023B	M	Triple 3-Input NAND Gates	14	0.04	0.50	F,M,N,RCA
4023UB	C	Triple 3-Input NAND Gates	14	0.04	0.28	M,RCA
4023UB	M	Triple 3-Input NAND Gates	14	0.04	0.50	M,RCA
4024A	C	7-Bit Ripple-Carry Binary Counter/Divider	14	3.50	1.06	RCA
4024A	M	7-Bit Ripple-Carry Binary Counter/Divider	14	1.50	1.85	RCA
4024B	C	7-Bit Ripple-Carry Binary Counter/Divider	14	0.75	0.66	F,M,N,RCA
4024B	M	7-Bit Ripple-Carry Binary Counter/Divider	14	0.75	1.12	F,M,RCA
4025A	C	Triple 3-Input NOR Gates	14	0.07	0.40	N,RCA
4025A	M	Triple 3-Input NOR Gates	14	0.02	0.78	RCA

TYPE	TEMP GRADE	DESCRIPTION	PINS	POWER (mW)	PRICE ($)	SUPPLIERS
4025B	C	Triple 3-Input NOR Gates	14	0.04	0.28	F,M,N,RCA
4025B	M	Triple 3-Input NOR Gates	14	0.04	0.50	F,M,N,RCA
4025UB	C	Triple 3-Input NOR Gates	14	0.04	0.28	M,RCA
4025UB	M	Triple 3-Input NOR Gates	14	0.04	0.50	M,RCA
4026A	M	Decade Counter/Divider with 7-Segment Outputs and Display Enable	16	1.50	7.54	RCA
4026B	C	Decade Counter/Divider with 7-Segment Outputs and Display Enable	16	0.75	2.06	RCA
4026B	M	Decade Counter/Divider with 7-Segment Outputs and Display Enable	16	0.75	2.89	RCA
4027A	C	Dual J-K Master-Slave Flip-Flops	16	0.70	0.78	RCA
4027A	M	Dual J-K Master-Slave Flip-Flops	16	0.30	1.34	RCA
4027B	C	Dual J-K Master-Slave Flip-Flops	16	0.15	0.45	F,M,N,RCA
4027B	M	Dual J-K Master-Slave Flip-Flops	16	0.15	0.89	F,M,N,RCA
4028A	C	BCD to Decimal Decoder	16	3.50	1.01	RCA
4028A	M	BCD to Decimal Decoder	16	1.50	2.15	RCA
4028B	C	BCD to Decimal Decoder	16	0.75	0.71	F,M,N,RCA
4028B	M	BCD to Decimal Decoder	16	0.75	1.25	F,M,N,RCA
4029A	C	4-Bit Binary or BCD Decade Presettable Up/Down Counter	16	3.50	1.40	RCA
4029A	M	4-Bit Binary or BCD Decade Presettable Up/Down Counter	16	1.50	5.16	RCA
4029B	C	4-Bit Binary or BCD Decade Presettable Up/Down Counter	16	0.75	0.83	F,M,N,RCA
4029B	M	4-Bit Binary or BCD Decade Presettable Up/Down Counter	16	0.75	1.40	F,M,N,RCA
4030A	C	Quad Exclusive-OR Gates	14	0.35	0.41	N,RCA
4030A	M	Quad Exclusive-OR Gates	14	0.15	0.89	N,RCA
4030B	C	Quad Exclusive-OR Gates	14	0.15	0.56	F,RCA

TYPE	TEMP GRADE	DESCRIPTION	PINS	POWER (mW)	PRICE ($)	SUPPLIERS
4030B	M	Quad Exclusive-OR Gates	14	0.15	1.26	F,RCA
4031A	M	64-Bit Static Shift Register	16	3.00	12.86	RCA
4031B	C	64-Bit Static Shift Register	16	0.75	2.69	N,RCA
4031B	M	64-Bit Static Shift Register	16	0.75	3.76	N,RCA
4032B	C	Triple Serial Positive Logic Adder	16	0.75	1.75	M,RCA
4032B	M	Triple Serial Positive Logic Adder	16	0.75	2.72	M,RCA
4033A	M	Decade Counter/Divider with 7-Segment Outputs and Ripple Blanking	16	1.50	7.54	RCA
4033B	C	Decade Counter/Divider with 7-Segment Outputs and Ripple Blanking	16	0.75	2.06	RCA
4033B	M	Decade Counter/Divider with 7-Segment Outputs and Ripple Blanking	16	0.75	3.30	RCA
4034A	M	8-Bit Bidirectional Serial/Parallel In, Parallel Out Shift Register	24	1.50	12.86	RCA
4034B	C	8-Bit Bidirectional Serial/Parallel In, Parallel Out Shift Register	24	0.75	2.31	M,N,RCA
4034B	M	8-Bit Bidirectional Serial/Parallel In, Parallel Out Shift Register	24	0.75	4.32	M,N,RCA
4035A	C	4-Bit Parallel In/Parallel Out Shift Register	16	3.50	1.85	RCA
4035A	M	4-Bit Parallel In/Parallel Out Shift Register	16	1.50	2.87	RCA
4035B	C	4-Bit Parallel In/Parallel Out Shift Register	16	0.75	0.83	F,M,N,RCA
4035B	M	4-Bit Parallel In/Parallel Out Shift Register	16	0.75	1.35	F,M,RCA
4037A	M	Triple AND/OR Bi-Phase Pairs	14	1.50	4.16	RCA
4038B	C	Triple Serial Negative Logic Adder	16	0.75	1.75	M,RCA
4038B	M	Triple Serial Negative Logic Adder	16	0.75	2.64	M,RCA
4040A	C	12-Bit Ripple-Carry Binary Counter/Divider	16	3.50	1.45	RCA
4040A	M	12-Bit Ripple-Carry Binary Counter/Divider	16	4.50	2.41	RCA

TYPE	TEMP GRADE	DESCRIPTION	PINS	POWER (mW)	PRICE ($)	SUPPLIERS
4040B	C	12-Bit Ripple-Carry Binary Counter/Divider	16	0.75	0.83	F,M,N,RCA
4040B	M	12-Bit Ripple-Carry Binary Counter/Divider	16	0.75	1.35	F,M,N,RCA
4041A	C	Quad True/Complement Buffer	14	0.15	1.16	N
4041A	M	Quad True/Complement Buffer	14	0.30	3.31	N,RCA
4041UB	C	Quad True/Complement Buffer	14	0.15	1.19	RCA
4041UB	M	Quad True/Complement Buffer	14	0.15	1.73	RCA
4042A	C	Quad Clocked D-Type Latch	16	0.70	1.06	RCA
4042A	M	Quad Clocked D-Type Latch	16	0.30	1.96	RCA
4042B	C	Quad Clocked D-Type Latch	16	0.15	0.66	F,M,N,RCA
4042B	M	Quad Clocked D-Type Latch	16	0.15	1.19	F,M,N,RCA
4043A	M	Quad NOR R/S Latch with 3-State Outputs	16	0.30	3.31	RCA
4043B	C	Quad NOR R/S Latch with 3-State Outputs	16	0.15	0.79	M,N,RCA
4043B	M	Quad NOR R/S Latch with 3-State Outputs	16	0.15	1.24	M,N,RCA
4044A	C	Quad NAND R/S Latch with 3-State Outputs	16	0.70	0.99	N,RCA
4044A	M	Quad NAND R/S Latch with 3-State Outputs	16	0.30	2.26	RCA
4044B	C	Quad NAND R/S Latch with 3-State Outputs	16	0.15	0.63	F,M,N,RCA
4044B	M	Quad NAND R/S Latch with 3-State Outputs	16	0.15	1.24	F,M,RCA
4045A	M	21-Bit Counter	16	4.50	11.50	RCA
4045B	C	21-Bit Counter	16	0.75	1.63	RCA
4045B	M	21-Bit Counter	16	0.75	2.48	RCA
4046A	C	Phase-Locked Loop	16	0.07	1.57	RCA
4046A	M	Phase-Locked Loop	16	0.07	3.56	RCA
4046B	C	Phase-Locked Loop	16	0.10	0.99	M,N,RCA
4046B	M	Phase-Locked Loop	16	0.10	1.68	M,RCA
4047A	C	Monostable/Astable Multivibrator	14	3.50	1.78	RCA

TYPE	TEMP GRADE	DESCRIPTION	PINS	POWER (mW)	PRICE ($)	SUPPLIERS
4047A	M	Monostable/Astable Multivibrator	14	1.50	3.73	RCA
4047B	C	Monostable/Astable Multivibrator	14	0.15	0.84	F,N,RCA
4047B	M	Monostable/Astable Multivibrator	14	0.15	2.31	F,N,RCA
4048A	C	Multifunction Expandable 8-Input Gate with 3-State Output	16	0.70	1.16	RCA
4048A	M	Multifunction Expandable 8-Input Gate with 3-State Output	16	0.30	1.85	RCA
4048B	C	Multifunction Expandable 8-Input Gate with 3-State Output	16	0.04	0.54	N,RCA
4048B	M	Multifunction Expandable 8-Input Gate with 3-State Output	16	0.04	1.40	N,RCA
4049A	C	Hex Inverting Buffers/Converters	16	0.21	0.41	N,RCA
4049A	M	Hex Inverting Buffers/Converters	16	0.10	1.19	RCA
4049UB	C	Hex Inverting Buffers/Converters	16	0.15	0.41	M,RCA
4049UB	M	Hex Inverting Buffers/Converters	16	0.15	0.89	M,RCA
4050A	C	Hex Buffers/Converters	16	0.21	0.71	N,RCA
4050A	M	Hex Buffers/Converters	16	0.10	1.19	RCA
4050B	C	Hex Buffers/Converters	16	0.15	0.41	F,M,N,RCA
4050B	M	Hex Buffers/Converters	16	0.15	0.89	F,M,N,RCA
4051B	C	8-Channel Analog Multiplexer	16	0.75	0.74	F,M,N,RCA
4051B	M	8-Channel Analog Multiplexer	16	0.75	1.52	F,M,RCA
4052B	C	Dual 4-Channel Analog Multiplexer	16	0.75	0.74	F,M,N,RCA
4052B	M	Dual 4-Channel Analog Multiplexer	16	0.75	1.52	F,M,RCA
4053B	C	Triple 2-Channel Analog Multiplexer	16	0.75	0.74	M,N,RCA
4053B	M	Triple 2-Channel Analog Multiplexer	16	0.75	1.52	M,N,RCA
4054B	C	4-Segment Decoder/Driver	16	0.75	1.75	RCA
4054B	M	4-Segment Decoder/Driver	16	0.75	2.48	RCA
4055B	C	BCD to 7-Segment Decoder/Driver	16	0.75	1.45	RCA

TYPE	TEMP GRADE	DESCRIPTION	PINS	POWER (mW)	PRICE ($)	SUPPLIERS
4055B	M	BCD to 7-Segment Decoder/Driver	16	0.75	2.18	RCA
4056B	C	BCD to 7-Segment Decoder/Driver with Strobed Latch Function	16	0.75	1.75	RCA
4056B	M	BCD to 7-Segment Decoder/Driver with Strobed Latch Function	16	0.75	2.48	RCA
4057A	M	4-Bit Arithmetic Logic Unit	28	0.75	48.90	RCA
4059A	C	Programmable Divide-by-N Counter	24	3.50	3.38	RCA
4059A	M	Programmable Divide-by-N Counter	24	1.50	4.73	RCA
4060A	C	14-Bit Ripple-Carry Binary Counter/Divider and Oscillator	16	3.50	1.67	RCA
4060A	M	14-Bit Ripple-Carry Binary Counter/Divider and Oscillator	16	4.50	4.52	RCA
4060B	C	14-Bit Ripple-Carry Binary Counter/Divider and Oscillator	16	0.75	0.97	M,N,RCA
4060B	M	14-Bit Ripple-Carry Binary Counter/Divider and Oscillator	16	0.75	1.40	M,N,RCA
4063B	C	4-Bit Magnitude Comparator	16	0.75	1.37	RCA
4063B	M	4-Bit Magnitude Comparator	16	0.75	2.15	RCA
4066A	C	Quad Analog Switch	14	0.07	0.79	RCA
4066A	M	Quad Analog Switch	14	0.04	2.48	RCA
4066B	C	Quad Analog Switch	14	0.75	0.38	F,M,N,RCA
4066B	M	Quad Analog Switch	14	0.75	0.99	F,M,N,RCA
4067B	C	16-Channel Analog Multiplexer	24	0.75	1.57	F,M,RCA
4067B	M	16-Channel Analog Multiplexer	24	0.75	4.55	F,M,RCA
4068B	C	8-Input NAND/AND Gate	14	0.04	0.28	M,RCA
4068B	M	8-Input NAND/AND Gate	14	0.04	0.50	M,RCA
4069UB	C	Hex Inverter	14	0.04	0.28	F,M,RCA
4069UB	M	Hex Inverter	14	0.04	0.50	F,M,RCA

TYPE	TEMP GRADE	DESCRIPTION	PINS	POWER (mW)	PRICE ($)	SUPPLIERS
4070B	C	Quad Exclusive-OR Gates	14	0.15	0.28	F,M,N,RCA
4070B	M	Quad Exclusive-OR Gates	14	0.15	0.50	F,M,N,RCA
4071B	C	Quad 2-Input OR Gates	14	0.04	0.28	F,M,N,RCA
4071B	M	Quad 2-Input OR Gates	14	0.04	0.50	F,M,N,RCA
4072B	C	Dual 4-Input OR Gates	14	0.04	0.28	M,N,RCA
4072B	M	Dual 4-Input OR Gates	14	0.04	0.50	M,RCA
4073B	C	Triple 3-Input AND Gates	14	0.04	0.28	M,N,RCA
4073B	M	Triple 3-Input AND Gates	14	0.04	0.50	M,N,RCA
4075B	C	Triple 3-Input OR Gates	14	0.04	0.28	M,N,RCA
4075B	M	Triple 3-Input OR Gates	14	0.04	0.50	M,N,RCA
4076B	C	4-Bit D-Type Register	16	0.75	0.78	F,M,N,RCA
4076B	M	4-Bit D-Type Register	16	0.75	1.25	F,M,N,RCA
4077B	C	Quad Exclusive-NOR Gates	14	0.15	0.28	M,RCA
4077B	M	Quad Exclusive-NOR Gates	14	0.15	0.50	M,RCA
4078B	C	8-Input OR/NOR Gate	14	0.04	0.28	M,RCA
4078B	M	8-Input OR/NOR Gate	14	0.04	0.50	M,RCA
4081B	C	Quad 2-Input AND Gates	14	0.04	0.28	F,M,N,RCA
4081B	M	Quad 2-Input AND Gates	14	0.04	0.50	F,M,N,RCA
4082B	C	Dual 4-Input AND Gates	14	0.04	0.28	M,N,RCA
4082B	M	Dual 4-Input AND Gates	14	0.04	0.50	M,RCA
4085B	C	Dual 2-Wide 2-Input AND-OR-INVERT Gates	14	0.15	0.78	RCA
4085B	M	Dual 2-Wide 2-Input AND-OR-INVERT Gates	14	0.15	1.32	RCA
4086B	C	Expandable 4-Wide 2-Input AND-OR-INVERT Gate	14	0.15	0.78	F,RCA
4086B	M	Expandable 4-Wide 2-Input AND-OR-INVERT Gate	14	0.15	1.32	F,RCA
4089B	C	Binary Rate Multiplier	16	0.75	2.06	N,RCA

TYPE	TEMP GRADE	DESCRIPTION	PINS	POWER (mW)	PRICE ($)	SUPPLIERS
4089B	M	Binary Rate Multiplier	16	0.75	2.97	RCA
4093B	C	Quad 2-Input NAND Schmitt Triggers	14	0.15	0.45	F,M,N,RCA
4093B	M	Quad 2-Input NAND Schmitt Triggers	14	0.15	0.96	F,M,N,RCA
4094B	C	8-Bit Shift and Store Bus Register	16	0.75	0.97	M,N,RCA
4094B	M	8-Bit Shift and Store Bus Register	16	0.75	1.57	M,RCA
4095B	C	Gated J-K Master-Slave Flip-Flop	14	0.15	0.78	RCA
4095B	M	Gated J-K Master-Slave Flip-Flop	14	0.15	1.28	RCA
4096B	C	Gated J-K Master-Slave Flip-Flop (Inverting and Non-Inverting Inputs)	14	0.15	0.69	RCA
4096B	M	Gated J-K Master-Slave Flip-Flop (Inverting and Non-Inverting Inputs)	14	0.15	1.24	RCA
4097B	C	Dual 8-Channel Analog Multiplexer	24	0.75	1.57	M,RCA
4097B	M	Dual 8-Channel Analog Multiplexer	24	0.75	2.82	M,RCA
4098B	C	Dual Monostable Multivibrators	16	0.15	0.86	RCA
4098B	M	Dual Monostable Multivibrators	16	0.15	2.06	RCA
4099B	C	8-Bit Addressable Latch	16	0.75	1.16	M,N,RCA
4099B	M	8-Bit Addressable Latch	16	0.75	2.15	M,N,RCA
4502B	C	Strobed Hex Inverter/Buffer with 3-State Outputs	16	0.15	0.89	M,RCA
4502B	M	Strobed Hex Inverter/Buffer with 3-State Outputs	16	0.15	1.40	M,RCA
4503B	C	Hex Buffer with 3-State Outputs	16	0.15	0.63	M,N,RCA
4503B	M	Hex Buffer with 3-State Outputs	16	0.15	1.04	M,N,RCA
4504B	C	Hex Level Shifter for TTL to CMOS or CMOS to CMOS	16	0.02	1.34	M,RCA
4504B	M	Hex Level Shifter for TTL to CMOS or CMOS to CMOS	16	0.02	2.00	M,RCA
4508B	C	Dual 4-Bit Latch	24	0.75	3.75	M,RCA

TYPE	TEMP GRADE	DESCRIPTION	PINS	POWER (mW)	PRICE ($)	SUPPLIERS
4508B	M	Dual 4-Bit Latch	24	0.75	5.36	M,RCA
4510B	C	Presettable BCD Up/Down Counter	16	0.75	0.78	F,M,N,RCA
4510B	M	Presettable BCD Up/Down Counter	16	0.75	1.40	F,M,RCA
4511B	C	BCD to 7-Segment Latch/Decoder/Driver	16	0.75	0.79	F,M,N,RCA
4511B	M	BCD to 7-Segment Latch/Decoder/Driver	16	0.75	1.78	F,M,RCA
4512B	C	8-Channel Data Selector	16	0.75	0.69	F,M,N,RCA
4512B	M	8-Channel Data Selector	16	0.75	1.35	F,M,N,RCA
4514B	C	4-Bit Latch/4-to-16 Line Decoder (Output High on Select)	24	0.75	1.90	M,N,RCA
4514B	M	4-Bit Latch/4-to-16 Line Decoder (Output High on Select)	24	0.75	3.60	M,RCA
4515B	C	4-Bit Latch/4-to-16 Line Decoder (Output Low on Select)	24	0.75	1.90	M,N,RCA
4515B	M	4-Bit Latch/4-to-16 Line Decoder (Output Low on Select)	24	0.75	3.60	M,RCA
4516B	C	Presettable Binary Up/Down Counter	16	0.75	0.78	F,M,N,RCA
4516B	M	Presettable Binary Up/Down Counter	16	0.75	1.35	F,M,RCA
4517B	C	Dual 64-Bit Static Shift Registers	16	0.75	2.06	M,RCA
4517B	M	Dual 64-Bit Static Shift Registers	16	0.75	2.89	M,RCA
4518B	C	Dual BCD Up Counters	16	0.75	0.71	F,M,N,RCA
4518B	M	Dual BCD Up Counters	16	0.75	1.40	F,M,RCA
4519B	C	4-Bit AND/OR Selector	16	0.15	0.42	M,N,RCA
4519B	M	4-Bit AND/OR Selector	16	0.15	0.86	M,RCA
4520B	C	Dual Binary Up Counters	16	0.75	0.71	F,M,N,RCA
4520B	M	Dual Binary Up Counters	16	0.75	1.40	F,M,N,RCA
4521B	C	24-Stage Frequency Divider	16	0.75	1.35	M,RCA
4521B	M	24-Stage Frequency Divider	16	0.75	3.97	M,RCA
4522B	C	Programmable Divide-by-N 4-Bit BCD Counter	16	0.75	0.86	M,N,RCA

TYPE	TEMP GRADE	DESCRIPTION	PINS	POWER (mW)	PRICE ($)	SUPPLIERS
4522B	M	Programmable Divide-by-N 4-Bit BCD Counter	16	0.75	1.75	M,RCA
4526B	C	Programmable Divide-by-N 4-Bit Binary Counter	16	0.75	0.87	M,N
4526B	M	Programmable Divide-by-N 4-Bit Binary Counter	16	0.75	1.75	M
4527B	C	BCD Rate Multiplier	16	0.75	0.78	M,N,RCA
4527B	M	BCD Rate Multiplier	16	0.75	1.73	M,RCA
4528B	C	Dual Monostable Multivibrator	16	0.75	0.71	F,M,N
4528B	M	Dual Monostable Multivibrator	16	0.75	1.50	F,M,N
4529B	C	Dual 4-Channel or Single 8-Channel Analog Data Selector	16	0.35	1.62	M,N,RCA
4529B	M	Dual 4-Channel or Single 8-Channel Analog Data Selector	16	0.30	2.26	M,N,RCA
4532B	C	8-Bit Priority Encoder	16	0.75	0.83	M,RCA
4532B	M	8-Bit Priority Encoder	16	0.75	2.01	M,RCA
4536B	C	Programmable Timer	16	0.75	4.01	M,RCA
4536B	M	Programmable Timer	16	0.75	5.78	M,RCA
4538B	C	Dual Precision Monostable Multivibrators	16	0.75	1.07	M,N,RCA
4538B	M	Dual Precision Monostable Multivibrators	16	0.75	2.24	M,RCA
4539B	C	Dual 4-Channel Data Selector/Multiplexer	16	0.75	0.72	F,M
4539B	M	Dual 4-Channel Data Selector/Multiplexer	16	0.75	1.37	F,M
4541B	C	Programmable Timer	14	0.75	0.83	M,N,RCA
4541B	M	Programmable Timer	14	0.75	1.68	M,RCA
4543B	C	BCD to 7-Segment Latch/Decoder/Driver	16	0.75	0.99	M,N,RCA
4543B	M	BCD to 7-Segment Latch/Decoder/Driver	16	0.75	1.68	M,N,RCA
4555B	C	Dual Binary 1-of-4 Decoders (Outputs High on Select)	16	0.75	0.59	F,M,RCA

TYPE	TEMP GRADE	DESCRIPTION	PINS	POWER (mW)	PRICE ($)	SUPPLIERS
4555B	M	Dual Binary 1-of-4 Decoders (Outputs High on Select)	16	0.75	1.26	F,M,RCA
4556B	C	Dual Binary 1-of-4 Decoders (Outputs Low on Select)	16	0.75	0.59	F,M,RCA
4556B	M	Dual Binary 1-of-4 Decoders (Outputs Low on Select)	16	0.75	1.26	F,M,RCA
4560B	C	NBCD Adder	16	0.75	3.14	M,RCA
4560B	M	NBCD Adder	16	0.75	4.08	M,RCA
4566B	C	Industrial Time Base Generator	16	0.75	1.96	M,RCA
4566B	M	Industrial Time Base Generator	16	0.75	2.94	M,RCA
4572UB	C	Hex Gate (4 Inverters, 2-Input NAND Gate, 2-Input NOR Gate)	16	0.02	0.64	M,RCA
4572UB	M	Hex Gate (4 Inverters, 2-Input NAND Gate, 2-Input NOR Gate)	16	0.01	0.83	M,RCA
4585B	C	4-Bit Magnitude Comparator	16	0.75	0.99	M,RCA
4585B	M	4-Bit Magnitude Comparator	16	0.75	1.68	M,RCA
4723B	C	Dual 4-Bit Addressable Latch	16	0.75	1.24	F,N
4723B	M	Dual 4-Bit Addressable Latch	16	0.75	2.80	F,N
4724B	C	8-Bit Addressable Latch	16	0.75	1.32	F,N,RCA
4724B	M	8-Bit Addressable Latch	16	0.75	1.85	F,N,RCA
40100B	C	32-Bit Static Left/Right Shift Register	16	0.75	2.21	RCA
40100B	M	32-Bit Static Left/Right Shift Register	16	0.75	3.10	RCA
40101B	C	9-Bit Parity Generator/Checker	14	0.75	1.11	RCA
40101B	M	9-Bit Parity Generator/Checker	14	0.75	1.55	RCA
40102B	C	Presettable 2-Decade BCD Synchronous Down Counter	16	0.75	1.68	RCA
40102B	M	Presettable 2-Decade BCD Synchronous Down Counter	16	0.75	2.36	RCA
40103B	C	Presettable 8-Bit Binary Synchronous Down Counter	16	0.75	1.68	RCA

TYPE	TEMP GRADE	DESCRIPTION	PINS	POWER (mW)	PRICE ($)	SUPPLIERS
40103B	M	Presettable 8-Bit Binary Synchronous Down Counter	16	0.75	2.36	RCA
40104B	C	4-Bit Bidirectional Universsal Shift Register	16	0.75	1.40	RCA
40104B	M	4-Bit Bidirectional Universsal Shift Register	16	0.75	1.96	RCA
40105B	C	4 Bits x 16 Words FIFO Register with 3-State Outputs	16	0.75	1.40	RCA
40105B	M	4 Bits x 16 Words FIFO Register with 3-State Outputs	16	0.75	2.03	RCA
40106B	C	Hex Schmitt Triggers	14	0.15	0.58	N,RCA
40106B	M	Hex Schmitt Triggers	14	0.15	1.32	N,RCA
40107B	C	Dual 2-Input NAND Buffer/Driver	14	0.15	0.84	RCA
40107B	M	Dual 2-Input NAND Buffer/Driver	14	0.15	1.19	RCA
40108B	C	4 x 4 Multiport Register with 3-State Outputs	24	0.75	4.78	RCA
40108B	M	4 x 4 Multiport Register with 3-State Outputs	24	0.75	6.70	RCA
40109B	C	Quad Low to High Voltage Level Shifter with 3-State Outputs	16	0.15	1.34	RCA
40109B	M	Quad Low to High Voltage Level Shifter with 3-State Outputs	16	0.15	1.86	RCA
40110B	C	Decade Up/Down Counter/Latch/Decoder Driver	16	0.75	2.11	RCA
40110B	M	Decade Up/Down Counter/Latch/Decoder Driver	16	0.75	2.97	RCA
40117B	C	Programmable Dual 4-Bit Terminator	14	0.04	0.66	RCA
40117B	M	Programmable Dual 4-Bit Terminator	14	0.04	3.48	RCA
40147B	C	10 to 4 Line BCD Priority Encoder	16	0.15	1.50	RCA
40147B	M	10 to 4 Line BCD Priority Encoder	16	0.15	2.10	RCA

TYPE	TEMP GRADE	DESCRIPTION	PINS	POWER (mW)	PRICE ($)	SUPPLIERS
40160B	C	Synchronous Decade Counter with Asynchronous Clear	14	0.75	0.83	M,N,RCA
40160B	M	Synchronous Decade Counter with Asynchronous Clear	14	0.75	1.40	M,N,RCA
40161B	C	Synchronous Binary Counter with Asynchronous Clear	14	0.75	0.83	F,M,N,RCA
40161B	M	Synchronous Binary Counter with Asynchronous Clear	14	0.75	1.40	F,M,N,RCA
40162B	C	Synchronous Decade Counter with Synchronous Clear	14	0.75	0.83	M,N,RCA
40162B	M	Synchronous Decade Counter with Synchronous Clear	14	0.75	1.40	M,N,RCA
40163B	C	Synchronous Binary Counter with Synchronous Clear	14	0.75	0.83	F,M,N,RCA
40163B	M	Synchronous Binary Counter with Synchronous Clear	14	0.75	1.40	F,M,N,RCA
40174B	C	Hex D-Type Flip-Flops	16	0.15	0.68	F,M,N,RCA
40174B	M	Hex D-Type Flip-Flops	16	0.15	1.24	F,M,N,RCA
40175B	C	Quad D-Type Flip-Flops	16	0.15	0.68	F,M,N,RCA
40175B	M	Quad D-Type Flip-Flops	16	0.15	1.24	F,M,N,RCA
40181B	C	4-Bit Arithmetic Logic Unit	24	0.75	3.18	RCA
40181B	M	4-Bit Arithmetic Logic Unit	24	0.75	4.46	RCA
40182B	C	Look-Ahead Carry Generator	16	0.75	1.14	RCA
40182B	M	Look-Ahead Carry Generator	16	0.75	1.60	RCA
40192B	C	Presettable 4-Bit BCD Up/Down Counter	16	0.75	1.20	N,RCA
40192B	M	Presettable 4-Bit BCD Up/Down Counter	16	0.75	1.68	N,RCA
40193B	C	Presettable 4-Bit Binary Up/Down Counter	16	0.75	0.88	F,N,RCA
40193B	M	Presettable 4-Bit Binary Up/Down Counter	16	0.75	1.82	F,N,RCA
40194B	C	4-Bit Bidirectional Universal Shift Register	16	0.75	0.83	M,RCA

TYPE	TEMP GRADE	DESCRIPTION	PINS	POWER (mW)	PRICE ($)	SUPPLIERS
40194B	M	4-Bit Bidirectional Universal Shift Register	16	0.75	1.40	M,RCA
40208B	C	4 x 4 Multiport Register with 3-State Outputs	24	0.75	5.38	RCA
40208B	M	4 x 4 Multiport Register with 3-State Outputs	24	0.75	7.52	RCA
40257B	C	Quad 2 to 1 Line Data Selector/Multiplexer	16	0.15	1.39	RCA
40257B	M	Quad 2 to 1 Line Data Selector/Multiplexer	16	0.15	1.98	RCA

Appendix C
Memories Index

TYPE	TEMP GRADE	DESCRIPTION	PINS	POWER (mW)	PRICE ($)	SUPPLIERS
18S030	C	32 x 8 TTL PROM 40 NS	16	577.50	1.65	TI
18S030	M	32 x 8 TTL PROM 50 NS	16	605.00	3.15	TI
18SA030	C	32 x 8 TTL PROM 40 NS	16	577.50	1.65	TI
2016	C	2K x 8 Static MOS RAM 45 NS	24	630.00	5.56	M
2016	C	2K x 8 Static MOS RAM 55 NS	24	630.00	4.88	M
2016	C	2K x 8 Static MOS RAM 70 NS	24	630.00	4.19	M
2101	C	256 x 4 Static MOS RAM 250 NS	22	367.50	3.93	AMD
2101	C	256 x 4 Static MOS RAM 300 NS	22	367.50	3.79	AMD
2101	C	256 x 4 Static MOS RAM 400 NS	22	367.50	3.65	AMD
2101	C	256 x 4 Static MOS RAM 500 NS	22	367.50	3.50	AMD
2101	C	256 x 4 Static MOS RAM 1000 NS	22	367.50	3.50	AMD
2111	C	256 x 4 Static MOS RAM 250 NS	18	367.50	4.65	AMD
2111	C	256 x 4 Static MOS RAM 300 NS	18	367.50	4.50	AMD
2111	C	256 x 4 Static MOS RAM 400 NS	18	367.50	4.36	AMD
2111	C	256 x 4 Static MOS RAM 500 NS	18	367.50	4.22	AMD
2111	C	256 x 4 Static MOS RAM 1000 NS	18	367.50	4.22	AMD
2112	C	256 x 4 Static MOS RAM 250 NS	16	367.50	5.01	AMD
2112	C	256 x 4 Static MOS RAM 300 NS	16	367.50	4.86	AMD
2112	C	256 x 4 Static MOS RAM 400 NS	16	367.50	4.72	AMD
2112	C	256 x 4 Static MOS RAM 1000 NS	16	367.50	4.58	AMD
2114	C	1K x 4 Static MOS RAM 150 NS	18	525.00	2.45	N
2114	C	1K x 4 Static MOS RAM 200 NS	18	367.50	2.80	I
2114	C	1K x 4 Static MOS RAM 200 NS	18	525.00	1.37	M,N
2114	M	1K x 4 Static MOS RAM 200 NS	18	385.00	9.85	I

TYPE	TEMP GRADE	DESCRIPTION	PINS	POWER (mW)	PRICE ($)	SUPPLIERS
2114	C	1K x 4 Static MOS RAM 250 NS	18	525.00	1.33	M,N
2114	M	1K x 4 Static MOS RAM 250 NS	18	385.00	9.50	I
2114	C	1K x 4 Static MOS RAM 300 NS	18	525.00	1.33	M,N
2114	C	1K x 4 Static MOS RAM 450 NS	18	525.00	1.33	M,N
2114L	C	1K x 4 Static MOS RAM 100 NS	18	210.00	3.05	I
2114L	C	1K x 4 Static MOS RAM 120 NS	18	210.00	2.95	I
2114L	C	1K x 4 Static MOS RAM 150 NS	18	210.00	2.75	I
2114L	C	1K x 4 Static MOS RAM 150 NS	18	367.50	2.55	N
2114L	M	1K x 4 Static MOS RAM 150 NS	18	275.00	15.35	I
2114L	C	1K x 4 Static MOS RAM 200 NS	18	210.00	2.75	I
2114L	C	1K x 4 Static MOS RAM 200 NS	18	367.50	2.25	N
2114L	M	1K x 4 Static MOS RAM 200 NS	18	275.00	13.50	I
2114L	C	1K x 4 Static MOS RAM 250 NS	18	367.50	2.15	N
2114L	C	1K x 4 Static MOS RAM 300 NS	18	367.50	2.10	N
2114L	C	1K x 4 Static MOS RAM 450 NS	18	367.50	2.00	N
2115	C	1K x 1 Static MOS RAM 30 NS	16	656.25	5.25	I
2115	C	1K x 1 Static MOS RAM 35 NS	16	656.25	4.40	I
2115	C	1K x 1 Static MOS RAM 45 NS	16	656.25	2.80	I
2115	C	1K x 1 Static MOS RAM 70 NS	16	656.25	2.50	I
2115L	C	1K x 1 Static MOS RAM 45 NS	16	393.75	3.00	I
2115L	C	1K x 1 Static MOS RAM 70 NS	16	393.75	3.30	I
2125	C	1K x 1 Static MOS RAM 20 NS	16	787.50	8.30	I
2125	C	1K x 1 Static MOS RAM 25 NS	16	656.25	7.30	I
2125	C	1K x 1 Static MOS RAM 35 NS	16	656.25	4.20	I
2125	C	1K x 1 Static MOS RAM 45 NS	16	656.25	3.30	I
2125	C	1K x 1 Static MOS RAM 70 NS	16	656.25	3.05	I

TYPE	TEMP GRADE	DESCRIPTION	PINS	POWER (mW)	PRICE ($)	SUPPLIERS
2125L	C	1K x 1 Static MOS RAM 45 NS	16	393.75	3.35	I
2125L	C	1K x 1 Static MOS RAM 70 NS	16	393.75	3.25	I
21L41	C	4K x 1 Static MOS RAM 120 NS	18	288.75	5.29	AMD
21L41	C	4K x 1 Static MOS RAM 150 NS	18	210.00	4.15	AMD
21L41	C	4K x 1 Static MOS RAM 200 NS	18	210.00	3.86	AMD
21L41	C	4K x 1 Static MOS RAM 250 NS	18	210.00	3.50	AMD
2147	C	4K x 1 Static MOS RAM 35 NS	18	945.00	4.25	AMD,I,N
2147	C	4K x 1 Static MOS RAM 45 NS	18	945.00	4.00	AMD,I,N
2147	M	4K x 1 Static MOS RAM 45 NS	18	990.00	28.75	AMD,I
2147	C	4K x 1 Static MOS RAM 55 NS	18	945.00	3.50	AMD,I,N
2147	M	4K x 1 Static MOS RAM 55 NS	18	990.00	20.15	AMD,I
2147	C	4K x 1 Static MOS RAM 70 NS	18	840.00	3.00	AMD,I,N
2147	M	4K x 1 Static MOS RAM 70 NS	18	990.00	13.78	AMD,I
2147L	C	4K x 1 Static MOS RAM 45 NS	18	656.25	5.65	AMD
2147L	C	4K x 1 Static MOS RAM 55 NS	18	656.25	3.70	AMD,N
2147L	C	4K x 1 Static MOS RAM 70 NS	18	656.25	4.29	AMD
2148	C	1K x 4 Static MOS RAM 35 NS	18	945.00	7.51	AMD
2148	C	1K x 4 Static MOS RAM 45 NS	18	945.00	4.85	AMD,I,N
2148	M	1K x 4 Static MOS RAM 45 NS	18	990.00	47.00	AMD
2148	C	1K x 4 Static MOS RAM 55 NS	18	945.00	4.25	AMD,I,N
2148	M	1K x 4 Static MOS RAM 55 NS	18	990.00	38.42	AMD,I
2148	C	1K x 4 Static MOS RAM 70 NS	18	945.00	3.35	AMD,I,N
2148	M	1K x 4 Static MOS RAM 70 NS	18	990.00	26.85	AMD,I
21L48	C	1K x 4 Static MOS RAM 45 NS	18	656.25	6.44	AMD
21L48/2148L	C	1K x 4 Static MOS RAM 55 NS	18	656.25	4.65	AMD,I,N
21L48/2148L	C	1K x 4 Static MOS RAM 70 NS	18	656.25	4.15	AMD,I,N

TYPE	TEMP GRADE	DESCRIPTION	PINS	POWER (mW)	PRICE ($)	SUPPLIERS
2149	C	1K x 4 Static MOS RAM 35 NS	18	945.00	7.51	AMD,I
2149	C	1K x 4 Static MOS RAM 45 NS	18	945.00	5.25	AMD,I
2149	M	1K x 4 Static MOS RAM 45 NS	18	990.00	47.00	AMD
2149	C	1K x 4 Static MOS RAM 55 NS	18	787.50	4.65	I
2149	C	1K x 4 Static MOS RAM 55 NS	18	945.00	4.65	AMD,I
2149	M	1K x 4 Static MOS RAM 55 NS	18	990.00	38.42	AMD
2149	C	1K x 4 Static MOS RAM 70 NS	18	945.00	3.35	AMD,I
2149	M	1K x 4 Static MOS RAM 70 NS	18	990.00	26.85	AMD
21L49	C	1K x 4 Static MOS RAM 45 NS	18	656.25	6.44	AMD
21L49	C	1K x 4 Static MOS RAM 55 NS	18	656.25	4.86	AMD
21L49/2149L	C	1K x 4 Static MOS RAM 70 NS	18	656.25	4.25	AMD,I
2167	C	16K x 1 Static MOS RAM 35 NS	20	630.00	14.40	AMD
2167	C	16K x 1 Static MOS RAM 45 NS	20	630.00	6.93	AMD,H
2167	M	16K x 1 Static MOS RAM 45 NS	20	880.00	104.00	AMD
2167	C	16K x 1 Static MOS RAM 55 NS	20	630.00	5.53	AMD,H
2167	M	16K x 1 Static MOS RAM 55 NS	20	880.00	72.00	AMD
2167	C	16K x 1 Static MOS RAM 70 NS	20	630.00	4.90	AMD,H
2167	M	16K x 1 Static MOS RAM 70 NS	20	880.00	56.00	AMD
24S10	C	256 x 4 TTL PROM 55 NS	16	525.00	2.17	TI
24S10	M	256 x 4 TTL PROM 75 NS	16	550.00	3.58	TI
24SA10	C	256 x 4 TTL PROM 65 NS	16	525.00	2.17	TI
24S41	C	1K x 4 TTL PROM 60 NS	18	735.00	4.90	TI
24SA41	C	1K x 4 TTL PROM 60 NS	18	735.00	4.90	TI
24S81	C	2K x 4 TTL PROM 70 NS	18	918.75	9.59	TI
24SA81	C	2K x 4 TTL PROM 70 NS	18	918.75	9.59	TI
27LS00	C	256 x 1 Static TTL RAM 35 NS	16	603.75	7.15	AMD

TYPE	TEMP GRADE	DESCRIPTION	PINS	POWER (mW)	PRICE ($)	SUPPLIERS
27LS00	C	256 x 1 Static TTL RAM 45 NS	16	367.50	4.20	AMD
27LS00	M	256 x 1 Static TTL RAM 45 NS	16	632.50	16.85	AMD
27LS00	M	256 x 1 Static TTL RAM 55 NS	16	385.00	11.25	AMD
27LS01	C	256 x 1 Static TTL RAM 35 NS	16	603.75	7.15	AMD
27LS01	C	256 x 1 Static TTL RAM 45 NS	16	367.50	4.20	AMD
27LS01	M	256 x 1 Static TTL RAM 45 NS	16	632.50	16.85	AMD
27LS01	M	256 x 1 Static TTL RAM 55 NS	16	385.00	11.25	AMD
27LS02	C	16 x 4 Static TTL RAM 55 NS	16	183.75	3.80	AMD
27LS02	M	16 x 4 Static TTL RAM 65 NS	16	209.00	10.65	AMD
27S02	C	16 x 4 Static TTL RAM 25 NS	16	525.00	4.10	AMD
27S02	M	16 x 4 Static TTL RAM 30 NS	16	577.50	11.50	AMD
27S02	C	16 x 4 Static TTL RAM 35 NS	16	525.00	2.35	AMD
27S02	M	16 x 4 Static TTL RAM 50 NS	16	577.50	8.75	AMD
27LS03	C	16 x 4 Static TTL RAM 55 NS	16	183.75	3.80	AMD
27LS03	M	16 x 4 Static TTL RAM 65 NS	16	209.00	10.65	AMD
27S03	C	16 x 4 Static TTL RAM 25 NS	16	525.00	4.10	AMD
27S03	M	16 x 4 Static TTL RAM 30 NS	16	577.50	11.50	AMD
27S03	C	16 x 4 Static TTL RAM 35 NS	16	525.00	2.35	AMD
27S03	M	16 x 4 Static TTL RAM 50 NS	16	577.50	8.75	AMD
27LS06	C	16 x 4 Static TTL RAM 55 NS	16	183.75	4.75	AMD
27LS06	M	16 x 4 Static TTL RAM 65 NS	16	209.00	13.15	AMD
27S06	C	16 x 4 Static TTL RAM 25 NS	16	525.00	6.35	AMD
27S06	M	16 x 4 Static TTL RAM 30 NS	16	577.50	15.50	AMD
27S06	C	16 x 4 Static TTL RAM 35 NS	16	525.00	4.75	AMD
27S06	M	16 x 4 Static TTL RAM 50 NS	16	577.50	10.15	AMD
27LS07	C	16 x 4 Static TTL RAM 55 NS	16	183.75	4.75	AMD

TYPE	TEMP GRADE	DESCRIPTION	PINS	POWER (mW)	PRICE ($)	SUPPLIERS
27LS07	M	16 x 4 Static TTL RAM 65 NS	16	209.00	13.15	AMD
27S07	C	16 x 4 Static TTL RAM 25 NS	16	525.00	6.35	AMD
27S07	M	16 x 4 Static TTL RAM 30 NS	16	577.50	15.50	AMD
27S07	C	16 x 4 Static TTL RAM 35 NS	16	525.00	4.75	AMD
27S07	M	16 x 4 Static TTL RAM 50 NS	16	577.50	10.15	AMD
27S12	C	512 x 4 TTL PROM 50 NS	16	682.50	2.90	AMD
27S12	M	512 x 4 TTL PROM 60 NS	16	715.00	6.90	AMD
27S12A	C	512 x 4 TTL PROM 30 NS	16	682.50	3.35	AMD
27S12A	M	512 x 4 TTL PROM 40 NS	16	715.00	7.15	AMD
27S13	C	512 x 4 TTL PROM 50 NS	16	682.50	2.90	AMD
27S13	M	512 x 4 TTL PROM 60 NS	16	715.00	6.90	AMD
27S13A	C	512 x 4 TTL PROM 30 NS	16	682.50	3.35	AMD
27S13A	M	512 x 4 TTL PROM 40 NS	16	715.00	7.15	AMD
27S15	C	512 x 8 TTL PROM 60 NS	24	918.75	8.00	AMD
27S15	M	512 x 8 TTL PROM 90 NS	24	1017.50	19.90	AMD
2716	M	2K x 8 Eraseable MOS PROM 450 NS 10% VCC 25V VPP	24	632.50	12.15	AMD, I
27C16	C	2K x 8 Eraseable CMOS PROM 350 NS 5% VCC 25V VPP	24	26.25	8.40	N
27C16	C	2K x 8 Eraseable CMOS PROM 450 NS 5% VCC 25V VPP	24	26.25	7.25	N
27C16	I	2K x 8 Eraseable CMOS PROM 450 NS 5% VCC 25V VPP	24	26.25	10.15	N
27LS18	C	32 x 8 TTL PROM 55 NS	16	420.00	5.35	AMD
27LS18	M	32 x 8 TTL PROM 70 NS	16	440.00	18.15	AMD
27S18	C	32 x 8 TTL PROM 40 NS	16	603.75	1.45	AMD
27S18	M	32 x 8 TTL PROM 50 NS	16	632.50	3.25	AMD
27S18A	C	32 x 8 TTL PROM 25 NS	16	603.75	1.45	AMD

TYPE	TEMP GRADE	DESCRIPTION	PINS	POWER (mW)	PRICE ($)	SUPPLIERS
27S18A	M	32 x 8 TTL PROM 35 NS	16	632.50	3.80	AMD
27S18SA	C	32 x 8 TTL PROM 15 NS	16	603.75	2.75	AMD
27S18SA	M	32 x 8 TTL PROM 20 NS	16	632.50	6.50	AMD
27LS19	C	32 x 8 TTL PROM 55 NS	16	420.00	5.35	AMD
27LS19	M	32 x 8 TTL PROM 70 NS	16	440.00	18.15	AMD
27S19	C	32 x 8 TTL PROM 40 NS	16	603.75	1.45	AMD
27S19	M	32 x 8 TTL PROM 50 NS	16	632.50	3.25	AMD
27S19A	C	32 x 8 TTL PROM 25 NS	16	603.75	1.45	AMD
27S19A	M	32 x 8 TTL PROM 35 NS	16	632.50	3.80	AMD
27S19SA	C	32 x 8 TTL PROM 15 NS	16	603.75	2.75	AMD
27S19SA	M	32 x 8 TTL PROM 20 NS	16	632.50	6.50	AMD
27S20	C	256 x 4 TTL PROM 45 NS	16	682.50	1.70	AMD
27S20	M	256 x 4 TTL PROM 60 NS	16	715.00	4.00	AMD
27S20A	C	256 x 4 TTL PROM 30 NS	16	682.50	1.70	AMD
27S20A	M	256 x 4 TTL PROM 40 NS	16	715.00	4.40	AMD
27S21	C	256 x 4 TTL PROM 45 NS	16	682.50	1.70	AMD
27S21	M	256 x 4 TTL PROM 60 NS	16	715.00	4.00	AMD
27S21A	C	256 x 4 TTL PROM 30 NS	16	682.50	1.70	AMD
27S21A	M	256 x 4 TTL PROM 40 NS	16	715.00	4.40	AMD
27S25	C	512 x 8 Registered TTL PROM 50 NS	24	971.25	8.50	AMD
27S25	M	512 x 8 Registered TTL PROM 55 NS	24	1017.50	23.00	AMD
27S25A	C	512 x 8 Registered TTL PROM 30 NS	24	971.25	11.75	AMD
27S25A	M	512 x 8 Registered TTL PROM 35 NS	24	1017.50	29.00	AMD
27S27	C	512 x 8 Registered TTL PROM 55 NS	22	971.25	12.35	AMD
27S27	M	512 x 8 Registered TTL PROM 65 NS	22	1017.50	30.45	AMD
27S28	C	512 x 8 TTL PROM 55 NS	20	840.00	4.35	AMD

TYPE	TEMP GRADE	DESCRIPTION	PINS	POWER (mW)	PRICE ($)	SUPPLIERS
27S28	M	512 x 8 TTL PROM 70 NS	20	880.00	9.40	AMD
27S28A	C	512 x 8 TTL PROM 40 NS	20	840.00	6.00	AMD
27S28A	M	512 x 8 TTL PROM 50 NS	20	880.00	10.90	AMD
27S29	C	512 x 8 TTL PROM 55 NS	20	840.00	4.35	AMD
27S29	M	512 x 8 TTL PROM 70 NS	20	880.00	9.40	AMD
27S29A	C	512 x 8 TTL PROM 40 NS	20	840.00	6.00	AMD
27S29A	M	512 x 8 TTL PROM 50 NS	20	880.00	10.90	AMD
27S30	C	512 x 8 TTL PROM 55 NS	24	918.75	4.80	AMD
27S30	M	512 x 8 TTL PROM 70 NS	24	962.50	9.85	AMD
27S30A	C	512 x 8 TTL PROM 40 NS	24	918.75	7.15	AMD
27S30A	M	512 x 8 TTL PROM 50 NS	24	962.50	12.20	AMD
27S31	C	512 x 8 TTL PROM 55 NS	24	918.75	4.80	AMD
27S31	M	512 x 8 TTL PROM 70 NS	24	962.50	9.85	AMD
27S31A	C	512 x 8 TTL PROM 40 NS	24	918.75	7.15	AMD
27S31A	M	512 x 8 TTL PROM 50 NS	24	962.50	12.20	AMD
2732	C	4K x 8 Eraseable MOS PROM 150 NS 10% VCC 21V VPP	24	550.00	17.55	AMD
2732	C	4K x 8 Eraseable MOS PROM 150 NS 5% VCC 21V VPP	24	656.25	6.32	AMD,TI
2732	C	4K x 8 Eraseable MOS PROM 200 NS 10% VCC 21V VPP	24	550.00	4.90	AMD,I
2732	C	4K x 8 Eraseable MOS PROM 200 NS 5% VCC 21V VPP	24	656.25	4.46	AMD,I,TI
2732	C	4K x 8 Eraseable MOS PROM 250 NS 5% VCC 21V VPP	24	656.25	4.05	AMD,I,TI
2732	C	4K x 8 Eraseable MOS PROM 250 NS 10% VCC 21V VPP	24	550.00	4.25	AMD,I
2732	M	4K x 8 Eraseable MOS PROM 250 NS 10% VCC 21V VPP	24	632.50	18.90	AMD,I

TYPE	TEMP GRADE	DESCRIPTION	PINS	POWER (mW)	PRICE ($)	SUPPLIERS
2732	C	4K x 8 Eraseable MOS PROM 300 NS 10% VCC 21V VPP	24	550.00	4.01	AMD, I
2732	C	4K x 8 Eraseable MOS PROM 300 NS 5% VCC 21V VPP	24	656.25	3.65	AMD, I, TI
2732	C	4K x 8 Eraseable MOS PROM 350 NS 5% VCC 21V VPP	24	656.25	5.14	TI
2732	C	4K x 8 Eraseable MOS PROM 450 NS 5% VCC 21V VPP	24	656.25	3.44	AMD, I, TI
2732	C	4K x 8 Eraseable MOS PROM 450 NS 10% VCC 21V VPP	24	550.00	5.00	I
2732	M	4K x 8 Eraseable MOS PROM 450 NS 10% VCC 21V VPP	24	632.50	13.50	AMD, I
27C32	C	4K x 8 Eraseable CMOS PROM 350 NS 5% VCC 25V VPP	24	26.25	11.00	N
27C32	C	4K x 8 Eraseable CMOS PROM 450 NS 5% VCC 25V VPP	24	26.25	10.15	N
27C32	I	4K x 8 Eraseable CMOS PROM 450 NS 5% VCC 25V VPP	24	26.25	12.30	N
27S32	C	1K x 4 TTL PROM 55 NS	18	735.00	3.80	AMD
27S32	M	1K x 4 TTL PROM 70 NS	18	797.50	9.25	AMD
27S32A	C	1K x 4 TTL PROM 35 NS	18	735.00	5.40	AMD
27S32A	M	1K x 4 TTL PROM 45 NS	18	797.50	12.70	AMD
27S33	C	1K x 4 TTL PROM 55 NS	18	735.00	3.80	AMD
27S33	M	1K x 4 TTL PROM 70 NS	18	797.50	9.25	AMD
27S33A	C	1K x 4 TTL PROM 35 NS	18	735.00	5.40	AMD
27S33A	M	1K x 4 TTL PROM 45 NS	18	797.50	12.70	AMD
27S35	C	1K x 8 TTL PROM 40 NS	24	971.25	13.25	AMD
27S35	M	1K x 8 TTL PROM 45 NS	24	1017.50	36.50	AMD
27S35A	C	1K x 8 TTL PROM 35 NS	24	971.25	18.00	AMD
27S35A	M	1K x 8 TTL PROM 40 NS	24	1017.50	48.00	AMD

TYPE	TEMP GRADE	DESCRIPTION	PINS	POWER (mW)	PRICE ($)	SUPPLIERS
27S37	C	1K x 8 TTL PROM 40 NS	24	971.25	13.25	AMD
27S37	M	1K x 8 TTL PROM 45 NS	24	1017.50	36.50	AMD
27S37A	C	1K x 8 TTL PROM 35 NS	24	971.25	18.00	AMD
27S37A	M	1K x 8 TTL PROM 40 NS	24	1017.50	48.00	AMD
27PS41	C	4K x 4 TTL PROM 50 NS	20	866.25	27.20	AMD
27PS41	M	4K x 4 TTL PROM 65 NS	20	935.00	77.25	AMD
27S41	C	4K x 4 TTL PROM 50 NS	20	866.25	15.50	AMD
27S41	M	4K x 4 TTL PROM 65 NS	20	935.00	34.00	AMD
27S41A	C	4K x 4 TTL PROM 35 NS	20	866.25	18.50	AMD
27S41A	M	4K x 4 TTL PROM 50 NS	20	935.00	41.75	AMD
27S43	C	4K x 8 TTL PROM 55 NS	24	971.25	26.10	AMD
27S43	M	4K x 8 TTL PROM 65 NS	24	1017.50	46.40	AMD
27S43A	C	4K x 8 TTL PROM 40 NS	24	971.25	33.35	AMD
27S43A	M	4K x 8 TTL PROM 55 NS	24	1017.50	51.00	AMD
27S45	C	2K x 8 TTL PROM 45 NS	24	971.25	22.00	AMD
27S45	M	2K x 8 TTL PROM 50 NS	24	1017.50	83.00	AMD
27S45A	C	2K x 8 TTL PROM 40 NS	24	971.25	27.00	AMD
27S45A	M	2K x 8 TTL PROM 45 NS	24	1017.50	105.75	AMD
27S47	C	2K x 8 TTL PROM 45 NS	24	971.25	22.00	AMD
27S47	M	2K x 8 TTL PROM 50 NS	24	1017.50	83.00	AMD
27S47A	C	2K x 8 TTL PROM 40 NS	24	971.25	27.00	AMD
27S47A	M	2K x 8 TTL PROM 45 NS	24	1017.50	105.75	AMD
27S49	C	8K x 8 TTL PROM 55 NS	24	997.50	53.65	AMD
27S49	M	8K x 8 TTL PROM 65 NS	24	1045.00	162.50	AMD
27S49A	C	8K x 8 TTL PROM 40 NS	24	997.50	71.00	AMD
27S49A	M	8K x 8 TTL PROM 55 NS	24	1045.00	210.25	AMD

TYPE	TEMP GRADE	DESCRIPTION	PINS	POWER (mW)	PRICE ($)	SUPPLIERS
2764	C	8K x 8 Eraseable MOS PROM 150 NS 10% VCC 12.5V VPP	28	550.00	6.75	AMD
2764	C	8K x 8 Eraseable MOS PROM 170 NS 5% VCC 12.5V VPP	28	787.50	5.40	AMD,TI
2764	C	8K x 8 Eraseable MOS PROM 180 NS 5% VCC 12.5V VPP	28	393.75	8.90	I
2764	C	8K x 8 Eraseable MOS PROM 200 NS 10% VCC 12.5V VPP	28	412.50	5.35	AMD,I
2764	C	8K x 8 Eraseable MOS PROM 200 NS 5% VCC 12.5V VPP	28	787.50	4.90	AMD,I,TI
2764	M	8K x 8 Eraseable MOS PROM 200 NS 10% VCC 12.5V VPP	28	550.00	47.25	AMD
2764	C	8K x 8 Eraseable MOS PROM 250 NS 5% VCC 12.5V VPP	28	787.50	4.40	AMD,I,TI
2764	C	8K x 8 Eraseable MOS PROM 250 NS 10% VCC 12.5V VPP	28	412.50	4.68	AMD,I
2764	M	8K x 8 Eraseable MOS PROM 250 NS 10% VCC 12.5V VPP	28	550.00	40.00	AMD,I
2764	C	8K x 8 Eraseable MOS PROM 300 NS 10% VCC 12.5V VPP	28	412.50	4.41	AMD,I
2764	C	8K x 8 Eraseable MOS PROM 300 NS 5% VCC 12.5V VPP	28	393.75	4.01	AMD,I
2764	M	8K x 8 Eraseable MOS PROM 350 NS 10% VCC 12.5V VPP	28	550.00	34.00	I
2764	C	8K x 8 Eraseable MOS PROM 450 NS 10% VCC 12.5V VPP	28	412.50	4.90	AMD,I
2764	C	8K x 8 Eraseable MOS PROM 450 NS 5% VCC 12.5V VPP	28	787.50	4.05	AMD,I,TI
2764	M	8K x 8 Eraseable MOS PROM 450 NS 10% VCC 12.5V VPP	28	550.00	33.75	AMD
27C64	C	8K x 8 Eraseable CMOS PROM 150 NS 5% VCC 12.5V VPP	28	52.50	7.50	I
27C64	C	8K x 8 Eraseable CMOS PROM 150 NS 10% VCC 12.5V VPP	28	55.00	6.00	I,N

TYPE	TEMP GRADE	DESCRIPTION	PINS	POWER (mW)	PRICE ($)	SUPPLIERS
27C64	I	8K x 8 Eraseable CMOS PROM 150 NS 10% VCC 12.5V VPP	28	55.00	7.30	N
27C64	C	8K x 8 Eraseable CMOS PROM 200 NS 5% VCC 12.5V VPP	28	52.50	6.40	I
27C64	C	8K x 8 Eraseable CMOS PROM 200 NS 10% VCC 12.5V VPP	28	55.00	4.95	I,N
27C64	I	8K x 8 Eraseable CMOS PROM 200 NS 10% VCC 12.5V VPP	28	55.00	6.35	N
27C64	M	8K x 8 Eraseable CMOS PROM 200 NS 10% VCC 12.5V VPP	28	55.00	14.00	I,N
27C64	C	8K x 8 Eraseable CMOS PROM 250 NS 10% VCC 12.5V VPP	28	55.00	5.90	I
27C64	C	8K x 8 Eraseable CMOS PROM 250 NS 5% VCC 12.5V VPP	28	52.50	5.40	I
27C64	M	8K x 8 Eraseable CMOS PROM 250 NS 10% VCC 12.5V VPP	28	55.00	10.75	I,N
27C64	C	8K x 8 Eraseable CMOS PROM 300 NS 5% VCC 12.5V VPP	28	52.50	5.40	I
27C64	C	8K x 8 Eraseable CMOS PROM 300 NS 10% VCC 12.5V VPP	28	55.00	5.90	I
27C64	M	8K x 8 Eraseable CMOS PROM 350 NS 10% VCC 12.5V VPP	28	55.00	56.50	I
27S65	C	1K x 4 Registered TTL PROM 30 NS	24	971.25	11.75	AMD
27S65	M	1K x 4 Registered TTL PROM 35 NS	24	1017.50	38.00	AMD
27S65A	C	1K x 4 Registered TTL PROM 23 NS	24	971.25	17.50	AMD
27S65A	M	1K x 4 Registered TTL PROM 27 NS	24	1017.50	49.00	AMD
27S75	C	2K x 4 Registered TTL PROM 30 NS	24	971.25	14.25	AMD
27S75	M	2K x 4 Registered TTL PROM 35 NS	24	1017.50	60.00	AMD
27S75A	C	2K x 4 Registered TTL PROM 25 NS	24	971.25	25.50	AMD
27S75A	M	2K x 4 Registered TTL PROM 30 NS	24	1017.50	77.00	AMD
27S85	C	4K x 4 Registered TTL PROM 35 NS	24	971.25	17.00	AMD

TYPE	TEMP GRADE	DESCRIPTION	PINS	POWER (mW)	PRICE ($)	SUPPLIERS
27S85	M	4K x 4 Registered TTL PROM 40 NS	24	1017.50	96.00	AMD
27S85A	C	4K x 4 Registered TTL PROM 27 NS	24	971.25	34.00	AMD
27S85A	M	4K x 4 Registered TTL PROM 30 NS	24	1017.50	120.00	AMD
27128	M	16K x 8 Eraseable MOS PROM 110 NS 10% VCC 12.5V VPP	28	770.00	523.85	I
27128	C	16K x 8 Eraseable MOS PROM 150 NS 5% VCC 21V VPP	28	525.00	24.30	AMD
27128	C	16K x 8 Eraseable MOS PROM 150 NS 10% VCC 21V VPP	28	550.00	27.00	AMD
27128	C	16K x 8 Eraseable MOS PROM 200 NS 5% VCC 21V VPP	28	525.00	19.60	AMD
27128	M	16K x 8 Eraseable MOS PROM 200 NS 10% VCC 21V VPP	28	550.00	81.00	AMD
27128	C	16K x 8 Eraseable MOS PROM 250 NS 5% VCC 21V VPP	28	525.00	5.70	AMD, I
27128	C	16K x 8 Eraseable MOS PROM 250 NS 10% VCC 21V VPP	28	550.00	6.60	AMD, I
27128	M	16K x 8 Eraseable MOS PROM 250 NS 10% VCC 21V VPP	28	550.00	60.75	AMD
27128	C	16K x 8 Eraseable MOS PROM 300 NS 10% VCC 21V VPP	28	550.00	6.60	AMD, I
27128	C	16K x 8 Eraseable MOS PROM 300 NS 5% VCC 21V VPP	28	525.00	5.70	AMD, I
27128	C	16K x 8 Eraseable MOS PROM 450 NS 10% VCC 21V VPP	28	550.00	6.60	AMD, I
27128	C	16K x 8 Eraseable MOS PROM 450 NS 5% VCC 21V VPP	28	525.00	5.70	AMD, I
27128	M	16K x 8 Eraseable MOS PROM 450 NS 10% VCC 21V VPP	28	550.00	47.25	AMD
27128A	C	16K x 8 Eraseable MOS PROM 150 NS 10% VCC 12.5V VPP	28	550.00	7.15	AMD
27128A	C	16K x 8 Eraseable MOS PROM 150 NS 5% VCC 12.5V VPP	28	525.00	6.50	AMD, I

TYPE	TEMP GRADE	DESCRIPTION	PINS	POWER (mW)	PRICE ($)	SUPPLIERS
27128A	M	16K x 8 Eraseable MOS PROM 150 NS 10% VCC 12.5V VPP	28	770.00	351.00	I
27128A	C	16K x 8 Eraseable MOS PROM 200 NS 5% VCC 12.5V VPP	28	525.00	5.40	AMD,I
27128A	C	16K x 8 Eraseable MOS PROM 200 NS 10% VCC 12.5V VPP	28	550.00	7.90	I
27128A	M	16K x 8 Eraseable MOS PROM 200 NS 10% VCC 12.5V VPP	28	770.00	81.00	AMD,I
27128A	C	16K x 8 Eraseable MOS PROM 250 NS 5% VCC 12.5V VPP	28	525.00	4.73	AMD,I
27128A	C	16K x 8 Eraseable MOS PROM 250 NS 10% VCC 12.5V VPP	28	550.00	5.20	AMD,I
27128A	M	16K x 8 Eraseable MOS PROM 250 NS 10% VCC 12.5V VPP	28	550.00	60.75	AMD
27128A	C	16K x 8 Eraseable MOS PROM 300 NS 5% VCC 12.5V VPP	28	525.00	4.27	AMD,I
27128A	C	16K x 8 Eraseable MOS PROM 300 NS 10% VCC 12.5V VPP	28	550.00	4.68	AMD,I
27128A	M	16K x 8 Eraseable MOS PROM 300 NS 10% VCC 12.5V VPP	28	770.00	52.50	I
27128A	C	16K x 8 Eraseable MOS PROM 450 NS 10% VCC 12.5V VPP	28	550.00	4.45	AMD
27128A	C	16K x 8 Eraseable MOS PROM 450 NS 5% VCC 12.5V VPP	28	525.00	4.27	AMD
27128A	M	16K x 8 Eraseable MOS PROM 450 NS 10% VCC 12.5V VPP	28	550.00	47.25	AMD
27C128	C	16K x 8 Eraseable CMOS PROM 150 NS 10% VCC 12.5V VPP	28	220.00	11.70	TI
27C128	C	16K x 8 Eraseable CMOS PROM 150 NS 5% VCC 12.5V VPP	28	210.00	9.75	TI
27C128	C	16K x 8 Eraseable CMOS PROM 200 NS 10% VCC 12.5V VPP	28	220.00	9.72	TI
27C128	C	16K x 8 Eraseable CMOS PROM 200 NS 5% VCC 12.5V VPP	28	210.00	8.45	TI

TYPE	TEMP GRADE	DESCRIPTION	PINS	POWER (mW)	PRICE ($)	SUPPLIERS
27C128	C	16K x 8 Eraseable CMOS PROM 250 NS 10% VCC 12.5V VPP	28	220.00	6.44	TI
27C128	C	16K x 8 Eraseable CMOS PROM 250 NS 5% VCC 12.5V VPP	28	210.00	5.85	TI
27C128	C	16K x 8 Eraseable CMOS PROM 300 NS 10% VCC 12.5V VPP	28	220.00	6.08	TI
27C128	C	16K x 8 Eraseable CMOS PROM 300 NS 5% VCC 12.5V VPP	28	210.00	5.53	TI
27C128	C	16K x 8 Eraseable CMOS PROM 450 NS 5% VCC 12.5V VPP	28	210.00	5.20	TI
27C128	C	16K x 8 Eraseable CMOS PROM 450 NS 10% VCC 12.5V VPP	28	220.00	5.72	TI
27S180	C	1K x 8 TTL PROM 60 NS	24	971.25	7.60	AMD
27S180	M	1K x 8 TTL PROM 80 NS	24	1017.50	16.50	AMD
27S180A	C	1K x 8 TTL PROM 35 NS	24	971.25	9.60	AMD
27S180A	M	1K x 8 TTL PROM 50 NS	24	1017.50	18.85	AMD
27PS181	C	1K x 8 TTL PROM 65 NS	24	971.25	11.45	AMD
27PS181	M	1K x 8 TTL PROM 75 NS	24	1017.50	25.25	AMD
27S181	C	1K x 8 TTL PROM 60 NS	24	971.25	7.60	AMD
27S181	M	1K x 8 TTL PROM 80 NS	24	1017.50	16.50	AMD
27S181A	C	1K x 8 TTL PROM 35 NS	24	971.25	9.60	AMD
27S181A	M	1K x 8 TTL PROM 50 NS	24	1017.50	18.85	AMD
27S184	C	2K x 4 TTL PROM 50 NS	18	787.50	8.35	AMD
27S184	M	2K x 4 TTL PROM 55 NS	18	825.00	13.80	AMD
27S184A	C	2K x 4 TTL PROM 35 NS	18	787.50	10.50	AMD
27S184A	M	2K x 4 TTL PROM 45 NS	18	825.00	21.75	AMD
27LS185	C	2K x 4 TTL PROM 60 NS	18	656.25	12.00	AMD
27LS185	M	2K x 4 TTL PROM 65 NS	18	687.50	33.75	AMD
27PS185	C	2K x 4 TTL PROM 50 NS	18	787.50	12.00	AMD

TYPE	TEMP GRADE	DESCRIPTION	PINS	POWER (mW)	PRICE ($)	SUPPLIERS
27PS185	M	2K x 4 TTL PROM 55 NS	18	825.00	33.75	AMD
27S185	C	2K x 4 TTL PROM 50 NS	18	787.50	8.35	AMD
27S185	M	2K x 4 TTL PROM 55 NS	18	825.00	13.80	AMD
27S185A	C	2K x 4 TTL PROM 35 NS	18	787.50	10.50	AMD
27S185A	M	2K x 4 TTL PROM 45 NS	18	825.00	21.75	AMD
27S190	C	2K x 8 TTL PROM 50 NS	24	971.25	14.25	AMD
27S190	M	2K x 8 TTL PROM 65 NS	24	1017.50	26.10	AMD
27S190A	C	2K x 8 TTL PROM 35 NS	24	971.25	17.35	AMD
27S190A	M	2K x 8 TTL PROM 50 NS	24	1017.50	34.80	AMD
27PS191	C	2K x 8 TTL PROM 65 NS	24	971.25	23.60	AMD
27PS191	M	2K x 8 TTL PROM 75 NS	24	1017.50	68.25	AMD
27S191	C	2K x 8 TTL PROM 50 NS	24	971.25	14.25	AMD
27S191	M	2K x 8 TTL PROM 65 NS	24	1017.50	26.10	AMD
27S191A	C	2K x 8 TTL PROM 35 NS	24	971.25	17.35	AMD
27S191A	M	2K x 8 TTL PROM 50 NS	24	1017.50	34.80	AMD
27256	C	32K x 8 Eraseable MOS PROM 170 NS 5% VCC 12.5V VPP	28	656.25	9.50	AMD, I
27256	M	32K x 8 Eraseable MOS PROM 170 NS 10% VCC 12.5V VPP	28	770.00	264.00	I
27256	C	32K x 8 Eraseable MOS PROM 200 NS 5% VCC 12.5V VPP	28	656.25	7.80	AMD, I
27256	C	32K x 8 Eraseable MOS PROM 200 NS 10% VCC 12.5V VPP	28	687.50	8.54	AMD, I
27256	M	32K x 8 Eraseable MOS PROM 200 NS 10% VCC 12.5V VPP	28	687.50	135.00	AMD, I
27256	C	32K x 8 Eraseable MOS PROM 250 NS 10% VCC 12.5V VPP	28	550.00	7.43	AMD, I
27256	C	32K x 8 Eraseable MOS PROM 250 NS 5% VCC 12.5V VPP	28	525.00	7.10	AMD, I

TYPE	TEMP GRADE	DESCRIPTION	PINS	POWER (mW)	PRICE ($)	SUPPLIERS
27256	M	32K x 8 Eraseable MOS PROM 250 NS 10% VCC 12.5V VPP	28	687.50	114.75	AMD, I
27256	C	32K x 8 Eraseable MOS PROM 300 NS 5% VCC 12.5V VPP	28	525.00	6.45	AMD, I
27256	C	32K x 8 Eraseable MOS PROM 300 NS 10% VCC 12.5V VPP	28	550.00	6.75	AMD, I
27256	M	32K x 8 Eraseable MOS PROM 350 NS 10% VCC 12.5V VPP	28	687.50	108.00	AMD, I
27256	C	32K x 8 Eraseable MOS PROM 450 NS 10% VCC 12.5V VPP	28	550.00	6.75	AMD
27256	C	32K x 8 Eraseable MOS PROM 450 NS 5% VCC 12.5V VPP	28	525.00	6.45	AMD
27256	M	32K x 8 Eraseable MOS PROM 450 NS 10% VCC 12.5V VPP	28	550.00	94.50	AMD
27256L	C	32K x 8 Eraseable MOS PROM 170 NS 5% VCC 12.5V VPP	28	525.00	21.40	I
27256L	C	32K x 8 Eraseable MOS PROM 200 NS 5% VCC 12.5V VPP	28	525.00	16.70	I
27256L	C	32K x 8 Eraseable MOS PROM 200 NS 10% VCC 12.5V VPP	28	550.00	18.30	I
27C256	C	32K x 8 Eraseable CMOS PROM 170 NS 5% VCC 12.5V VPP	28	210.00	17.50	TI
27C256	C	32K x 8 Eraseable CMOS PROM 170 NS 10% VCC 12.5V VPP	28	220.00	21.00	TI
27C256	C	32K x 8 Eraseable CMOS PROM 200 NS 5% VCC 12.5V VPP	28	210.00	10.00	N, TI
27C256	C	32K x 8 Eraseable CMOS PROM 200 NS 10% VCC 12.5V VPP	28	220.00	14.09	TI
27C256	M	32K x 8 Eraseable CMOS PROM 200 NS 10% VCC 12.5V VPP	28	55.00	150.00	I
27C256	C	32K x 8 Eraseable CMOS PROM 250 NS 5% VCC 12.5V VPP	28	210.00	8.96	N, TI
27C256	C	32K x 8 Eraseable CMOS PROM 250 NS 10% VCC 12.5V VPP	28	220.00	9.86	N, TI

TYPE	TEMP GRADE	DESCRIPTION	PINS	POWER (mW)	PRICE ($)	SUPPLIERS
27C256	I	32K x 8 Eraseable CMOS PROM 250 NS 10% VCC 12.5V VPP	28	55.00	13.50	N
27C256	M	32K x 8 Eraseable CMOS PROM 250 NS 10% VCC 12.5V VPP	28	55.00	24.00	I,N
27C256	C	32K x 8 Eraseable CMOS PROM 300 NS 10% VCC 12.5V VPP	28	220.00	9.24	TI
27C256	C	32K x 8 Eraseable CMOS PROM 300 NS 5% VCC 12.5V VPP	28	210.00	8.40	TI
27C256	M	32K x 8 Eraseable CMOS PROM 350 NS 10% VCC 12.5V VPP	28	55.00	20.00	I,N
27C256	C	32K x 8 Eraseable CMOS PROM 450 NS 10% VCC 12.5V VPP	28	220.00	8.93	TI
27C256	C	32K x 8 Eraseable CMOS PROM 450 NS 5% VCC 12.5V VPP	28	210.00	8.12	N,TI
27S280	C	1K x 8 TTL PROM 60 NS	24	971.25	7.60	AMD
27S280	M	1K x 8 TTL PROM 80 NS	24	1017.50	25.00	AMD
27S280A	C	1K x 8 TTL PROM 35 NS	24	971.25	9.60	AMD
27S280A	M	1K x 8 TTL PROM 50 NS	24	1017.50	33.00	AMD
27S281	C	1K x 8 TTL PROM 60 NS	24	971.25	7.60	AMD
27S281	M	1K x 8 TTL PROM 80 NS	24	1017.50	25.00	AMD
27S281A	C	1K x 8 TTL PROM 35 NS	24	971.25	9.60	AMD
27S281A	M	1K x 8 TTL PROM 50 NS	24	1017.50	33.00	AMD
27S290	C	2K x 8 TTL PROM 50 NS	24	971.25	14.25	AMD
27S290	M	2K x 8 TTL PROM 65 NS	24	1017.50	26.10	AMD
27S290A	C	2K x 8 TTL PROM 35 NS	24	971.25	17.35	AMD
27S290A	M	2K x 8 TTL PROM 50 NS	24	1017.50	34.80	AMD
27PS291	C	2K x 8 TTL PROM 65 NS	24	971.25	28.30	AMD
27PS291	M	2K x 8 TTL PROM 75 NS	24	1017.50	82.00	AMD
27S291	C	2K x 8 TTL PROM 50 NS	24	971.25	14.25	AMD

TYPE	TEMP GRADE	DESCRIPTION	PINS	POWER (mW)	PRICE ($)	SUPPLIERS
27S291	M	2K x 8 TTL PROM 65 NS	24	1017.50	26.10	AMD
27S291A	C	2K x 8 TTL PROM 35 NS	24	971.25	18.50	AMD
27S291A	M	2K x 8 TTL PROM 50 NS	24	1017.50	34.80	AMD
27512	C	64K x 8 Eraseable MOS PROM 200 NS 5% VCC 12.5V VPP	28	656.25	20.00	I
27512	C	64K x 8 Eraseable MOS PROM 200 NS 10% VCC 12.5V VPP	28	687.50	22.00	I
27512	C	64K x 8 Eraseable MOS PROM 250 NS 5% VCC 12.5V VPP	28	656.25	15.70	AMD,I
27512	C	64K x 8 Eraseable MOS PROM 250 NS 10% VCC 12.5V VPP	28	687.50	17.30	AMD,I
27512	M	64K x 8 Eraseable MOS PROM 250 NS 10% VCC 12.5V VPP	28	825.00	309.00	I
27512	C	64K x 8 Eraseable MOS PROM 300 NS 10% VCC 12.5V VPP	28	687.50	15.70	AMD,I
27512	C	64K x 8 Eraseable MOS PROM 300 NS 5% VCC 12.5V VPP	28	656.25	14.30	AMD,I
27512	M	64K x 8 Eraseable MOS PROM 350 NS 10% VCC 12.5V VPP	28	825.00	206.00	I
27512	M	64K x 8 Eraseable MOS PROM 450 NS 10% VCC 12.5V VPP	28	660.00	243.00	AMD
28L22	C	256 x 8 TTL PROM 70 NS	20	525.00	3.91	TI
28L22	M	256 x 8 TTL PROM 75 NS	20	550.00	5.72	TI
28LA22	C	256 x 8 TTL PROM 75 NS	20	525.00	3.91	TI
28L42	C	512 x 8 TTL PROM 95 NS	20	446.25	5.58	TI
28L42	M	512 x 8 TTL PROM 110 NS	20	467.50	10.73	TI
28S42	C	512 x 8 TTL PROM 60 NS	20	708.75	5.33	TI
28S42	M	512 x 8 TTL PROM 70 NS	20	742.50	8.58	TI
28SA42	C	512 x 8 TTL PROM 65 NS	20	708.75	5.33	TI
28L46	C	512 x 8 TTL PROM 95 NS	24	446.25	5.86	TI

TYPE	TEMP GRADE	DESCRIPTION	PINS	POWER (mW)	PRICE ($)	SUPPLIERS
28S46	C	512 x 8 TTL PROM 60 NS	24	708.75	5.33	TI
28SA46	C	512 x 8 TTL PROM 65 NS	24	708.75	5.25	TI
28L86A	C	1K x 8 TTL PROM 110 NS	24	420.00	9.66	TI
28L86A	M	1K x 8 TTL PROM 200 NS	24	522.50	20.74	TI
28S86A	C	1K x 8 TTL PROM 65 NS	24	866.25	9.52	TI
28L166	C	2K x 8 TTL PROM 125 NS	24	577.50	12.44	TI
28S166	C	2K x 8 TTL PROM 75 NS	24	918.75	11.37	TI
34L10-25	C	256 x 4 TTL PROM 25 NS	16	262.50	1.70	TI
34L10-35	C	256 x 4 TTL PROM 35 NS	16	262.50	1.32	TI
34S10-18	C	256 x 4 TTL PROM 18 NS	16	498.75	5.05	TI
34S10-25	C	256 x 4 TTL PROM 25 NS	16	498.75	1.32	TI
34SA10-25	C	256 x 4 TTL PROM 25 NS	16	498.75	1.32	TI
38S030-25	C	32 x 8 TTL PROM 25 NS	16	656.25	1.17	TI
38SA030-25	C	32 x 8 TTL PROM 25 NS	16	656.25	1.17	TI
38L165-35	C	2K x 8 TTL PROM 35 NS	24	525.00	18.15	TI
38L165-45	C	2K x 8 TTL PROM 45 NS	24	525.00	10.11	TI
38S165-25	C	2K x 8 TTL PROM 25 NS	24	840.00	29.86	TI
38S165-35	C	2K x 8 TTL PROM 35 NS	24	840.00	10.66	TI
4164	C	64K x 1 Dynamic MOS RAM 120 NS	16	252.00	2.32	TI
4164	M	64K x 1 Dynamic MOS RAM 120 NS	16	264.00	26.81	TI
4164	C	64K x 1 Dynamic MOS RAM 150 NS	16	236.25	2.00	TI
4164	M	64K x 1 Dynamic MOS RAM 150 NS	16	247.50	21.45	TI
4164	C	64K x 1 Dynamic MOS RAM 200 NS	16	194.25	2.00	TI
4164	M	64K x 1 Dynamic MOS RAM 200 NS	16	203.50	19.31	TI
4256	C	256K x 1 Dynamic MOS RAM 120 NS	16	409.50	5.60	TI
4256	C	256K x 1 Dynamic MOS RAM 150 NS	16	357.00	4.80	TI

TYPE	TEMP GRADE	DESCRIPTION	PINS	POWER (mW)	PRICE ($)	SUPPLIERS
4256	M	256K x 1 Dynamic MOS RAM 150 NS	16	412.50	107.25	TI
4256	C	256K x 1 Dynamic MOS RAM 200 NS	16	304.50	4.80	TI
4256	M	256K x 1 Dynamic MOS RAM 200 NS	16	330.00	92.95	TI
4257	C	256K x 1 Dynamic MOS RAM 120 NS	16	409.50	5.60	TI
4257	C	256K x 1 Dynamic MOS RAM 150 NS	16	357.00	4.80	TI
4257	C	256K x 1 Dynamic MOS RAM 200 NS	16	304.50	4.80	TI
4416	C	16K x 4 Dynamic MOS RAM 120 NS	18	283.50	3.20	TI
4416	C	16K x 4 Dynamic MOS RAM 150 NS	18	252.00	2.56	TI
4416	M	16K x 4 Dynamic MOS RAM 150 NS	18	264.00	34.50	TI
4416	C	16K x 4 Dynamic MOS RAM 200 NS	18	220.50	2.56	TI
4416	M	16K x 4 Dynamic MOS RAM 200 NS	18	231.00	30.36	TI
4464	C	64K x 4 Dynamic MOS RAM 120 NS	18	420.00	5.60	TI
4464	C	64K x 4 Dynamic MOS RAM 150 NS	18	367.50	4.80	TI
4464	C	64K x 4 Dynamic MOS RAM 200 NS	18	315.00	4.80	TI
4517	C	16K x 1 Dynamic MOS RAM 100 NS	16	162.75	1.75	M
4517	C	16K x 1 Dynamic MOS RAM 120 NS	16	147.00	1.54	M
4517	C	16K x 1 Dynamic MOS RAM 150 NS	16	131.25	1.47	M
4517	C	16K x 1 Dynamic MOS RAM 200 NS	16	120.75	1.40	M
51C66	C	16K x 1 Static CMOS RAM 25 NS	20	420.00	17.00	I
51C66	C	16K x 1 Static CMOS RAM 30 NS	20	420.00	15.25	I
51C66	C	16K x 1 Static CMOS RAM 35 NS	20	420.00	12.50	I
51C66L	C	16K x 1 Static CMOS RAM 35 NS	20	315.00	15.25	I
51C67	C	16K x 1 Static CMOS RAM 30 NS	20	420.00	15.25	I
51C67	C	16K x 1 Static CMOS RAM 35 NS	20	420.00	12.50	I
51C67	M	16K x 1 Static CMOS RAM 35 NS	20	550.00	67.14	I
51C67	M	16K x 1 Static CMOS RAM 45 NS	20	550.00	53.70	I

TYPE	TEMP GRADE	DESCRIPTION	PINS	POWER (mW)	PRICE ($)	SUPPLIERS
51C67	M	16K x 1 Static CMOS RAM 55 NS	20	550.00	47.67	I
51C67L	C	16K x 1 Static CMOS RAM 35 NS	20	315.00	15.25	I
51C68	C	4K x 4 Static CMOS RAM 30 NS	20	472.50	16.88	I
51C68	C	4K x 4 Static CMOS RAM 35 NS	20	472.50	13.85	I
51C68	M	4K x 4 Static CMOS RAM 35 NS	20	550.00	67.14	I
51C68	M	4K x 4 Static CMOS RAM 45 NS	20	550.00	53.70	I
51C68	M	4K x 4 Static CMOS RAM 55 NS	20	550.00	47.67	I
51C68	M	4K x 4 Static CMOS RAM 70 NS	20	550.00	38.15	I
51C68L	C	4K x 4 Static CMOS RAM 35 NS	20	341.25	16.88	I
51C69	C	4K x 4 Static CMOS RAM 30 NS	20	472.50	16.88	I
51C69	C	4K x 4 Static CMOS RAM 35 NS	20	472.50	13.85	I
51C69L	C	4K x 4 Static CMOS RAM 35 NS	20	341.25	16.88	I
53S080	M	32 x 8 TTL PROM 35 NS	16	687.50	3.34	MMI
53S081	M	32 x 8 TTL PROM 35 NS	16	687.50	3.34	MMI
53S140	M	256 x 4 TTL PROM 55 NS	16	715.00	3.42	MMI
53S141	M	256 x 4 TTL PROM 55 NS	16	715.00	3.42	MMI
53S141A	M	256 x 4 TTL PROM 40 NS	16	715.00	4.34	MMI
53S240	M	512 x 4 TTL PROM 55 NS	16	715.00	4.68	MMI
53S241	M	512 x 4 TTL PROM 55 NS	16	715.00	4.68	MMI
53S241A	M	512 x 4 TTL PROM 45 NS	16	715.00	5.61	MMI
53S280	M	256 x 8 TTL PROM 50 NS	20	770.00	5.18	MMI
53S281	M	256 x 8 TTL PROM 50 NS	20	770.00	5.18	MMI
53S281A	M	256 x 8 TTL PROM 40 NS	20	770.00	5.36	MMI
53S440	M	1K x 4 TTL PROM 55 NS	18	770.00	7.26	MMI
53DA441	M	1K x 4 Registered TTL PROM 45 NS	24	990.00	22.55	MMI
53S441	M	1K x 4 TTL PROM 55 NS	18	770.00	7.26	MMI

TYPE	TEMP GRADE	DESCRIPTION	PINS	POWER (mW)	PRICE ($)	SUPPLIERS
53S441A	M	1K x 4 TTL PROM 50 NS	18	770.00	8.27	MMI
53DA442	M	1K x 4 Registered TTL PROM 45 NS	24	990.00	22.55	MMI
53S480	M	512 x 8 TTL PROM 50 NS	20	852.50	9.02	MMI
53RA481	M	512 x 8 Registered TTL PROM 45 NS	24	990.00	18.04	MMI
53RA481A	M	512 x 8 Registered TTL PROM 35 NS	24	990.00	21.64	MMI
53S481	M	512 x 8 TTL PROM 50 NS	20	852.50	9.02	MMI
53S481A	M	512 x 8 TTL PROM 40 NS	20	852.50	10.82	MMI
53DA841	M	2K x 4 Registered TTL PROM 45 NS	24	1017.50	38.33	MMI
53S841	M	2K x 4 TTL PROM 55 NS	18	825.00	11.02	MMI
53S841A	M	2K x 4 TTL PROM 50 NS	18	825.00	11.62	MMI
53RS881	M	1K x 8 Registered TTL PROM 45 NS	24	990.00	23.38	MMI
53RS881A	M	1K x 8 Registered TTL PROM 40 NS	24	990.00	29.23	MMI
53D1641	M	4K x 4 Registered TTL PROM 45 NS	24	1045.00	45.09	MMI
53S1641	M	4K x 4 TTL PROM 65 NS	20	962.50	24.88	MMI
53S1641A	M	4K x 4 TTL PROM 50 NS	20	962.50	26.64	MMI
53DA1643	M	4K x 4 Registered TTL PROM 45 NS	24	1045.00	45.09	MMI
53RA1681	M	2K x 8 Registered TTL PROM 45 NS	24	1017.50	33.65	MMI
53RA1681A	M	2K x 8 Registered TTL PROM 40 NS	24	1017.50	38.33	MMI
53RS1681	M	2K x 8 Registered TTL PROM 45 NS	24	1017.50	33.65	MMI
53RS1681A	M	2K x 8 Registered TTL PROM 40 NS	24	1017.50	38.33	MMI
53S1681	M	2K x 8 TTL PROM 60 NS	24	962.50	20.54	MMI
53S1681A	M	2K x 8 TTL PROM 45 NS	24	962.50	22.63	MMI
53S3281	M	4K x 8 TTL PROM 60 NS	24	1045.00	41.08	MMI
53S3281A	M	4K x 8 TTL PROM 50 NS	24	1045.00	45.26	MMI
54S188	M	32 x 8 TTL PROM 45 NS	16	605.00	2.60	N
54F189	M	16 x 4 Static TTL RAM 32 NS	16	302.50	12.87	F

TYPE	TEMP GRADE	DESCRIPTION	PINS	POWER (mW)	PRICE ($)	SUPPLIERS
54LS189	M	16 x 4 Static TTL RAM 90 NS	16	330.00	4.50	TI
54S189	M	16 x 4 Static TTL RAM 30 NS	16	550.00	8.70	N
54S189	M	16 x 4 Static TTL RAM 50 NS	16	605.00	4.20	N
54F219	M	16 x 4 Static TTL RAM 32 NS	16	302.50	20.59	F
54LS219	M	16 x 4 Static TTL RAM 90 NS	16	330.00	4.50	TI
54S287	M	256 x 4 TTL PROM 60 NS	16	715.00	2.85	N
54S288	M	32 x 8 TTL PROM 45 NS	16	605.00	2.60	N
54LS289	M	16 x 4 Static TTL RAM 90 NS	16	330.00	4.50	TI
54S289	M	16 x 4 Static TTL RAM 35 NS	16	605.00	4.20	N
54LS319	M	16 x 4 Static TTL RAM 90 NS	16	330.00	4.50	TI
54S387	M	256 x 4 TTL PROM 60 NS	16	715.00	2.85	N
54LS471	M	256 x 8 TTL PROM 70 NS	20	550.00	6.40	N
54S472	M	512 x 8 TTL PROM 75 NS	20	852.50	7.10	N
54S472A	M	512 x 8 TTL PROM 60 NS	20	852.50	8.50	N
54S472B	M	512 x 8 TTL PROM 50 NS	20	852.50	10.15	N
54S473	M	512 x 8 TTL PROM 75 NS	20	852.50	7.10	N
54S473A	M	512 x 8 TTL PROM 60 NS	20	852.50	8.50	N
54S474	M	512 x 8 TTL PROM 75 NS	24	935.00	8.10	N
54S474A	M	512 x 8 TTL PROM 60 NS	24	935.00	9.85	N
54S474B	M	512 x 8 TTL PROM 50 NS	24	935.00	11.80	N
54S475	M	512 x 8 TTL PROM 75 NS	24	935.00	8.10	N
54S475A	M	512 x 8 TTL PROM 60 NS	24	935.00	9.85	N
54S570	M	512 x 4 TTL PROM 65 NS	16	715.00	4.85	N
54S570A	M	512 x 4 TTL PROM 60 NS	16	715.00	5.80	N
54S571	M	512 x 4 TTL PROM 65 NS	16	715.00	4.85	N
54S571A	M	512 x 4 TTL PROM 60 NS	16	715.00	5.80	N

TYPE	TEMP GRADE	DESCRIPTION	PINS	POWER (mW)	PRICE ($)	SUPPLIERS
54S571B	M	512 x 4 TTL PROM 50 NS	16	715.00	6.95	N
54S572	M	1K x 4 TTL PROM 75 NS	18	770.00	8.35	N
54S572A	M	1K x 4 TTL PROM 60 NS	18	770.00	10.00	N
54S573	M	1K x 4 TTL PROM 75 NS	18	770.00	8.35	N
54S573A	M	1K x 4 TTL PROM 60 NS	18	770.00	10.00	N
54S573B	M	1K x 4 TTL PROM 50 NS	18	770.00	12.00	N
54S572	C	1K x 4 TTL PROM 60 NS	18	735.00	4.55	N
54S572A	C	1K x 4 TTL PROM 45 NS	18	735.00	4.55	N
54S573	C	1K x 4 TTL PROM 60 NS	18	735.00	4.55	N
54S573A	C	1K x 4 TTL PROM 45 NS	18	735.00	4.55	N
54S573B	C	1K x 4 TTL PROM 35 NS	18	735.00	6.60	N
6116	C	2K x 8 Static CMOS RAM 25 NS	24	420.00	11.04	IDT
6116	C	2K x 8 Static CMOS RAM 30 NS	24	420.00	9.20	IDT
6116	C	2K x 8 Static CMOS RAM 35 NS	24	420.00	7.50	IDT
6116	M	2K x 8 Static CMOS RAM 35 NS	24	495.00	94.80	IDT
6116	C	2K x 8 Static CMOS RAM 45 NS	24	420.00	5.20	IDT
6116	M	2K x 8 Static CMOS RAM 45 NS	24	495.00	79.60	IDT
6116	C	2K x 8 Static CMOS RAM 55 NS	24	420.00	3.60	IDT
6116	M	2K x 8 Static CMOS RAM 55 NS	24	495.00	63.70	IDT
6116	C	2K x 8 Static CMOS RAM 70 NS	24	420.00	3.20	IDT
6116	M	2K x 8 Static CMOS RAM 70 NS	24	495.00	53.50	IDT
6116	C	2K x 8 Static CMOS RAM 90 NS	24	420.00	2.80	IDT
6116	M	2K x 8 Static CMOS RAM 90 NS	24	495.00	46.20	IDT
6116	M	2K x 8 Static CMOS RAM 120 NS	24	495.00	40.15	IDT
6116	M	2K x 8 Static CMOS RAM 150 NS	24	495.00	37.00	IDT
6116L	C	2K x 8 Static CMOS RAM 25 NS	24	393.75	13.80	IDT

TYPE	TEMP GRADE	DESCRIPTION	PINS	POWER (mW)	PRICE ($)	SUPPLIERS
6116L	C	2K x 8 Static CMOS RAM 30 NS	24	393.75	11.50	IDT
6116L	C	2K x 8 Static CMOS RAM 35 NS	24	393.75	9.50	IDT
6116L	M	2K x 8 Static CMOS RAM 35 NS	24	467.50	105.00	IDT
6116L	C	2K x 8 Static CMOS RAM 45 NS	24	393.75	6.50	IDT
6116L	M	2K x 8 Static CMOS RAM 45 NS	24	467.50	87.56	IDT
6116L	C	2K x 8 Static CMOS RAM 55 NS	24	393.75	4.50	IDT
6116L	M	2K x 8 Static CMOS RAM 55 NS	24	467.50	70.07	IDT
6116L	C	2K x 8 Static CMOS RAM 70 NS	24	393.75	4.00	IDT
6116L	M	2K x 8 Static CMOS RAM 70 NS	24	467.50	58.36	IDT
6116L	C	2K x 8 Static CMOS RAM 90 NS	24	393.75	3.50	IDT
6116L	M	2K x 8 Static CMOS RAM 90 NS	24	467.50	50.82	IDT
6116L	M	2K x 8 Static CMOS RAM 120 NS	24	467.50	44.17	IDT
6116L	M	2K x 8 Static CMOS RAM 150 NS	24	467.50	40.00	IDT
6147	C	4K x 1 Static MOS RAM 55 NS	18	183.75	2.80	M
6147	C	4K x 1 Static MOS RAM 70 NS	18	183.75	2.59	M
61L47	C	4K x 1 Static MOS RAM 55 NS	18	183.75	2.94	M
61L47	C	4K x 1 Static MOS RAM 70 NS	18	183.75	2.73	M
6167	C	16K x 1 Static CMOS RAM 15 NS	20	472.50	33.30	IDT
6167	C	16K x 1 Static CMOS RAM 20 NS	20	472.50	17.37	IDT
6167	M	16K x 1 Static CMOS RAM 20 NS	20	495.00	156.33	IDT
6167	C	16K x 1 Static CMOS RAM 25 NS	20	472.50	12.87	IDT
6167	M	16K x 1 Static CMOS RAM 25 NS	20	495.00	115.83	IDT
6167	C	16K x 1 Static CMOS RAM 35 NS	20	472.50	7.11	IDT
6167	M	16K x 1 Static CMOS RAM 35 NS	20	495.00	63.99	IDT
6167	C	16K x 1 Static CMOS RAM 45 NS	20	472.50	5.67	IDT
6167	M	16K x 1 Static CMOS RAM 45 NS	20	495.00	51.03	IDT

TYPE	TEMP GRADE	DESCRIPTION	PINS	POWER (mW)	PRICE ($)	SUPPLIERS
6167	C	16K x 1 Static CMOS RAM 55 NS	20	472.50	4.82	IDT
6167	M	16K x 1 Static CMOS RAM 55 NS	20	495.00	43.34	IDT
6167	M	16K x 1 Static CMOS RAM 70 NS	20	495.00	36.11	IDT
6167	M	16K x 1 Static CMOS RAM 85 NS	20	495.00	30.09	IDT
6167	M	16K x 1 Static CMOS RAM 100 NS	20	495.00	25.08	IDT
6167L	C	16K x 1 Static CMOS RAM 15 NS	20	288.75	37.00	IDT
6167L	C	16K x 1 Static CMOS RAM 20 NS	20	288.75	19.30	IDT
6167L	M	16K x 1 Static CMOS RAM 20 NS	20	330.00	173.70	IDT
6167L	C	16K x 1 Static CMOS RAM 25 NS	20	288.75	14.30	IDT
6167L	M	16K x 1 Static CMOS RAM 25 NS	20	330.00	128.70	IDT
6167L	C	16K x 1 Static CMOS RAM 35 NS	20	288.75	7.90	IDT
6167L	M	16K x 1 Static CMOS RAM 35 NS	20	330.00	71.10	IDT
6167L	C	16K x 1 Static CMOS RAM 45 NS	20	288.75	6.30	IDT
6167L	M	16K x 1 Static CMOS RAM 45 NS	20	330.00	56.70	IDT
6167L	C	16K x 1 Static CMOS RAM 55 NS	20	288.75	5.35	IDT
6167L	M	16K x 1 Static CMOS RAM 55 NS	20	330.00	48.15	IDT
6167L	M	16K x 1 Static CMOS RAM 70 NS	20	330.00	40.13	IDT
6167L	M	16K x 1 Static CMOS RAM 85 NS	20	330.00	33.44	IDT
6167L	M	16K x 1 Static CMOS RAM 100 NS	20	330.00	27.86	IDT
6168	C	4K x 4 Static CMOS RAM 20 NS	20	472.50	17.37	IDT
6168	C	4K x 4 Static CMOS RAM 25 NS	20	472.50	12.87	IDT
6168	M	4K x 4 Static CMOS RAM 25 NS	20	550.00	117.76	IDT
6168	C	4K x 4 Static CMOS RAM 35 NS	20	472.50	7.11	IDT
6168	M	4K x 4 Static CMOS RAM 35 NS	20	550.00	65.06	IDT
6168	C	4K x 4 Static CMOS RAM 45 NS	20	472.50	5.67	IDT
6168	M	4K x 4 Static CMOS RAM 45 NS	20	550.00	51.88	IDT

TYPE	TEMP GRADE	DESCRIPTION	PINS	POWER (mW)	PRICE ($)	SUPPLIERS
6168	C	4K x 4 Static CMOS RAM 55 NS	20	472.50	4.82	IDT
6168	M	4K x 4 Static CMOS RAM 55 NS	20	550.00	44.06	IDT
6168	M	4K x 4 Static CMOS RAM 70 NS	20	550.00	36.71	IDT
6168	M	4K x 4 Static CMOS RAM 85 NS	20	550.00	30.60	IDT
6168	M	4K x 4 Static CMOS RAM 100 NS	20	550.00	25.50	IDT
6168L	C	4K x 4 Static CMOS RAM 20 NS	20	367.50	19.30	IDT
6168L	C	4K x 4 Static CMOS RAM 25 NS	20	367.50	14.30	IDT
6168L	M	4K x 4 Static CMOS RAM 25 NS	20	440.00	130.85	IDT
6168L	C	4K x 4 Static CMOS RAM 35 NS	20	367.50	7.90	IDT
6168L	M	4K x 4 Static CMOS RAM 35 NS	20	440.00	72.29	IDT
6168L	C	4K x 4 Static CMOS RAM 45 NS	20	367.50	6.30	IDT
6168L	M	4K x 4 Static CMOS RAM 45 NS	20	440.00	94.50	IDT
6168L	C	4K x 4 Static CMOS RAM 55 NS	20	367.50	5.35	IDT
6168L	M	4K x 4 Static CMOS RAM 55 NS	20	440.00	48.95	IDT
6168L	M	4K x 4 Static CMOS RAM 70 NS	20	440.00	40.79	IDT
6168L	M	4K x 4 Static CMOS RAM 85 NS	20	440.00	33.99	IDT
6168L	M	4K x 4 Static CMOS RAM 100 NS	20	440.00	28.33	IDT
63S080	C	32 x 8 TTL PROM 25 NS	16	656.25	1.50	MMI
63S081	C	32 x 8 TTL PROM 25 NS	16	656.25	1.50	MMI
63S081A	C	32 x 8 TTL PROM 15 NS	16	656.25	2.25	MMI
63S140	C	256 x 4 TTL PROM 45 NS	16	682.50	1.59	MMI
63S141	C	256 x 4 TTL PROM 45 NS	16	682.50	1.59	MMI
63S141A	C	256 x 4 TTL PROM 30 NS	16	682.50	2.00	MMI
63S240	C	512 x 4 TTL PROM 45 NS	16	682.50	2.76	MMI
63S241	C	512 x 4 TTL PROM 45 NS	16	682.50	2.76	MMI
63S241A	C	512 x 4 TTL PROM 35 NS	16	682.50	3.09	MMI

TYPE	TEMP GRADE	DESCRIPTION	PINS	POWER (mW)	PRICE ($)	SUPPLIERS
63S280	C	256 x 8 TTL PROM 45 NS	20	735.00	3.34	MMI
63S281	C	256 x 8 TTL PROM 45 NS	20	735.00	3.34	MMI
63S281A	C	256 x 8 TTL PROM 28 NS	20	735.00	3.67	MMI
63S440	C	1K x 4 TTL PROM 45 NS	18	735.00	3.51	MMI
63DA441	C	1K x 4 Registered TTL PROM 35 NS	24	945.00	10.02	MMI
63S441	C	1K x 4 TTL PROM 45 NS	18	735.00	3.51	MMI
63S441A	C	1K x 4 TTL PROM 35 NS	18	735.00	3.84	MMI
63DA442	C	1K x 4 Registered TTL PROM 35 NS	24	945.00	10.02	MMI
63S480	C	512 x 8 TTL PROM 45 NS	20	813.75	4.18	MMI
63RA481	C	512 x 8 Registered TTL PROM 35 NS	24	945.00	7.52	MMI
63RA481A	C	512 x 8 Registered TTL PROM 30 NS	24	945.00	9.44	MMI
63S481	C	512 x 8 TTL PROM 45 NS	20	813.75	4.18	MMI
63S481A	C	512 x 8 TTL PROM 30 NS	20	813.75	4.51	MMI
63DA841	C	2K x 4 Registered TTL PROM 40 NS	24	971.25	16.28	MMI
63S841	C	2K x 4 TTL PROM 50 NS	18	787.50	5.43	MMI
63S841A	C	2K x 4 TTL PROM 35 NS	18	787.50	5.85	MMI
63RS881	C	1K x 8 Registered TTL PROM 35 NS	24	945.00	10.35	MMI
63RS881A	C	1K x 8 Registered TTL PROM 30 NS	24	945.00	12.94	MMI
63D1641	C	4K x 4 Registered TTL PROM 40 NS	24	997.50	20.04	MMI
63S1641	C	4K x 4 TTL PROM 50 NS	20	918.75	14.20	MMI
63S1641A	C	4K x 4 TTL PROM 35 NS	20	918.75	16.70	MMI
63DA1643	C	4K x 4 Registered TTL PROM 40 NS	24	997.50	20.04	MMI
63RA1681	C	2K x 8 Registered TTL PROM 40 NS	24	971.25	14.20	MMI
63RA1681A	C	2K x 8 Registered TTL PROM 35 NS	24	971.25	16.28	MMI
63RS1681	C	2K x 8 Registered TTL PROM 40 NS	24	971.25	14.20	MMI
63RS1681A	C	2K x 8 Registered TTL PROM 35 NS	24	971.25	16.28	MMI

TYPE	TEMP GRADE	DESCRIPTION	PINS	POWER (mW)	PRICE ($)	SUPPLIERS
63S1681	C	2K x 8 TTL PROM 50 NS	24	918.75	6.68	MMI
63S1681A	C	2K x 8 TTL PROM 35 NS	24	918.75	8.35	MMI
63S3281	C	4K x 8 TTL PROM 50 NS	24	997.50	17.54	MMI
63S3281A	C	4K x 8 TTL PROM 40 NS	24	997.50	19.62	MMI
6504	I	4K x 1 Static CMOS RAM 120 NS	18	38.50	10.40	H
6504	M	4K x 1 Static CMOS RAM 120 NS	18	38.50	18.88	H
6504	I	4K x 1 Static CMOS RAM 220 NS	18	38.50	6.02	H
6504	M	4K x 1 Static CMOS RAM 220 NS	18	38.50	10.61	H
6508	I	1K x 1 Static CMOS RAM 180 NS	16	22.00	7.94	H
6508	M	1K x 1 Static CMOS RAM 180 NS	16	22.00	12.76	H
6508	I	1K x 1 Static CMOS RAM 250 NS	16	22.00	5.91	H
6508	M	1K x 1 Static CMOS RAM 250 NS	16	22.00	9.85	H
6508	C	1K x 1 Static CMOS RAM 310 NS	16	21.00	4.94	H
6514	I	1K x 4 Static CMOS RAM 120 NS	18	38.50	10.40	H
6514	M	1K x 4 Static CMOS RAM 120 NS	18	38.50	21.14	H
6514	I	1K x 4 Static CMOS RAM 220 NS	18	38.50	7.59	H
6514	M	1K x 4 Static CMOS RAM 220 NS	18	38.50	15.43	H
6514	I	1K x 4 Static CMOS RAM 320 NS	18	38.50	6.02	H
6514	M	1K x 4 Static CMOS RAM 320 NS	18	38.50	11.87	H
6516	I	2K x 8 Static CMOS RAM 120 NS	24	55.00	27.60	H
6516	M	2K x 8 Static CMOS RAM 120 NS	24	55.00	94.58	H
6516	I	2K x 8 Static CMOS RAM 200 NS	24	55.00	21.23	H
6516	M	2K x 8 Static CMOS RAM 200 NS	24	55.00	70.06	H
6518	I	1K x 1 Static CMOS RAM 180 NS	18	22.00	7.94	H
6518	M	1K x 1 Static CMOS RAM 180 NS	18	22.00	12.81	H
6518	I	1K x 1 Static CMOS RAM 250 NS	18	22.00	5.91	H

TYPE	TEMP GRADE	DESCRIPTION	PINS	POWER (mW)	PRICE ($)	SUPPLIERS
6518	M	1K x 1 Static CMOS RAM 250 NS	18	22.00	9.85	H
6518	C	1K x 1 Static CMOS RAM 310 NS	18	21.00	4.28	H
6551	I	256 x 4 Static CMOS RAM 220 NS	22	22.00	9.09	H
6551	M	256 x 4 Static CMOS RAM 220 NS	22	22.00	14.58	H
6551	I	256 x 4 Static CMOS RAM 300 NS	22	22.00	6.86	H
6551	M	256 x 4 Static CMOS RAM 300 NS	22	22.00	11.23	H
6561	I	256 x 4 Static CMOS RAM 220 NS	18	22.00	9.09	H
6561	M	256 x 4 Static CMOS RAM 220 NS	18	22.00	14.58	H
6561	I	256 x 4 Static CMOS RAM 300 NS	18	22.00	6.86	H
6561	M	256 x 4 Static CMOS RAM 300 NS	18	22.00	11.23	H
65162	I	2K x 8 Static CMOS RAM 70 NS	24	385.00	21.52	H
65162	M	2K x 8 Static CMOS RAM 70 NS	24	385.00	75.33	H
65162	I	2K x 8 Static CMOS RAM 90 NS	24	385.00	15.94	H
65162	I	2K x 8 Static CMOS RAM 90 NS	24	385.00	13.55	H
65162	M	2K x 8 Static CMOS RAM 90 NS	24	385.00	55.80	H
65162	M	2K x 8 Static CMOS RAM 90 NS	24	385.00	39.06	H
65262	I	16K x 1 Static CMOS RAM 70 NS	20	275.00	21.52	H
65262	M	16K x 1 Static CMOS RAM 70 NS	20	275.00	75.33	H
65262	I	16K x 1 Static CMOS RAM 85 NS	20	275.00	13.55	H
65262	I	16K x 1 Static CMOS RAM 85 NS	20	275.00	15.94	H
65262	M	16K x 1 Static CMOS RAM 85 NS	20	275.00	55.80	H
6616	I	2K x 8 CMOS PROM 140 NS	24	82.50	22.00	H
6616	M	2K x 8 CMOS PROM 140 NS	24	82.50	66.00	H
6641	I	512 x 8 CMOS PROM 250 NS	24	82.50	15.52	H
6641	M	512 x 8 CMOS PROM 250 NS	24	82.50	27.94	H
6810	C	128 x 8 Static MOS RAM 450 NS	24	420.00	1.75	M

TYPE	TEMP GRADE	DESCRIPTION	PINS	POWER (mW)	PRICE ($)	SUPPLIERS
6810	I	128 x 8 Static MOS RAM 450 NS	24	440.00	2.90	M
68A10	C	128 x 8 Static MOS RAM 360 NS	24	525.00	2.20	M
68A10	I	128 x 8 Static MOS RAM 360 NS	24	550.00	3.20	M
68B10	C	128 x 8 Static MOS RAM 250 NS	24	525.00	2.85	M
68764	C	8K x 8 Eraseable MOS PROM 450 NS 5% VCC 25V VPP	24	446.25	11.20	M
68766	C	8K x 8 Eraseable MOS PROM 350 NS 5% VCC 25V VPP	24	446.25	12.60	M
68766	C	8K x 8 Eraseable MOS PROM 450 NS 5% VCC 25V VPP	24	446.25	11.20	M
7164L	C	8K x 8 Static CMOS RAM 30 NS	28	420.00	37.20	IDT
7164L	C	8K x 8 Static CMOS RAM 35 NS	28	420.00	26.40	IDT
7164L	M	8K x 8 Static CMOS RAM 35 NS	28	495.00	268.00	IDT
7164L	C	8K x 8 Static CMOS RAM 45 NS	28	420.00	19.20	IDT
7164L	M	8K x 8 Static CMOS RAM 45 NS	28	495.00	223.00	IDT
7164L	C	8K x 8 Static CMOS RAM 55 NS	28	420.00	17.40	IDT
7164L	M	8K x 8 Static CMOS RAM 55 NS	28	495.00	186.00	IDT
7164L	C	8K x 8 Static CMOS RAM 70 NS	28	420.00	15.00	IDT
7164L	M	8K x 8 Static CMOS RAM 70 NS	28	495.00	155.00	IDT
7164L	M	8K x 8 Static CMOS RAM 85 NS	28	495.00	129.00	IDT
7164L	M	8K x 8 Static CMOS RAM 100 NS	28	495.00	108.00	IDT
7164L	M	8K x 8 Static CMOS RAM 120 NS	28	495.00	108.00	IDT
7164L	M	8K x 8 Static CMOS RAM 150 NS	28	495.00	108.00	IDT
7164L	M	8K x 8 Static CMOS RAM 200 NS	28	495.00	108.00	IDT
7164S	C	8K x 8 Static CMOS RAM 30 NS	28	472.50	30.50	IDT
7164S	C	8K x 8 Static CMOS RAM 35 NS	28	472.50	21.50	IDT
7164S	M	8K x 8 Static CMOS RAM 35 NS	28	550.00	246.00	IDT

TYPE	TEMP GRADE	DESCRIPTION	PINS	POWER (mW)	PRICE ($)	SUPPLIERS
7164S	C	8K x 8 Static CMOS RAM 45 NS	28	472.50	15.50	IDT
7164S	M	8K x 8 Static CMOS RAM 45 NS	28	550.00	205.00	IDT
7164S	C	8K x 8 Static CMOS RAM 55 NS	28	472.50	14.00	IDT
7164S	M	8K x 8 Static CMOS RAM 55 NS	28	550.00	171.00	IDT
7164S	C	8K x 8 Static CMOS RAM 70 NS	28	472.50	12.00	IDT
7164S	M	8K x 8 Static CMOS RAM 70 NS	28	550.00	142.00	IDT
7164S	M	8K x 8 Static CMOS RAM 85 NS	28	550.00	118.00	IDT
7164S	M	8K x 8 Static CMOS RAM 100 NS	28	550.00	99.00	IDT
7164S	M	8K x 8 Static CMOS RAM 120 NS	28	550.00	99.00	IDT
7164S	M	8K x 8 Static CMOS RAM 150 NS	28	550.00	99.00	IDT
7164S	M	8K x 8 Static CMOS RAM 200 NS	28	550.00	99.00	IDT
7165L	C	8K x 8 Static CMOS RAM 30 NS	28	420.00	44.60	IDT
7165L	C	8K x 8 Static CMOS RAM 35 NS	28	420.00	31.70	IDT
7165L	M	8K x 8 Static CMOS RAM 35 NS	28	495.00	310.00	IDT
7165L	C	8K x 8 Static CMOS RAM 45 NS	28	420.00	23.00	IDT
7165L	M	8K x 8 Static CMOS RAM 45 NS	28	495.00	258.00	IDT
7165L	C	8K x 8 Static CMOS RAM 55 NS	28	420.00	20.90	IDT
7165L	M	8K x 8 Static CMOS RAM 55 NS	28	495.00	215.00	IDT
7165L	C	8K x 8 Static CMOS RAM 70 NS	28	420.00	18.00	IDT
7165L	M	8K x 8 Static CMOS RAM 70 NS	28	495.00	179.00	IDT
7165L	M	8K x 8 Static CMOS RAM 85 NS	28	495.00	122.00	IDT
7165S	C	8K x 8 Static CMOS RAM 30 NS	28	472.50	36.60	IDT
7165S	C	8K x 8 Static CMOS RAM 35 NS	28	472.50	25.80	IDT
7165S	M	8K x 8 Static CMOS RAM 35 NS	28	550.00	282.00	IDT
7165S	C	8K x 8 Static CMOS RAM 45 NS	28	472.50	18.60	IDT
7165S	M	8K x 8 Static CMOS RAM 45 NS	28	550.00	235.00	IDT

TYPE	TEMP GRADE	DESCRIPTION	PINS	POWER (mW)	PRICE ($)	SUPPLIERS
7165S	C	8K x 8 Static CMOS RAM 55 NS	28	472.50	16.80	IDT
7165S	M	8K x 8 Static CMOS RAM 55 NS	28	550.00	196.00	IDT
7165S	C	8K x 8 Static CMOS RAM 70 NS	28	472.50	14.40	IDT
7165S	M	8K x 8 Static CMOS RAM 70 NS	28	550.00	163.00	IDT
7165S	M	8K x 8 Static CMOS RAM 85 NS	28	550.00	135.00	IDT
7187L	C	64K x 1 Static CMOS RAM 25 NS	22	367.50	49.50	IDT
7187L	M	64K x 1 Static CMOS RAM 25 NS	22	467.50	297.00	IDT
7187L	C	64K x 1 Static CMOS RAM 30 NS	22	367.50	44.00	IDT
7187L	M	64K x 1 Static CMOS RAM 30 NS	22	467.50	264.00	IDT
7187L	C	64K x 1 Static CMOS RAM 35 NS	22	367.50	38.50	IDT
7187L	M	64K x 1 Static CMOS RAM 35 NS	22	467.50	231.00	IDT
7187L	C	64K x 1 Static CMOS RAM 45 NS	22	367.50	27.50	IDT
7187L	M	64K x 1 Static CMOS RAM 45 NS	22	467.50	177.69	IDT
7187L	C	64K x 1 Static CMOS RAM 55 NS	22	367.50	19.80	IDT
7187L	M	64K x 1 Static CMOS RAM 55 NS	22	467.50	142.15	IDT
7187L	C	64K x 1 Static CMOS RAM 70 NS	22	367.50	13.20	IDT
7187L	M	64K x 1 Static CMOS RAM 70 NS	22	467.50	118.46	IDT
7187L	M	64K x 1 Static CMOS RAM 85 NS	22	467.50	103.01	IDT
7187S	C	64K x 1 Static CMOS RAM 25 NS	22	472.50	45.00	IDT
7187S	M	64K x 1 Static CMOS RAM 25 NS	22	577.50	270.00	IDT
7187S	C	64K x 1 Static CMOS RAM 30 NS	22	472.50	40.00	IDT
7187S	M	64K x 1 Static CMOS RAM 30 NS	22	577.50	240.00	IDT
7187S	C	64K x 1 Static CMOS RAM 35 NS	22	472.50	35.00	IDT
7187S	M	64K x 1 Static CMOS RAM 35 NS	22	577.50	210.00	IDT
7187S	C	64K x 1 Static CMOS RAM 45 NS	22	472.50	25.00	IDT
7187S	M	64K x 1 Static CMOS RAM 45 NS	22	577.50	161.54	IDT

TYPE	TEMP GRADE	DESCRIPTION	PINS	POWER (mW)	PRICE ($)	SUPPLIERS
7187S	C	64K x 1 Static CMOS RAM 55 NS	22	472.50	18.00	IDT
7187S	M	64K x 1 Static CMOS RAM 55 NS	22	577.50	129.23	IDT
7187S	C	64K x 1 Static CMOS RAM 70 NS	22	472.50	12.00	IDT
7187S	M	64K x 1 Static CMOS RAM 70 NS	22	577.50	107.69	IDT
7187S	M	64K x 1 Static CMOS RAM 85 NS	22	577.50	93.65	IDT
7188L	C	16K x 4 Static CMOS RAM 25 NS	22	367.50	49.50	IDT
7188L	M	16K x 4 Static CMOS RAM 25 NS	22	467.50	297.00	IDT
7188L	C	16K x 4 Static CMOS RAM 30 NS	22	367.50	44.00	IDT
7188L	M	16K x 4 Static CMOS RAM 30 NS	22	467.50	264.00	IDT
7188L	C	16K x 4 Static CMOS RAM 35 NS	22	367.50	38.50	IDT
7188L	M	16K x 4 Static CMOS RAM 35 NS	22	467.50	231.00	IDT
7188L	C	16K x 4 Static CMOS RAM 45 NS	22	367.50	27.50	IDT
7188L	M	16K x 4 Static CMOS RAM 45 NS	22	467.50	177.69	IDT
7188L	C	16K x 4 Static CMOS RAM 55 NS	22	367.50	19.80	IDT
7188L	M	16K x 4 Static CMOS RAM 55 NS	22	467.50	142.15	IDT
7188L	C	16K x 4 Static CMOS RAM 70 NS	22	367.50	13.20	IDT
7188L	M	16K x 4 Static CMOS RAM 70 NS	22	467.50	118.46	IDT
7188L	M	16K x 4 Static CMOS RAM 85 NS	22	467.50	103.01	IDT
7188S	C	16K x 4 Static CMOS RAM 25 NS	22	472.50	45.00	IDT
7188S	M	16K x 4 Static CMOS RAM 25 NS	22	577.50	270.00	IDT
7188S	C	16K x 4 Static CMOS RAM 30 NS	22	472.50	40.00	IDT
7188S	M	16K x 4 Static CMOS RAM 30 NS	22	577.50	240.00	IDT
7188S	C	16K x 4 Static CMOS RAM 35 NS	22	472.50	35.00	IDT
7188S	M	16K x 4 Static CMOS RAM 35 NS	22	577.50	210.00	IDT
7188S	C	16K x 4 Static CMOS RAM 45 NS	22	472.50	25.00	IDT
7188S	M	16K x 4 Static CMOS RAM 45 NS	22	577.50	161.54	IDT

TYPE	TEMP GRADE	DESCRIPTION	PINS	POWER (mW)	PRICE ($)	SUPPLIERS
7188S	C	16K x 4 Static CMOS RAM 55 NS	22	472.50	18.00	IDT
7188S	M	16K x 4 Static CMOS RAM 55 NS	22	577.50	129.23	IDT
7188S	C	16K x 4 Static CMOS RAM 70 NS	22	472.50	12.00	IDT
7188S	M	16K x 4 Static CMOS RAM 70 NS	22	577.50	107.69	IDT
7188S	M	16K x 4 Static CMOS RAM 85 NS	22	577.50	93.65	IDT
7198L	C	16K x 4 Static CMOS RAM 25 NS	24	446.25	49.50	IDT
7198L	C	16K x 4 Static CMOS RAM 30 NS	24	446.25	44.00	IDT
7198L	M	16K x 4 Static CMOS RAM 30 NS	24	522.50	259.88	IDT
7198L	C	16K x 4 Static CMOS RAM 35 NS	24	446.25	38.50	IDT
7198L	M	16K x 4 Static CMOS RAM 35 NS	24	522.50	231.00	IDT
7198L	C	16K x 4 Static CMOS RAM 45 NS	24	446.25	27.50	IDT
7198L	M	16K x 4 Static CMOS RAM 45 NS	24	522.50	177.69	IDT
7198L	C	16K x 4 Static CMOS RAM 55 NS	24	446.25	19.80	IDT
7198L	M	16K x 4 Static CMOS RAM 55 NS	24	522.50	142.15	IDT
7198L	C	16K x 4 Static CMOS RAM 70 NS	24	446.25	13.20	IDT
7198L	M	16K x 4 Static CMOS RAM 70 NS	24	522.50	118.46	IDT
7198L	M	16K x 4 Static CMOS RAM 85 NS	24	522.50	103.01	IDT
7198S	C	16K x 4 Static CMOS RAM 25 NS	24	525.00	45.00	IDT
7198S	C	16K x 4 Static CMOS RAM 30 NS	24	525.00	40.00	IDT
7198S	M	16K x 4 Static CMOS RAM 30 NS	24	605.00	240.00	IDT
7198S	C	16K x 4 Static CMOS RAM 35 NS	24	525.00	35.00	IDT
7198S	M	16K x 4 Static CMOS RAM 35 NS	24	605.00	210.00	IDT
7198S	C	16K x 4 Static CMOS RAM 45 NS	24	525.00	25.00	IDT
7198S	M	16K x 4 Static CMOS RAM 45 NS	24	605.00	161.54	IDT
7198S	C	16K x 4 Static CMOS RAM 55 NS	24	525.00	18.00	IDT
7198S	M	16K x 4 Static CMOS RAM 55 NS	24	605.00	129.23	IDT

TYPE	TEMP GRADE	DESCRIPTION	PINS	POWER (mW)	PRICE ($)	SUPPLIERS
7198S	C	16K x 4 Static CMOS RAM 70 NS	24	525.00	12.00	IDT
7198S	M	16K x 4 Static CMOS RAM 70 NS	24	605.00	107.69	IDT
7198S	M	16K x 4 Static CMOS RAM 85 NS	24	605.00	93.65	IDT
71681L	C	4K x 4 Static CMOS RAM 20 NS	24	367.50	22.25	IDT
71681L	C	4K x 4 Static CMOS RAM 25 NS	24	367.50	16.45	IDT
71681L	M	4K x 4 Static CMOS RAM 25 NS	24	440.00	148.05	IDT
71681L	C	4K x 4 Static CMOS RAM 35 NS	24	367.50	9.10	IDT
71681L	M	4K x 4 Static CMOS RAM 35 NS	24	440.00	81.90	IDT
71681L	C	4K x 4 Static CMOS RAM 45 NS	24	367.50	7.25	IDT
71681L	M	4K x 4 Static CMOS RAM 45 NS	24	440.00	65.25	IDT
71681L	C	4K x 4 Static CMOS RAM 55 NS	24	367.50	6.15	IDT
71681L	M	4K x 4 Static CMOS RAM 55 NS	24	440.00	55.35	IDT
71681L	M	4K x 4 Static CMOS RAM 70 NS	24	440.00	46.13	IDT
71681L	M	4K x 4 Static CMOS RAM 85 NS	24	440.00	38.44	IDT
71681L	M	4K x 4 Static CMOS RAM 100 NS	24	440.00	32.03	IDT
71681S	C	4K x 4 Static CMOS RAM 20 NS	24	472.50	20.03	IDT
71681S	C	4K x 4 Static CMOS RAM 25 NS	24	472.50	14.81	IDT
71681S	M	4K x 4 Static CMOS RAM 25 NS	24	550.00	133.25	IDT
71681S	C	4K x 4 Static CMOS RAM 35 NS	24	472.50	8.19	IDT
71681S	M	4K x 4 Static CMOS RAM 35 NS	24	550.00	73.71	IDT
71681S	C	4K x 4 Static CMOS RAM 45 NS	24	472.50	6.53	IDT
71681S	M	4K x 4 Static CMOS RAM 45 NS	24	550.00	58.73	IDT
71681S	C	4K x 4 Static CMOS RAM 55 NS	24	472.50	5.54	IDT
71681S	M	4K x 4 Static CMOS RAM 55 NS	24	550.00	49.82	IDT
71681S	M	4K x 4 Static CMOS RAM 70 NS	24	550.00	41.51	IDT
71681S	M	4K x 4 Static CMOS RAM 85 NS	24	550.00	34.59	IDT

TYPE	TEMP GRADE	DESCRIPTION	PINS	POWER (mW)	PRICE ($)	SUPPLIERS
71681S	M	4K x 4 Static CMOS RAM 100 NS	24	550.00	28.83	IDT
71682L	C	4K x 4 Static CMOS RAM 20 NS	24	367.50	22.25	IDT
71682L	C	4K x 4 Static CMOS RAM 25 NS	24	367.50	16.45	IDT
71682L	M	4K x 4 Static CMOS RAM 25 NS	24	440.00	148.05	IDT
71682L	C	4K x 4 Static CMOS RAM 35 NS	24	367.50	9.10	IDT
71682L	M	4K x 4 Static CMOS RAM 35 NS	24	440.00	81.90	IDT
71682L	C	4K x 4 Static CMOS RAM 45 NS	24	367.50	7.25	IDT
71682L	M	4K x 4 Static CMOS RAM 45 NS	24	440.00	65.25	IDT
71682L	C	4K x 4 Static CMOS RAM 55 NS	24	367.50	6.15	IDT
71682L	M	4K x 4 Static CMOS RAM 55 NS	24	440.00	55.35	IDT
71682L	M	4K x 4 Static CMOS RAM 70 NS	24	440.00	46.13	IDT
71682L	M	4K x 4 Static CMOS RAM 85 NS	24	440.00	38.44	IDT
71682L	M	4K x 4 Static CMOS RAM 100 NS	24	440.00	32.03	IDT
71682S	C	4K x 4 Static CMOS RAM 20 NS	24	472.50	20.03	IDT
71682S	C	4K x 4 Static CMOS RAM 25 NS	24	472.50	14.81	IDT
71682S	M	4K x 4 Static CMOS RAM 25 NS	24	550.00	133.25	IDT
71682S	C	4K x 4 Static CMOS RAM 35 NS	24	472.50	8.19	IDT
71682S	M	4K x 4 Static CMOS RAM 35 NS	24	550.00	73.71	IDT
71682S	C	4K x 4 Static CMOS RAM 45 NS	24	472.50	6.53	IDT
71682S	M	4K x 4 Static CMOS RAM 45 NS	24	550.00	58.73	IDT
71682S	C	4K x 4 Static CMOS RAM 55 NS	24	472.50	5.54	IDT
71682S	M	4K x 4 Static CMOS RAM 55 NS	24	550.00	49.82	IDT
71682S	M	4K x 4 Static CMOS RAM 70 NS	24	550.00	41.51	IDT
71682S	M	4K x 4 Static CMOS RAM 85 NS	24	550.00	34.59	IDT
71632S	M	4K x 4 Static CMOS RAM 100 NS	24	550.00	28.83	IDT
71981L	C	16K x 4 Static CMOS RAM 25 NS	28	446.25	56.93	IDT

TYPE	TEMP GRADE	DESCRIPTION	PINS	POWER (mW)	PRICE ($)	SUPPLIERS
71981L	C	16K x 4 Static CMOS RAM 30 NS	28	446.25	50.60	IDT
71981L	M	16K x 4 Static CMOS RAM 30 NS	28	522.50	433.13	IDT
71981L	C	16K x 4 Static CMOS RAM 35 NS	28	446.25	44.28	IDT
71981L	M	16K x 4 Static CMOS RAM 35 NS	28	522.50	385.00	IDT
71981L	C	16K x 4 Static CMOS RAM 45 NS	28	446.25	31.63	IDT
71981L	M	16K x 4 Static CMOS RAM 45 NS	28	522.50	296.15	IDT
71981L	C	16K x 4 Static CMOS RAM 55 NS	28	446.25	22.77	IDT
71981L	M	16K x 4 Static CMOS RAM 55 NS	28	522.50	236.92	IDT
71981L	C	16K x 4 Static CMOS RAM 70 NS	28	446.25	15.18	IDT
71981L	M	16K x 4 Static CMOS RAM 70 NS	28	522.50	197.44	IDT
71981L	M	16K x 4 Static CMOS RAM 85 NS	28	522.50	171.68	IDT
71981S	C	16K x 4 Static CMOS RAM 25 NS	28	525.00	51.75	IDT
71981S	C	16K x 4 Static CMOS RAM 30 NS	28	525.00	46.00	IDT
71981S	M	16K x 4 Static CMOS RAM 30 NS	28	605.00	393.75	IDT
71981S	C	16K x 4 Static CMOS RAM 35 NS	28	525.00	40.25	IDT
71981S	M	16K x 4 Static CMOS RAM 35 NS	28	605.00	350.00	IDT
71981S	C	16K x 4 Static CMOS RAM 45 NS	28	525.00	28.75	IDT
71981S	M	16K x 4 Static CMOS RAM 45 NS	28	605.00	269.23	IDT
71981S	C	16K x 4 Static CMOS RAM 55 NS	28	525.00	20.70	IDT
71981S	M	16K x 4 Static CMOS RAM 55 NS	28	605.00	215.38	IDT
71981S	C	16K x 4 Static CMOS RAM 70 NS	28	525.00	13.80	IDT
71981S	M	16K x 4 Static CMOS RAM 70 NS	28	605.00	179.49	IDT
71981S	M	16K x 4 Static CMOS RAM 85 NS	28	605.00	156.08	IDT
71982L	C	16K x 4 Static CMOS RAM 25 NS	28	446.25	56.93	IDT
71982L	C	16K x 4 Static CMOS RAM 30 NS	28	446.25	50.60	IDT
71982L	M	16K x 4 Static CMOS RAM 30 NS	28	522.50	433.13	IDT

TYPE	TEMP GRADE	DESCRIPTION	PINS	POWER (mW)	PRICE ($)	SUPPLIERS
71982L	C	16K x 4 Static CMOS RAM 35 NS	28	446.25	44.28	IDT
71982L	M	16K x 4 Static CMOS RAM 35 NS	28	522.50	385.00	IDT
71982L	C	16K x 4 Static CMOS RAM 45 NS	28	446.25	31.63	IDT
71982L	M	16K x 4 Static CMOS RAM 45 NS	28	522.50	296.15	IDT
71982L	C	16K x 4 Static CMOS RAM 55 NS	28	446.25	22.77	IDT
71982L	M	16K x 4 Static CMOS RAM 55 NS	28	522.50	236.92	IDT
71982L	C	16K x 4 Static CMOS RAM 70 NS	28	446.25	15.18	IDT
71982L	M	16K x 4 Static CMOS RAM 70 NS	28	522.50	197.44	IDT
71982L	M	16K x 4 Static CMOS RAM 85 NS	28	522.50	171.68	IDT
71982S	C	16K x 4 Static CMOS RAM 25 NS	28	525.00	51.75	IDT
71982S	C	16K x 4 Static CMOS RAM 30 NS	28	525.00	46.00	IDT
71982S	M	16K x 4 Static CMOS RAM 30 NS	28	605.00	393.75	IDT
71982S	C	16K x 4 Static CMOS RAM 35 NS	28	525.00	40.25	IDT
71982S	M	16K x 4 Static CMOS RAM 35 NS	28	605.00	350.00	IDT
71982S	C	16K x 4 Static CMOS RAM 45 NS	28	525.00	28.75	IDT
71982S	M	16K x 4 Static CMOS RAM 45 NS	28	605.00	269.23	IDT
71982S	C	16K x 4 Static CMOS RAM 55 NS	28	525.00	20.70	IDT
71982S	M	16K x 4 Static CMOS RAM 55 NS	28	605.00	215.38	IDT
71982S	C	16K x 4 Static CMOS RAM 70 NS	28	525.00	13.80	IDT
71982S	M	16K x 4 Static CMOS RAM 70 NS	28	605.00	179.49	IDT
71982S	M	16K x 4 Static CMOS RAM 85 NS	28	605.00	156.08	IDT
7489	C	16 x 4 Static TTL RAM 60 NS	16	551.25	1.96	TI
74S188	C	32 x 8 TTL PROM 35 NS	16	577.50	1.45	N
74F189	C	16 x 4 Static TTL RAM 27 NS	16	288.75	4.29	F
74LS189	C	16 x 4 Static TTL RAM 80 NS	16	315.00	3.60	TI
74S189	C	16 x 4 Static TTL RAM 25 NS	16	525.00	3.25	N

TYPE	TEMP GRADE	DESCRIPTION	PINS	POWER (mW)	PRICE ($)	SUPPLIERS
74S189	C	16 x 4 Static TTL RAM 35 NS	16	577.50	2.15	N,TI
74S201	C	256 x 1 Static TTL RAM 65 NS	16	735.00	4.32	TI
74F219	C	16 x 4 Static TTL RAM 27 NS	16	288.75	4.29	F
74LS219	C	16 x 4 Static TTL RAM 80 NS	16	315.00	3.60	TI
74S287	C	256 x 4 TTL PROM 50 NS	16	682.50	1.50	N
74S288	C	32 x 8 TTL PROM 35 NS	16	577.50	1.45	N
74LS289	C	16 x 4 Static TTL RAM 80 NS	16	315.00	3.60	TI
74S289	C	16 x 4 Static TTL RAM 35 NS	16	577.50	2.15	N,TI
74S301	C	256 x 1 Static TTL RAM 65 NS	16	735.00	4.32	TI
74LS319	C	16 x 4 Static TTL RAM 80 NS	16	315.00	3.60	TI
74S387	C	256 x 4 TTL PROM 50 NS	16	682.50	1.50	N
74LS471	C	256 x 8 TTL PROM 60 NS	20	525.00	3.25	N
74S472	C	512 x 8 TTL PROM 60 NS	20	813.75	4.35	N
74S472A	C	512 x 8 TTL PROM 45 NS	20	813.75	4.35	N
74S472B	C	512 x 8 TTL PROM 35 NS	20	813.75	6.25	N
74S473	C	512 x 8 TTL PROM 60 NS	20	813.75	4.35	N
74S473A	C	512 x 8 TTL PROM 45 NS	20	813.75	4.35	N
74S474	C	512 x 8 TTL PROM 65 NS	24	892.50	4.80	N
74S474A	C	512 x 8 TTL PROM 45 NS	24	892.50	4.80	N
74S474B	C	512 x 8 TTL PROM 35 NS	24	892.50	6.95	N
74S475	C	512 x 8 TTL PROM 65 NS	24	892.50	4.80	N
74S475A	C	512 x 8 TTL PROM 45 NS	24	892.50	4.80	N
74S570	C	512 x 4 TTL PROM 55 NS	16	682.50	2.55	N
74S570A	C	512 x 4 TTL PROM 45 NS	16	682.50	3.35	N
74S571	C	512 x 4 TTL PROM 55 NS	16	682.50	2.55	N
74S571A	C	512 x 4 TTL PROM 45 NS	16	682.50	3.35	N

TYPE	TEMP GRADE	DESCRIPTION	PINS	POWER (mW)	PRICE ($)	SUPPLIERS
75S06	M	16 x 4 Static TTL RAM 50 NS	16	550.00	8.70	N
75S07	M	16 x 4 Static TTL RAM 50 NS	16	550.00	8.70	N
77S180	M	1K x 8 TTL PROM 75 NS	24	935.00	14.15	N
77LS181	M	1K x 8 TTL PROM 120 NS	24	550.00	21.60	N
77S181	M	1K x 8 TTL PROM 75 NS	24	935.00	14.15	N
77S181A	M	1K x 8 TTL PROM 75 NS	24	935.00	16.95	N
77SR181	M	1K x 8 Registered TTL PROM 50 NS	24	962.50	35.35	N
77S184	M	2K x 4 TTL PROM 70 NS	18	770.00	15.10	N
77S185	M	2K x 4 TTL PROM 70 NS	18	770.00	15.10	N
77S185A	M	2K x 4 TTL PROM 60 NS	18	770.00	12.10	N
77S185B	M	2K x 4 TTL PROM 50 NS	18	770.00	21.75	N
77S190	M	2K x 8 TTL PROM 70 NS	24	962.50	23.40	N
77S190A	M	2K x 8 TTL PROM 60 NS	24	962.50	29.35	N
77S191	M	2K x 8 TTL PROM 70 NS	24	962.50	23.40	N
77S191A	M	2K x 8 TTL PROM 60 NS	24	962.50	29.35	N
77S191B	M	2K x 8 TTL PROM 50 NS	24	962.50	35.20	N
77S195A	M	4K x 4 TTL PROM 60 NS	20	935.00	22.75	N
77S195B	M	4K x 4 TTL PROM 50 NS	20	935.00	27.90	N
77S280	M	1K x 8 TTL PROM 75 NS	24	935.00	17.70	N
77S281	M	1K x 8 TTL PROM 75 NS	24	935.00	17.70	N
77S281A	M	1K x 8 TTL PROM 75 NS	24	935.00	21.25	N
77S290	M	2K x 8 TTL PROM 70 NS	24	962.50	34.65	N
77S290A	M	2K x 8 TTL PROM 60 NS	24	962.50	41.60	N
77S291	M	2K x 8 TTL PROM 70 NS	24	962.50	34.65	N
77S291B	M	2K x 8 TTL PROM 50 NS	24	962.50	49.90	N
77S321	M	4K x 8 TTL PROM 65 NS	24	1017.50	60.30	N

TYPE	TEMP GRADE	DESCRIPTION	PINS	POWER (mW)	PRICE ($)	SUPPLIERS
77S421	M	4K x 8 TTL PROM 65 NS	24	1017.50	60.30	N
77SR476	M	512 x 8 Registered TTL PROM 55 NS	24	1017.50	15.00	N
82S23	C	32 x 8 TTL PROM 50 NS	16	504.00	1.00	S
82S23	M	32 x 8 TTL PROM 65 NS	16	605.00	2.86	S
82S23A	C	32 x 8 TTL PROM 25 NS	16	504.00	1.45	S
82S23A	M	32 x 8 TTL PROM 35 NS	16	605.00	3.56	S
82S115	C	512 x 8 TTL PROM 60 NS	24	918.75	7.35	S
82S115	M	512 x 8 TTL PROM 90 NS	24	1017.50	16.61	S
82S123	C	32 x 8 TTL PROM 50 NS	16	504.00	1.07	S
82S123	M	32 x 8 TTL PROM 65 NS	16	605.00	2.87	S
82S123A	C	32 x 8 TTL PROM 25 NS	16	504.00	1.45	S
82S123A	M	32 x 8 TTL PROM 35 NS	16	605.00	3.47	S
82S126	C	256 x 4 TTL PROM 50 NS	16	630.00	1.30	S
82S126	M	256 x 4 TTL PROM 70 NS	16	687.50	3.87	S
82S126A	C	256 x 4 TTL PROM 30 NS	16	630.00	1.30	S
82S126A	M	256 x 4 TTL PROM 35 NS	16	687.50	4.28	S
82S129	C	256 x 4 TTL PROM 50 NS	16	630.00	1.30	S
82S129	M	256 x 4 TTL PROM 70 NS	16	687.50	3.87	S
82S129A	C	256 x 4 TTL PROM 27 NS	16	630.00	1.30	S
82S129A	M	256 x 4 TTL PROM 35 NS	16	687.50	4.28	S
82S130	C	512 x 4 TTL PROM 50 NS	16	735.00	2.46	S
82S130	M	512 x 4 TTL PROM 70 NS	16	770.00	5.66	S
82S130A	C	512 x 4 TTL PROM 33 NS	16	735.00	2.91	S
82S130A	M	512 x 4 TTL PROM 35 NS	16	770.00	10.27	S
82S131	C	512 x 4 TTL PROM 50 NS	16	735.00	2.46	S
82S131	M	512 x 4 TTL PROM 70 NS	16	770.00	5.66	S

TYPE	TEMP GRADE	DESCRIPTION	PINS	POWER (mW)	PRICE ($)	SUPPLIERS
82S131A	C	512 x 4 TTL PROM 30 NS	16	735.00	2.91	S
82S131A	M	512 x 4 TTL PROM 35 NS	16	770.00	10.27	S
82LS135	C	256 x 8 TTL PROM 100 NS	20	525.00	3.36	S
82S135	C	256 x 8 TTL PROM 45 NS	20	787.50	3.43	S
82S137	C	1K x 4 TTL PROM 60 NS	18	735.00	2.45	S
82S137	M	1K x 4 TTL PROM 80 NS	18	825.00	7.93	S
82S137A	C	1K x 4 TTL PROM 45 NS	18	735.00	2.65	S
82S137A	M	1K x 4 TTL PROM 55 NS	18	825.00	12.33	S
82S137B	C	1K x 4 TTL PROM 35 NS	18	735.00	3.73	S
82S141	M	1K x 8 TTL PROM 90 NS	24	907.50	8.26	S
82S147	C	512 x 8 TTL PROM 60 NS	20	813.75	2.50	S
82S147	M	512 x 8 TTL PROM 75 NS	20	907.50	7.86	S
82S147A	C	512 x 8 TTL PROM 45 NS	20	813.75	2.85	S
82S181	C	1K x 8 TTL PROM 70 NS	24	918.75	4.65	S
82S181	M	1K x 8 TTL PROM 90 NS	24	1017.50	8.33	S
82S181A	C	1K x 8 TTL PROM 55 NS	24	918.75	5.30	S
82S181A	M	1K x 8 TTL PROM 55 NS	24	1017.50	11.33	S
82S181C	C	1K x 8 TTL PROM 35 NS	24	918.75	6.27	S
82S183	C	1K x 8 TTL PROM 60 NS	24	918.75	16.90	S
82S185	C	2K x 4 TTL PROM 100 NS	18	630.00	5.00	S
82S185	M	2K x 4 TTL PROM 115 NS	18	715.00	13.50	S
82S185A	C	2K x 4 TTL PROM 50 NS	18	813.75	5.37	S
82S185A	M	2K x 4 TTL PROM 55 NS	18	880.00	20.75	S
82S185B	C	2K x 4 TTL PROM 45 NS	18	813.75	5.75	S
82HS187	C	1K x 8 Registered TTL PROM 35 NS	24	918.75	9.80	S
82HS187A	C	1K x 8 Registered TTL PROM 30 NS	24	918.75	12.65	S

TYPE	TEMP GRADE	DESCRIPTION	PINS	POWER (mW)	PRICE ($)	SUPPLIERS
82HS187A	M	1K x 8 Registered TTL PROM 40 NS	24	1017.50	36.50	S
82HS189	C	1K x 8 Registered TTL PROM 35 NS	24	918.75	9.80	S
82HS189A	C	1K x 8 Registered TTL PROM 30 NS	24	918.75	12.65	S
82HS189A	M	1K x 8 Registered TTL PROM 40 NS	24	1017.50	36.50	S
82S191	C	2K x 8 TTL PROM 80 NS	24	918.75	7.15	S
82S191	M	2K x 8 TTL PROM 100 NS	24	1017.50	11.33	S
82S191A	C	2K x 8 TTL PROM 55 NS	24	918.75	8.21	S
82S191A	M	2K x 8 TTL PROM 55 NS	24	1017.50	14.57	S
82S191C	C	2K x 8 TTL PROM 35 NS	24	918.75	10.71	S
82HS195	C	4K x 4 TTL PROM 45 NS	20	761.25	12.15	S
82HS195A	C	4K x 4 TTL PROM 35 NS	20	761.25	14.00	S
82HS195A	M	4K x 4 TTL PROM 35 NS	20	852.50	38.33	S
82HS195B	C	4K x 4 TTL PROM 25 NS	20	761.25	21.00	S
82HS321	C	4K x 8 TTL PROM 45 NS	24	918.75	15.00	S
82HS321A	C	4K x 8 TTL PROM 35 NS	24	918.75	17.00	S
82HS321A	M	4K x 8 TTL PROM 45 NS	24	1017.50	41.42	S
82HS321B	C	4K x 8 TTL PROM 30 NS	24	918.75	20.70	S
82HS641	C	8K x 8 TTL PROM 55 NS	24	918.75	32.85	S
82HS641A	C	8K x 8 TTL PROM 45 NS	24	918.75	37.00	S
82HS641A	M	8K x 8 TTL PROM 55 NS	24	1017.50	156.00	S
82HS641B	C	8K x 8 TTL PROM 35 NS	24	918.75	41.50	S
82S2708	M	1K x 8 TTL PROM 90 NS	24	1017.50	42.30	S
85S06	C	16 x 4 Static TTL RAM 35 NS	16	525.00	2.60	N
85S07	C	16 x 4 Static TTL RAM 25 NS	16	525.00	3.60	N
85S07	C	16 x 4 Static TTL RAM 35 NS	16	525.00	2.60	N

TYPE	TEMP GRADE	DESCRIPTION	PINS	POWER (mW)	PRICE ($)	SUPPLIERS
87C64	C	8K x 8 Eraseable CMOS PROM 150 NS 5% VCC 12.5V VPP	28	52.50	7.50	I
87C64	C	8K x 8 Eraseable CMOS PROM 150 NS 10% VCC 12.5V VPP	28	55.00	8.30	I
87C64	C	8K x 8 Eraseable CMOS PROM 200 NS 5% VCC 12.5V VPP	28	52.50	6.40	I
87C64	C	8K x 8 Eraseable CMOS PROM 200 NS 10% VCC 12.5V VPP	28	55.00	7.10	I
87C64	C	8K x 8 Eraseable CMOS PROM 250 NS 10% VCC 12.5V VPP	28	55.00	5.90	I
87C64	C	8K x 8 Eraseable CMOS PROM 250 NS 10% VCC 12.5V VPP	28	55.00	5.40	I
87C64	C	8K x 8 Eraseable CMOS PROM 300 NS 5% VCC 12.5V VPP	28	52.50	5.40	I
87C64	C	8K x 8 Eraseable CMOS PROM 300 NS 10% VCC 12.5V VPP	28	55.00	5.90	I
87S180	C	1K x 8 TTL PROM 55 NS	24	892.50	7.95	N
87LS181	C	1K x 8 TTL PROM 100 NS	24	525.00	12.95	N
87S181	C	1K x 8 TTL PROM 55 NS	24	892.50	7.95	N
87S181A	C	1K x 8 TTL PROM 45 NS	24	892.50	9.55	N
87SR181	C	1K x 8 Registered TTL PROM 40 NS	24	918.75	9.90	N
87S184	C	2K x 4 TTL PROM 55 NS	18	735.00	8.60	N
87S185	C	2K x 4 TTL PROM 55 NS	18	735.00	8.60	N
87S185A	C	2K x 4 TTL PROM 45 NS	18	735.00	10.35	N
87S185B	C	2K x 4 TTL PROM 35 NS	18	735.00	12.40	N
87S190	C	2K x 8 TTL PROM 55 NS	24	918.75	11.95	N
87S190A	C	2K x 8 TTL PROM 45 NS	24	918.75	14.35	N
87S191	C	2K x 8 TTL PROM 55 NS	24	918.75	11.95	N
87S191A	C	2K x 8 TTL PROM 45 NS	24	918.75	14.35	N
87S191B	C	2K x 8 TTL PROM 35 NS	24	918.75	17.25	N

TYPE	TEMP GRADE	DESCRIPTION	PINS	POWER (mW)	PRICE ($)	SUPPLIERS
87S195A	C	4K x 4 TTL PROM 45 NS	20	892.50	17.40	N
87S195B	C	4K x 4 TTL PROM 35 NS	20	892.50	21.75	N
87S280	C	1K x 8 TTL PROM 55 NS	24	892.50	7.95	N
87S281	C	1K x 8 TTL PROM 55 NS	24	892.50	7.95	N
87S281A	C	1K x 8 TTL PROM 45 NS	24	892.50	9.55	N
87S290	C	2K x 8 TTL PROM 55 NS	24	918.75	11.95	N
87S290A	C	2K x 8 TTL PROM 45 NS	24	918.75	14.35	N
87S291	C	2K x 8 TTL PROM 55 NS	24	918.75	11.95	N
87S291A	C	2K x 8 TTL PROM 45 NS	24	918.75	14.35	N
87S291B	C	2K x 8 TTL PROM 35 NS	24	918.75	17.25	N
87S321	C	4K x 8 TTL PROM 55 NS	24	971.25	17.14	N
87S421	C	4K x 8 TTL PROM 55 NS	24	971.25	21.43	N
87SR474	C	512 x 8 Registered TTL PROM 50 NS	24	971.25	6.80	N
87SR474B	C	512 x 8 Registered TTL PROM 35 NS	24	971.25	9.00	N
87SR476	C	512 x 8 Registered TTL PROM 50 NS	24	971.25	6.80	N
87SR476B	C	512 x 8 Registered TTL PROM 35 NS	24	971.25	9.00	N
9044	C	4K x 1 Static MOS RAM 200 NS	18	367.50	5.72	AMD
9044	C	4K x 1 Static MOS RAM 250 NS	18	367.50	5.43	AMD
9044	M	4K x 1 Static MOS RAM 250 NS	18	440.00	29.32	AMD
9044	C	4K x 1 Static MOS RAM 300 NS	18	367.50	5.15	AMD
9044	M	4K x 1 Static MOS RAM 300 NS	18	440.00	28.24	AMD
9044	C	4K x 1 Static MOS RAM 450 NS	18	367.50	4.86	AMD
9044	M	4K x 1 Static MOS RAM 450 NS	18	440.00	27.55	AMD
90L44	C	4K x 1 Static MOS RAM 250 NS	18	262.50	6.79	AMD
90L44	C	4K x 1 Static MOS RAM 300 NS	18	262.50	6.51	AMD
90L44	C	4K x 1 Static MOS RAM 450 NS	18	262.50	6.22	AMD

TYPE	TEMP GRADE	DESCRIPTION	PINS	POWER (mW)	PRICE ($)	SUPPLIERS
9101	C	256 x 4 Static MOS RAM 250 NS	22	315.00	3.93	AMD
9101	C	256 x 4 Static MOS RAM 300 NS	22	315.00	3.79	AMD
9101	M	256 x 4 Static MOS RAM 300 NS	22	357.50	30.39	AMD
9101	C	256 x 4 Static MOS RAM 400 NS	22	288.75	3.65	AMD
9101	M	256 x 4 Static MOS RAM 400 NS	22	330.00	19.88	AMD
9101	C	256 x 4 Static MOS RAM 500 NS	22	288.75	3.50	AMD
9101	M	256 x 4 Static MOS RAM 500 NS	22	330.00	13.80	AMD
91L01	C	256 x 4 Static MOS RAM 300 NS	22	189.00	3.93	AMD
91L01	M	256 x 4 Static MOS RAM 300 NS	22	220.00	34.75	AMD
91L01	C	256 x 4 Static MOS RAM 400 NS	22	173.25	3.79	AMD
91L01	M	256 x 4 Static MOS RAM 400 NS	22	203.50	21.09	AMD
91L01	C	256 x 4 Static MOS RAM 500 NS	22	173.25	3.65	AMD
91L01	M	256 x 4 Static MOS RAM 500 NS	22	203.50	16.37	AMD
9111	C	256 x 4 Static MOS RAM 250 NS	18	315.00	4.65	AMD
9111	C	256 x 4 Static MOS RAM 300 NS	18	315.00	4.50	AMD
9111	M	256 x 4 Static MOS RAM 300 NS	18	357.50	30.39	AMD
9111	C	256 x 4 Static MOS RAM 400 NS	18	288.75	4.36	AMD
9111	M	256 x 4 Static MOS RAM 400 NS	18	330.00	18.45	AMD
9111	C	256 x 4 Static MOS RAM 500 NS	18	288.75	4.22	AMD
9111	M	256 x 4 Static MOS RAM 500 NS	18	330.00	13.80	AMD
91L11	C	256 x 4 Static MOS RAM 300 NS	18	189.00	4.80	AMD
91L11	M	256 x 4 Static MOS RAM 300 NS	18	220.00	34.75	AMD
91L11	C	256 x 4 Static MOS RAM 400 NS	18	173.25	4.65	AMD
91L11	M	256 x 4 Static MOS RAM 400 NS	18	203.50	21.09	AMD
91L11	C	256 x 4 Static MOS RAM 500 NS	18	173.25	4.50	AMD
91L11	M	256 x 4 Static MOS RAM 500 NS	18	203.50	16.37	AMD

TYPE	TEMP GRADE	DESCRIPTION	PINS	POWER (mW)	PRICE ($)	SUPPLIERS
9112	C	256 x 4 Static MOS RAM 250 NS	16	315.00	5.01	AMD
9112	C	256 x 4 Static MOS RAM 300 NS	16	315.00	4.86	AMD
9112	M	256 x 4 Static MOS RAM 300 NS	16	357.50	30.39	AMD
9112	C	256 x 4 Static MOS RAM 400 NS	16	288.75	4.72	AMD
9112	M	256 x 4 Static MOS RAM 400 NS	16	330.00	18.45	AMD
9112	C	256 x 4 Static MOS RAM 500 NS	16	288.75	4.58	AMD
9112	M	256 x 4 Static MOS RAM 500 NS	16	330.00	13.80	AMD
91L12	C	256 x 4 Static MOS RAM 300 NS	16	189.00	5.15	AMD
91L12	M	256 x 4 Static MOS RAM 300 NS	16	220.00	34.75	AMD
91L12	C	256 x 4 Static MOS RAM 400 NS	16	173.25	5.00	AMD
91L12	M	256 x 4 Static MOS RAM 400 NS	16	203.50	21.09	AMD
91L12	C	256 x 4 Static MOS RAM 500 NS	16	173.25	4.90	AMD
91L12	M	256 x 4 Static MOS RAM 500 NS	16	203.50	16.37	AMD
9114	C	1K x 4 Static MOS RAM 200 NS	18	367.50	5.15	AMD
9114	M	1K x 4 Static MOS RAM 200 NS	18	440.00	12.70	AMD
9114	C	1K x 4 Static MOS RAM 300 NS	18	367.50	1.95	AMD
9114	M	1K x 4 Static MOS RAM 300 NS	18	440.00	8.70	AMD
9114	C	1K x 4 Static MOS RAM 450 NS	18	367.50	1.90	AMD
9114	M	1K x 4 Static MOS RAM 450 NS	18	440.00	7.95	AMD
91L14	C	1K x 4 Static MOS RAM 200 NS	18	262.50	2.75	AMD
91L14	C	1K x 4 Static MOS RAM 300 NS	18	262.50	2.54	AMD
91L14	M	1K x 4 Static MOS RAM 300 NS	18	330.00	9.80	AMD
91L14	C	1K x 4 Static MOS RAM 450 NS	18	262.50	2.47	AMD
91L14	M	1K x 4 Static MOS RAM 450 NS	18	330.00	8.70	AMD
9122	C	256 x 4 Static MOS RAM 25 NS	22	630.00	15.02	AMD
9122	C	256 x 4 Static MOS RAM 35 NS	22	630.00	8.45	AMD

TYPE	TEMP GRADE	DESCRIPTION	PINS	POWER (mW)	PRICE ($)	SUPPLIERS
9122	M	256 x 4 Static MOS RAM 35 NS	22	742.50	39.80	AMD
91L22	C	256 x 4 Static MOS RAM 35 NS	22	420.00	14.30	AMD
91L22	C	256 x 4 Static MOS RAM 45 NS	22	420.00	7.25	AMD
91L22	M	256 x 4 Static MOS RAM 45 NS	22	495.00	39.80	AMD
9124	C	1K x 4 Static MOS RAM 300 NS	18	367.50	3.58	AMD
9124	M	1K x 4 Static MOS RAM 300 NS	18	440.00	15.95	AMD
9124	C	1K x 4 Static MOS RAM 450 NS	18	367.50	3.43	AMD
9124	M	1K x 4 Static MOS RAM 450 NS	18	440.00	14.50	AMD
91L24	C	1K x 4 Static MOS RAM 300 NS	18	262.50	3.93	AMD
91L24	M	1K x 4 Static MOS RAM 300 NS	18	330.00	17.30	AMD
91L24	C	1K x 4 Static MOS RAM 450 NS	18	262.50	3.79	AMD
91L24	M	1K x 4 Static MOS RAM 450 NS	18	330.00	15.73	AMD
9128	C	2K x 8 Static MOS RAM 70 NS	24	735.00	9.57	AMD
9128	M	2K x 8 Static MOS RAM 90 NS	24	990.00	84.85	AMD
9128	C	2K x 8 Static MOS RAM 100 NS	24	630.00	4.71	AMD
9128	M	2K x 8 Static MOS RAM 120 NS	24	825.00	61.65	AMD
9128	C	2K x 8 Static MOS RAM 150 NS	24	525.00	4.35	AMD
9128	M	2K x 8 Static MOS RAM 150 NS	24	825.00	43.50	AMD
9128	C	2K x 8 Static MOS RAM 200 NS	24	735.00	3.98	AMD
9128	M	2K x 8 Static MOS RAM 200 NS	24	825.00	36.25	AMD
9150-20	C	1K x 4 Static MOS RAM 20 NS	24	945.00	22.95	AMD
9150-25	C	1K x 4 Static MOS RAM 25 NS	24	945.00	19.50	AMD
9150-25	M	1K x 4 Static MOS RAM 25 NS	24	990.00	65.00	AMD
9150-35	C	1K x 4 Static MOS RAM 35 NS	24	945.00	17.45	AMD
9150-35	M	1K x 4 Static MOS RAM 35 NS	24	990.00	55.00	AMD
9150-45	C	1K x 4 Static MOS RAM 45 NS	24	945.00	15.90	AMD

TYPE	TEMP GRADE	DESCRIPTION	PINS	POWER (mW)	PRICE ($)	SUPPLIERS
9150-45	M	1K x 4 Static MOS RAM 45 NS	24	990.00	50.00	AMD
91L50-25	C	1K x 4 Static MOS RAM 25 NS	24	682.50	22.45	AMD
91L50-35	C	1K x 4 Static MOS RAM 35 NS	24	682.50	20.00	AMD
91L50-45	C	1K x 4 Static MOS RAM 45 NS	24	682.50	18.25	AMD
9151-40	C	1K x 4 Static MOS RAM 40 NS	24	945.00	12.50	AMD
9151-50	C	1K x 4 Static MOS RAM 50 NS	24	945.00	10.50	AMD
9151-50	M	1K x 4 Static MOS RAM 50 NS	24	990.00	50.00	AMD
9151-60	C	1K x 4 Static MOS RAM 60 NS	24	945.00	9.35	AMD
9151-60	M	1K x 4 Static MOS RAM 60 NS	24	990.00	45.00	AMD
9244	C	4K x 1 Static MOS RAM 200 NS	18	367.50	5.72	AMD
9244	C	4K x 1 Static MOS RAM 250 NS	18	367.50	5.43	AMD
9244	M	4K x 1 Static MOS RAM 250 NS	18	440.00	29.32	AMD
9244	C	4K x 1 Static MOS RAM 300 NS	18	367.50	5.15	AMD
9244	M	4K x 1 Static MOS RAM 300 NS	18	440.00	28.24	AMD
9244	C	4K x 1 Static MOS RAM 450 NS	18	367.50	4.86	AMD
9244	M	4K x 1 Static MOS RAM 450 NS	18	440.00	27.17	AMD
92L44	C	4K x 1 Static MOS RAM 250 NS	18	262.50	6.79	AMD
92L44	C	4K x 1 Static MOS RAM 300 NS	18	262.50	6.51	AMD
92L44	M	4K x 1 Static MOS RAM 300 NS	18	330.00	40.00	AMD
92L44	C	4K x 1 Static MOS RAM 450 NS	18	262.50	6.22	AMD
92L44	M	4K x 1 Static MOS RAM 450 NS	18	330.00	38.40	AMD
93412	C	256 x 4 Static TTL RAM 35 NS	22	813.75	7.25	AMD
93412	C	256 x 4 Static TTL RAM 45 NS	22	813.75	5.75	AMD
93412	M	256 x 4 Static TTL RAM 45 NS	22	935.00	22.60	AMD
93412	M	256 x 4 Static TTL RAM 60 NS	22	935.00	19.70	AMD
93L412	C	256 x 4 Static TTL RAM 45 NS	22	420.00	7.25	AMD

TYPE	TEMP GRADE	DESCRIPTION	PINS	POWER (mW)	PRICE ($)	SUPPLIERS
93L412	M	256 x 4 Static TTL RAM 55 NS	22	495.00	22.60	AMD
93L412	C	256 x 4 Static TTL RAM 60 NS	22	420.00	5.75	AMD
93L412	M	256 x 4 Static TTL RAM 75 NS	22	495.00	19.70	AMD
93415	C	1K x 1 Static TTL RAM 20 NS	16	813.75	13.25	AMD
93415	C	1K x 1 Static TTL RAM 25 NS	16	656.25	5.29	F
93415	C	1K x 1 Static TTL RAM 30 NS	16	813.75	4.00	AMD,F
93415	M	1K x 1 Static TTL RAM 30 NS	16	935.00	29.00	AMD,F
93415	M	1K x 1 Static TTL RAM 40 NS	16	935.00	13.59	AMD,F
93415	C	1K x 1 Static TTL RAM 45 NS	16	813.75	4.25	AMD,F
93415	M	1K x 1 Static TTL RAM 60 NS	16	935.00	10.72	AMD,F
93L415	C	1K x 1 Static TTL RAM 35 NS	16	341.25	5.29	F
93L415	M	1K x 1 Static TTL RAM 40 NS	16	742.50	16.45	F
93L415	C	1K x 1 Static TTL RAM 45 NS	16	420.00	3.93	AMD,F
93L415	M	1K x 1 Static TTL RAM 50 NS	16	412.50	15.02	F
93L415	M	1K x 1 Static TTL RAM 55 NS	16	495.00	18.25	AMD
93L415	C	1K x 1 Static TTL RAM 60 NS	16	420.00	4.10	AMD,F
93L415	M	1K x 1 Static TTL RAM 70 NS	16	495.00	15.02	AMD,F
93422	C	256 x 4 Static TTL RAM 35 NS	22	813.75	4.72	AMD,F
93422	C	256 x 4 Static TTL RAM 45 NS	22	813.75	4.29	AMD,F
93422	M	256 x 4 Static TTL RAM 45 NS	22	935.00	19.31	AMD,F
93422	M	256 x 4 Static TTL RAM 60 NS	22	935.00	16.45	AMD,F
93L422	C	256 x 4 Static TTL RAM 45 NS	22	420.00	6.44	AMD,F
93L422	M	256 x 4 Static TTL RAM 55 NS	22	495.00	17.88	AMD,F
93L422	C	256 x 4 Static TTL RAM 60 NS	22	420.00	5.01	AMD,F
93L422	M	256 x 4 Static TTL RAM 75 NS	22	495.00	15.02	AMD,F
93425	C	1K x 1 Static TTL RAM 20 NS	16	813.75	13.25	AMD

TYPE	TEMP GRADE	DESCRIPTION	PINS	POWER (mW)	PRICE ($)	SUPPLIERS
93425	C	1K x 1 Static TTL RAM 25 NS	16	656.25	5.29	F
93425	C	1K x 1 Static TTL RAM 30 NS	16	813.75	4.00	AMD,F
93425	M	1K x 1 Static TTL RAM 30 NS	16	935.00	29.00	AMD,F
93425	M	1K x 1 Static TTL RAM 40 NS	16	935.00	13.59	AMD,F
93425	C	1K x 1 Static TTL RAM 45 NS	16	813.75	4.25	AMD,F
93425	M	1K x 1 Static TTL RAM 60 NS	16	935.00	10.30	AMD,F
93L425	C	1K x 1 Static TTL RAM 35 NS	16	341.25	5.29	F
93L425	M	1K x 1 Static TTL RAM 40 NS	16	742.50	16.45	F
93L425	C	1K x 1 Static TTL RAM 45 NS	16	420.00	3.93	AMD,F
93L425	M	1K x 1 Static TTL RAM 50 NS	16	412.50	15.02	F
93L425	M	1K x 1 Static TTL RAM 55 NS	16	495.00	18.25	AMD
93L425	C	1K x 1 Static TTL RAM 60 NS	16	420.00	5.01	AMD,F
93L425	M	1K x 1 Static TTL RAM 70 NS	16	495.00	15.37	AMD,F
93Z451	C	1K x 8 TTL PROM 40 NS	24	708.75	5.36	F
93Z451	M	1K x 8 TTL PROM 55 NS	24	742.50	8.58	F
93Z451A	C	1K x 8 TTL PROM 35 NS	24	708.75	6.01	F
93Z451A	M	1K x 8 TTL PROM 45 NS	24	742.50	11.44	F
93479	C	256 x 9 Static TTL RAM 35 NS	22	971.25	24.31	F
93479	C	256 x 9 Static TTL RAM 45 NS	22	971.25	20.74	F
93479	M	256 x 9 Static TTL RAM 45 NS	22	1100.00	30.75	F
93479	M	256 x 9 Static TTL RAM 60 NS	22	1100.00	27.89	F
93Z511	C	2K x 8 TTL PROM 45 NS	24	918.75	10.01	F
93Z511	M	2K x 8 TTL PROM 55 NS	24	962.50	12.87	F
93Z565	C	8K x 8 TTL PROM 55 NS	24	945.00	32.89	F
93Z565	M	8K x 8 TTL PROM 65 NS	24	990.00	114.40	F
93Z565A	C	8K x 8 TTL PROM 45 NS	24	945.00	38.61	F

TYPE	TEMP GRADE	DESCRIPTION	PINS	POWER (mW)	PRICE ($)	SUPPLIERS
93Z565A	M	8K x 8 TTL PROM 55 NS	24	990.00	121.55	F
99C58-20	C	4K x 4 Static CMOS RAM 20 NS	24	945.00	24.75	AMD
99C58-25	C	4K x 4 Static CMOS RAM 25 NS	24	945.00	19.95	AMD
99C58-35	C	4K x 4 Static CMOS RAM 35 NS	24	945.00	17.25	AMD
99C58-45	C	4K x 4 Static CMOS RAM 45 NS	24	945.00	16.00	AMD
99C59-20	C	4K x 4 Static CMOS RAM 20 NS	24	945.00	24.75	AMD
99C59-25	C	4K x 4 Static CMOS RAM 25 NS	24	945.00	19.95	AMD
99C59-35	C	4K x 4 Static CMOS RAM 35 NS	24	945.00	17.25	AMD
99C59-45	C	4K x 4 Static CMOS RAM 45 NS	24	945.00	16.00	AMD
99C68-35	C	4K x 4 Static CMOS RAM 35 NS	20	525.00	8.00	AMD
99C68-45	C	4K x 4 Static CMOS RAM 45 NS	20	525.00	5.35	AMD
99C68-55	C	4K x 4 Static CMOS RAM 55 NS	20	525.00	4.75	AMD
99C68-55	M	4K x 4 Static CMOS RAM 55 NS	20	660.00	60.00	AMD
99C68-70	C	4K x 4 Static CMOS RAM 70 NS	20	525.00	4.00	AMD
99C68-70	M	4K x 4 Static CMOS RAM 70 NS	20	660.00	51.20	AMD
99CL68-45	C	4K x 4 Static CMOS RAM 45 NS	20	525.00	14.96	AMD
99CL68-55	C	4K x 4 Static CMOS RAM 55 NS	20	525.00	10.56	AMD
99CL68-55	M	4K x 4 Static CMOS RAM 55 NS	20	660.00	62.00	AMD
99CL68-70	C	4K x 4 Static CMOS RAM 70 NS	20	525.00	9.68	AMD
99CL68-70	M	4K x 4 Static CMOS RAM 70 NS	20	660.00	53.20	AMD
99C88-10	C	8K x 8 Static CMOS RAM 100 NS	28	315.00	14.25	AMD
99C88-10	M	8K x 8 Static CMOS RAM 100 NS	28	330.00	215.00	AMD
99C88-12	M	8K x 8 Static CMOS RAM 120 NS	28	330.00	175.00	AMD
99C88-15	M	8K x 8 Static CMOS RAM 150 NS	28	330.00	145.00	AMD
99C88-20	M	8K x 8 Static CMOS RAM 200 NS	28	330.00	130.00	AMD
99C88-20	M	8K x 8 Static CMOS RAM 200 NS	28	330.00	130.00	AMD

TYPE	TEMP GRADE	DESCRIPTION	PINS	POWER (mW)	PRICE ($)	SUPPLIERS
99C88-70	C	8K x 8 Static CMOS RAM 70 NS	28	315.00	55.00	AMD
99C88-70	M	8K x 8 Static CMOS RAM 70 NS	28	330.00	245.00	AMD
99CL88-10	C	8K x 8 Static CMOS RAM 100 NS	28	210.00	17.00	AMD
99CL88-70	C	8K x 8 Static CMOS RAM 70 NS	28	210.00	66.00	AMD
99CS88-70	M	8K x 8 Static CMOS RAM 70 NS	28	330.00	245.00	AMD
99C641-25	C	64K x 1 Static CMOS RAM 25 NS	22	682.50	55.80	AMD
99C641-35	C	64K x 1 Static CMOS RAM 35 NS	22	577.50	36.25	AMD
99C641-45	C	64K x 1 Static CMOS RAM 45 NS	22	472.50	28.30	AMD
99C641-55	C	64K x 1 Static CMOS RAM 55 NS	22	472.50	24.40	AMD
99C641-70	C	64K x 1 Static CMOS RAM 70 NS	22	472.50	21.80	AMD

Appendix D
6500 Index

TYPE	TEMP GRADE	DESCRIPTION	PINS	POWER (mW)	PRICE ($)	SUPPLIERS
6500/1E	C	8-Bit Microprocessor with RAM, Counters & I/O 1 MHz	64	1200.00	10.98	RI
6500/1EA	C	8-Bit Microprocessor with RAM, Counters & I/O 2 MHz	64	1200.00	12.07	RI
6501	C	8-Bit Microprocessor with RAM, Counters & I/O 1 MHz	64	1100.00	11.69	RI
6501A	C	8-Bit Microprocessor with RAM, Counters & I/O 2 MHz	64	1100.00	12.86	RI
6502	C	8-Bit NMOS Microprocessor with Clock 1 MHz	40	700.00	4.80	RI
6502	I	8-Bit NMOS Microprocessor with Clock 1 MHz	40	700.00	5.50	RI
6502A	C	8-Bit NMOS Microprocessor with Clock 2 MHz	40	700.00	5.30	RI
6502A	I	8-Bit NMOS Microprocessor with Clock 2 MHz	40	700.00	6.10	RI
6503	C	8-Bit NMOS Microprocessor with Clock 1 MHz	28	700.00	5.30	RI
6503	I	8-Bit NMOS Microprocessor with Clock 1 MHz	28	700.00	6.10	RI
6503A	C	8-Bit NMOS Microprocessor with Clock 2 MHz	28	700.00	5.85	RI
6503A	I	8-Bit NMOS Microprocessor with Clock 2 MHz	28	700.00	6.65	RI
6504	C	8-Bit NMOS Microprocessor with Clock 1 MHz	28	700.00	5.30	RI
6504	I	8-Bit NMOS Microprocessor with Clock 1 MHz	28	700.00	6.10	RI
6504A	C	8-Bit NMOS Microprocessor with Clock 2 MHz	28	700.00	5.85	RI
6504A	I	8-Bit NMOS Microprocessor with Clock 2 MHz	28	700.00	6.65	RI
6505	C	8-Bit NMOS Microprocessor with Clock 1 MHz	28	700.00	5.30	RI

TYPE	TEMP GRADE	DESCRIPTION	PINS	POWER (mW)	PRICE ($)	SUPPLIERS
6505	I	8-Bit NMOS Microprocessor with Clock 1 MHz	28	700.00	6.10	RI
6505A	C	8-Bit NMOS Microprocessor with Clock 2 MHz	28	700.00	5.85	RI
6505A	I	8-Bit NMOS Microprocessor with Clock 2 MHz	28	700.00	6.65	RI
6506	C	8-Bit NMOS Microprocessor with Clock 1 MHz	28	700.00	5.30	RI
6506	I	8-Bit NMOS Microprocessor with Clock 1 MHz	28	700.00	6.10	RI
6506A	C	8-Bit NMOS Microprocessor with Clock 2 MHz	28	700.00	5.85	RI
6506A	I	8-Bit NMOS Microprocessor with Clock 2 MHz	28	700.00	6.65	RI
6507	C	8-Bit NMOS Microprocessor with Clock 1 MHz	28	700.00	4.00	RI
6507	I	8-Bit NMOS Microprocessor with Clock 1 MHz	28	700.00	4.60	RI
6507A	C	8-Bit NMOS Microprocessor with Clock 2 MHz	28	700.00	4.40	RI
6507A	I	8-Bit NMOS Microprocessor with Clock 2 MHz	28	700.00	5.05	RI
6511	C	8-Bit Microprocessor with RAM, Counters & I/O 1 MHz	64	1100.00	11.69	RI
6511A	C	8-Bit Microprocessor with RAM, Counters & I/O 2 MHz	64	1100.00	12.86	RI
6512	C	8-Bit NMOS Microprocessor 1 MHz	40	700.00	6.30	RI
6512	I	8-Bit NMOS Microprocessor 1 MHz	40	700.00	7.25	RI
6512A	C	8-Bit NMOS Microprocessor 2 MHz	40	700.00	7.00	RI
6512A	I	8-Bit NMOS Microprocessor 2 MHz	40	700.00	8.10	RI
6518	C	8-Bit Microprocessor with RAM, Counters & I/O 1 MHz	40	1000.00	8.78	RI

TYPE	TEMP GRADE	DESCRIPTION	PINS	POWER (mW)	PRICE ($)	SUPPLIERS
6518A	C	8-Bit Microprocessor with RAM, Counters & I/O 2 MHz	40	1000.00	9.67	RI
6520	C	Peripheral Interface Adapter 1 MHz	40	500.00	3.15	RI
6520	I	Peripheral Interface Adapter 1 MHz	40	500.00	3.60	RI
6520A	C	Peripheral Interface Adapter 2 MHz	40	500.00	3.60	RI
6520A	I	Peripheral Interface Adapter 2 MHz	40	500.00	4.15	RI
6522	C	Versatile Interface Adapter 1 MHz	40	700.00	4.10	RI
6522	I	Versatile Interface Adapter 1 MHz	40	700.00	5.40	RI
6522A	C	Versatile Interface Adapter 2 MHz	40	700.00	4.60	RI
6522A	I	Versatile Interface Adapter 2 MHz	40	700.00	6.05	RI
6532	C	RAM-I/O-Timer 1 MHz	40	1000.00	6.10	RI
6532	I	RAM-I/O-Timer 1 MHz	40	1000.00	7.00	RI
6532A	C	RAM-I/O-Timer 2 MHz	40	1000.00	6.70	RI
6545A	C	CRT Controller 2 MHz Bus 2.5 MHz Character Clock	40	700.00	5.65	RI
6545A	I	CRT Controller 2 MHz Bus 2.5 MHz Character Clock	40	800.00	6.50	RI
6545EA	C	CRT Controller 2 MHz Bus 3.7 MHz Character Clock	40	700.00	6.70	RI
6545EA	I	CRT Controller 2 MHz Bus 3.7 MHz Character Clock	40	800.00	7.70	RI
6551	C	Asynchronous Communications Interface Adapter 1 MHz	28	300.00	5.15	RI
6551A	I	Asynchronous Communications Interface Adapter 2 MHz	28	300.00	5.90	RI
65C02P1	C	8-Bit CMOS Microprocessor with Clock 1 MHz	40	21.00	4.95	RI
65C02P1	I	8-Bit CMOS Microprocessor with Clock 1 MHz	40	21.00	5.05	RI
65C02P2	C	8-Bit CMOS Microprocessor with Clock 2 MHz	40	42.00	5.45	RI

TYPE	TEMP GRADE	DESCRIPTION	PINS	POWER (mW)	PRICE ($)	SUPPLIERS
65C02P2	I	8-Bit CMOS Microprocessor with Clock 2 MHz	40	42.00	5.80	RI
65C02P3	C	8-Bit CMOS Microprocessor with Clock 3 MHz	40	63.00	6.80	RI
65C02P3	I	8-Bit CMOS Microprocessor with Clock 3 MHz	40	63.00	7.85	RI
65C02P4	C	8-Bit CMOS Microprocessor with Clock 4 MHz	40	84.00	8.25	RI
65C02P4	I	8-Bit CMOS Microprocessor with Clock 4 MHz	40	84.00	9.50	RI
65C21P1	C	Peripheral Interface Adapter 1 MHz	40	10.00	3.35	RI
65C21P1	I	Peripheral Interface Adapter 1 MHz	40	10.00	3.95	RI
65C21P2	C	Peripheral Interface Adapter 2 MHz	40	20.00	3.80	RI
65C21P2	I	Peripheral Interface Adapter 2 MHz	40	20.00	4.35	RI
65C21P3	C	Peripheral Interface Adapter 3 MHz	40	30.00	4.25	RI
65C21P3	I	Peripheral Interface Adapter 3 MHz	40	30.00	5.00	RI
65C21P4	C	Peripheral Interface Adapter 4 MHz	40	40.00	5.10	RI
65C21P4	I	Peripheral Interface Adapter 4 MHz	40	40.00	6.00	RI
65C22P1	C	Versatile Interface Adapter 1 MHz	40	10.00	4.35	RI
65C22P1	I	Versatile Interface Adapter 1 MHz	40	10.00	5.10	RI
65C22P2	C	Versatile Interface Adapter 2 MHz	40	20.00	4.75	RI
65C22P2	I	Versatile Interface Adapter 2 MHz	40	20.00	5.60	RI
65C22P3	C	Versatile Interface Adapter 3 MHz	40	30.00	5.50	RI
65C22P3	I	Versatile Interface Adapter 3 MHz	40	30.00	6.45	RI
65C22P4	C	Versatile Interface Adapter 4 MHz	40	40.00	6.60	RI
65C22P4	I	Versatile Interface Adapter 4 MHz	40	40.00	7.75	RI
65C24P1	C	Peripheral Interface Adapter/Timer 1 MHz	40	10.00	4.05	RI

TYPE	TEMP GRADE	DESCRIPTION	PINS	POWER (mW)	PRICE ($)	SUPPLIERS
65C24P1	I	Peripheral Interface Adapter/Timer 1 MHz	40	10.00	4.55	RI
65C24P2	C	Peripheral Interface Adapter/Timer 2 MHz	40	20.00	4.40	RI
65C24P2	I	Peripheral Interface Adapter/Timer 2 MHz	40	20.00	5.00	RI
65C24P3	C	Peripheral Interface Adapter/Timer 3 MHz	40	30.00	5.10	RI
65C24P3	I	Peripheral Interface Adapter/Timer 3 MHz	40	30.00	5.75	RI
65C24P4	C	Peripheral Interface Adapter/Timer 4 MHz	40	40.00	6.15	RI
65C24P4	I	Peripheral Interface Adapter/Timer 4 MHz	40	40.00	6.90	RI
65C51P1	C	Asynchronous Communications Interface Adapter 1 MHz	28	10.00	5.30	RI
65C51P1	I	Asynchronous Communications Interface Adapter 1 MHz	28	10.00	5.45	RI
65C51P2	C	Asynchronous Communications Interface Adapter 2 MHz	28	20.00	6.95	RI
65C52P1	C	Dual Asynchronous Communications Interface Adapter 1 MHz	40	10.00	8.50	RI
65C52P1	I	Dual Asynchronous Communications Interface Adapter 1 MHz	40	10.00	9.25	RI
65C52P2	C	Dual Asynchronous Communications Interface Adapter 2 MHz	40	20.00	9.35	RI*
65C52P2	I	Dual Asynchronous Communications Interface Adapter 2 MHz	40	20.00	10.20	RI
65C52P3	C	Dual Asynchronous Communications Interface Adapter 3 MHz	40	30.00	10.30	RI
65C52P3	I	Dual Asynchronous Communications Interface Adapter 3 MHz	40	30.00	11.20	RI
65C52P4	C	Dual Asynchronous Communications Interface Adapter 4 MHz	40	40.00	17.05	RI

TYPE	TEMP GRADE	DESCRIPTION	PINS	POWER (mW)	PRICE ($)	SUPPLIERS
65C52P4	I	Dual Asynchronous Communications Interface Adapter 4 MHz	40	40.00	18.45	RI
65C102P1	C	8-Bit CMOS Microprocessor with Clock 1 MHz	40	36.75	4.95	RI
65C102P1	I	8-Bit CMOS Microprocessor with Clock 1 MHz	40	36.75	5.05	RI
65C102P2	C	8-Bit CMOS Microprocessor with Clock 2 MHz	40	73.50	5.45	RI
65C102P2	I	8-Bit CMOS Microprocessor with Clock 2 MHz	40	73.50	5.80	RI
65C102P3	C	8-Bit CMOS Microprocessor with Clock 3 MHz	40	110.25	6.80	RI
65C102P3	I	8-Bit CMOS Microprocessor with Clock 3 MHz	40	110.25	7.85	RI
65C102P4	C	8-Bit CMOS Microprocessor with Clock 4 MHz	40	147.00	8.25	RI
65C102P4	I	8-Bit CMOS Microprocessor with Clock 4 MHz	40	147.00	9.50	RI
65C112P1	C	8-Bit CMOS Microprocessor 1 MHz	40	21.00	4.95	RI
65C112P1	I	8-Bit CMOS Microprocessor 1 MHz	40	21.00	5.05	RI
65C112P2	C	8-Bit CMOS Microprocessor 2 MHz	40	42.00	5.45	RI
65C112P2	I	8-Bit CMOS Microprocessor 2 MHz	40	42.00	5.80	RI
65C112P3	C	8-Bit CMOS Microprocessor 3 MHz	40	63.00	6.80	RI
65C112P3	I	8-Bit CMOS Microprocessor 3 MHz	40	63.00	7.85	RI

Appendix E
6800/68000 Index

TYPE	TEMP GRADE	DESCRIPTION	PINS	POWER (mW)	PRICE ($)	SUPPLIERS
6800	C	8-Bit NMOS Microprocessor 1 MHz	40	1000.00	2.85	M
6800C	I	8-Bit NMOS Microprocessor 1 MHz	40	1000.00	5.95	M
68A00	C	8-Bit NMOS Microprocessor 1.5 MHz	40	1000.00	4.45	M
68A00C	I	8-Bit NMOS Microprocessor 1.5 MHz	40	1000.00	6.90	M
68B00	C	8-Bit NMOS Microprocessor 2 MHz	40	1000.00	4.75	M
6802	C	8-Bit NMOS Microprocessor 1 MHz with Clock & 128 x 8 RAM	40	1000.00	2.65	M
6802C	I	8-Bit NMOS Microprocessor 1 MHz with Clock & 128 x 8 RAM	40	1000.00	7.02	M
68A02	C	8-Bit NMOS Microprocessor 1.5 MHz with Clock & 128 x 8 RAM	40	1000.00	5.10	M
68B02	C	8-Bit NMOS Microprocessor 2 MHz with Clock & 128 x 8 RAM	40	1000.00	5.80	M
6809	C	8-Bit NMOS Microprocessor 1 MHz with Clock	40	1000.00	3.75	M
68A09	C	8-Bit NMOS Microprocessor 1.5 MHz with Clock	40	1000.00	7.00	M
68B09	C	8-Bit NMOS Microprocessor 2 MHz with Clock	40	1000.00	8.55	M
6809E	C	8-Bit NMOS Microprocessor 1 MHz	40	1000.00	5.40	M
68A09E	C	8-Bit NMOS Microprocessor 1.5 MHz	40	1000.00	7.00	M
68B09E	C	8-Bit NMOS Microprocessor 2 MHz	40	1000.00	7.85	M
6810	C	128 x 8 Static MOS RAM 1.0 MHz	24	420.00	1.75	M
6810C	I	128 x 8 Static MOS RAM 1.0 MHz	24	420.00	2.90	M
68A10	C	128 x 8 Static MOS RAM 1.5 MHz	24	525.00	2.20	M
68A10C	I	128 x 8 Static MOS RAM 1.5 MHz	24	525.00	3.20	M
68B10C	I	128 x 8 Static MOS RAM 2.0 MHz	24	525.00	2.85	M
6821	C	Peripheral Interface Adapter 1.0 MHz	40	550.00	1.30	M

TYPE	TEMP GRADE	DESCRIPTION	PINS	POWER (mW)	PRICE ($)	SUPPLIERS
6821C	I	Peripheral Interface Adapter 1.0 MHz	40	550.00	3.10	M
68A21	C	Peripheral Interface Adapter 1.5 MHz	40	550.00	2.20	M
68A21C	I	Peripheral Interface Adapter 1.5 MHz	40	550.00	4.10	M
68B21	C	Peripheral Interface Adapter 2.0 MHz	40	550.00	2.50	M
6840	C	Programmable Timer 1.0 MHz	28	700.00	2.75	M
6840C	I	Programmable Timer 1.0 MHz	28	700.00	6.30	M
68A40	C	Programmable Timer 1.5 MHz	28	700.00	4.75	M
68A40C	I	Programmable Timer 1.5 MHz	28	700.00	6.21	M
68B40	C	Programmable Timer 2.0 MHz	28	700.00	5.20	M
6844	C	DMA Controller 1.0 MHz	40	750.00	13.95	M
68A44	C	DMA Controller 1.5 MHz	40	750.00	14.75	M
68B44	C	DMA Controller 2.0 MHz	40	750.00	15.35	M
6845	C	CRT Controller 1.0 MHz	40	750.00	5.00	M
6845C	I	CRT Controller 1.0 MHz	40	750.00	6.75	M
68A45	C	CRT Controller 1.5 MHz	40	750.00	7.00	M
68B45	C	CRT Controller 2.0 MHz	40	750.00	7.60	M
6847	C	Video Display Generator	40	600.00	7.87	M
6850	C	Asynchronous Communications Interface Adapter 1 MHz	24	525.00	1.30	M
6850C	I	Asynchronous Communications Interface Adapter 1 MHz	24	525.00	2.55	M
68A50	C	Asynchronous Communications Interface Adapter 1.5 MHz	24	525.00	2.20	M
68B50	C	Asynchronous Communications Interface Adapter 2.0 MHz	24	525.00	2.50	M
6852	C	Synchronous Serial Data Adapter 1.0 MHz	24	525.00	3.68	M
6852C	I	Synchronous Serial Data Adapter 1.0 MHz	24	525.00	6.00	M
68A52	C	Synchronous Serial Data Adapter 1.5 MHz	24	525.00	5.70	M

TYPE	TEMP GRADE	DESCRIPTION	PINS	POWER (mW)	PRICE ($)	SUPPLIERS
68B52	C	Synchronous Serial Data Adapter 2.0 MHz	24	525.00	5.05	M
6854	C	Advanced Data-Link Controller 1.0 MHz	28	850.00	4.70	M
6854C	I	Advanced Data-Link Controller 1.0 MHz	28	850.00	6.54	M
68A54	C	Advanced Data-Link Controller 1.5 MHz	28	850.00	6.21	M
68B54	C	Advanced Data-Link Controller 2.0 MHz	28	850.00	6.20	M
6859	C	Data Security Device	24	1000.00	6.45	M
6875	C	6800 Clock Generator	16	787.50	6.42	M
6875A	M	6800 Clock Generator	16	787.50	17.14	M
6880A	C	Quad 3-State Bus Transceiver Inverting	16	456.75	1.00	M
6885	C	Hex 3-State Buffers Non-Inverting	16	514.50	0.79	M
6886	C	Hex 3-State Buffers Inverting	16	467.25	0.79	M
6887	C	Hex 3-State Buffers Non-Inverting	16	514.50	0.79	M
6888	C	Hex 3-State Buffers Inverting	16	467.25	0.79	M
6889	C	Quad 3-State Bus Transceiver Non-Inverting	16	577.50	0.87	M
68000P8	C	16-Bit NMOS Microprocessor 8 MHz	64	1500.00	10.00	M
68000P10	C	16-Bit NMOS Microprocessor 10 MHz	64	1500.00	12.50	M
68000P12	C	16-Bit NMOS Microprocessor 12.5 MHz	64	1500.00	25.00	M
68HC000L8	C	16-Bit CMOS Microprocessor 8 MHz	64	130.00	30.00	M
68HC000L10	C	16-Bit CMOS Microprocessor 10 MHz	64	160.00	39.00	M
68HC000L12	C	16-Bit CMOS Microprocessor 12.5 MHz	64	190.00	51.00	M
68008P8	C	16-Bit NMOS Microprocessor 8 MHz with 8-Bit Data Bus	48	1500.00	10.67	M
68008P10	C	16-Bit NMOS Microprocessor 10 MHz with 8-Bit Data Bus	48	1500.00	18.31	M
68010P8	C	16-Bit NMOS Virtual Memory Microprocessor 8 MHz	64	1500.00	20.85	M

TYPE	TEMP GRADE	DESCRIPTION	PINS	POWER (mW)	PRICE ($)	SUPPLIERS
68010P10	C	16–Bit NMOS Virtual Memory Microprocessor 10 MHz	64	1500.00	29.20	M
68010P12	C	16–Bit NMOS Virtual Memory Microprocessor 12.5 MHz	64	1500.00	83.40	M
68020RC12	C	32–Bit NMOS Virtual Memory Microprocessor 12.5 MHz	114	2000.00	173.75	M
68020RC16	C	32–Bit NMOS Virtual Memory Microprocessor 16.67 MHz	114	2000.00	311.25	M
68020RC20	C	32–Bit NMOS Virtual Memory Microprocessor 20 MHz	114	2000.00	579.00	M
68230P8	C	Parallel Interface/Timer 8 MHz	48	750.00	9.97	M
68230P10	C	Parallel Interface/Timer 10 MHz	48	750.00	13.26	M
68450L8	C	DMA Controller 8 MHz	64	2000.00	33.60	M
68450L10	C	DMA Controller 10 MHz	64	2000.00	58.80	M
68451L8	C	Memory Management Unit 8 MHz	64	1500.00	38.96	M
68451L10	C	Memory Management Unit 10 MHz	64	1500.00	116.88	M
68452	C	Bus Arbitration Module	28	682.50	19.00	M
68652	C	Multi–Protocol Communications Controller 1 MHz	40	750.00	7.00	M
68652P2	C	Multi–Protocol Communications Controller 2 MHz	40	750.00	9.10	M
68661A	C	Enhanced Programmable Communications Interrface	28	787.50	3.50	M
68661B	C	Enhanced Programmable Communications Interrface	28	787.50	3.50	M
68661C	C	Enhanced Programmable Communications Interrface	28	787.50	3.50	M
68681	C	Dual Asynchronous Receiver/Transmitter	40	787.50	6.86	M
68881RC12	C	Floating-Point Coprocessor 12.5 MHz	68	750.00	131.25	M
68881RC16	C	Floating-Point Coprocessor 16.67 MHz	68	750.00	193.75	M
68881RC20	C	Floating-Point Coprocessor 20 MHz	68	750.00	622.00	M
68901	C	Multi-Function Peripheral	48	1500.00	7.66	M

Appendix F
8000/80000 Index

TYPE	TEMP GRADE	DESCRIPTION	PINS	POWER (mW)	PRICE ($)	SUPPLIERS
8031AH	C	Single-Chip 8-Bit Microcomputer without ROM 12 MHz	40	840.00	4.15	AMD,I
8031AH	I	Single-Chip 8-Bit Microcomputer without ROM 12 MHz	40	880.00	8.00	AMD
8031AH	M	Single-Chip 8-Bit Microcomputer without ROM 12 MHz	40	880.00	107.00	AMD,I
8032AH	C	Single-Chip 8-Bit Microcomputer without ROM 12 MHz	40	962.50	7.60	I
8035AHL	C	Single-Chip 8-Bit Microcomputer without ROM 11 MHz	40	357.50	4.00	I,N
8035AHL	M	Single-Chip 8-Bit Microcomputer without ROM 11 MHz	40	577.50	33.00	I
8039AHL	C	Single-Chip 8-Bit Microcomputer without ROM 11 MHz	40	385.00	4.30	I,N
8040AHL	C	Single-Chip 8-Bit Microcomputer without ROM 11 MHz	40	440.00	10.10	I,N
8080A	C	8-Bit N-Channel Microprocessor 2 MHz	40	1307.25	5.87	AMD,I
8080A	I	8-Bit N-Channel Microprocessor 2 MHz	40	1611.50	23.65	AMD
8080A	M	8-Bit N-Channel Microprocessor 2 MHz	40	1611.50	35.70	AMD,I
8080A-1	C	8-Bit N-Channel Microprocessor 3 MHz	40	1307.25	7.87	AMD,I
8080A-2	C	8-Bit N-Channel Microprocessor 2.6 MHz	40	1307.25	6.70	AMD,I
8080A-2	I	8-Bit N-Channel Microprocessor 2.6 MHz	40	1611.50	31.85	AMD
8080A-2	M	8-Bit N-Channel Microprocessor 2.6 MHz	40	1611.50	45.46	AMD
8085A	C	8-Bit Microprocessor 3 MHz	40	892.50	3.35	AMD
8085A	I	8-Bit Microprocessor 3 MHz	40	1100.00	18.40	AMD
8085A	M	8-Bit Microprocessor 3 MHz	40	1100.00	41.80	AMD
8085A-2	C	8-Bit Microprocessor 5 MHz	40	892.50	4.00	AMD

TYPE	TEMP GRADE	DESCRIPTION	PINS	POWER (mW)	PRICE ($)	SUPPLIERS
8085A-2	M	8-Bit Microprocessor 5 MHz	40	1100.00	48.30	AMD
8085AH	C	8-Bit HMOS Microprocessor 3 MHz	40	742.50	3.55	AMD,I
8085AH	I	8-Bit HMOS Microprocessor 3 MHz	40	1100.00	17.27	AMD
8085AH	M	8-Bit HMOS Microprocessor 3 MHz	40	1100.00	42.85	I
8085AH-1	C	8-Bit HMOS Microprocessor 6 MHz	40	1100.00	12.65	AMD,I
8085AH-2	C	8-Bit HMOS Microprocessor 5 MHz	40	742.50	4.30	AMD,I
8086	C	16-Bit HMOS Microprocessor 5 MHz	40	1870.00	9.65	AMD,I
8086	I	16-Bit HMOS Microprocessor 5 MHz	40	1870.00	27.99	AMD
8086	M	16-Bit HMOS Microprocessor 5 MHz	40	1870.00	175.00	AMD,I
8086-1	C	16-Bit HMOS Microprocessor 10 MHz	40	1890.00	23.35	AMD,I
8086-2	C	16-Bit HMOS Microprocessor 8 MHz	40	1837.50	11.45	AMD,I
8086-2	I	16-Bit HMOS Microprocessor 8 MHz	40	2178.75	29.35	AMD
8086-2	M	16-Bit HMOS Microprocessor 8 MHz	40	2178.75	211.00	AMD,I
8087	C	Numeric Data Coprocessor 5 MHz	40	2493.75	134.00	I
8087	M	Numeric Data Coprocessor 5 MHz	40	2493.75	312.00	I
8087-1	C	Numeric Data Coprocessor 10 MHz	40	2493.75	250.00	I
8087-2	C	Numeric Data Coprocessor 8 MHz	40	2493.75	179.00	I
8087-2	M	Numeric Data Coprocessor 8 MHz	40	2493.75	436.00	I
8088	C	8-Bit HMOS Microprocessor 5 MHz	40	1870.00	6.90	AMD,I
8088	I	8-Bit HMOS Microprocessor 5 MHz	40	1870.00	22.50	AMD
8088	M	8-Bit HMOS Microprocessor 5 MHz	40	1870.00	126.67	AMD,I
8088-1	C	8-Bit HMOS Microprocessor 10 MHz	40	1925.00	13.50	AMD
8088-2	C	8-Bit HMOS Microprocessor 8 MHz	40	1925.00	9.30	AMD,I
8088-2	I	8-Bit HMOS Microprocessor 8 MHz	40	1925.00	28.00	AMD
8089-3	C	I/O Processor for 5 MHz 8086/8088	40	1925.00	38.70	I
8089-3	M	I/O Processor for 5 MHz 8086/8088	40	2362.50	164.00	I

TYPE	TEMP GRADE	DESCRIPTION	PINS	POWER (mW)	PRICE ($)	SUPPLIERS
8094	C	Single–Chip 16–Bit Microcomputer without ROM	48	1188.00	32.05	I
8095	C	8094 with On–Chip 10–Bit A/D	48	1188.00	36.55	I
8096	C	Single–Chip 16–Bit Microcomputer without ROM	68	1188.00	24.75	I
8097	C	8096 with On–Chip 10–Bit A/D	68	1188.00	29.30	I
8097	M	8096 with On–Chip 10–Bit A/D	68	1160.50	400.20	I
8155	C	2048–Bit Static RAM with I/O Ports and Timer 400 ns	40	990.00	3.35	AMD
8155	I	2048–Bit Static RAM with I/O Ports and Timer 400 ns	40	990.00	17.35	AMD
8155	M	2048–Bit Static RAM with I/O Ports and Timer 400 ns	40	990.00	41.66	AMD
8155–2	C	2048–Bit Static RAM with I/O Ports and Timer 300 ns	40	990.00	4.80	AMD
8155–2	I	2048–Bit Static RAM with I/O Ports and Timer 300 ns	40	990.00	20.00	AMD
8155H	C	2048–Bit Static HMOS RAM with I/O Ports and Timer 400 ns	40	687.50	4.15	AMD, I
8155H	I	2048–Bit Static HMOS RAM with I/O Ports and Timer 400 ns	40	687.50	24.00	AMD
8155H	M	2048–Bit Static HMOS RAM with I/O Ports and Timer 400 ns	40	687.50	42.85	I
8155H–2	C	2048–Bit Static HMOS RAM with I/O Ports and Timer 300 ns	40	687.50	6.00	AMD, I
8155H–2	I	2048–Bit Static HMOS RAM with I/O Ports and Timer 300 ns	40	687.50	25.20	AMD
8156	C	2048–Bit Static RAM with I/O Ports and Timer 400 ns	40	990.00	3.35	AMD
8156	M	2048–Bit Static RAM with I/O Ports and Timer 400 ns	40	990.00	34.33	AMD
8156–2	C	2048–Bit Static RAM with I/O Ports and Timer 300 ns	40	990.00	4.80	AMD

TYPE	TEMP GRADE	DESCRIPTION	PINS	POWER (mW)	PRICE ($)	SUPPLIERS
8156H	C	2046-Bit Static HMOS RAM with I/O Ports and Timer 400 ns	40	687.50	4.15	AMD,I
8156H-2	C	2048-Bit Static HMOS RAM with I/O Ports and Timer 300 ns	40	687.50	6.00	AMD,I
8185	C	1024 x 8 Static RAM 300 ns	18	550.00	21.45	I
8185-2	C	1024 x 8 Static RAM 200 ns	18	550.00	27.85	I
8203	C	64K Dynamic RAM Controller	40	1595.00	28.90	I
8203-1	C	64K Dynamic RAM Controller with Internal Clock	40	1595.00	31.80	I
8203-3	C	64K Dynamic RAM Controller with Internal Clock	40	1522.50	28.90	I
8206	C	Error Detection and Correction Unit 67ns Correction	68	1485.00	44.35	I
8206	M	Error Detection and Correction Unit 67ns Correction	68	1485.00	115.00	I
8206-1	C	Error Detection and Correction Unit 55ns Correction	68	1485.00	51.50	I
8207	M	Dual Port Dynamic RAM Controller 16 MHz	68	2388.75	115.00	I
8207-16	C	Dual Port Dynamic RAM Controller 16 MHz	68	2388.75	48.75	I
8207-8	C	Dual Port Dynamic RAM Controller 8 MHz	68	2502.50	44.35	I
8208	C	Dynamic RAM Controller 8 MHz	48	1650.00	24.60	I
8208-16	C	Dynamic RAM Controller 16 MHz	48	1650.00	31.05	I
8212	C	8-Bit I/O Port	24	682.50	2.15	AMD,I,N
8212	M	8-Bit I/O Port	24	797.50	3.75	AMD,N
8214	C	Priority Interrupt Control Unit	24	715.00	5.50	I
8216	C	Non-Inverting 4-Bit Bus Transceiver	16	682.50	2.00	AMD,I,N
8216	M	Non-Inverting 4-Bit Bus Transceiver	16	715.00	4.90	AMD,N

TYPE	TEMP GRADE	DESCRIPTION	PINS	POWER (mW)	PRICE ($)	SUPPLIERS
8224	C	8080A Clock Generator and Driver	16	754.95	2.60	I,N
8224	M	8080A Clock Generator and Driver	16	754.95	17.90	I
8226	C	Inverting 4-Bit Bus Transceiver	16	682.50	2.00	AMD,I,N
8226	M	Inverting 4-Bit Bus Transceiver	16	715.00	4.90	AMD,N
8228	C	8080A System Controller and Bus Driver	28	997.50	4.65	AMD,I,N
8228	M	8080A System Controller and Bus Driver	28	1155.00	7.90	AMD,I,N
8231A	C	Arithmetic Processing Unit 4 MHz	24	1776.50	135.00	I
8231A-8	C	Arithmetic Processing Unit 2 MHz	24	1776.50	120.00	I
8237A	C	Programmable DMA Controller 3 MHz	40	787.50	4.35	AMD,I
8237A	I	Programmable DMA Controller 3 MHz	40	962.50	19.95	AMD
8237A-4	C	Programmable DMA Controller 4 MHz	40	787.50	5.10	AMD,I
8237A-5	C	Programmable DMA Controller 5 MHz	40	787.50	5.75	AMD,I
8238	C	8080A System Controller and Bus Driver	28	997.50	4.65	AMD,I,N
8238	M	8080A System Controller and Bus Driver	28	1155.00	7.90	AMD,N
8243	C	8048 Family I/O Expander	24	110.00	4.75	I,N
8243	M	8048 Family I/O Expander	24	110.00	26.00	I
8251	C	Programmable Communications Interface 2.4 MHz	28	420.00	8.00	AMD
8251	I	Programmable Communications Interface 2.4 MHz	28	660.00	16.35	AMD
8251	M	Programmable Communications Interface 2.4 MHz	28	660.00	54.72	AMD
8251A	C	Programmable Communications Interface 3 MHz	28	525.00	3.00	AMD,I
8251A	I	Programmable Communications Interface 3 MHz	28	825.00	14.15	AMD

TYPE	TEMP GRADE	DESCRIPTION	PINS	POWER (mW)	PRICE ($)	SUPPLIERS
8251A	M	Programmable Communications Interface 3 MHz	28	825.00	31.40	AMD,I
8253	C	Programmable Interval Timer 2.6 MHz	24	770.00	3.00	AMD,I
8253	I	Programmable Interval Timer 2.6 MHz	24	880.00	14.50	AMD
8253	M	Programmable Interval Timer 2.6 MHz	24	880.00	23.00	AMD,I
8253-2	C	Programmable Interval Timer 5 MHz	24	770.00	4.00	AMD
8253-5	C	Programmable Interval Timer 2.6 MHz	24	770.00	3.33	AMD,I
8253-5	I	Programmable Interval Timer 2.6 MHz	24	880.00	15.60	AMD
8253-5	M	Programmable Interval Timer 2.6 MHz	24	880.00	47.65	AMD
8254	C	Programmable Interval Timer 8 MHz	24	935.00	4.15	I
8254	M	Programmable Interval Timer 8 MHz	24	935.00	40.00	I
8254-2	C	Programmable Interval Timer 10 MHz	24	935.00	6.45	I
8254-5	C	Programmable Interval Timer 5 MHz	24	935.00	3.60	I
8255A	C	Programmable Peripheral Interface 2.5 MHz	40	660.00	2.70	AMD,I
8255A	I	Programmable Peripheral Interface 2.5 MHz	40	660.00	14.35	AMD
8255A	M	Programmable Peripheral Interface 2.5 MHz	40	660.00	22.75	AMD,I
8255A-5	C	Programmable Peripheral Interface 3.3 MHz	40	660.00	3.00	AMD,I
8255A-5	I	Programmable Peripheral Interface 3.3 MHz	40	660.00	14.86	AMD
8255A-5	M	Programmable Peripheral Interface 3.3 MHz	40	660.00	25.35	AMD
8256AH	C	Multifunction Microprocessor Support Controller	40	880.00	8.60	I
8257	C	Programmable DMA Controller 2 MHz	40	630.00	8.80	I
8257	M	Programmable DMA Controller 2 MHz	40	825.00	50.00	I
8257-5	C	Programmable DMA Controller 3 MHz	40	660.00	10.55	I

TYPE	TEMP GRADE	DESCRIPTION	PINS	POWER (mW)	PRICE ($)	SUPPLIERS
8259A	C	Programmable Interrupt Controller 5 MHz	28	467.50	3.00	AMD,I
8259A	I	Programmable Interrupt Controller 5 MHz	28	467.50	11.55	AMD
8259A	M	Programmable Interrupt Controller 5 MHz	28	467.50	22.14	AMD,I
8259A-2	C	Programmable Interrupt Controller 8 MHz	28	467.50	3.55	AMD,I
8259A-2	I	Programmable Interrupt Controller 8 MHz	28	467.50	17.30	AMD
8259A-8	C	Programmable Interrupt Controller 2 MHz	28	446.25	5.15	I
8272A	C	Single/Double Density Floppy Disk Controller	40	660.00	6.01	I
8273	C	Programmable HDLC/SDLC Protocol Controller 64K Baud	40	990.00	35.75	I
8273-4	C	Programmable HDLC/SDLC Protocol Controller 56K Baud	40	990.00	32.15	I
8274	C	Multi-Protocol Serial Controller	40	990.00	13.40	I
8274	M	Multi-Protocol Serial Controller	40	1320.00	138.00	I
8275	C	Programmable CRT Controller 2 MHz	40	880.00	23.40	I
8275-2	C	Programmable CRT Controller 3 MHz	40	880.00	29.30	I
8276	C	Small System CRT Controller 2 MHz	40	880.00	18.40	I
8276-2	C	Small System CRT Controller 3 MHz	40	880.00	21.00	I
8279	C	Programmable Keyboard/Display Interface 2 MHz	40	660.00	6.40	I
8279-5	C	Programmable Keyboard/Display Interface 3 MHz	40	660.00	6.80	I
8282	C	Octal Latch	20	880.00	8.95	I
8282	M	Octal Latch	20	880.00	32.60	I
8283	C	Octal Latch	20	880.00	8.95	I

TYPE	TEMP GRADE	DESCRIPTION	PINS	POWER (mW)	PRICE ($)	SUPPLIERS
8283	M	Octal Latch	20	880.00	32.60	I
8284A	C	Clock Generator/Driver for 8086/8088	18	935.00	2.90	AMD,I
8284A	M	Clock Generator/Driver for 8086/8088	18	850.50	28.70	AMD,I
8284A-1	C	10 MHz Clock Generator/Driver for 8086/8088	18	935.00	8.55	AMD,I
8286	C	Octal Bus Transceiver	20	880.00	4.50	AMD,I
8286	M	Octal Bus Transceiver	20	880.00	23.50	AMD,I
8287	C	Octal Bus Transceiver	20	715.00	4.50	AMD,I
8287	M	Octal Bus Transceiver	20	715.00	33.40	I
8288	C	Bus Controller for 8086/8088	20	1265.00	4.70	AMD,I
8288	M	Bus Controller for 8086/8088	20	1265.00	69.40	I
8289	C	Bus Arbiter	20	907.50	16.80	I
8289	M	Bus Arbiter	20	907.50	108.00	I
8289-1	C	10 MHz Bus Arbiter	20	907.50	33.55	I
8291A	C	GPIB Talker/Listener	40	660.00	23.15	I
8292	C	GPIB Controller	40	687.50	18.85	I
8293	C	GPIB Transceiver	28	962.50	13.95	I
8294	C	Data Encryption Unit	40	687.50	19.95	I
8344AH	C	8031 with On-Chip Serial Interface Unit 12 MHz	40	1100.00	22.20	I
8741A	C	Universal Peripheral Interface 6 MHz	40	687.50	21.45	I
8741A-8	C	Universal Peripheral Interface 3.6 MHz	40	687.50	18.25	I
8742	C	Universal Peripheral Interface 12 MHz	40	742.50	31.45	I
8744AH	C	8751 with On-Chip Serial Interface Unit 12 MHz	40	1100.00	112.15	I
8744H	M	8751 with On-Chip Serial Interface Unit 12 MHz	40	1650.00	470.00	I

TYPE	TEMP GRADE	DESCRIPTION	PINS	POWER (mW)	PRICE ($)	SUPPLIERS
8748H	C	Single-Chip 8-Bit Microcomputer with EPROM 11 MHz	40	495.00	12.30	I
8748H	M	Single-Chip 8-Bit Microcomputer with EPROM 11 MHz	40	770.00	129.95	I
8749H	C	Single-Chip 8-Bit Microcomputer with EPROM 11 MHz	40	605.00	14.85	I
8751H	C	Single-Chip 8-Bit Microcomputer with EPROM 12 MHz	40	1375.00	52.00	AMD, I
8751H-88	M	Single-Chip 8-Bit Microcomputer with EPROM 8 MHz	40	1512.50	268.90	I
8755A	C	16,384-Bit EPROM with I/O 3 MHz	40	1102.50	15.70	I
8755A-2	C	16,384-Bit EPROM with I/O 5 MHz	40	1155.00	28.55	I
80186-10	C	High Integration 16-Bit Microprocessor 10 MHz	68	3025.00	26.80	AMD, I
80186-6	C	High Integration 16-Bit Microprocessor 6 MHz	68	3025.00	15.95	AMD, I
80186-6	M	High Integration 16-Bit Microprocessor 6 MHz	68	3150.00	265.00	AMD, I
80186	C	High Integration 16-Bit Microprocessor 8 MHz	68	3025.00	21.35	AMD, I
80186-8	M	High Integration 16-Bit Microprocessor 8 MHz	68	3150.00	310.00	AMD, I
80188	C	High Integration 8-Bit Microprocessor 8 MHz	68	3025.00	21.25	AMD, I
80188-10	C	High Integration 8-Bit Microprocessor 10 MHz	68	3025.00	35.00	I
80188-6	C	High Integration 8-Bit Microprocessor 6 MHz	68	3025.00	18.95	AMD
80286-10	C	High Performance 16-Bit Microprocessor 10 MHz	68	3150.00	93.00	AMD, I
80286-6	C	High Performance 16-Bit Microprocessor 6 MHz	68	3150.00	50.00	AMD, I
80286-6	M	High Performance 16-Bit Microprocessor 6 MHz	68	3300.00	665.00	I

TYPE	TEMP GRADE	DESCRIPTION	PINS	POWER (mW)	PRICE ($)	SUPPLIERS
80286-8	C	High Performance 16-Bit Microprocessor 8 MHz	68	3150.00	78.60	AMD,I
80286-8	M	High Performance 16-Bit Microprocessor 8 MHz	68	3300.00	784.00	I
80287-10	C	80-Bit HMOS Numeric Processor Extension 10 MHz	40	3150.00	328.00	I
80287-10	M	80-Bit HMOS Numeric Processor Extension 10 MHz	40	3150.00	829.00	I
80287-6	C	80-Bit HMOS Numeric Processor Extension 6 MHz	40	3150.00	185.00	I
80287-8	M	80-Bit HMOS Numeric Processor Extension 8 MHz	40	3150.00	659.00	I
80287-8	C	80-Bit HMOS Numeric Processor Extension 8 MHz	40	3150.00	287.00	I
82188	C	Integrated Bus Controller for 8086/8088, 80186/80188	28	550.00	15.00	I
82188	M	Integrated Bus Controller for 8086/8088, 80186/80188	28	550.00	49.90	I
82258-6	C	Advanced DMA Coprocessor 6 MHz	68	2362.50	95.00	I
82284-10	C	Clock Generator/Driver for 80286-10	18	761.25	16.20	I
82284-6	C	Clock Generator/Driver for 80286-6	18	761.25	7.50	I
82284-8	C	Clock Generator/Driver for 80286-8	18	761.25	10.80	I
82288-6	C	Bus Controller for 80286-6	20	630.00	7.50	I
82288-6	M	Bus Controller for 80286-6	20	770.00	73.95	I
82288-8	C	Bus Controller for 80286-8	20	630.00	10.80	I
82288-8	M	Bus Controller for 80286-8	20	770.00	87.02	I
82289	C	Bus Arbiter for 80286	20	630.00	51.95	I
82289	M	Bus Arbiter for 80286	20	630.00	129.00	I
82501	C	Ethernet Serial Interface	20	1375.00	38.50	I
82502	C	Ethernet Serial Interface	16	445.50	38.50	I

TYPE	TEMP GRADE	DESCRIPTION	PINS	POWER (mW)	PRICE ($)	SUPPLIERS
82530	C	Serial Communications Controller 4 MHz	40	1375.00	10.25	I
82530-6	C	Serial Communications Controller 6 MHz	40	1375.00	15.50	I
82586	C	Local Area Network Coprocessor 8 MHz	48	3025.00	68.00	I
82586-10	C	Local Area Network Coprocessor 10 MHz	48	3025.00	85.20	I
82588	C	Single Chip LAN Controller	28	2090.00	39.70	I
82720	C	Graphics Display Controller 4 MHz	40	1485.00	32.20	I
82720	M	Graphics Display Controller 4 MHz	40	1650.00	177.00	I
82720-1	C	Graphics Display Controller 5 MHz	40	1485.00	37.55	I
82730	C	Text Coprocessor	68	2200.00	84.50	I

TYPE	TEMP GRADE	DESCRIPTION	PINS	POWER (mW)	PRICE ($)	SUPPLIERS
80C31BH	C	CMOS Single Chip Microcomputer without ROM 3.5-12 MHz	40	120.00	10.80	I
80C31BH	M	CMOS Single Chip Microcomputer without ROM 3.5-12 MHz	40	120.00	171.90	I
80C31BH-1	C	CMOS Single Chip Microcomputer without ROM 3.5-16 MHz	40	150.00	13.50	I
80C31BH-2	C	CMOS Single Chip Microcomputer without ROM 0.5-12 MHz	40	120.00	12.40	I
80C86	C	CMOS 16-Bit Microprocessor 5 MHz	40	275.00	20.00	H
80C86	I	CMOS 16-Bit Microprocessor 5 MHz	40	275.00	26.01	H
80C86	M	CMOS 16-Bit Microprocessor 5 MHz	40	275.00	194.00	H,I
80C86-2	C	CMOS 16-Bit Microprocessor 8 MHz	40	440.00	43.11	H
80C86-2	I	CMOS 16-Bit Microprocessor 8 MHz	40	440.00	56.03	H
80C86-2	M	CMOS 16-Bit Microprocessor 8 MHz	40	420.00	239.00	H,I
80C88	C	CMOS 8-Bit Microprocessor 5 MHz	40	275.00	12.20	H,I
80C88	I	CMOS 8-Bit Microprocessor 5 MHz	40	275.00	19.08	H
80C88	M	CMOS 8-Bit Microprocessor 5 MHz	40	275.00	143.00	H
82C08-10	C	CMOS Dynamic RAM Controller 10 MHz	48	330.00	26.75	I
82C08-16	C	CMOS Dynamic RAM Controller 16 MHz	48	330.00	26.75	I
82C08-8	C	CMOS Dynamic RAM Controller 8 MHz	48	330.00	24.30	I
82C37A	C	CMOS Programmable DMA Controller 8 MHz	40	88.00	25.72	H
82C37A	I	CMOS Programmable DMA Controller 8 MHz	40	88.00	26.75	H
82C37A	M	CMOS Programmable DMA Controller 8 MHz	40	88.00	100.47	H
82C37A-5	C	CMOS Programmable DMA Controller 5 MHz	40	55.00	17.15	H
82C37A-5	I	CMOS Programmable DMA Controller 5 MHz	40	55.00	20.58	H

TYPE	TEMP GRADE	DESCRIPTION	PINS	POWER (mW)	PRICE ($)	SUPPLIERS
82C37A-5	M	CMOS Programmable DMA Controller 5 MHz	40	55.00	91.34	H
82C50A-5	C	CMOS Asynchronous Communications Element	40	33.00	10.81	H
82C50A-5	I	CMOS Asynchronous Communications Element	40	33.00	12.98	H
82C50A-5	M	CMOS Asynchronous Communications Element	40	33.00	69.55	H
82C52	C	CMOS Serial Controller Interface	28	16.50	13.50	H
82C52	I	CMOS Serial Controller Interface	28	16.50	16.49	H
82C52	M	CMOS Serial Controller Interface	28	16.50	42.68	H
82C54	C	CMOS Programmable Interval Timer 8 MHz	24	55.00	8.61	H, I
82C54	I	CMOS Programmable Interval Timer 8 MHz	24	55.00	20.93	H
82C54	M	CMOS Programmable Interval Timer 8 MHz	24	55.00	40.00	H, I
82C54-2	C	CMOS Programmable Interval Timer 10 MHz	24	55.00	10.35	I
82C55A	C	CMOS Programmable Peripheral Interface 8 MHz	40	55.00	6.57	H, I
82C55A	I	CMOS Programmable Peripheral Interface 8 MHz	40	55.00	12.80	H
82C55A	M	CMOS Programmable Peripheral Interface 8 MHz	40	55.00	42.47	H
82C55A-5	C	CMOS Programmable Peripheral Interface 5 MHz	40	55.00	3.99	H
82C55A-5	I	CMOS Programmable Peripheral Interface 5 MHz	40	55.00	11.52	H
82C55A-5	M	CMOS Programmable Peripheral Interface 5 MHz	40	55.00	28.32	H
82C59A	C	CMOS Priority Interrupt Controller 8 MHz	28	27.50	4.00	H, I

TYPE	TEMP GRADE	DESCRIPTION	PINS	POWER (mW)	PRICE ($)	SUPPLIERS
82C59A	I	CMOS Priority Interrupt Controller 8 MHz	28	27.50	14.51	H
82C59A	M	CMOS Priority Interrupt Controller 8 MHz	28	27.50	25.10	I
82C59A-5	C	CMOS Priority Interrupt Controller 5 MHz	28	17.20	4.80	H
82C59A-5	I	CMOS Priority Interrupt Controller 5 MHz	28	17.20	13.06	H
82C82	C	CMOS Octal Latching Bus Driver	20	5.50	4.69	H
82C82	I	CMOS Octal Latching Bus Driver	20	5.50	7.55	H
82C82	M	CMOS Octal Latching Bus Driver	20	5.50	29.10	H
82C83H	C	CMOS Octal Latching Inverting Bus Driver	20	5.50	8.96	H
82C83H	I	CMOS Octal Latching Inverting Bus Driver	20	5.50	12.51	H
82C83H	M	CMOS Octal Latching Inverting Bus Driver	20	5.50	33.62	H
82C84A	C	CMOS Clock Generator Driver for 8 MHz 80C86/80C88	18	220.00	3.67	H
82C84A	I	CMOS Clock Generator Driver for 8 MHz 80C86/80C88	18	220.00	9.27	H
82C84A	M	CMOS Clock Generator Driver for 8 MHz 80C86/80C88	18	220.00	28.69	H,I
82C84A-5	C	CMOS Clock Generator Driver for 5 MHz 80C86/80C88	18	55.00	4.00	I
82C85	C	CMOS Static Clock Generator/Driver	24	275.00	7.95	H
82C85	I	CMOS Static Clock Generator/Driver	24	275.00	9.54	H
82C85	M	CMOS Static Clock Generator/Driver	24	275.00	44.04	H
82C86H	C	CMOS Octal Bus Transceivers 32 ns	20	5.50	9.22	H
82C86H	I	CMOS Octal Bus Transceivers 32 ns	20	5.50	12.61	H
82C86H-5	C	CMOS Octal Bus Transceivers 35 ns	20	5.50	6.65	H

TYPE	TEMP GRADE	DESCRIPTION	PINS	POWER (mW)	PRICE ($)	SUPPLIERS
82C86H-5	I	CMOS Octal Bus Transceivers 35 ns	20	5.50	11.35	H
82C86H-5	M	CMOS Octal Bus Transceivers 35 ns	20	5.50	33.43	H
82C87H	C	CMOS Octal Inverting Bus Transceivers 30 ns	20	5.50	9.22	H
82C87H	I	CMOS Octal Inverting Bus Transceivers 30 ns	20	5.50	12.61	H
82C87H-5	C	CMOS Octal Inverting Bus Transceivers 35 ns	20	5.50	6.65	H
82C87H-5	I	CMOS Octal Inverting Bus Transceivers 35 ns	20	5.50	11.35	H
82C87H-5	M	CMOS Octal Inverting Bus Transceivers 35 ns	20	5.50	33.43	H
82C88	C	CMOS Bus Controller	20	44.00	8.48	H,I
82C88	I	CMOS Bus Controller	20	44.00	10.17	H
82C88	M	CMOS Bus Controller	20	44.00	69.39	H,I

Appendix G
Z80/Z8000 Index

TYPE	TEMP GRADE	DESCRIPTION	PINS	POWER (mW)	PRICE ($)	SUPPLIERS
Z8001	C	Z8000 SEG CPU 16-Bit NMOS Microprocessor 4 MHz	48	1575.00	12.00	AMD
Z8001	M	Z8000 SEG CPU 16-Bit NMOS Microprocessor 4 MHz	48	2200.00	96.74	AMD,Z
Z8001A	C	Z8000 SEG CPU 16-Bit NMOS Microprocessor 6 MHz	48	1575.00	13.10	AMD,Z
Z8001A	I	Z8000 SEG CPU 16-Bit NMOS Microprocessor 6 MHz	48	2100.00	57.04	Z
Z8001A	M	Z8000 SEG CPU 16-Bit NMOS Microprocessor 6 MHz	48	2200.00	120.26	AMD,Z
Z8001A-8	C	Z8000 SEG CPU 16-Bit NMOS Microprocessor 8 MHz	48	1575.00	17.50	AMD
Z8001B	C	Z8000 SEG CPU 16-Bit NMOS Microprocessor 10 MHz	48	2100.00	18.57	Z
Z8001B	M	Z8000 SEG CPU 16-Bit NMOS Microprocessor 10 MHz	48	2200.00	519.00	Z
Z8002	C	Z8000 NONSEG CPU 16-Bit NMOS Microprocessor 4 MHz	40	1575.00	8.80	AMD,Z
Z8002	M	Z8000 NONSEG CPU 16-Bit NMOS Microprocessor 4 MHz	40	2200.00	68.33	Z
Z8002A	C	Z8000 NONSEG CPU 16-Bit NMOS Microprocessor 6 MHz	40	1575.00	9.35	AMD,Z
Z8002A	I	Z8000 NONSEG CPU 16-Bit NMOS Microprocessor 6 MHz	40	2100.00	29.29	Z
Z8002A	M	Z8000 NONSEG CPU 16-Bit NMOS Microprocessor 6 MHz	40	2200.00	133.79	AMD,Z
Z8002A-8	C	Z8000 NONSEG CPU 16-Bit NMOS Microprocessor 8 MHz	40	1575.00	14.40	AMD
Z8002B	C	Z8000 NONSEG CPU 16-Bit NMOS Microprocessor 10 MHz	40	2100.00	14.14	Z
Z8002B	M	Z8000 NONSEG CPU 16-Bit NMOS Microprocessor 10 MHz	40	2200.00	498.00	Z
Z8010A	C	Z8000 MMU Memory Management Unit 6 MHz	48	1575.00	13.89	Z

TYPE	TEMP GRADE	DESCRIPTION	PINS	POWER (mW)	PRICE ($)	SUPPLIERS
Z8010B	C	Z8000 MMU Memory Management Unit 10 MHz	48	1575.00	27.16	Z
Z8016	C	Z8000 DTC Direct Memory Access Transfer Controller 4 MHz	48	1837.50	5.83	AMD,Z
Z8016A	C	Z8000 DTC Direct Memory Access Transfer Controller 6 MHz	48	1837.50	8.57	AMD,Z
Z8030	C	Z8000 SCC Serial Communications Controller 4 MHz	40	1312.50	6.45	AMD
Z8030	M	Z8000 SCC Serial Communications Controller 4 MHz	40	1312.50	107.30	Z
Z8030A	C	Z8000 SCC Serial Communications Controller 6 MHz	40	1312.50	4.86	AMD,Z
Z8030A	I	Z8000 SCC Serial Communications Controller 6 MHz	40	1312.50	22.57	Z
Z8030A	M	Z8000 SCC Serial Communications Controller 6 MHz	40	1312.50	132.40	Z
Z8031	C	Z8000 ASCC Async Serial Communications Controller 4 MHz	40	1312.50	6.50	AMD
Z8031A	C	Z8000 ASCC Async Serial Communications Controller 6 MHz	40	1312.50	4.86	AMD,Z
Z8036	M	Z8000 CIO Counter/Timer and Parallel I/O Unit 4 MHz	40	1050.00	84.23	Z
Z8036A	C	Z8000 CIO Counter/Timer and Parallel I/O Unit 6 MHz	40	1050.00	5.54	Z
Z8036A	I	Z8000 CIO Counter/Timer and Parallel I/O Unit 6 MHz	40	1050.00	18.53	Z
Z8036A	M	Z8000 CIO Counter/Timer and Parallel I/O Unit 6 MHz	40	1050.00	132.40	Z
Z8038	C	Z8000 FIO FIFO Input/Output Interface Unit 4 MHz	40	1050.00	11.16	Z
Z8038A	C	Z8000 FIO FIFO Input/Output Interface Unit 6 MHz	40	1050.00	13.49	Z
Z8060	C	Z8000 FIFO Buffer Unit and FIO Expander 4 MHz	28	1050.00	9.60	AMD,Z

TYPE	TEMP GRADE	DESCRIPTION	PINS	POWER (mW)	PRICE ($)	SUPPLIERS
Z8060	M	Z8000 FIFO Buffer Unit and FIO Expander 4 MHz	28	1050.00	133.35	AMD
Z8400A	C	Z80A CPU 8-Bit NMOS Microprocessor 4 MHz	40	1050.00	1.71	Z
Z8400A	I	Z80A CPU 8-Bit NMOS Microprocessor 4 MHz	40	1050.00	3.57	Z
Z8400A	M	Z80A CPU 8-Bit NMOS Microprocessor 4 MHz	40	1050.00	74.29	Z
Z8400B	C	Z80B CPU 8-Bit NMOS Microprocessor 6 MHz	40	1050.00	1.86	Z
Z8400B	I	Z80B CPU 8-Bit NMOS Microprocessor 6 MHz	40	1050.00	4.71	Z
Z8400H	C	Z80H CPU 8-Bit NMOS Microprocessor 8 MHz	40	1050.00	3.21	Z
Z8410A	C	Z80A DMA Direct Memory Access Controller 4 MHz	40	1050.00	4.29	Z
Z8420A	C	Z80A PIO Parallel Input/Output Controller 4 MHz	40	525.50	1.71	Z
Z8420A	I	Z80A PIO Parallel Input/Output Controller 4 MHz	40	525.50	3.36	Z
Z8420A	M	Z80A PIO Parallel Input/Output Controller 4 MHz	40	550.00	65.71	Z
Z8420B	C	Z80B PIO Parallel Input/Output Controller 6 MHz	40	525.50	1.93	Z
Z8420B	I	Z80B PIO Parallel Input/Output Controller 6 MHz	40	525.50	4.43	Z
Z8430A	C	Z80A CTC Counter/Timer Circuit 4 MHz	28	630.00	1.71	Z
Z8430A	I	Z80A CTC Counter/Timer Circuit 4 MHz	28	630.00	3.43	Z
Z8430A	M	Z80A CTC Counter/Timer Circuit 4 MHz	28	660.00	82.86	Z
Z8430B	C	Z80B CTC Counter/Timer Circuit 6 MHz	28	630.00	2.21	Z
Z8430B	I	Z80B CTC Counter/Timer Circuit 6 MHz	28	630.00	5.64	Z
Z8440A	C	Z80A SIO/0 Serial Input/Output Controller 4 MHz	40	525.00	2.64	Z
Z8440A	I	Z80A SIO/0 Serial Input/Output Controller 4 MHz	40	525.00	6.00	Z
Z8440A	M	Z80A SIO/0 Serial Input/Output Controller 4 MHz	40	550.00	108.57	Z

TYPE	TEMP GRADE	DESCRIPTION	PINS	POWER (mW)	PRICE ($)	SUPPLIERS
Z8440B	C	Z80B SIO/0 Serial Input/Output Controller 6 MHz	40	525.00	3.00	Z
Z8440B	I	Z80B SIO/0 Serial Input/Output Controller 6 MHz	40	525.00	7.50	Z
Z8441A	C	Z80A SIO/1 Serial Input/Output Controller 4 MHz	40	525.00	2.64	Z
Z8441A	I	Z80A SIO/1 Serial Input/Output Controller 4 MHz	40	525.00	6.00	Z
Z8441A	M	Z80A SIO/1 Serial Input/Output Controller 4 MHz	40	550.00	108.57	Z
Z8441B	C	Z80B SIO/1 Serial Input/Output Controller 6 MHz	40	525.00	3.00	Z
Z8441B	I	Z80B SIO/1 Serial Input/Output Controller 6 MHz	40	525.00	7.50	Z
Z8442A	C	Z80A SIO/2 Serial Input/Output Controller 4 MHz	40	525.00	2.64	Z
Z8442A	I	Z80A SIO/2 Serial Input/Output Controller 4 MHz	40	525.00	6.00	Z
Z8442A	M	Z80A SIO/2 Serial Input/Output Controller 4 MHz	40	550.00	108.57	Z
Z8442B	C	Z80B SIO/2 Serial Input/Output Controller 6 MHz	40	525.00	3.00	Z
Z8442B	I	Z80B SIO/2 Serial Input/Output Controller 6 MHz	40	525.00	7.50	Z
Z8470A	C	Z80A DART Dual Asynchronous Receiver/Transmitter 4 MHz	40	525.00	2.64	Z
Z8470B	C	Z80B DART Dual Asynchronous Receiver/Transmitter 6 MHz	40	525.00	3.00	Z
Z84C00-4	C	Z80C CPU 8-Bit CMOS Microprocessor 4 MHz	40	137.50	2.07	Z
Z84C00-4	I	Z80C CPU 8-Bit CMOS Microprocessor 4 MHz	40	137.50	2.50	Z
Z84C00-6	C	Z80C CPU 8-Bit CMOS Microprocessor 6 MHz	40	206.25	3.36	Z
Z84C00-6	I	Z80C CPU 8-Bit CMOS Microprocessor 6 MHz	40	206.25	5.00	Z

TYPE	TEMP GRADE	DESCRIPTION	PINS	POWER (mW)	PRICE ($)	SUPPLIERS
Z84C00-8	C	Z80C CPU 8-Bit CMOS Microprocessor 8 MHz	40	275.00	5.14	Z
Z84C20-4	C	Z80C PIO Parallel Input/Output 4 MHz	40	27.50	1.86	Z
Z84C20-4	I	Z80C PIO Parallel Input/Output 4 MHz	40	27.50	2.29	Z
Z84C20-6	C	Z80C PIO Parallel Input/Output 6 MHz	40	41.25	3.43	Z
Z84C20-6	I	Z80C PIO Parallel Input/Output 6 MHz	40	41.25	4.50	Z
Z84C30-4	C	Z80C CTC Counter/Timer Circuit 4 MHz	28	38.50	1.93	Z
Z84C30-4	I	Z80C CTC Counter/Timer Circuit 4 MHz	28	38.50	2.36	Z
Z84C30-6	C	Z80C CTC Counter/Timer Circuit 6 MHz	28	57.75	3.50	Z
Z84C30-6	I	Z80C CTC Counter/Timer Circuit 6 MHz	28	57.75	4.86	Z
Z84C40-4	C	Z80C SIO/0 Serial Input/Output 4 MHz	40	82.50	3.00	Z
Z84C40-4	I	Z80C SIO/0 Serial Input/Output 4 MHz	40	82.50	6.93	Z
Z84C40-6	C	Z80C SIO/0 Serial Input/Output 6 MHz	40	123.75	6.29	Z
Z84C41-4	C	Z80C SIO/1 Serial Input/Output 4 MHz	40	82.50	3.00	Z
Z84C41-4	I	Z80C SIO/1 Serial Input/Output 4 MHz	40	82.50	6.93	Z
Z84C41-6	C	Z80C SIO/1 Serial Input/Output 6 MHz	40	123.75	6.29	Z
Z84C42-4	C	Z80C SIO/2 Serial Input/Output 4 MHz	40	82.50	3.00	Z
Z84C42-4	I	Z80C SIO/2 Serial Input/Output 4 MHz	40	82.50	6.93	Z
Z84C42-6	C	Z80C SIO/2 Serial Input/Output 6 MHz	40	123.75	6.29	Z
Z8516	C	Z8500 DTC DMA Transfer Controller 4 MHz	48	1837.50	10.86	Z
Z8516A	C	Z8500 DTC DMA Transfer Controller 6 MHz	48	1837.50	14.29	Z
Z8530	C	Z8500 SCC Serial Communications Controller 4 MHz	40	1312.50	5.00	AMD,Z
Z8530	M	Z8500 SCC Serial Communications Controller 4 MHz	40	1312.50	76.30	AMD,Z
Z8530A	C	Z8500 SCC Serial Communications Controller 6 MHz	40	1312.50	5.86	AMD,Z
Z8530A	I	Z8500 SCC Serial Communications Controller 6 MHz	40	1312.50	10.64	Z

TYPE	TEMP GRADE	DESCRIPTION	PINS	POWER (mW)	PRICE ($)	SUPPLIERS
Z8530A	M	Z8500 SCC Serial Communications Controller 6 MHz	40	1312.50	135.39	Z
Z8531	C	Z8500 ASCC Async Serial Communications Controller 4 MHz	40	1312.50	6.50	AMD
Z8531A	C	Z8500 ASCC Async Serial Communications Controller 6 MHz	40	1312.50	7.40	AMD
Z8536	M	Z8500 CIO Counter/Timer and Parallel I/O Unit 4 MHz	40	1050.00	85.27	Z
Z8536A	C	Z8500 CIO Counter/Timer and Parallel I/O Unit 6 MHz	40	1050.00	5.50	Z
Z8536A	I	Z8500 CIO Counter/Timer and Parallel I/O Unit 6 MHz	40	1050.00	7.99	Z
Z8536A	M	Z8500 CIO Counter/Timer and Parallel I/O Unit 6 MHz	40	1050.00	132.96	Z
Z8581	C	Z8500 CGC Clock Generator and Controller 6 MHz	18	787.50	3.51	Z
Z8581	I	Z8500 CGC Clock Generator and Controller 6 MHz	18	787.50	5.79	Z
Z8581	M	Z8500 CGC Clock Generator and Controller 6 MHz	18	825.00	93.13	Z
Z8581-10	C	Z8500 CGC Clock Generator and Controller 10 MHz	18	787.50	5.43	Z
Z8581-10	M	Z8500 CGC Clock Generator and Controller 10 MHz	18	825.00	180.93	Z

Appendix H
32000 Index

TYPE	TEMP GRADE	DESCRIPTION	PINS	POWER (mW)	PRICE ($)	SUPPLIERS
32008-6	C	High Performance 8-Bit Microprocessor 6 MHz	48	1575.00	12.50	N
32008-8	C	High Performance 8-Bit Microprocessor 8 MHz	48	1575.00	31.10	N
32008-10	C	High Performance 8-Bit Microprocessor 10 MHz	48	1575.00	41.45	N
32016-6	C	High Performance 16-Bit Microprocessor 6 MHz	48	1575.00	14.95	N
32016-8	C	High Performance 16-Bit Microprocessor 8 MHz	48	1575.00	40.70	N
32016-10	C	High Performance 16-Bit Microprocessor 10 MHz	48	1575.00	70.00	N
32032-6	C	High Performance 32-Bit Microprocessor 6 MHz	68	1575.00	30.95	N
32032-8	C	High Performance 32-Bit Microprocessor 8 MHz	68	1575.00	98.55	N
32032-10	C	High Performance 32-Bit Microprocessor 10 MHz	68	1575.00	178.60	N
32081-6	C	Floating-Point Unit 6 MHz	24	1575.00	17.75	N
32081-8	C	Floating-Point Unit 8 MHz	24	1575.00	84.30	N
32081-10	C	Floating-Point Unit 10 MHz	24	1575.00	98.60	N
32082-6	C	Memory Management Unit 6 MHz	48	1575.00	13.55	N
32082-8	C	Memory Management Unit 8 MHz	48	1575.00	121.45	N
32082-10	C	Memory Management Unit 10 MHz	48	1575.00	131.45	N
32201-6	C	Timing Control Unit 6 MHz	24	1365.00	3.50	N
32201-8	C	Timing Control Unit 8 MHz	24	1365.00	13.60	N
32201-10	C	Timing Control Unit 10 MHz	24	1365.00	14.30	N
32202-6	C	Interrupt Control Unit 6 MHz	40	1575.00	9.25	N
32202-8	C	Interrupt Control Unit 8 MHz	40	1575.00	64.30	N
32202-10	C	Interrupt Control Unit 10 MHz	40	1575.00	70.00	N

Appendix I
2900 Index

TYPE	TEMP GRADE	DESCRIPTION	PINS	POWER (mW)	PRICE ($)	SUPPLIERS
2901C	C	4-Bit Bipolar Microprocessor Slice	40	1391.25	6.65	AMD
2901C	M	4-Bit Bipolar Microprocessor Slice	40	1540.00	33.50	AMD
2902A	C	High-Speed Look-Ahead Carry Generator	16	572.25	1.80	AMD
2902A	M	High-Speed Look-Ahead Carry Generator	16	544.50	6.75	AMD
2903A	C	4-Bit Bipolar Microprocessor Slice	48	1837.50	20.50	AMD
2903A	M	4-Bit Bipolar Microprocessor Slice	48	2172.50	52.50	AMD
2904	C	Status and Shift Control Unit	40	1669.50	16.95	AMD
2904	M	Status and Shift Control Unit	40	1914.00	68.70	AMD
2905	C	Quad 2-Input OC Bus Transceiver with 3-State Receiver	24	551.25	5.40	AMD
2905	M	Quad 2-Input OC Bus Transceiver with 3-State Receiver	24	577.50	17.25	AMD
2906	C	Quad 2-Input OC Bus Transceiver with Parity	24	551.25	7.45	AMD
2906	M	Quad 2-Input OC Bus Transceiver with Parity	24	577.50	21.25	AMD
2907	C	Quad Bus Transceiver with Interface Logic	20	577.50	4.75	AMD
2907	M	Quad Bus Transceiver with Interface Logic	20	605.00	14.80	AMD
2908	C	Quad Bus Transceiver with Interface Logic	20	630.00	4.75	AMD
2908	M	Quad Bus Transceiver with Interface Logic	20	660.00	15.00	AMD
2909A	C	Microprogram Sequencer	28	682.50	5.25	AMD
2909A	M	Microprogram Sequencer	28	770.00	26.70	AMD
2910A	C	Microprogram Controller	40	1806.00	13.35	AMD

TYPE	TEMP GRADE	DESCRIPTION	PINS	POWER (mW)	PRICE ($)	SUPPLIERS
2910A	M	Microprogram Controller	40	1870.00	49.00	AMD
2911A	C	Microprogram Sequencer	20	682.50	3.35	AMD
2911A	M	Microprogram Sequencer	20	770.00	21.00	AMD
2912	C	Quad Bus Transceiver	16	367.50	2.10	AMD
2912	M	Quad Bus Transceiver	16	385.00	4.57	AMD
2913	C	Priority Interrupt Expander	20	126.00	1.93	AMD
2913	M	Priority Interrupt Expander	20	132.00	6.40	AMD
2914	C	Vectored Priority Interrupt Controller	40	1601.25	18.00	AMD
2914	M	Vectored Priority Interrupt Controller	40	1705.00	68.75	AMD
2915A	C	Quad 3-State Bus Transceiver with Interface Logic	24	498.75	5.40	AMD
2915A	M	Quad 3-State Bus Transceiver with Interface Logic	24	522.50	17.25	AMD
2916A	C	Quad 3-State Bus Transceiver with Interface Logic	24	577.50	7.45	AMD
2916A	M	Quad 3-State Bus Transceiver with Interface Logic	24	605.00	21.25	AMD
2917A	C	Quad 3-State Bus Transceiver with Interface Logic	20	498.75	4.75	AMD
2917A	M	Quad 3-State Bus Transceiver with Interface Logic	20	522.50	16.70	AMD
2918	C	Quad D Register with Standard and 3-State Outputs	16	682.50	2.88	AMD
2918	M	Quad D Register with Standard and 3-State Outputs	16	715.00	12.75	AMD
29LS18	C	Quad D Register with Standard and 3-State Outputs	16	147.00	2.75	AMD
29LS18	M	Quad D Register with Standard and 3-State Outputs	16	154.00	7.02	AMD

TYPE	TEMP GRADE	DESCRIPTION	PINS	POWER (mW)	PRICE ($)	SUPPLIERS
2919	C	Quad Register with Dual 3-State Outputs	20	204.75	2.53	AMD
2919	M	Quad Register with Dual 3-State Outputs	20	198.00	6.20	AMD
2920	C	Octal 3-State D Flip-Flop with Clear and Clock Enable	22	194.25	2.55	AMD
2920	M	Octal 3-State D Flip-Flop with Clear and Clock Enable	22	203.50	6.20	AMD
2921	C	1-of-8 Decoder with 3-State Outputs and Polarity Control	20	178.50	2.08	AMD
2921	M	1-of-8 Decoder with 3-State Outputs and Polarity Control	20	187.00	5.25	AMD
2922	C	8 Input Multiplexer with Control Register	20	777.00	3.55	AMD
2922	M	8 Input Multiplexer with Control Register	20	814.00	9.95	AMD
2923	C	8 Input Multiplexer	16	446.25	1.40	AMD
2923	M	8 Input Multiplexer	16	467.50	3.15	AMD
2924	C	3 to 8 Line Decoder/Demultiplexer	16	388.50	1.40	AMD
2924	M	3 to 8 Line Decoder/Demultiplexer	16	407.00	3.15	AMD
2925	C	Clock Generator and Microcycle Length Controller	24	630.00	12.99	AMD
2925	M	Clock Generator and Microcycle Length Controller	24	660.00	54.31	AMD
2927	C	Quad 3-State Bus Transceiver with Clock Enable	20	971.25	5.70	AMD
2927	M	Quad 3-State Bus Transceiver with Clock Enable	20	1017.50	15.00	AMD
2928	C	Quad 3-State Bus Transceiver with Clock Enable	20	997.50	5.70	AMD
2928	M	Quad 3-State Bus Transceiver with Clock Enable	20	1045.00	15.00	AMD
2930	C	Program Control Unit	28	1155.00	19.95	AMD

TYPE	TEMP GRADE	DESCRIPTION	PINS	POWER (mW)	PRICE ($)	SUPPLIERS
2930	M	Program Control Unit	28	1314.50	67.10	AMD
2932	C	Program Control Unit	20	997.50	17.95	AMD
2932	M	Program Control Unit	20	1155.00	66.65	AMD
2940	C	DMA Address Generator	28	1522.50	18.15	AMD
2940	M	DMA Address Generator	28	1732.50	67.95	AMD
2942	C	Programmable Timer/Counter or DMA Address Generator	22	1391.25	13.00	AMD
2942	M	Programmable Timer/Counter or DMA Address Generator	22	1567.50	53.90	AMD
2946	C	Octal Inverting 3-State Bus Transceivers	20	787.50	3.10	AMD
2946	M	Octal Inverting 3-State Bus Transceivers	20	825.00	7.30	AMD
2947	C	Octal 3-State Bus Transceivers	20	735.00	3.10	AMD
2947	M	Octal 3-State Bus Transceivers	20	770.00	7.03	AMD
2948	C	Octal Inverting 3-State Bus Transceivers	20	787.50	3.90	AMD
2948	M	Octal Inverting 3-State Bus Transceivers	20	825.00	6.05	AMD
2949	C	Octal 3-State Bus Transceivers	20	735.00	3.90	AMD
2949	M	Octal 3-State Bus Transceivers	20	770.00	6.05	AMD
2950A	C	8-Bit Bidirectional I/O Ports with Handshake	28	1443.75	4.85	AMD
2950A	M	8-Bit Bidirectional I/O Ports with Handshake	28	1699.50	12.35	AMD
2951A	C	8-Bit Bidirectional I/O Ports with Handshake	28	1443.75	4.85	AMD
2951A	M	8-Bit Bidirectional I/O Ports with Handshake	28	1699.50	12.35	AMD
2952A	C	8-Bit Bidirectional I/O Ports with Handshake	24	1443.75	4.50	AMD

TYPE	TEMP GRADE	DESCRIPTION	PINS	POWER (mW)	PRICE ($)	SUPPLIERS
2952A	M	8-Bit Bidirectional I/O Ports with Handshake	24	1699.50	12.00	AMD
2953A	C	8-Bit Bidirectional I/O Ports with Handshake	24	1443.75	4.50	AMD
2953A	M	8-Bit Bidirectional I/O Ports with Handshake	24	1699.50	12.00	AMD
2954	C	Octal Register with 3-State Outputs	20	735.00	2.65	AMD
2954	M	Octal Register with 3-State Outputs	20	770.00	11.65	AMD
2955	C	Octal Register with Inverting 3-State Outputs	20	735.00	3.20	AMD
2955	M	Octal Register with Inverting 3-State Outputs	20	770.00	11.65	AMD
2956	C	Octal Latch with 3-State Outputs	20	840.00	2.70	AMD
2956	M	Octal Latch with 3-State Outputs	20	880.00	11.65	AMD
2957	C	Octal Latch with Inverting 3-State Outputs	20	882.00	3.20	AMD
2957	M	Octal Latch with Inverting 3-State Outputs	20	924.00	11.65	AMD
2960	C	16-Bit Error Detection and Correction Unit	48	2100.00	23.50	AMD
2960	M	16-Bit Error Detection and Correction Unit	48	2200.00	104.11	AMD
2961	C	4-Bit Error Correction Multiple Bus Inverting Buffer	24	813.75	5.50	AMD
2961	M	4-Bit Error Correction Multiple Bus Inverting Buffer	24	852.50	11.50	AMD
2962	C	4-Bit Error Correction Multiple Bus Buffer	24	813.75	5.50	AMD
2962	M	4-Bit Error Correction Multiple Bus Buffer	24	852.50	11.50	AMD
2964B	C	Dynamic Memory Controller	40	908.25	10.00	AMD
2964B	M	Dynamic Memory Controller	40	902.00	37.44	AMD

TYPE	TEMP GRADE	DESCRIPTION	PINS	POWER (mW)	PRICE ($)	SUPPLIERS
2965	C	Octal 3-State Dynamic Memory Inverting Driver	20	656.25	2.05	AMD
2965	M	Octal 3-State Dynamic Memory Inverting Driver	20	687.50	9.50	AMD
2966	C	Octal 3-State Dynamic Memory Driver	20	787.50	2.05	AMD
2966	M	Octal 3-State Dynamic Memory Driver	20	825.00	9.50	AMD
2968A	C	Dynamic Memory Controller	48	1470.00	20.52	AMD
2968A	M	Dynamic Memory Controller	48	1622.50	96.92	AMD
29116	C	16-Bit Bipolar Microprocessor	52	3858.75	95.00	AMD
29116	M	16-Bit Bipolar Microprocessor	52	4097.50	560.00	AMD
29118	C	8-Bit I/O Support for 29116	24	1443.75	8.85	AMD
29203	C	4-Bit Bipolar Microprocessor Slice	48	1837.50	20.50	AMD
29203	M	4-Bit Bipolar Microprocessor Slice	48	2172.50	65.60	AMD
29501	C	Multi-Port Pipelined Processor	64	2100.00	47.00	AMD
29501	M	Multi-Port Pipelined Processor	64	2300.00	192.50	AMD
29510	C	16 X 16 Multiplier Accumulator	64	4725.00	68.00	AMD
29510	M	16 X 16 Multiplier Accumulator	64	5500.00	185.00	AMD
29L510	C	Low Power 16 X 16 Multiplier Accumulator	64	2362.50	58.00	AMD
29L510	M	Low Power 16 X 16 Multiplier Accumulator	64	2942.50	135.00	AMD
29516	C	16 X 16 Multiplier 65 ns	64	4200.00	56.00	AMD
29516	M	16 X 16 Multiplier 75 ns	64	4950.00	130.00	AMD
29516A	C	16 X 16 Multiplier 38 ns	64	4200.00	88.00	AMD
29L516	C	16 X 16 Multiplier 90 ns	64	2100.00	39.00	AMD
29L516	M	16 X 16 Multiplier 100 ns	64	2420.00	100.00	AMD
29517	C	16 X 16 Multiplier 65 ns	64	4200.00	56.00	AMD

TYPE	TEMP GRADE	DESCRIPTION	PINS	POWER (mW)	PRICE ($)	SUPPLIERS
29517	M	16 X 16 Multiplier 75 ns	64	4950.00	128.00	AMD
29L517	C	16 X 16 Multiplier 90 ns	64	2100.00	39.00	AMD
29L517	M	16 X 16 Multiplier 100 ns	64	2420.00	100.00	AMD
29520	C	Multilevel Pipeline Register	24	971.25	6.50	AMD
29520	M	Multilevel Pipeline Register	24	1100.00	23.35	AMD
29521	C	Multilevel Pipeline Register	24	971.25	6.50	AMD
29521	M	Multilevel Pipeline Register	24	1100.00	23.35	AMD
29526	C	Sine Generator Most Significant Byte	24	971.25	35.00	AMD
29526	M	Sine Generator Most Significant Byte	24	971.25	101.50	AMD
29527	C	Sine Generator Least Significant Byte	24	971.25	35.00	AMD
29527	M	Sine Generator Least Significant Byte	24	971.25	101.50	AMD
29528	C	Cosine Generator Most Significant Byte	24	971.25	35.00	AMD
29528	M	Cosine Generator Most Significant Byte	24	971.25	101.50	AMD
29529	C	Cosine Generator Least Significant Byte	24	971.25	35.00	AMD
29529	M	Cosine Generator Least Significant Byte	24	971.25	101.50	AMD
29540	C	Programmable FFT Address Sequencer	40	2362.50	45.00	AMD
29540	M	Programmable FFT Address Sequencer	40	2585.00	160.00	AMD
29705A	C	16-Word by 4-Bit 2-Port RAM	28	1102.50	5.50	AMD
29705A	M	16-Word by 4-Bit 2-Port RAM	28	1155.00	37.50	AMD
29707	C	16-Word by 4-Bit 2-Port RAM	28	1102.50	10.35	AMD
29803	C	16-Way Branch Control Unit	16	682.50	4.30	AMD
29803	M	16-Way Branch Control Unit	16	715.00	7.15	AMD

TYPE	TEMP GRADE	DESCRIPTION	PINS	POWER (mW)	PRICE ($)	SUPPLIERS
29806	C	6-Bit Chip Select Decoder	24	262.50	3.10	AMD
29806	M	6-Bit Chip Select Decoder	24	275.00	9.40	AMD
29809	C	9-Bit Equal-to-Comparator	24	262.50	3.10	AMD
29809	M	9-Bit Equal-to-Comparator	24	275.00	9.35	AMD
29811A	C	Next Address Control Unit	16	603.75	2.85	AMD
29811A	M	Next Address Control Unit	16	632.50	5.00	AMD
29818	C	8-Bit Pipeline Register with Shadow Register	24	813.75	3.30	AMD
29818	M	8-Bit Pipeline Register with Shadow Register	24	907.50	12.15	AMD
29821	C	10-Bit Register	24	735.00	2.40	AMD
29821	M	10-Bit Register	24	770.00	7.70	AMD
29822	C	10-Bit Register Inverting	24	735.00	2.40	AMD
29822	M	10-Bit Register Inverting	24	770.00	7.70	AMD
29823	C	9-Bit Register	24	735.00	2.40	AMD
29823	M	9-Bit Register	24	770.00	7.70	AMD
29824	C	9-Bit Register Inverting	24	735.00	2.40	AMD
29824	M	9-Bit Register Inverting	24	770.00	7.70	AMD
29825	C	8-Bit Register	24	735.00	2.40	AMD
29825	M	8-Bit Register	24	770.00	7.70	AMD
29826	C	8-Bit Register Inverting	24	735.00	2.40	AMD
29826	M	8-Bit Register Inverting	24	770.00	7.70	AMD
29827A	C	10-Bit Buffer	24	420.00	2.80	AMD
29827A	M	10-Bit Buffer	24	440.00	13.70	AMD
29828A	C	10-Bit Buffer Inverting	24	420.00	2.80	AMD
29828A	M	10-Bit Buffer Inverting	24	440.00	13.70	AMD

TYPE	TEMP GRADE	DESCRIPTION	PINS	POWER (mW)	PRICE ($)	SUPPLIERS
29833A	C	Parity Bus Transceiver Register Option	24	1023.75	5.95	AMD
29833A	M	Parity Bus Transceiver Register Option	24	1072.50	16.40	AMD
29834A	C	Parity Bus Transceiver Inverting, Register Option	24	1023.75	5.95	AMD
29834A	M	Parity Bus Transceiver Inverting, Register Option	24	1072.50	16.40	AMD
29841	C	10-Bit Latch	24	630.00	2.40	AMD
29841	M	10-Bit Latch	24	660.00	7.70	AMD
29842	C	10-Bit Latch Inverting	24	630.00	2.40	AMD
29842	M	10-Bit Latch Inverting	24	660.00	7.70	AMD
29843	C	9-Bit Latch	24	630.00	2.40	AMD
29843	M	9-Bit Latch	24	660.00	7.70	AMD
29844	C	9-Bit Latch Inverting	24	630.00	2.40	AMD
29844	M	9-Bit Latch Inverting	24	660.00	7.70	AMD
29845	C	8-Bit Latch	24	630.00	2.40	AMD
29845	M	8-Bit Latch	24	660.00	7.70	AMD
29846	C	8-Bit Latch Inverting	24	630.00	2.40	AMD
29846	M	8-Bit Latch Inverting	24	660.00	7.70	AMD
29853A	C	Parity Bus Transceiver Latch Option	24	1023.75	5.95	AMD
29853A	M	Parity Bus Transceiver Latch Option	24	1072.50	16.40	AMD
29854A	C	Parity Bus Transceiver Inverting, Latch Option	24	1023.75	5.95	AMD
29854A	M	Parity Bus Transceiver Inverting, Latch Option	24	1072.50	16.40	AMD
29861A	C	10-Bit Transceiver	24	840.00	2.80	AMD
29861A	M	10-Bit Transceiver	24	880.00	13.70	AMD

TYPE	TEMP GRADE	DESCRIPTION	PINS	POWER (mW)	PRICE ($)	SUPPLIERS
29862A	C	10-Bit Transceiver Inverting	24	840.00	2.80	AMD
29862A	M	10-Bit Transceiver Inverting	24	880.00	13.70	AMD
29863A	C	9-Bit Transceiver	24	840.00	2.80	AMD
29863A	M	9-Bit Transceiver	24	880.00	13.70	AMD
29864A	C	9-Bit Transceiver Inverting	24	840.00	2.80	AMD
29864A	M	9-Bit Transceiver Inverting	24	880.00	13.70	AMD
IDT39C01C	C	4-Bit CMOS Microprocessor Slice 32 MHz	40	157.50	6.25	IDT
IDT39C01C	M	4-Bit CMOS Microprocessor Slice 31 MHz	40	192.50	25.00	IDT
IDT39C01D	C	4-Bit CMOS Microprocessor Slice 43 MHz	40	183.75	8.25	IDT
IDT39C01D	M	4-Bit CMOS Microprocessor Slice 37 MHz	40	220.00	39.90	IDT
IDT39C01E	C	4-Bit CMOS Microprocessor Slice 50 MHz	40	210.00	10.75	IDT
IDT39C01E	M	4-Bit CMOS Microprocessor Slice 46 MHz	40	247.50	51.85	IDT
IDT39C02A	C	Look-Ahead Carry Generator	16	13.13	1.95	IDT
IDT39C02A	M	Look-Ahead Carry Generator	16	13.75	12.00	IDT
IDT39C03A	C	4-Bit CMOS Microprocessor Slice 16.7 MHz	48	262.50	18.25	IDT
IDT39C03A	M	4-Bit CMOS Microprocessor Slice 16.7 MHz	48	330.00	39.50	IDT
IDT39C09A	C	4-Bit Microprogram Sequencer	28	236.25	5.00	IDT
IDT39C09A	M	4-Bit Microprogram Sequencer	28	302.50	20.00	IDT
IDT39C10B	C	12-Bit Microprogram Sequencer 20 MHz	40	393.75	12.50	IDT
IDT39C10B	M	12-Bit Microprogram Sequencer 19.6 MHz	40	495.00	36.75	IDT

TYPE	TEMP GRADE	DESCRIPTION	PINS	POWER (mW)	PRICE ($)	SUPPLIERS
IDT39C10C	C	12-Bit Microprogram Sequencer 28.6 MHz	40	393.75	17.00	IDT
IDT39C10C	M	12-Bit Microprogram Sequencer 25 MHz	40	495.00	51.45	IDT
IDT39C11A	C	4-Bit Microprogram Sequencer	20	236.25	3.25	IDT
IDT39C11A	M	4-Bit Microprogram Sequencer	20	302.50	15.75	IDT
IDT49C402	C	16-Bit CMOS Microprocessor Slice 20.8 MHz	68	656.25	27.90	IDT
IDT49C402	M	16-Bit CMOS Microprocessor Slice 20 MHz	68	825.00	102.00	IDT
IDT49C402A	C	16-Bit CMOS Microprocessor Slice 32.3 MHz	68	656.25	44.00	IDT
IDT49C402A	M	16-Bit CMOS Microprocessor Slice 27.8 MHz	68	825.00	144.00	IDT
IDT49C410	C	16-Bit Microprogram Sequencer 20 MHz	48	393.75	17.65	IDT
IDT49C410	M	16-Bit Microprogram Sequencer 19.6 MHz	48	495.00	58.50	IDT
IDT49C410A	C	16-Bit Microprogram Sequencer 28.6 MHz	48	393.75	24.70	IDT
IDT49C410A	M	16-Bit Microprogram Sequencer 25 MHz	48	495.00	81.90	IDT

Appendix J
Supplier Codes

CODE	SUPPLIER
AMD	ADVANCED MICRO DEVICES
F	FAIRCHILD
H	HARRIS
I	INTEL
IDT	INTEGRATED DEVICE TECHNOLOGY
M	MOTOROLA
MM	MONOLITHIC MEMORIES
N	NATIONAL SEMICONDUCTOR
RCA	RCA
RI	ROCKWELL INTERNATIONAL
S	SIGNETICS
TI	TEXAS INSTRUMENTS
Z	ZILOG

Index

Index

Edited by Roland S. Phelps

Other Bestsellers From TAB

□ **IMPROVING TV SIGNAL RECEPTION: MASTERING ANTENNAS AND SATELLITE DISHES**—Dick Glass

Practical, proven techniques for solving the antenna and distribution problems that can hamper proper TV reception! This is a practical, easy-to-follow introduction to antenna technology. It provides practical solutions to all the common and not-so-common problems that prevent your TV from receiving a clear, distortion-free picture—no matter whether your TV signal comes from a satellite dish, a TV antenna on the roof, a master antenna system in an apartment complex, or cable company. 192 pp., 150 illus.

Paper $18.95   **Book No. 2970**

□ **ILLUSTRATED DICTIONARY OF ELECTRONICS—4TH EDITION**—Rufus P. Turner and Stan Gibilisco

Whether you are an electronics technician, student, educator, hobbyist, radio operator, or are just technically curious, this collection of terms is THE most comprehensive dictionary available. Including all practical electronics and computer terms, it is as up-to-date as the latest advances in the field itself! 640 pp., 584 illus.

Paper $24.95   **Book No. 2900**

□ **62 HOME REMOTE CONTROL AND AUTOMATION PROJECTS**—Delton T. Horn

Here are 62 different remote control and automation units that anyone can build. All parts and components are readily obtainable and the cost is only a fraction of that charged for ready-built devices in electronics stores . . . some of the devices can't be purchased commercially at any price! Just think how you can make your home safer and more convenient with these devices. 294 pp., 222 illus.

Paper $10.95   **Book No. 2735**

□ **55 EASY-TO-BUILD ELECTRONIC PROJECTS**—Editors of *Elementary Electronics*

If you're looking for a gold mine of exciting, fun-to-build, *and useful* electronics projects that are both easy and inexpensive to put together . . . here's where you'll hit pay dirt!! Here are more than 50 unique electronic projects selected from the best that have been published in *Elementary Electronics* Magazine . . . projects that have been tested and proven! 256 pp., 256 illus.

Paper $12.95   **Hard $14.95**
Book No. 1999

□ **ELECTRONIC DATABOOK—4th Edition**—Rudolf F. Graf

If it's electronic, it's here—current, detailed, and comprehensive! Use this book to broaden your electronics information base. Revised and expanded to include all up-to-date information, the fourth edition of *Electronic Databook* will make any electronic job easier and less time-consuming. This edition includes information that will aid in the design of local area networks, computer interfacing structure, and more! 528 pp., 131 illus.

Paper $25.95   **Book No. 2958**

□ **THE BENCHTOP ELECTRONICS REFERENCE MANUAL**—Victor F.C. Veley

One strength of this book lies in its unique format which divides the various topics into five subject areas that include direct-current principles, tubes, alternating-current principles, principles of radio communications, and solid-state devices. But, what really sets this electronics sourcebook apart from all the others is the wide range of information given on each of the 160 topics including basic principles and mathematical derivations. 672 pp., 282 illus.

Paper $27.95   **Hard $34.95**
Book No. 2785

□ **BUILD YOUR OWN WORKING FIBEROPTIC, INFRARED AND LASER SPACE-AGE PROJECTS**—Robert E. Iannini

Here are plans for a variety of useful electronic and scientific devices, including a high sensitivity laser light detector and a high voltage laboratory generator (useful in all sorts of laser, plasma ion, and particle applications as well as for lighting displays and special effects). And that's just the beginning of the exciting space age technology that you'll be able to put to work! 288 pp., 198 illus.

Paper $18.95   **Hard $24.95**
Book No. 2724

□ **THE ENCYCLOPEDIA OF ELECTRONIC CIRCUITS**—Rudolf F. Graf

Here is every professionals's dream treasury of analog and digital circuits—nearly 100 circuit categories . . . over 1,200 individual circuits designed for long-lasting applications potential. Adding even more to the value of this resource is the exhaustively thorough index which gives you instant access to exactly the circuits you need each and every time! 768 pp., 1,762 illus.

Paper $39.95   **Hard $60.00**
Book No. 1938

Other Bestsellers From TAB